CHEMICAL ACTIVITIES

" . . . a mutable and treacherous tribe"—von Haller

CHEMICAL
ACTIVITIES OF FUNGI

BY

JACKSON W. FOSTER

Professor of Bacteriology, University of Texas, Austin, Texas

1949

ACADEMIC PRESS INC., PUBLISHERS

NEW YORK, N. Y.

Dedicated with much appreciation

to

My microbiological mentors

PROFESSOR S. A. WAKSMAN
PROFESSOR R. L. STARKEY
PROFESSOR C. B. VAN NIEL

and to numerous colleagues, especially at the
New Jersey Agricultural Experimental Station,
Hopkins Marine Station, Stanford University,
University of California, Merck and Co., Inc.,
and the University of Texas, whose scientific
fraternization with me through my career has
better prepared me to undertake this work.

PREFACE

This book is the result of my bewilderment when as a beginning graduate student in 1936, I was assigned by Dr. Waksman to a problem in mold metabolism. The bewilderment was a direct consequence of the unavailability of a suitable treatise comprehensive enough to orientate a non-specialist in this field. What impressed me particularly was the tremendous amount of work that had been done, and the fact that it was widely scattered in innumerable literature sources, predominately foreign at that time. Furthermore, much of the work on the major phases of the subject was so contradictory that the beginner could scarcely avoid a sensation of confusion.

What was needed was an authoritative, critical book integrating and evaluating the field, and I was presumptuous enough to tell Dr. Waksman that he ought to write such a volume. Whereupon he suggested that I work five years in the field, then write it myself. It has taken me thirteen years to become so bold as to do it.

Considering the enormous developments during this time, the plight of the beginning student has, I should imagine, become a great deal worse. It is primarily for such persons that this book is designed, though obviously many other groups of individuals may find it valuable. Consequently the didactic approach is conspicuous throughout, perhaps to the point of being repetitious at times. In fact, development of the subject matter was made with an eye toward the use of this book as a text for college courses at the upperclass or graduate level. The giant developments in this field, both academic and technological, are convincing evidence that mold metabolism as a distinct entity "has arrived." It would appear that the inclusion of a college course on this subject is essential for a well-rounded curriculum in mycology or general microbiology, and this book is designed to meet the needs of such a course.

This book is not an exhaustive compilation, but, instead, is a treatise in which the main outlines of the field are developed around the theme of comparative biochemistry. A definite attempt to synthesize the field has been made. The long-known facts have been reinterpreted and presented in terms of modern concepts of biology and biochemistry. Oftentimes this has necessitated a discussion of the merits and flaws in theories contradicting each other; and there is no dearth of such instances! The reader will seek in vain a list, for example, of all the pigments or antibiotics produced by fungi, for my purpose has been to stress the subject matter from the standpoint of dynamics, that is, *transformations* effected by fungi, and not merely to list all facts regardless of their significance.

Similarly, details of certain processes such as production of riboflavin by *Eremothecium asbyii* have been omitted on the grounds that they are largely empirical and illustrate no new principles—they merely reflect other principles discussed throughout the book.   Admittedly, this is an arbitrary basis, but it was done advisedly, to keep the size of the book within bounds.

Also arbitrary has been the interpretation of "Fungi" as used in the title.   In general this book is limited to the filamentous forms, the so-called "lower fungi" or "molds" according to the definition in Chapter 1.   This ordinarily will mean fungi which are easily handled as experimental material in the laboratory.

Inasmuch as fungi are very much a part of the industrial scene nowadays, the evolution of a process to industrial scale is treated in connection with the particular transformation; yet this book is not one on applied microbiology.   Nevertheless, factors involved in the industrial approach of necessity depend on and capitalize on principles of physiology of the organism, and this has provided me with an excellent opportunity to draw upon my own industrial experience.   A great many of the industrial features presented here have never appeared in student texts.

Another feature deliberately incorporated is the historical development and evolution of each major line of work with a special aim to associate names and personalities with definite contributions.   This policy I adopted when I commenced writing the book in November, 1945, and it was a source of great satisfaction to see the noted scientist-educator J. B. Conant espouse this very cause some two years later in his book "On Understanding Science."

I do not doubt that many important sins of omission and commission are embraced by this book.   I am cognizant of many; and I would sincerely welcome any and all corrections, criticisms and different points of view from readers, so that if possible, the book can be amended in the future.

My acknowledgments and gratitude are due to innumerable people for expediting the preparation of this book in various ways.   In the professional field, for advice and criticism of certain parts of the MS, I wish to thank Drs. R. P. Wagner, B. S. Gould, F. F. Nord, and also O. Wyss for exchanges of opinions on certain subjects.   Thanks are due also to Dr. Otto Behrens for permission to utilize some information on artificial penicillins prior to its publication.

Thanks are due of course to various authors and publishers for permission to use certain cuts and illustrations, and especially to Dr. G. W. Beadle because I used so many of his.   In the physical task of preparation appreciation is due Merck and Co., Inc. for the unsurpassed services of their research library, and for the able typing services of the Misses Olga Myna and Jenny Yankow.   At the University of Texas I am grateful to the Misses Marjorie Borel and Patricia Mackey for transcribing my longhand, and particularly to Miss Doris McGuire for much typing and for the odious task of making corrections and for "patching up" the MS.   My thanks also to J. B. Davis for his service in reading and checking the proof.

No gratitude could be too much for my devoted wife who not only aided in the typing but spent many a long and lonely night and weekend vigil at home while I worked on the book at the laboratory.

Jackson W. Foster

Austin, Texas

CONTENTS

CONTENTS

CHAPTER 8

LACTIC ACID FORMATION BY FUNGI 282

CHAPTER 9

ALCHOLIC FERMENTATION BY MOLDS. 296

CHAPTER 10

OXALIC ACID METABOLISM 326

CHAPTER 18

CHAPTER 19

CHAPTER 1

INTRODUCTION, HISTORY, PERSPECTIVE

Historically, the initial developments in the organized study of fungi (mycology), very much like the classical approach to other systems of biology throughout the history of science, were primarily descriptive, centering at first mainly on what fungi are, including the evolutionary sequence within the group itself, and classification and identification (taxonomy), these being based on morphological characters, gross and microscopic. With the recognition that the reproductive structures and processes are the distinctive features about legions of otherwise indistinguishable organisms within the group, emphasis on these aspects led to rapid accumulation of knowledge about sporulation and reproduction mechanisms and complicated life cycles in the more highly evolved fungus forms. Particular attention was paid, naturally, to fungus forms of practical importance, and up until the last two or three decades this had come to mean traditionally those fungi responsible for diseases of cultivated crops and other plants, and of man and animals. It is not surprising, therefore, that until a recent era the study of fungi was almost exclusively the domain of the plant pathologist, who usually was a botanist, horticulturist, naturalist, mycologist, histologist, microscopist, agronomist, or combinations thereof, and whose generalized interest could best be described as plant biology. The study of molds was, then, a very logical extension of the classical botany, and, indeed, the early history of the study of fungi is closely associated with the names of the active botanists and plant pathologists of the day. Their influence is still widely felt in the study of fungi, for, judging from the texts available, the teaching of mycology is largely based on the classical themes of morphology, reproduction, and host-parasite relationships, and a good deal of art work, with only incidental attention to such aspects as modern concepts of ecology, artificial cultivation, nutrition, physiology, and biochemistry. Indeed, the impression is all too wide spread that mycology teaching today consists of the study of herbarium specimens and is handled jointly with plant pathology, if not actually considered synonymous with it. Nevertheless, the tremendous significance of plant pathology in mycology certainly cannot be underestimated, as E. C. Large has so scholarly revealed in his magnificent treatise *Advance of the*

1

Fungi (1940). The use of herbarium specimens is, in addition to revealing the characteristics of the infection, a consequence of the inability so far to cultivate many of the forms and sexual bodies apart from the host tissues. But this in turn is the result of lack of information on the cultural, physiological, and biochemical aspects of the fungus itself, as compared to what is known of the process of parasitism of the plant.

Mycology, then, as organized subject matter was for a long time thought of as being principally the province of plant pathology, directly or indirectly. However, this certainly was not due to any dearth of numbers and varieties of purely saprophytic fungi, whose very abundance and diversity, physiologically as well as morphologically, and whose ease of cultivation in pure culture, provide a tempting lure for an understanding of the intimate character of the organisms themselves.

While this has been true to a greater or lesser degree in the past, the emergence of the study of the behavior of the organism itself and of the factors contributing to it has become unmistakable and has been largely attributable to the application of physiological and biochemical approaches to the organism in the living state. Microbiology has spawned a new but substantial family member—Mold Metabolism.

A definition of terms is not out of place here, because the word mold is not clearly defined in standard treatises on fungi (in Henrici's *Molds, Yeasts and Actinomycetes* this definition is lacking). "Mold" has no strict taxonomic or even scientific meaning and its interpretation doubtless varies with different authorities. It is, perhaps, a colloquialism in microbiology. Nevertheless it is possible to shape the general connotation of the term, leaving disputable issues a matter of individual viewpoint.

The term "mold" connotes certain types of fungi. It is very frequently used by the English ("mould") who synonymize it with "lower fungi." Similarly the German "Schimmelpilze" connotes one type of fungi apart from all others, i.e., mold fungi, literally. It has come to have very narrow applications in some connections, mainly non-technical. Thus there is "black-mold," "white-mold," "bread-mold," "water-mold." Sometimes by "mold" is meant mildew and in other cases the term is used to denote any member of the Mucorales.

However, to workers in the field the designation has broader significance, meaning fungi (Eumycetes) whose characteristic nature is distinctively filamentous, but which do not form any organized specialized fleshy fruiting structures of macroscopic dimensions. It at once rules out the great numbers of so-called ascocarpous and mushroom-type organisms. Mushroom spawn, for example, exclusively mycelial, usually is not called mold because the organism typically forms a fleshy fruiting body. On the other hand, it does not exclude all fungi which bear sexual spores in specialized structures, only the macroscopic fleshy types. Thus many filamentous genera like Penicillium, Aspergillus, etc., bear spores in specialized structures under certain conditions, but mainly in microscopic fruiting structures, at least not in structures that could be called fleshy.

In mycology, the larger and more complex the fruiting body is, the "higher" the fungus is said to be. This stems from the fact that in an evolutionary sense those forms are more highly specialized, adapted, or evolved. Conversely, organisms with relatively simple and inconspicuous fruiting bodies, or with none known, are considered "lower" forms or lower fungi.

Historical Development of Mold Metabolism

It can well be said that bacteriology as a science in the sense that we know it today stems from the fact that bacteria are of extremely great practical importance in the economy of man and civilization. Indeed, the "Golden Age of Bacteriology," perhaps not yet in its stage of highest development, was a direct result of Pasteur's elegant demonstration in a convincing and unequivocal scientific manner, of the role of bacteria as causative instruments of disease in animals, and of the undesirable changes in spoilage of fermented beverages. The impetus this work bestowed upon the field and upon the subsequent autocatalytic development of medical and agricultural bacteriology is too well known to dwell upon here. Sanitary and industrial bacteriology next became the high points in the field. Out of these pursuits came understanding of the profound and intimate characters of the bacteria themselves. Particularly did this work take a tremendous spurt with the revelation of the stepwise chemical and enzymic nature of the mechanisms of respiration, fermentation, and biological oxidations through the pioneering work of Harden and Young, Neuberg, Meyerhof, Wieland, Warburg, and many others. Not only did yeast and muscle biochemistry find ready confirmation and corraboration with bacteria but, not long after, the very reverse became true—bacteria, because of their simplicity, ease of handling, etc. became fair game for the study of phenomena of fundamental biological significance and application to biological systems at large. Indeed, from this has been synthesized the beautiful pattern of the doctrine of comparative biochemistry (van Niel, 1943) first clearly enunciated in 1926 by Kluyver and Donker in their epochal article, *Die Einheit in der Biochemie*.

Detailed consideration is given here to the development of bacterial metabolism because it is a perfect orientation for the development of mold metabolism, standing as the latter does in striking parallelism to it, and affording, as it were, a precedent. As emphasized above, molds first and for a long time were the property of the descriptive botanist and mycologist, and earned their first importance in plant pathology. Nevertheless, in a less spectacular way, the role of fungi in diseases of plants was as important a stimulus for the study of mold metabolism as human and animal diseases were for bacteriology.

The development was not, however, exclusively from the standpoint of mycology and pathology. What may be called mold physiology was very much in evidence, as far back as a half century ago, but here again physiology was of the classic variety, based a good deal on physiology in a dynamic and physical sense—response to stimuli of various kinds—a carry-over from the plant physiology of the day. In fact, the mold physiologists were the plant physiologists of the day (Pfeffer, Wehmer, Bertrand, Brefeld, etc.). This does not mean that the problems of the activities and workings of molds were not being attacked at all before this field became well-defined. Indeed, numerous isolated historical examples could be given of molds being studied for what they do and what they produce, and of a practical utilization of the findings. In fact, practically all of the cornerstones of the study of mold metabolism as we know it today can be traced back to pioneering researches of the last century. The point is that more and more representative processes were revealed, but they failed to develop further because they were ahead of their times: the tools, mechanisms, and concepts of the newer knowledge of physiology, biochemistry, and nutrition were yet undiscovered and the approaches were not far from empirical. One is reminded of the comment of the great German biochemist Otto Warburg when, some twenty years ago, he decided to abandon his researches on tumor metabolism simply because the tools and concepts essential for the successful prosecution of the problem were not available and because it would not be worthwhile to resume the problem until they were. Twenty years later Warburg did return to the problem with modern techniques and theories (largely developed by himself!). In the same way some aspects of mold metabolism were already well defined considerably before the close of the last century and never realized the fullest academic exploitation in the sense we now know is possible simply because of limited experimental means. It is worth-while to mention a few of these, for they were the forerunners of the science of mold metabolism as we know it today, and occupy a unique historical significance in the development of this now definite branch of microbiology. (1) Van Tieghem, 1867: Conversion of tannin in gall nuts to gallic acid by fungi. (2) Raulin, 1867: Mineral nutrition of fungi. (3) Wehmer, 1891: Organic acid production from sugar by fungi.

The amount and trend of research in this field has even been the subject of an interesting compilation and statistical analysis by Japanese workers. Using the genus Aspergillus as the index, Tamiya and Morita (1929–30) listed by year and title every paper published on this subject from the first recorded one in 1729 through 1928, in which year there were 135, an aggregate total of 2424 papers. Tamiya (1931) subjected the bibliographical data to mathematical analysis and showed that the rate of publications conformed to an autocatalytic curve, still ascending in 1928. Data for the years 1930 and 1931 in which the incomplete combined total exceeded 300 papers (Iwanoff, 1932) certainly bear out Tamiya's conclusion. Statistics subsequent to 1931 appear not to have been made, but one gets the general impression that, with the exception of the war years, the rate increase continues unabated through the present time.

As in the case of bacteriology, the stimulation of organized studies on mold metabolism is the direct result of technological utilization of molds. Roughly these may be designated as follows: Commercial production of enzymes, especially proteolytic, pectinolytic, and diastatic enzymes; production of chemicals, particularly citric acid; development of fungicide research; agricultural, with emphasis on fungus transformations in soil, etc.; molds in food manufacturing, notably soy sauce and cheese; fungi in food spoilage; rotting of textiles, etc.; and more lately, antibiotics. A vast amount of investigation has been devoted to these subjects, and there is reason to believe that a good deal of it has never been published and remains as trade secrets of commercial laboratories. The many magnificent studies of the genetics of molds also deserve to be mentioned in this group, which, as will be seen presently, have opened the way for a whole new branch of mold metabolism. Also, the development of the awareness of importance of fungi in the economy of the soil might well be mentioned, especially their vital role in the carbon and nitrogen cycles, and the association of specific forms with specific processes.

MODERN DEVELOPMENTS

The modern era of mold metabolism has only scarcely begun, but the signs of an immense advance in the numerous phases of the field are unmistakable. Their importance is recognized, practically and academically. The fertility of the field awaiting exploitation is fully apparent, and the tools and concepts of modern biochemistry can now be brought to bear on this subject. As examples, one may include the following: respiration, growth factors and nutrition, enzymes, introduction of shaking or submerged culture techniques, stabilization of cultures, isolation and identification of intermediary products of metabolism, particularly phosphorylated compounds, activity of cell-free juices, oxidative assimilation and biochemical syntheses.

1. MOLDS AS AGENTS OF CHEMICAL SYNTHESIS

Chronologically, and perhaps with considerable arbitrariness, one could very well associate the beginning of the newer science of mold metabolism with the systematic survey of the chemical substances resulting from the growth of molds undertaken in 1922 on a comprehensive scale by Raistrick and numerous collaborators at the London School of Hygiene and Tropical Medicine, and continuing even at the present time. The appearance of their monograph, *Studies in the Biochemistry of Micro-organisms*, published in 1931 marks a milestone in the development of mold metabolism. And yet, peculiarly, the work of the Raistrick school is in itself not representative of the field, for it deals largely with the isolation, identification, and where new, synthesis of chemical substances formed by molds. Little attention was devoted to the metabolism of the molds studied, the role of these substances in the metabolism of the organisms producing them, the mechanism of and conditions influencing their formation, and numerous other aspects generally inherent in a microbiological approach. Here then, the interest was not in the dynamics of the mold systems themselves, but more in the chemicals formed as a result of metabolism. One might, therefore, consider this study to be the organic chemistry of mold products rather than mold metabolism since the biochemical transformations of these substances were not involved.

The signal position these studies have, from the standpoint of mold physiology and biochemistry, is that they made clear the vast potentialities of molds in regard to the number and diversity of hitherto unknown substances. These studies made it evident that an understanding of the transformations involving these substances would be a great contribution to fundamental biochemistry, and possibly might be suitable for practical utilization. They exposed the field, so to speak. Raistrick and his associates were so impressed by the heterogeneity of compounds synthesized by molds that they designated this feature of molds as "Polychemism."

Probably polychemism is distinctive to molds only in a relative sense, if even that. Of the other different groups of microorganisms, bacteria, yeasts, actinomycetes, protozoa, algae, etc., wherever they have been studied extensively, a sufficiently large number and heterogeneity of chemical substances has been isolated and characterized to justify the application of the term polychemism to them also. Along these lines, a great deal came out of the much-studied bacteria simply because this group has been the subject of so much attention. One can hardly refrain from incorporating the well-known tubercle bacillus within the scope of this designation since this organism, as the extensive studies of Anderson and coworkers have shown, synthesizes an astonishingly diverse array of new chemical substances, a great many of which have now been isolated in pure form and had their structures elucidated. Truly the cause of the "white death" is a formidable candidate for polychemism!

This bacterial species happens to have been the subject of organized attack, but to lesser degrees the same holds for many other bacterial species, particularly those groups whose polysaccharides have been studied for their importance in immunological problems. Wherever the organic- and biochemist have had cause for applying themselves to the study of bacteria, examples of polychemism in bacteria appear. The currently fruitful results obtained from study of the antibiotic substances of all types produced by bacteria are a more recent example of this. The same could be said for the yeasts, and although still in its infancy, there is no doubt that the polychemism of actinomycetes will be revealed as a result of the stimulated interest in the antagonistic properties of many members of this group.

Notwithstanding the polychemism of other groups, the association of polychemism with molds relates to their high capacity for synthesis, which in its overall aspects is manifested by a large amount of cell growth. It is this characteristic that facilitated the recognition of polychemism in the molds, because this, together with the ease of cultivation of the organisms studied, especially the rapid and abundant development on synthetic media (and in a majority of cases with carbohydrate the only organic ingredient in the medium) has made the fungi ideal subject matter. Investigators who have attempted to collect large amounts of bacterial cell material for chemical studies under laboratory conditions can attest to the superiority of molds in this respect. Cultivated in surface or stationary conditions, the luxurious growth itself tends to accentuate, as manifested by differences in appearances, qualitative variations in the synthetic powers of the molds, thus attracting attention to their occurrence. This probably explains why so many of the compounds studied by the Raistrick group were pigments.

Along the lines mentioned earlier, some developments in biochemistry evolved only in the past few years, mostly by the West coast school of microbiologists (van Niel, Barker, Doudoroff, and Clifton), permit an interpretation of the extraordinary ability of molds to build up large amounts of cell material rapidly, and provide a fine example of the workings of the doctrine of comparative biochemistry. Having been demonstrated for many different bacteria and substrates, it is now well recognized that oxidative assimilation (the ability to convert a portion of the substrates into complex material within the cells under favorable conditions of aeration) is probably a general phenomenon among the bacteria, and it is quite evident now that molds can convert substrates into cell substance with reproducibly high efficiency (see Chapter 2). Efficiency coefficients for actively growing mold cultures would indicate that molds stand clearly above the bacteria. However, this is fallacious—the surface habits of molds insure an abundance of oxygen for efficient growth whereas most aerobic bacteria characteristically grow throughout the liquid and are limited by the rate of solution of oxygen. When air is made available mechanically the bacteria as a group, and yeasts and actinomycetes also, prove to be as efficient as molds in converting substrate into cell material. The molds are not, therefore, the superior biological machines they appear to be.

This very efficiency of molds has, interestingly enough, been a barrier to the mold biochemist in his attempts to accumulate facts which would permit a conclusive picture of the mechanism of formation of the numerous products arising through the dissimilation of carbohydrates. The chemical sequence of events leading to their formation is well known for almost all the bacterial metabolic products which have been studied because quantitative balance sheets between substrate decomposed and substances produced are obtainable, the bacteria serving essentially as an enzyme system effecting the transformations. Conclusive proof of mechanisms of origin of most of the mold dissimilation products is lacking owing to the diversion of so much of the substrate into cell material (and CO_2), thus making a quantitative chemical balance sheet impossible to obtain. As a matter of fact, it appears not unjustified to say that because of this, what we know about many mechanisms in molds results from knowledge of similar transformations by bacterial, yeast, or animal tissue as applied to molds by comparative biochemistry. The most that can be said of much chemical evidence available on fungi is that it is suggestive or provides only presumptive evidence.

It is a surprising fact, though typical of molds, that the occurrence of phosphorylated intermediary products of carbohydrate metabolism has not yet been conclusively demonstrated. The elimination of this very real stumbling block to the elucidation of dissimilation mechanisms of molds doubtless can be achieved, to a large extent at least, by the development of methods for obtaining active cell-free juices of mold mycelium, so that the study then becomes one of isolated enzyme action rather than cellular action. There may be dangers in applying such results to the intact cell, but experience with bacteria and yeast leave no question as to the value of this type of approach.

2. MOLDS AS AGENTS OF DISSIMILATION

Notwithstanding the handicaps just described, the elucidation and study of the chemical transformations of the substrate and the genesis of the metabolic products, with particular emphasis on those ("breakdown products") resulting from carbohydrates as contrasted to the synthetic metabolism, is without question one of the most important aspects of the modern attack on mold physiology and biochemistry. Often new and hitherto unknown substances are not involved, as in the case of poly-chemism, though, needless to say, many compounds distinctive to fungi could be cited. Encountered here are many metabolic products long familiar from other phases of microbiology and biochemistry, where, to a large extent, their dynamics is known. In the case of the molds, however, they still offer rich research possibilities from the standpoint of the mechanism of their origin and fate, the enzymes concerned in these transformations, their participation in the overall economy of the cell, and intimate influences on their accumulation and persistence. A good portion of this book deals with what has been done along these lines, and although it immediately becomes evident that a vast amount of study has been devoted to such work, the results, insofar as a unified concept goes, have not reached anywhere near the stage of development and intergration that similar studies have on the bacteria. As a matter of fact, this book makes perhaps the first comprehensive attempt to achieve this.

It is worth making a point of the nature of carbohydrate dissimilation end-products of mold metabolism as compared with those of bacteria. A great variety of dissimilation products is known to occur throughout the many well-defined physiological groups of bacteria, and with very few exceptions these are produced by anaerobes, facultative anaerobes or microaerophiles. Almost all the classically recognized end-products of carbohydrate breakdown, ethyl alcohol, acetic acid, formic acid, glycerol, butanol, acetone, propionic acid, acetone, lactic acid, and many others, are recognized as fermentation products, i.e., formed under anaerobic conditions. On the other hand, it takes a bit of reflection to recall the few instances where the products (aside from CO_2) result from aerobic metabolism. Included here are the partial oxidations of the various substrates by bacteria of the genus Acetobacter, of which *Acetobacter suboxydans* is the notable example; this generalized power seems to be highly specific to organisms of this genus. Although many different substrates can be oxidized, the reaction in all cases is substantially one, namely, the dehydrogenation of a hydroxy group without any change in the carbon skeleton of the compound undergoing oxidation. Usually two hydrogens are lost.   The principal other bacterial oxidation products are the group of sugar acids, 2-ketogluconic and 5-ketogluconic acid, derived from glucose, and the bionic acids obtained from reducing dissaccharides by members of the Pseudomonas and Phytomonas genera. These all are simple dehydrogenations, and it may be not without significance that, where aerobic oxidation products occur in bacteria, the carbon skeleton of the substrate is unchanged or at least not drastically disrupted.

With the molds, particularly the mycelial types, quite the reverse is true. Not only are there numerous and different oxidation products, but most of them obviously are derived from cleavage products of the carbohydrate carbon chain.   Indeed, the view seems justified that the cleavage is primarily a reaction independent of air (oxygen), followed by secondary reactions utilizing oxygen for the reactions yielding oxidation products.   From the aerobic tendencies of the molds, one would expect dissimilation products to consist principally of compounds whose formation involves reactions utilizing molecular oxygen, namely, organic acids, and this is indeed the case.   Those most frequently encountered are: citric, oxalic, gluconic, acetic, fumaric, itaconic, kojic, and succinic. In fact, some forty-odd different organic acids have been isolated and identified as products of mold metabolism, but not all may be regarded as dissimilation products.

As mentioned above, one is struck by the fact that many of the mold acids have been identified as important in the intermediary metabolism of other biological systems.   In these systems (animal tissues, bacteria, yeast) they are never present in more than traces, being transitory in nature, formed and transformed so quickly that they never accumulate. What the significance is of their accumulation in mold cultures in yields often over 50 per cent of the sugar consumed is bound to have basic importance, for in many instances it has been demonstrated that the very organism accumulating a particular product, does have, under certain conditions, the power to metabolize the substance further.   There is some evidence that permeability conditions may be an important factor in this situation.

Many of the fermentation products of bacteria are not known to arise from molds, at least from carbohydrates: propionic and butyric acid, propyl, isopropyl and butyl alcohols, acetone, butylene glycol, hydrogen gas, and possibly others.

In biology it may be said that the exception reveals the rule.   Thus it is that certain aerobic fungi belonging to the Mucorales are known to produce the most typical product of anaerobic bacterial metabolism, namely, lactic acid.   The formation and accumulation of large amounts of lactic acid by certain molds (up to 75 per cent of the carbohydrate consumed), appears to be the first instance where molecular oxygen has a distinctly beneficial effect on the formation of lactic acid by a biological system. Invariably lactic acid formation in plant, animal, and bacterial cells has been a strictly anaerobic process independent of molecular oxygen, and in fact, usually adversely affected by the presence of oxygen —the Pasteur reaction.

To say that fungi do not form the so-called characteristic fermentation products which bacteria do is to a certain extent a fallacy, for it evidently depends on the particular substrate furnished to the organism. Though it is true that no fungi are known to produce acetone from carbohydrate, the formation of this solvent from citric acid is an established fact. Similarly, the formation and utilization of formic acid is generally ascribed to bacteria, and not fungi; yet, furnished the appropriate substrate, formate is formed by the latter group, and many fungi avidly metabolize this 1-carbon compound. One scarcely thinks of propionic acid formation as a property of any organism except bacteria and actinomycetes, yet *Botrytis cinerea* has been found to produce propionate from lactate. This particular feature, formation from other substrates of a substance not formed from carbohydrates is doubtless one of the largest as yet unexplored potentialities in the field of industrial fermentations, for up to the present time this field has for the most part been confined to utilization of carbohydrates, a consequence of their low cost.

3. MOLDS AS PHYSIOLOGICAL MODELS

Referring again to the high rate of efficiency of the utilization of substrate by fungi, one ramification facilitates approaches to problems which, in other microbial systems, are not so easy to attack. The effect of imposed environmental conditions leads to very marked alterations in metabolism, accentuating phases of particular interest and thereby exposing them to investigation. It is remarkable how great an effect on mold growth (in synthetic media) 1 p.p.m. of heavy metals has and how profoundly the balance between cell material, CO_2, and organic acids is disturbed. Similarly, a mere shift of a few pH units in the medium determines if strains of Aspergillus produce oxalic acid or citric acid exclusively. Many examples of this type could be given, and they all relate to easy disturbances in metabolism caused by simple changes in environment, ultimately ascribable to enzyme action. This is the property which more and more is making molds favorite experimental material nowadays.

All this makes it clear that the investigator of molds utilizes them as physiological models; the biochemist, too, perceives the advantages of mold systems as working material. In two respects molds may be considered physiological models: first, as a means of studying, under better controlled conditions, general biochemical reactions of animal tissues which occur with greater intensity in molds. The best example of this are the various steps in the complex "citric acid cycle" in animal muscle, all of which individually have their counterparts in molds. Citric acid was long known as a metabolic product of molds before its occurrence and importance in intermediary metabolism of animal muscle was recognized. Second are those new biochemical reactions, distinctive to molds, and previously not studied much in other biological systems. Their discovery in molds may well pave the way for their identification in other systems, and an understanding of their role there.

As examples here, one could cite oxalic, kojic, aconitic, and itaconic acid formation, the transformation of arsenic into numerous organic compounds, and the synthesis of numerous other substances, particularly ring type compounds, identified only in molds so far. The unique polysaccharides described by the Raistrick school are another fine example.

4. THE CONTRIBUTION OF MOLD METABOLISM TO METHODS

In yet another way has mold biochemistry left its mark on general microbiology, and that is by the development of the shaking (submerged) technique for physiological and biochemical studies, particularly on growing cultures. In this aspect of technique, the relatively new subject of molds has reversed the usual order of things and has made a significant contribution to the long and extensively studied sister subject of bacteriology. First utilized in an effective scientific fashion by Kluyver and Perquin, who pointed out numerous of its advantageous and necessary features, the shake culture technique has rapidly become indispensable for mold work, having reached its highest stage of application in the study of penicillin production. The remarkable acceleration in growth and metabolic reactions, as well as the reproducibility obtainable as a result of the uniform physiological conditions, applies just as much to bacterial cultures, and it is a safe assumption that within a very short time metabolism studies on bacteria growing in stationary (surface or "still") cultures will be considered obsolete, for, as discussed in detail in Chapter 2, such conditions are hardly optimum for experimental work. It is not an exaggeration to say that for such work a shaking device is as essential to the modern bacteriological laboratory as incubators, and is a must for industrial microbiology. Actually many successful practical applications have already demonstrated the superiority of this technique for bacteria: vinegar and sorbose production by *Acetobacter suboxydans*, tyrothricin formation by *Bacillus brevis*, organic acid formation by species of Pseudomonas and Phytomonas, toxin production by Clostridium and Corynebacter. Recently there has been interest in the propagation of the tubercle bacillus under submerged conditions to manufacture tuberculin. One is surprised that the extensive use of the Warburg technique, with its shaking to secure good aeration and uniform diffusion conditions, did not lead much earlier to an appreciation of the necessity for utilizing this principle for growing cultures.

Incidentally, the washed cell technique itself was employed in mold research long before the general application of shake or submerged cultivation. It was used extensively with the ordinary surface (stationary) growth by allowing the development of a mature mold pad in a complete growth medium, then aseptically removing the spent medium, leaving the mold growth in the original flask. Residual medium is washed out by a few rinses with sterile water and a fresh sugar or other solution intended for investigation is introduced under the pad in such a manner that the mold pad finally floats on the surface. Usually the replacement liquid is deficient in nitrogen or minerals so as to prevent the incorporation, via growth, of a substantial portion of the substrate into cell material. Thus the substrate is dissimilated by the mold, the bulk of the substrate accumulating as soluble products. The earliest workers recognized the complicating factor of growth, and the omission of nitrogen has long been known to be of aid in separating the growth and dissimilation phases of metabolism. Actually, as mentioned above, this technique does not eliminate the oxidative assimilation so pronounced with molds, but it has found extremely wide application in research in mold metabolism.

5. FUNGI IN NATURAL PROCESSES

Next as a modern development in mold metabolism may be considered the role of fungi in the economy of organic matter in nature and the specific processes involved. Since time immemorial fungi have always been associated with spoilage and destruction of foodstuffs, and with the rotting and decay of organic debris of dead plants and animals. This association obviously was the result of easy recognition of the conspicuous fungus growth, such as is almost always present when plant remains, particularly woody materials, exist under high moisture conditions. Here the higher or fleshy type fungi are frequently involved as evidenced by the fruiting structures and by the abundance of coarse mycelial development throughout the moist substrate. Similarly, in the spoilage of foods, particularly bread and fresh and preserved fruits, a substantial amount of mold growth is evident to the naked eye.

Not so apparent, however, is the part played by molds in the destruction and conservation of the organic matter of the soil, for these are not apparent to the eye, and only in the last few decades has the understanding of these important activities come to light through the research of the soil microbiologist. The investigations of Waksman and associates have been largely responsible for much of our knowledge on this subject, and in particular for first clearly establishing the existence of an active fungus population in the soil. The situation existing up until the beginning of Waksman's studies and the paucity of specific information pertaining even to the existence of an active fungus population of the soil can be epitomized perhaps by the title of one of Waksman's papers published in 1916, when he commenced to explore this field: "*Do fungi live and produce mycelium in the soil.*"

With the demonstration that an autochtonous (indigenous) fungus flora does exist in the soil as physiologically active vegetative mycelium, together with spores, subsequent development of methods for their isolation and study *in vitro* and in the soil itself, has, during the past three decades led to the amassing of a great amount of information and understanding of the part fungi play in soil processes. After conclusive proof of the normal existence of vegetative mycelium in soil, there soon followed data on the large numbers and varieties of soil fungi, ecological influences on the nature of the fungus population, biochemical studies on the fungal breakdown of plant remains in pure culture and in the soil complex. Cellulose, proteins, hemicelluloses, and lignin were organic fractions of particular interest because of their participation in the formation of the permanent nutrient reservoir of the soil, namely, humus. Revelations were also made of symbiotic associations of fungi with the roots of certain plants (mycorrhizae) and also saprophytic relations to plant roots (rhizopheres). Their important role as contributors to and stabilizers of the essential residual humus of the soil, and antagonistic effects among themselves and the other members of the soil population has been developed into a rational pattern.

All these problems are interrelated with soil fertility and plant nutrition, and the varied aspects and characteristics of soil fungi provide the very basis for the study of the physiology and biochemistry of fungi, for they reveal the true workings of fungi as biological systems in the cycle of nature. The imposing progress which was made in this broad aspect of soil microbiology has been synthesized and integrated into a comprehensive picture by Waksman, the duration and substance of whose own multifarious contributions are again epitomized by the title of his reflective exposition, *Three decades with soil fungi*, published in 1944.

As time goes on, the realization of the basic value and importance of a background in soil microbiology for the student and research worker interested in the metabolism of fungi (the same holds for bacteria) becomes more evident. Study of the activities of a fungus in pure culture under the highly artificial conditions of the laboratory, where environmental conditions are usually something the organism is never exposed to in nature, cannot be expected to present a true picture of the natural metabolic performance of any one organism. It means that the laboratory findings are just another type of biochemical experiment, without regard to the biology of the fungus itself. All too often the activities and physiological processes of fungi in the soil comprise a vague and mysterious body of knowledge to the biochemist, who uses microbes merely to catalyze the reactions he happens to be interested in, and who is not concerned with the innumerable physiological aspects and influences at play during the growth of the organism in nature. The organism is not often thought of as a part of the extremely complex and constantly changing dynamics of the soil—the unstable equilibrium of Waksman—and there was and is still a feeling that the biochemist holds as his preserve only the organism under laboratory conditions, and that any and all study relative to the organism in nature is considered to be the pursuit reserved for the agricultural scientist. Actually, the two approaches are part of the same thing and for a true appreciation of the biology of the organism there cannot be an arbitrary division between biochemistry and physiology; the place where one leaves off and the other begins is imperceptible.

This brings up the question, more and more important as increasing numbers of organisms originating from soil are now studied individually in the laboratory, as to how much the performance of the organism in the laboratory is related to the activities of the same organism in the soil or under conditions of existence in nature. There is a good basis for believing, at least insofar as dissimilation metabolism goes, that there is little relation (see Chapter 4). The metabolism revealed in the highly controlled artificial conditions of the laboratory might well be considered as "pathological," a manifestation of reaction to conditions of nutrition quite foreign to anything the organism encounters under the vicissitudes of survival in the soil complex. One need not invoke the highly controversial issue of what is "normal" or "abnormal" for an organism. Regardless of whether or not one places teleological implications upon an organism's "normal" metabolism, a factual comparison can be made, by direction or indirection, of how a fungus behaves in the laboratory and in the soil; it is difficult to see how they could be very much alike.

This matter will be treated in detail in a later chapter (4), but it is well to point out here another problem always associated with this issue, one of sufficient import to warrant emphasis by the "dean of soil micro-biologists," Sergei Winogradsky. This distinguished scientist cautioned that after an organism is isolated from soil, or other natural systems, the very cultivation of the organism in the laboratory soon leads to changes in the organism's characteristics so that it gradually resembles less and less the culture as it existed in soil and when it was freshly isolated. This results probably from the forces of selection. Winogradsky called such organisms "hot-house" cultures.

Very much in the limelight since about 1940 has been the fad in microbiology pertaining to antibiotics and antagonistic effects among microorganisms. The same story applies here: it is a simple matter to demonstrate antagonism between organisms in the laboratory, but it is quite a different matter to project such findings and generalize as to the significance of antibiotic substances in controlling other groups of organisms in nature.

The conditions under which antagonists (and this is particularly true of fungi) form antibotic substances are highly specific and within rela-tively narrow limits, and it is likely that these "ideal" conditions only rarely, if ever, occur in the uncontrolled expanses of nature. The antibiotic substance as a natural force has yet to be demonstrated. There seems to be a more rational explanation for the unstable equilib-rium among the multifarious members of the soil population. This would be based not on substances synthesized by certain organisms which are repressive to other organisms, but rather on substances synthesized which *favor and which are beneficial to*, and which are more readily utilized by certain groups of organisms than others. Such substances include those readily utilized by the scavenger organisms for energy and carbon and those which may be assimilated by others unchanged for use in enzyme systems (coenzymes) or incorporation as building blocks for cell materials. According to this idea, then, the stability of the soil popula-tion is determined by the amount and type and availability of nutrients instead of by poisons and inhibitory substances produced by other organisms.

The fungi are of particular significance in this connection because they probably account for the bulk of the microbial cell material synthesized in the soil. Reserving a detailed discussion for Chapter 4, it may merely be mentioned here that in the case of fungi, organisms with highly oxidative tendencies, the products of metabolism in soil are most likely only cell material and CO_2. Products of incomplete dissimilation prob-ably are not often formed; most likely they make an insignificant con-tribution to the nourishment of the rest of the soil population. On the other hand, once dead, the cell material at once becomes a substrate for other microorganisms. Indeed, if one may be permitted the license of teleological venture, it may be said that in the natural complex that is soil, the aerobic inhabitants (and this applies in particular to fungi) have evolved to that stage and their metabolism so adjusted through continuous existence in the jungle of the soil, that they are 100 per cent biologically efficient in the utilization of available carbon substrates. Thus it would be that the only products formed are those resulting from perfect biological efficiency, namely cell material and CO_2 (and water).

6. BIOCHEMICAL SYNTHESES

Probably the most recent fundamental development in mold metabolism has been the field opened by the splendid work of Beadle and his coworkers (now at the California Institute of Technology) dealing with the genetic control of biochemical reactions. For various advantages such as ease of handling, rapid rate of growth, and knowledge of its (sexual) life cycle and genetics, an ascomycete mold, *Neurospora crassa*, has proved to be almost the ideal biological system for this work. Based on the appreciation of the fact that the synthesis of the vital chemical constituents of cell material involves a number of successive step-wise chemical reactions, eventuating in the ultimate appearance of the final compound through various intermediates, Beadle and Tatum, in 1941 (see 1945 paper), proved that the individual steps in the synthetic series are genetically controlled, each in fact being governed by a single gene. They developed methods and have, by artificial irradiation of Neurospora conidiospores with ultraviolet or x-rays, been able to secure mutants of the parent wild type which differ from the parent only in the lack of ability to effect a single biochemical reaction. Many of these reactions have proved to be one of the steps in the synthetic sequence during the genesis of the cellular amino acids, vitamins, nucleic acids, etc. The mutants are capable of carrying the synthesis of a given cellular substance to a certain stage only. By identification of these intermediate stages in various mutants it has been possible to establish the exact biochemical mechanisms of the synthesis of numerous cellular substances.

Projection of information of this kind through the instrument of comparative biochemistry makes possible an understanding of the origin of these substances in other biological systems, although there is ample evidence already that more than one pathway of biochemical synthesis of any given compound may exist; what may hold for Neurospora may not necessarily apply to other organisms, but in general a uniformity prevails.

The implications that this ingenious approach has for the future of mold biochemistry (indeed, microbiological biochemistry) can scarcely be fully realized or appreciated at this time.   Innumerable potentialities, academic as well as applied, have suddenly been created with the advent of this work.   The missing link in mold (or even general) biochemistry, has now been supplied in the form of a tool facilitating the approach to the intermediate steps in the origin of compounds synthesized by molds. This is true biochemistry of molds, as contrasted to the organic chemistry of the final product.   The vast majority of studies on intermediary mold metabolism has previously dealt with dissimilation (catabolic) processes merely for want of a suitable approach to assimilation (anabolic) processes. Already, marked success is noted in our understanding of the biochemical synthesis of such key biological compounds as arginine, lysine, trypto-phane, adenine, thiamine, nicotinic acid, and many others, through the use of induced mutants.

Approximately one-hundred gene mutants for various compounds have been obtained thus far in fungi.   In those already worked out, the intermediates have all been known chemicals, suspected to be precursors in the particular sequences.   There are untold possibilities for the detec-tion and identification of biochemical precursors, which are as yet unknown chemical substances, considering the innumerable synthetic products of mold metabolism.   For example, attack is now possible on the precursors of the various mold pigments described by the Raistrick group; the study of enzymes effecting transformation of the successive precursors will be a corollary.   The same holds for the various antibiotic substances produced by molds, and how valuable it would be to fill in the wide gap in our knowledge of the precursors in the biosynthesis of such remarkably useful substances as penicillin and streptomycin.   Real, practical application for higher yields of these substances might be envisaged from the identification, synthesis, and the addition of the synthetic intermediate to the medium in which, for example, penicillin is produced, so that high concentrations of the intermediate could be converted to the desired product by the mold.   Phenylacetic acid is already known to function in this manner, but precursors of the nucleus of the penicillin molecule are needed.   This idea would be particularly appealing if that precursor would be added whose biological synthesis by the mold is the limiting one in the overall synthesis of penicillin.   The practicability of this idea would depend, of course, on the cost of manu-facturing the precursor in relation to the amount converted, and espe-cially in relation to the worth of the finished penicillin.

Not only can induced mutants be obtained in which the synthetic sequence is blocked at a certain stage so that the end product is not pro-duced at all, but mutants may also be obtained in which the reverse is true—the substance in question is not only still synthesized but it is synthesized in appreciably larger quantities than the original culture. Such mutants are stable and presumably genetic in character and the mechanism of their origin is discussed in Chapter 6. This particular type of mutation is the special interest of the industrial microbiologist, for this technique, judiciously exploited, can lead to the development of strains capable of giving high yields of industrially valuable compounds. Phenomenal success in this way has been achieved with penicillin-producing molds. Some measure of improved yields have also been achieved with the production of citric acid by *Aspergillus niger* and itaconic acid by *A. terreus*. The technique has also been applied to streptothricin and streptomycin production by *Streptomyces lavendulae* and *S. griseus*, respectively.

Just as the shake or submerged growth technique was shown to be an indispensable tool for metabolic studies on molds, so may it be predicted that induced mutations are destined to be by far the most valuable tool of the industrial microbiologist from the standpoint of major increases in yields. Indeed, this has already proved itself. Without a doubt, with few exceptions all microbial processes of industrial value will be exhaustively exploited in the mutation sense, and should be so until the yield of the substance approachs that possible from theoretical considerations of substrate consumed, chemical reactions involved, CO_2 produced and product formed. Theoretically, in the case of synthetic products of metabolism, the concentrations obtainable are unlimited, within physiological concentrations of the substrate. Equally attractive possibilities present themselves for application of the mutation technique to problems of dissimilation of sugar in fungi.

Genetic control of physiological or biochemical reactions as a means of inducing inherent alterations in the metabolism can be achieved in certain organisms in quite another way—hybridization. Where viable spores are obtainable from organisms exhibiting the perfect sexual stage, it is possible to mate spores representing strains with different desirable features and secure a hybrid possessing the desired characteristics. Seemingly it should be possible to obtain by such breeding methods a strain possessing many if not all of the characteristics desired in an organism utilized in an industrial process. One might also perceive possibilities for improving rate of growth and the tolerance of the organism to temperature, pH, salt concentrations, accumulation of metabolic products, concentration of substrate, etc. Hybridization of yeasts and of Neurospora has been achieved with striking success by Lindegren and by Dodge. Physiological characters were concerned with the yeasts, and cultural and morphological properties in the case of the Neurospora work.

Excellent possibilities lie ahead in physiological hybridization, both theoretical and practical, with such organisms as lactic and fumaric acid formation in certain Mucorales, riboflavin synthesis in the ascomycete *Eremothecium ashbyii*, in improving edibility of fleshy fungi of the higher Ascomycetes and Basidiomycetes.

To complete this purview of mutations and physiological genetics one should mention the well-known spontaneous mutation, which accounts for the instability or physiological degeneration of stock cultures. Possibly this accounts for the occurrence in nature of numberless strains of a given species of mold.

7. FUNGI AS ANALYTICAL TOOLS

Fungi have found an important position in the list of analytical working tools available to the chemist, biologist, nutritionist, and numerous other specialized branches of science. Particularly is this true in the cases of quantitative determination, i.e., assay, of substances occurring in, or undergoing transformation in other biological systems or materials. Microbiological methods of analysis have become just as much a part of the analytical resources of the biochemist and physiologist as such well known techniques as Van Slyke amino nitrogen determination, Warburg manometry, phosphate estimations, and innumerable other parts of the stock and trade of the researcher. Although methods employing bacteria and yeasts are at the present time more numerous, several analytical methods using fungi have already been developed. In general, they have the advantages over chemical methods common to almost all microbiological assays, namely, small size of sample required for assay, high specificity for the substance being assayed, and, particularly in the case of fungi, reliability in the case of the highly colored or turbid extracts which generally are encountered in the analysis of natural materials.

Mold assays have come to be associated with the enormous developments in microbiological vitamin and amino acid assays which occurred during the last 5 to 8 years, but fungi have been utilized as successful analytical reagents ever since the time of Pasteur (1860), whose ingenious use of the lowly *Penicillium glaucum* to assimilate selectively *d*-tartaric acid from a racemic mixture permitting isolation of the unchanged unnatural *l*-tartrate was instrumental in the brilliant concept of molecular asymmetry, now known as stereoisomerism. In another classic experiment some years later, Pasteur was to employ again the physiological action of a fungus, *Mucor rouxii*, as corroboration of his revolutionary concept that alcohol formation in fermentation by yeast is a universal mechanism for aerobic organisms existing in the absence of air.

Little known too, outside their fields of special application, are the nice methods worked out for the quantitative determinations of the trace heavy metals, for the detection of arsenic and for the estimation of phosphorous and potassium occurring in soils in forms available to plants. The beautiful studies of Mulder (1939) in Holland using *Aspergillus niger* to measure copper and of Mehlich in this country using *Cunninghamella blakesleeana* to estimate the available phosphorus, have demonstrated these methods as valuable adjuncts in the study of soil fertility and the mineral content of soils in relation to crop requirements. Indeed, a standard Cunninghamella culture dish is a stock item of equipment available from laboratory supply houses.

When Schopfer in 1935 found that *Phycomyces blakesleanus* required vitamin B_1 (thiamine), he developed what appears to be the first microbiological assay procedure devised for determination of vitamin content of natural materials. It was based on dry weight growth response of the fungus in an assay medium devoid of the substance under test (thiamine), but otherwise nutritionally complete. It now appears possible to secure fungus assays made to order, so to speak, for any of the multifarious compounds in living mold cells. This has already been demonstrated by Beadle and associates by the technique of induced mutations whereby the desired assay organism is obtained simply by destroying a gene controlling the synthesis of the particular compound. No longer does a microbiological assay depend on the discovery of a naturally-occurring organism deficient in the ability to synthesize a given compound. Mutants of Neurospora deficient in twelve different amino acids and in seven of the B vitamins are already available and specific assay procedures have already been worked out for several of these. *A priori*, with this technique there is no reason why satisfactory Neurospora assays could not be worked out for biological molecules such as cholesterol, fatty acids, purine bases, and a host of other essential constituents of the cell. Every time a new mold assay is devised there ensues an accelerated physiological and biochemical study on the organism, because only after a thorough understanding of these aspects insofar as they relate to nutrition and growth, can the assay be considered acceptable.

8. INDUSTRIAL APPLICATIONS

Modern industrial fermentations represent the embodiment of all the points discussed in the foregoing paragraphs. The type of organized attack on microbiological processes of potential commercial value is reminiscent of the manner in which industrial and chemical technology developed, which led to mass production at low cost. In many instances industries that formerly were engaged exclusively in organic chemistry have centered and applied their extensive resources to the actively expanding field of producing chemicals through the intermediary agency of microorganisms. Particularly is this true of the pharmaceutical industry. The synthetic chemist has more than met his match in the microbe!

In recent years the fungi have been the most promising group in this respect, and most of the big advances have been in mold processes. This again bears out the observation made earlier that the variety and numbers of fungi provides abundant opportunity for the discovery of new chemicals for which uses may already exist or can be found. The greatest single impetus has been the antibiotic substances of which penicillin has been, of course, the signal example.

The collaborative efforts of the mycologist, microbiologist, biochemist, organic chemist, and engineer all find an important part in the large-scale development of an industrial fermentation process. Once established as producing a substance of value, the organism is exhaustively studied by the microbiologist in order that every character likely to be favorable for the production of the desired substance can be capitalized upon. Meantime the mycologist is concerned with the development of new and more potent strains. Selective culture isolation from natural sources and from various culture collections is employed, and, in addition, substrain testing and artificial induction of mutations are extensively prosecuted.

After laboratory conditions are evaluated, the process passes to the pilot plant stage where valuable data on physical environment and rate of production are obtained. From these results large-scale production units involving fermenters up to 15,000 gallons capacity are designed and constructed. Research on the process is almost endless, even after the process has reached the final stage of commercial production. There is always room for improvement, for new raw materials continually make their appearance as potential substrates, and the selection of a new strain, or even substrain, means extensive reviewal of the influence of all the basic factors because the new strain may behave quite differently from the parent in many respects. Many results of fundamental academic importance come out of such applied studies. At least, it may be said that practical exploitation of a microbial process has a direct positive effect on the stimulation of research on the organism concerned, and frequently on related ones. Often results or details are not published or made available though the scientific journals, but usually these are the practical aspects, the trade secrets, which have patentable value. Sooner or later the fundamental principles involved find their way into the scientific literature for other workers to utilize.

Although the developments in antibiotics far overshadow the field at the present time, it is worthwhile to list commercial processes in which molds are the active agents. In the field of hydrolytic enzymes, the production of proteolytic, diastatic and pectic enzymes is well established. Organic acids produced commercially by fungi include gluconic acid, citric acid, fumaric acid, gallic acid, and, potentially, itaconic acid. Actual commercial production of antibiotics by mold processes is limited to penicillin, notwithstanding the numerous different antibiotics known to be produced by molds, but so far useless therapeutically.

A number of mold products have been produced in sufficiently high concentrations, and optimum conditions for working processes elucidated, so as to make their commercial manufacture by fermentation methods feasible were it not for the fact that practical uses for the products are not known, or where known, the fermentation product cannot compete with other materials on a cost basis. Included here are kojic acid, d-lactic acid, and itaconic acid. Furthermore, should utility be shown for any of the scores of other compounds known to occur in small amounts in fungus culture fluids, it seems likely that through the approaches discussed in the previous sections, satisfactory industrial mold fermentation processes could be worked out. Recent emphasis in the field of nutrition has focused on the need for vitamins either in the pure state, or incorporated in crude form in feed mixtures for poultry and other animals. Riboflavin, pure and crude, is manufactured on a huge scale today by use of the fungus *Eremothecium ashbyii*, and this development is as new as penicillin. The possibilities are evident for economical synthesis by molds of complex substances valuable in nutrition, by converting cheap source materials of sugar, minerals, and nitrogen.

Molds have proved their value in other ways. Biotin, probably the most elusive of all the water-soluble vitamins in respect to its concentrations in natural materials, for years resisted isolation in sufficient quantities to permit study of its chemical structure until it was found to accumulate in relatively high concentrations during the production of fumaric acid by *Rhizopus nigricans*. A further recent interesting example of this type is the report that antibacillin, a naturally-occurring inhibitor for the antibiotic substance bacillin, is found to exist most abundantly in the waste mycelium of *Penicillium chrysogenum* obtained in commercial penicillin production.

These examples provide the justification for, and are intended to stress a principle that in the future might very well be the guide to more rapid exploitation of, and success in, the isolation of new growth factors of general biological significance. Once a substance is demonstrated to be of widespread use there is every reason to believe that through a systematic microbiological study utilizing all the approaches previously summarized, a mold can be found and proper conditions defined, which will result in cultures far richer in the active substance than the usual biological source materials like liver, yeast, milk, cereals, etc. Often the impurities are fewer and more varied, facilitating the preparation of crude concentrates and subsequent isolation in pure form. Most molds can develop on glucose-salts media, thus eliminating impurities contributed by complex organic nitrogenous ingredients. The future of new growth factors must, indeed, look to the molds.

What new types of compounds in mold cultures will prove to be of value next, only time can tell. Molds synthesize protein from molasses and inorganic nitrogen sources, and possibly may be of value in the preparation of certain amino acids or even in the manufacture of protein hydrolysates. The same holds for fat production by molds. Another prospect not too remote to contemplate, is the production by means of molds of substances having pharmacological action in the animal and human body. These might prove to be safer and more effective than drugs presently available for certain pharmacological effects such as heart stimulants, blood pressure regulators, respiration effects, pyrogenic reactions, metabolism stimulation, etc. Ergot production by the smut fungus *Claviceps purpurea* is a good example of a pharmaceutical produced by a fungus. Evidence already exists for the elicitation of various pharmacological effects by products of mold metabolism. Some of the so-called toxic antibiotics are in this class.

In agriculture, and particularly in certain specialized phases such as greenhouse, nursery and general horticultural practices, there is a real indication that antibiotic pretreatment of seeds affords protection against plant pathogens, particularly fungi in damping-off diseases, which cause a high mortality in seedlings. General agricultural use of antibiotics would not be excluded on a cost basis if the antibiotic could be used in crude form, as for example, the spray-dried product of the whole culture medium without any purification. The control of obnoxious fungi in still another respect, is a distinct possibility. Mildewing and rotting of textiles is a major problem of the textile industry. Particularly is this true under the warm and moist conditions of the tropics, as experience in the war brought home forcibly.

All the above-mentioned applications of antibiotics refer to their use in the exact chemical form in which they are produced. Untold possibilities lie ahead for altering the chemical structures of known antibiotics, and for the preparation of derivatives to endow special desired properties on these substances. Thus, the ultimate production may turn out to be a joint process—first, the biological synthesis of the metabolic product;

second, its use by the synthetic chemist for further modification. The fertile possibilities implicit here have ample substantiation from the spectacular progress made in the sulfonamides, synthetic antivitamins, and other biochemical substances. Actually this has already been achieved with some antibiotics. The potency of penicillin has been materially enhanced by the introduction of substituent groups in the penicillin molecule. The very fact that different types of penicillins having different antibacterial potencies are produced by fungi shows the validity of the hypothesis. The most striking example of this type of approach is the reduction in toxicity of gramicidin to one-quarter of its original toxicity, without a corresponding reduction in antibacterial potency, by reacting the gramicidin with formaldehyde. Also, the very low water-solubility of gramicidin was previously a disadvantage, and the modified gramicidin has a substantially greater solubility.

Finally, returning to the therapeutic uses of antibiotics, one cannot overlook the possibilities awaiting the discovery of antibiotics effective in a number of infections of man and animals for which no treatment is satisfactory. Thus, protozoan infections, especially malaria, await chemotherapeutic agents superior to quinine and atebrine. Other types of infections, usually associated with tropical climates, such as trypano-somiasis, leischmaniasis, and fungus infections are in a similar situation. The report by Dunham and Rake in 1945 that non-penicillin impurities contained in commercial penicillin preparations are mostly responsible for the antispirochetal action curing rabbits of experimental syphilis, is bound to have implications for the chemotherapy of this disease in humans. It shows that antibiotic substance(s) which are more effective than pure penicillin against *Treponema pallida* are produced by molds.

The field of viruses is practically untouched in this regard and the promise for antibiotics active against this type of disease agent is limit-less. Already information exists pointing to the presence of substances in culture filtrates of certain fungi which destroy the infectivity of yellow fever virus and tobacco mosaic virus. Vast research possibilities are implied here. Quite parallel is the report published in 1943 that impurities in commercial penicillin preparations were effective inhibitors *in vitro* of growing malignant tissue cells, whereas cells from normal tissue were unaffected. The implications for future research and development on this subject are self evident.

REFERENCES

Beadle, G. W., and Tatum, E. L. 1945. *Am. J. Botany* **32**, 678–686.
Dunham, W. B., and Rake, G. 1945. *Am. J. Syphilis, Gonorrhea, Venereal Diseases* **29**, 214–228.
Iwanoff, N. N. 1932. *Ann. Rev. Biochem.* **1**, 675–697.

Kluyver, A. J., and Donker, H. J. L. 1926. *Chem. Zelle u. Gewebe* **13**, 134–140.

Large, E. C. 1940. Advance of the Fungi. Henry Holt & Co., New York, 488 pp.

Mulder, E. G. 1939. *Arch. Mikrobiol.* **10**, 72–86.

Pasteur, L. 1860. *Compt. rend.* **51**, 298–299.

Raistrick, H., *et al.* 1931. *Trans. Roy. Soc. London* **B220**, 1–367.

Raistrick, H. 1937. In Perspectives in Biochemistry. J. Needham, Ed., University Press, Cambridge, England.

Schopfer, W. H. 1935. In Plants and Vitamins. 1943. Chronica Botanica, Waltham, Massachusetts, 293 pp.

Tamiya, H. 1931. *Botan. Mag. Tokyo* **45**, No. 530, 8 pp.

Tamiya, H., and Morita, S. 1929–1930. *Botan. Mag. Tokyo* **43**, No. 506 through **44**, No. 524, 204 pp.

van Niel, C. B. 1943. Occasional Publ. Am. Assoc. Adv. Sci. **14**, 106–119.

Waksman, S. A. 1916. *Science* **44**, 320–322.

Waksman, S. A. 1944. *Soil Sci.* **58**, 89–114.

Winogradsky, S. 1928. *Soil Sci.* **25**, 37–43; **43**, 327–340; 1937.

CHAPTER 2

THE METHODOLOGY OF MOLD METABOLISM

This chapter is concerned with the general methods peculiar to the study of the physiological and biochemical properties of fungi. These fall logically into two groups: (1) those involving cultivation and growth and (2) those concerned with the biochemical activities of the mold cell material under conditions where growth, in the common sense of the term, and as connoted in group 1 above, does not take place. Almost always this utilizes preformed cell material, and thus is merely a logical extension of growth experiments.

A certain interdependence between the two always exists and is self-evident, for the activity of the organisms, whether judged by cultural observation or chemical analysis, is obviously the resultant of innumerable synthetic and degradative biochemical reactions. Synthesis eventually predominates although dissimilation proceeds more or less concomitantly. On the other hand, there is much evidence that the enzymic makeup of mold cell material, and consequently its biochemical behavior, directly depends on the cultivation conditions of the organism during its growth phase. The composition of mold cell material is not one and invariable; the growth conditions provide the determining factor. Even when the identity of cell material during a growth experiment and a post-growth physiological experiment is certain, there is no assurance of the presence and operation of the same biochemical reaction in both cases. In all, however, a fairly representative evaluation of the inherent biochemical character and potentialities of the fungus under study can be obtained by a combination of both approaches.

Growth Technique

1. SOLID SUBSTRATES

Much preliminary information and orientation can be obtained from study of a particular fungus on various solid substrates. Indeed, frequently it is only on such media that certain types of information are obtainable, and results from this simple technique often provide guidance for subsequent detailed and specialized studies. Most useful in this respect are ordinary agar cultures and friable materials such as cereal grains and bran. A variety of media may be used in agar cultures, depending on the purpose of the experiment, and the effect on the fungus of various medium constituents and other added chemical substances can be compared. This is probably the best means of studying the organism as a biological entity. Cultural and microscopical observation can be made on the undisturbed colony, and structure and fine details examined *in situ*. It is the most useful method for observing the behavior of fungi as a response to the physical environment. Included here are features like rate of growth and general cultural characteristics of the mold colony, amount and other special characters of sporulation, and the effect of light and temperature on the overall development. More and more cases of morphological differentiation as a function of nutritional environment are being studied in this way, e.g., conidiospore formation as a result of mineral nutrition, perithecia formation as a function of vitamin nutrition, etc.

Methods for quantitative determination of amino acids and vitamins depending on the rate of growth of fungus surface colonies on agar have been worked out. Agar colony cultures are particularly useful, almost indispensable, in the production and detection of mutants or variants, both those occurring naturally or spontaneously, and those induced artificially by chemicals, exposure to abnormal physical environments, and irradiation, X-ray and ultraviolet. In mutation work the agar colony technique has the limitation of permitting detection only of those colonies whose mutation is reflected by conspicuous change in cultural or morphological appearance. Probably a far greater number of physiological mutants are produced that vary in one or more biochemical properties but are morphologically indistinguishable from each other and from the parent culture, both micro- and macroscopically. Appropriate selection of the culture medium aids in the detection of biochemical mutants.

Many rough diagnostic or survey tests indicating the physiological or biochemical nature of fungi can be accomplished easily with agar cultures. Thus, the formation of colored substances can be readily followed and described, and classified as to color and as to whether they are retained in the cell material or diffuse out into the surrounding medium. It was from such an observation that a newly discovered fungus, *Eremothecium ashbyii* was found to produce a diffusible yellow fluorescent pigment, which was identified as riboflavin. A fermentation industry based on the microbiological production of riboflavin using this fungus has been developed. A drop of acid or alkali placed near the periphery of a colony on agar serves to categorize a soluble pigment, especially if it changes color according to hydrogen ion concentration.

Characterization of the organism as an acid-producer is performed easily by addition of a drop of a suitable pH indicator near the periphery of the colony. Another approach capable of revealing the formation of acidic products in substantial amounts, is to have 0.5–1.0 per cent precipitated calcium carbonate incorporated in the agar at the time of preparation. The carbonate makes a chalky background except for clear areas around the fungus colony where the acid formed has dissolved the carbonate. Depending on the width of the clear zone, the organism may be classified as a strong or weak acid former. Actually, in the case of certain types of acid-producing fungi, among which are Penicillia, Fusaria, and Mucorales, the organism may be inhibited by the high concentration of free acid it produces, resulting in inhibited growth, and possible abnormal colony formation. In such cases, calcium carbonate serves a dual purpose; (1) detection of acid by dissolution and (2) maintenance of a favorable pH by neutralization.

Based on this technique principle, various modifications can be devised by the ingenious investigator to suit the needs of special interests or problems. Thus, not only can the selection of acid-forming fungi be facilitated as just described, but, by appropriate qualitative tests applied directly to the agar culture the presence and identity of various specific acids, or other metabolic products of the fungus can be ascertained. To determine, for example, if the organic acidity revealed by the calcium carbonate test is due to kojic acid, at least in part, a drop of 0.1 per cent freshly-prepared $FeCl_3$ solution placed about 1 mm. away from the edge of the fungus colony. The formation of a deep reddish color in or adjacent to the solution indicates a positive test for kojic acid. Although the chances are that a red coloration is due to kojic acid, the possibility always exists that some other as yet unknown metabolic product may give a similar reaction, but in any case a positive test is good presumptive evidence for the presence of kojic acid. A negative test, of course, definitely eliminates it. The ferric chloride test, according to Yabuta, can detect one part of kojic acid in 200,000 (5 μg./ml.). A simplification for routine testing of kojic acid in agar cultures consists of placing a small piece of filter paper previously moistened with $FeCl_3$ solution flat on the agar (at the edge of the fungus colony). After a short period of time the kojic acid diffuses into the paper, turning it red. Another easily applied test is to remove a small plug (2-mm. diameter) of agar from the peripheral zone with a cork borer and to fill the hole with the particular reagent necessary to detect the substance sought. In many respects, the latter technique is probably the best for the conditions and better for diffusion between the liquid in the hole and the agar.

Ferric chloride reacts with other organic acids, all known products of mold metabolism, to yield yellow colors, for example, with malic and lactic acids. So far, no mold is known that produces any one of these acids and kojic acid simultaneously. Lactic acid can be eliminated from this group if the organism giving a yellow $FeCl_3$ test does not belong to the easily recognizable Mucorales order since, with only one or two exceptions, all molds known to produce lactic acid are of this group. Other rough qualitative reactions with $FeCl_3$ are (a) blue or violet color with phenolic acids and (b) various reactions with specific substances such as citromycetin (green color) and citrinin (brown color). Where more than one substance is known to give the same reaction, a combination of two or more qualitative tests can be applied to eliminate the likelihood of all but the one substance actually present.

Other organic acids may be identified in analogous fashion, depending on the availability of a qualitative test for the individual acids. Crystals of the insoluble calcium oxalate are easily distinguished from residual $CaCO_3$ in the agar, especially if finely divided precipitated carbonate is used.

These qualitative tests can, where useful, be extended from the agar culture to test tubes. A sizeable block of agar from near or underneath the mold colony is placed in a centrifuge tube with a few milliliters of water to permit diffusion of the acid from the agar into the water. A few minutes standing is sufficient if the agar is macerated in the test tube with a stirring rod. The tube is centrifuged and the supernatant liquid, containing the acid, is now subjected to chemical tests impossible to carry out in the agar. Thus the guaiacol or thiophene color reaction for lactic acid is performed by boiling the liquid for a few moments to expel any acetaldehyde that may be present, adding concentrated H_2SO_4, heating in a boiling water bath for several minutes, cooling, and carefully adding a dilute solution of guaiacol (alcoholic) or thiophene. A red coloration is a positive test for lactic acid. The thiophene test requires a drop of saturated copper sulfate solution. Citric acid may be detected in the same way using Denige's reaction, Stehre's reaction, or the sodium nitroprusside test. Fumaric acid may be suspected when rapid decolorization of dilute $KMnO_4$ or Br_2 solutions takes place.

Workers in the Raistrick group at the London School of Tropical Medicine and Hygiene (Birkinshaw *et al.*, 1931) state that the ferric chloride test may be used as a specific diagnostic test for *Penicillium digitatum*. Czapek-Dox culture liquids of 18 strains of this organism all showed a "permanent, beautiful, emerald green color" with a slight excess of $FeCl_3$. When bleaching powder solution (CaOCl) was added, the green changed to purple. These reactions were not shown by any other fungi tested. While a test of this nature may be presumptive evidence for *P. digitatum*, newer concepts of mold metabolism indicate it is extremely unusual for a metabolic specificity to be as rigid as this.

Without going into further detail as to the chemical detection of other specific organic acids, it is evident that special tests can be devised to meet the particular requirements of the investigator. The purpose of this brief discussion is not to formulate a specific, systematic routine testing procedure but rather to demonstrate the possibilities available to the investigator. In the final analysis the ingenuity of the investigator in adapting the technique to suit his special needs determines his success.

Nowadays the extensive developments in industrial microbiology oft times necessitates a survey of acid-producing fungi with the objective of finding new organisms producing a particular acid of interest. H. Davis (1948) has utilized the surface colony technique in a screening procedure designed to reveal and permit direct isolation of acid-forming fungi in the midst of non-acid-formers. Soil, manure, or other natural materials are plated in dilutions on peptone-glucose agar (0.5 and 5.0 per cent respectively) adjusted to pH 4.5, and containing bromcresol green indicator (yellow, acid; blue, alkaline). The optimum concentration of indicator stock solution was 10 times (i.e., 0.4 per cent) that normally employed in pH indicators and 6.7 ml. was added to each 100 ml. of medium. The initial reaction of pH 4.5 inhibits almost all the bacteria and actinomycetes in the sample and permits the bulk of the fungi to develop. The normal color of the indicator medium at this pH is a deep blue-green. If a fungus colony produces acid, the zone surrounding the colony changes in color, from an intense yellow to a green color hardly discernable from the blue-green color of the background, the unchanged original. The diameter of the acid zone and the degree of change in color are proportional to the quantity of acid produced by the colony. By holding the plate up to the window (daylight is best) acid-forming colonies are easily distinguished by the contrasting zone colors. The changes in zone colors are detectable while the colonies are, in some cases, barely visible to the naked eye, and almost always by the time they are only 1 or a few millimeters in diameter. This is of great advantage because mature colonies or those in low dilutions crowd each other, causing overlapping of zones which increase greatly in size as the colony ages. Considering the very small percentage of all the fungi in natural materials that have proved to be acid-formers, the value of this selective method is evident.

One of the most successful and widely used applications of the agar plate colony technique is in the field of antibiotics, where fungi producing antibiotics are easily distinguished. Here also a number of testing methods are used but, in contrast to the chemical reactions described for organic acids (dissimilation products), these are based on the distinctive property of all antibiotic substances, namely, their ability to inhibit the growth of various microorganisms. In such cases, the test microorganisms are the reagents, and their inhibition indicates the presence of antibiotic substances. In principle, most of these tests are based on a clear circular zone of bacterial inhibition around a fungus colony, the clear zone delineated by bacterial (or other microbial) growth in the region of the plate beyond which the antibiotic has not diffused. The comparative potency and/or amount of the antibiotic is roughly indicated by the width of the inhibition zone, but this is influenced by a number of factors, and is useful only under controlled and specific conditions. Fleming's celebrated discovery of penicillin was made in this way as was the discovery of streptomycin. Frequently, as described for organic acids, a block of agar may be recovered from the periphery of a mold colony, placed in a medium, agar, solid, or liquid, seeded with test bacteria, and judged to contain an antibiotic substance according to whether inhibition of bacterial growth occurred during a suitable incubation period. The various techniques and their applications in the field of antibiotics are available in Waksman's (1947) monograph on antibiotics.

The greatly intensified interest in various aspects of biochemical activities of molds in recent years quite generally has led to a search for new and different organisms capable of performing any given function, or in the case of any function of special interest, for different strains of the same species capable of carrying out the particular function in a superior manner. This is particularly true of molds or processes of actual or potential industrial importance. Usually three approaches have been followed: (1) testing pure cultures available in stock culture collections, (2) isolating new strains from nature (soil, fruits, etc), and (3) obtaining substrains either through routine testing of progeny by single colony isolates or through induced mutation.

Where the chief concern is the ability of the fungus to produce a particular substance, as so often is the case, the idea of new strains has definite limitations if the substance in question is a dissimilation product derived directly from the substrate through metabolic activity of the mold. Worthy of mention here simply because they are best known, but by no means the only ones, are the organic acids originating from carbohydrate, including gluconic, citric, oxalic, kojic, succinic, fumaric, lactic, and itaconic acid. From what is known of the immediate precursors of these substances and of the mechanisms of their formation by the mold, it is possible to calculate the conversion yields theoretically obtainable from the available carbohydrate, and, at least with those organic acids mentioned, the bulk of the carbohydrate consumed by appropriate molds can be converted into those metabolic products, and often in amounts approaching the theory. Considering that some of the substrate goes into cell substance, respiratory carbon dioxide, storage products, and minor amounts of other associated metabolic products, the great preponderance of the one type of metabolic chain in an organism is one of the outstanding phenomena of mold metabolism. Thus, with this type of metabolic product (i.e., direct dissimilation products of carbohydrates) the amount of effort to go into such a search, and the likelihood of significant improvement obtainable in new fungus strains, can be fairly critically and accurately evaluated on purely theoretical grounds. This is an extremely important consideration for the economics of industrial production, for costs can be compared with competing processes and products on the basis of yields actually obtained, those likely to be obtained, and the maximum obtainable on theoretical grounds.

The other great group of substances produced by molds are the innumerable products of the synthetic metabolism of the organisms. In a rough way, this group is distinguished from the former by the greater diversity of substances, their considerably more complex chemical structures, and, with some exceptions, their extremely small yields, figured on amount of substrate utilized by the fungi during their formation. Worthy of note here, again simply because of their practical interest and industrial importance, are certain enzymes, antibiotics, vitamins, and proteins. Because of the relatively large molecular weight and extreme complexity of chemical structure of most of these so-called synthetic products of mold metabolism, almost nothing is known of the mechanisms of their formation, and accordingly, yields of such substances theoretically attainable from the substrate are virtually impossible to ascertain. In fact, the only criterion available in this respect, and especially helpful in view of the extremely small amounts of synthetic products frequently derived from substrates, is based on a weight for weight basis. The absolute amounts of the vitamins, antibiotics, enzymes, pigments, etc. produced by molds under ordinary conditions are almost invariably of such a small order that the theoretical limit becomes almost an academic question. Nevertheless, under highly refined conditions, particularly with selected high-yielding mutant strains, up to 10 per cent of the substrate can be converted into one such substance, streptomycin, by *Streptomyces griseus* (Woodruff and Ruger, 1948). An enormous amount of developmental work on selected strains of fungi has led to the production of these substances in amounts exceeding 1 mg./ml. of culture medium, so in the final analysis any statement regarding the efficiency of an organism with respect to synthetic powers must be tempered with a consideration of the amount of work devoted to the subject. This, of course, invariably relates to its economic importance. For practical purposes, opportunities for increased yields are still far from the limits imposed by theoretical reasoning. The remarkable successes achieved in the formation of proteolytic, diastatic, and pectinolytic enzymes by fungi, and of high potency penicillin-producing strains of Penicillia, and of riboflavin and fat synthesis by molds are good examples of this kind.

The previous two paragraphs indicate the almost unlimited opportunities for the utilization and application of simple methods relating to the recognition and the selection of mold species and strains in connection with their ability to synthesize specific substances. A carefully devised system involving, as the initial step, agar colony culture technique is a most valuable and efficient tool for this kind of work. Regardless of whether the interest is in entirely new organisms or strains from soil or other natural sources, or whether improved strains are sought among the naturally occurring or mutated progeny of a given parent strain of known capacity, the problem is essentially one of elimination, i.e., screening out those organisms or colonies that are negative or inferior in the desired property. This is known as selective culturing and, as applied to synthetic substances, is little used or known as compared to selective culture methods for isolation of organisms capable of decomposing, or utilizing for growth, specific medium constituents. The latter is a rather straightforward technique based simply on the self evident premise that to isolate organisms capable of decomposing or utilizing a pentose for example, the particular pentose is incorporated as the sole carbon source in a basal medium inoculated with soil suspension or pure cultures. Naturally only those organisms capable of utilizing the pentose can develop substantially, eliminating thereby all organisms lacking this power, and greatly increasing the pentose utilizers. Agar plate methods, permitting as they do the separation and growth of different colonies, and containing the medium as described, are traditionally standard for this purpose.

With products of synthetic metabolism, the problem is not so simple. It is not possible to prevent the growth of all organisms except those that synthesize the desired substances. There is no method known that permits the selective cultivation of organisms producing specific synthetic products of metabolism except in those cases where the products happen to be required for the actual growth of the organism. Specifically, the only instances of this kind are vitamins and amino acids, and occasionally other substances, but this can scarcely be considered as selective because the vast majority of fungi can grow on synthetic media in the absence of added growth factors or amino acids and synthesize them.

Applied to synthetic substances of metabolism, then, selectivity cannot be achieved by suppressing the growth or appearance of extraneous colonies, but rather by securing the growth in colony form on agar plates of as large a number of different cultures as is feasible, and by the application of suitable qualitative or indicator tests, discarding all those colonies giving negative tests. If this screening test can be made semiquantitative, the most interesting strains can be selected directly from others performing the particular function relatively weakly. Here also the ingenuity of the investigator in applying the test is the determining factor in the efficiency of the screening from the standpoint of specificity and in revealing the full potentialities of all organisms under examination. Efficiency in such testing depends on predisposing, to the fullest extent possible, the conditions of the plating and testing to meet the specific requirements.

A few illustrations will serve to exemplify the point. In a systematic search for organisms producing new antibiotic substances, conventional plating methods on conventional nutrient or yeast extract-dextrose or Czapek-agar will easily reveal many such organisms if the agar is seeded with suitable test bacteria, positive tests being indicated by a circular zone of inhibition surrounding the various plated colonies. A large number of antibiotics secured in this way will be found to be known antibiotics, and the organisms identical or closely related to those known already to produce those antibiotics. Furthermore, if *Staphylococcus aureus* or *Escherichia coli*, the conventional test bacteria for this purpose, are used, the antibiotic might not be active against some other specific organism of interest, as for example, *Mycobacterium tuberculosis*. To predispose chances in favor of obtaining a *new* antibiotic active against the tubercle bacillus, one should expose, and make available for screening, various groups of organisms of the soil population not ordinarily able to develop on the usual media and thus not usually subjected to testing for antagonistic properties. Thus, for example, it was desired to examine soil actinomycetes and mycobacteria for their ability to form antibiotics, active particularly against *M. tuberculosis* (Foster and Woodruff 1945). Accordingly a tumbler of soil was enriched in actinomycetes and mycobacteria by adding fatty and waxy substances to the soil as a source of energy. These, being subject to attack by the desired groups of organisms, enrich the soil in this group as compared to most of the remaining soil groups ordinarily obtained. Various pseudomonads and aerobic sporeformers also may develop, and the soil is plated in various dilutions in agar seeded with *M. tuberculosis*. The plates are incubated for 4 to 7 days at 25°C., at which most of the soil colonies develop and form anti-biotic substances if they can, but *M. tuberculosis* does not grow. The plates then are transferred to 37° for a week, in which time the *M. tuberculosis* cells develop, except where the *preformed* antibiotics occur, permitting the isolation of the antagonist in further studies. When antagonist and test organism grow simultaneously the test organism may be fully grown before the antagonist produces the antibiotic and the presence of the latter would then be overlooked. This is an example of predisposing chances to the maximum.

The relative ability of fungi to synthesize (for example) the vitamin folic acid complex can be evaluated by plating fungus colonies in folic acid-less (no folic acid) agar media in Petri plates. After sizeable colony development, the plates are streaked with a suspension of a folic acid-requiring organism, which will grow along the streak only as far as sufficient folic acid has diffused from the mold colony. The width of this zone is an indication of relative folic acid synthesis by the mold. Actually, not all the folic acid synthesized by the mold diffuses out, some remains in the cells in bound form. In general, the amount excreted is fairly indicative of the synthetic power of the organism, at least where highest amounts are of interest. This type of test is, in essence, the reverse of that used to detect antibiotics. In such tests it is important to use as test bacteria only those capable of growing under the conditions, namely, aerobic organisms, and to insure against inhibition by organic acid formation, etc.

In similar fashion preliminary selection based on relative ability of molds to produce diastatic, proteolytic, or pectinolytic enzymes can be achieved by comparative growth rates and observation of peripheral zones of digestion, accompanied, if necessary, by appropriate chemical tests.

The concept of strain specificity (see Chapter 5), and the availability and exploitation of screening and selection techniques along the lines already discussed, should provide an impetus for the investigation and study of many biochemical characters of fungi quite apart from those of commercial or practical importance. Instead of accepting the particular reaction as nature provides it in any particular organism in which the reaction happens first to have been identified, the investigator now has means of greatly intensifying the reactions quantitatively, thereby rendering them considerably more accessible and, to a large extent, minimizing interference from extraneous biochemical activities. What at first exists as a minor physiological character, seemingly insignificant in the complexity of the main metabolic stream of an organism and thus impossible to segregate and isolate enzymatically or chemically, can be manipulated into a position much more prominent in the economy of the organism. This approach, selection, together with optimum environmental conditions, combine to give any study of physiological or biochemical mechanisms in fungi its most favorable auspices. Before the study commences one creates, so to speak, the ideal subject material.

Before leaving this discussion of strain selection, natural and artificial, (see also Chapters 5 and 6) one ought to realize (and it will become more and more evident throughout this book) that in the last decade since the discovery of penicillin this idea has become the dominant philosophy in applied microbiology. The thesis that the most crucial criterion of any industrial fermentation, namely yield per hour, depends for advancement more on strain improvement than an physiological conditions has been repeatedly proven. Increments in yields obtainable by exhaustive search for optimum combinations of nutritional and cultural factors are relatively minor compared to what can be obtained from selected strains, natural or mutant, inherently superior in the ability to do the particular process. Naturally, any particular strain is influenced by the environmental factors and these must be established, but it should be appreciated that in most cases greatest advances in yield gains are to be realized from an induced-mutation program. Before the advent of penicillin, and the success of this avenue in penicillin, artificial mutations as a means of enhancing yields of industrially important microbiological products were unheard of.

There are, however, definite limitations in the agar colony technique. First, the physiological conditions existing within the colony, and thus the chemical behavior of the organism as a whole, are heterogeneous and are in general typical of all surface type growth of fungi. Details of this point are given later. Second, strains selected in this manner do not behave quantitatively the same under conditions of submerged cultivation. This has been amply demonstrated for citric acid production and for penicillin formation. Third, the specificity is not as narrow as would be desirable. In this connection, one point is worthy of emphasis. Once some insight is gained into the mechanism of formation of particular substances, especially complex ones, and definite chemical intermediates identified as precursors of the desired products, a much higher degree of specificity may be obtained by incorporating the intermediates directly into the isolation and selection medium. By this means conditions are greatly in favor of the biochemical types of organisms particularly sought. This is a good example of predisposing the conditions to suit the requirements. There is no doubt that as knowledge of mold biochemistry advances, so will the value and applicability of plate culture techniques.

Surface Growth on Loose Solid Materials

This method utilizes the principle that the surface area of any given weight or volume of solid material is enormously increased proportionally to the smallness, and, therefore, to the number of individual particles making up the total weight or volume. Thus, the total surface area available for the growth of a fungus on for example, 10 g. of moist wheat bran spread evenly in a Petri plate, is far in excess of the 13 square inches provided by 10 g. of agar medium in the same agar plate. This surface feature of mold growth is predicated primarily on the fact that molds are aerobic organisms, and aeration, with solid substrates, is a function of surface area in free contact with the atmosphere. This also applies to mycelial forms of actinomycetes, particularly those producing aerial mycelia (Streptomyces).

The particular substrates may be natural materials like whole grains, bran, oatmeal, sugar beet slices, etc., which supply not only the physical structure but the nutrients for the mold as well. Sufficient water, to which may be added certain supplementary nutrients, is added to dry grains or cereal products so as to have them very moist after absorption. A thin layer of excess liquid resting on the bottom of the vessel is desirable, for through capillary action it keeps the particles moist, and through evaporation, maintains a high humidity in the vessel. This is favorable for mold growth, and it prevents the top portions from drying out. On the other hand, inert materials can serve as structural material if suitable nutrients are supplied. The best materials for this purpose are those having porosity or absorptive properties so they can retain the nutrients and moisture without having to be in direct contact with a body of liquid. Natural materials have this property. Wood chips or shavings, sawdust, fibrous materials such as straws, cornhusks, etc. are useful and wheat meal, horse chestnuts, and lupine seeds have been used. In general, non-absorptive materials are not useful, because the success of this method depends on surface growth not in contact with free liquid. The available surface on any non-absorptive material in contact with free liquid would be very small compared to absorptive substances.

Because of the nature of solid substrates, particular care must be given to their sterilization. Heat transfer is very slow and effective sterilization time in the autoclave will depend on the porosity, density, size of air spaces between particles, and thickness of the layers being sterilized. Steam sterilization, by softening grains, brans, etc., is a good conditioner for these materials.

Occasionally, certain natural substrates fail to support growth of a particular fungus, even though its nutritional requirements are adequately satisfied. Fortunately, the variety of different ones available makes it easy to secure a satisfactory solid substrate. Failure to grow usually can be traced to naturally occurring toxic materials, and this appears to be characteristic of wood chips, straw, etc., containing resins, waxes, and similar materials inhibitory to microorganisms. If necessary, these can be removed by ether or alcohol extraction prior to use. In other cases it has been possible to adapt an organism to a substrate by successive transfers through that substrate, so that in the end the organism develops rapidly and profusely. Whether this is an adaptation toward overcoming inhibitory materials, or in the utilization of some required nutrient (adaptive enzymes), or selection following mutation is not known, but, in view of the general nutritional completeness of cereal and grains, the former alternative seems more plausible, with selection the mechanism.

The main use of this type of culture as a laboratory tool is for the preparation of spore inoculum, for use in the inoculation of large numbers of vessels containing media for experimental purposes, or for production purposes. Because of the size of surface area, and the nutrient completeness, most fungi sporulate profusely in such cultures, and if the full-grown culture is allowed to evaporate to dryness the spores easily dislodge, and can be transferred in the dry state with pieces of the substrate as a carrier, or the whole can be shaken vigorously with sterile water and used as a liquid suspension. The use of heavily sporulated material, such as is obtainable in bran or oatmeal cultures, serves a very important purpose in experimental work on liquid cultures, where large numbers of vessels under different treatments must be inoculated heavily and uniformly in order to eliminate inconsistencies in rate of growth and the formation of a continuous surface pad commonly resulting from variable and otherwise inadequate inoculum. Growth and biochemical results are then true reflections of the imposed treatments and are not subject to the influence of variable inoculum; massive inoculation is the only way of minimizing this influence. Unfortunately, this technique for preparing mold inoculum does not enjoy widespread use in microbiological laboratories, but comparison with the usual agar or liquid media traditionally used for inoculum production readily demonstrates its superiority over the conventional method.

Bran cultures have been utilized successfully for the production of various products of mold growth on a commercial scale. The large-scale production of diastatic and proteolytic enzymes is conducted by propagating the organism on moistened bran aerated with sterile air in rotating horizontal drums. The movement and the air stream aids in dissipating the large amounts of heat generated by the fungus during oxidation of the carbohydrate and other assimilable materials. Usually water sprayed on the outside of the tank also is necessary to prevent the temperature from rising to a level inhibitory to the growth of the organism. The poor heat conductance of the bran is responsible for the temperature rise. The bran method is superior to other known methods of producing mold enzymes, though recently considerable attention has been given to the possibilities of submerged production of enzymes (LeMense et al., 1947; Erb et al., 1948). It seems likely that the inherent advantages of the submerged process (see later) will eventually displace the bran process.

Penicillin production on wheat bran was developed very successfully and for some time was actually used by certain commercial manufacturers of penicillin. However, the great strides made in the development of strains of penicillia adapted to high yields in liquid media in submerged culture in tanks equipped with aeration and agitation later superseded the bran process. The problem of heat dissipation was critical here. Streptomycin and streptothricin can be produced in high yields (900 μg. per gram dry bran) on rice bran after adaptation of the organism to this material. *Streptomyces lavendulae* and *S. griseus*, respectively, the organisms producing these antibiotic substances, are definitely inhibited by wheat bran. It is entirely likely that other antibiotics and other mold products especially favored by surface growth could be produced on solid substrates. Riboflavin and riboflavin concentrates have been manufactured in Japan since 1936 by the rice-bran process on a commercial scale. *Eremothecium asbyii* is the organism.

After a suitable growth period, the moldy bran mass is extracted or leached with water, and the active fractions isolated in concentrated form after further purification. In general, the bran production method is best applicable in those instances where absolute purity of the finished product is not necessary. Besides other metabolic products of the organism, the extraction step also removes quantities of water-soluble substances unattacked by the fungus and derived from the original natural material.

Another modification of the solid substrate technique is the so-called "trickling method" where the structural material, which may be wood chips or sugar beet pulp, etc., is packed in columns or towers, saturated with a suitable medium, and inoculated with the desired organism. Fresh sterile medium introduced from the top is allowed to trickle down over the pieces covered with mold growth, and in the course of transit is acted on by the mold; the free liquid containing the metabolic products is tapped off from the bottom. In this manner a continuous or intermittent process is possible. Sterile air is introduced from the bottom, and it bubbles up through the trickling liquid via the air spaces and aids in the distribution and oxygenation of the falling liquid. This method has been developed for the production of citric acid and penicillin and, while it was an attractive possibility before the availability of submerged culture methods, does not appear as likely competition for these more efficient methods now extant. Progress in mold research within the past five years has made it evident that the possibilities for developing submerged methods for any mold process are extremely good, thus obviating the less efficient "trickling" methods.

Other interesting applied aspects of the bran process relates to the use of the bran containing the mold growth essentially as an enzyme complex. This is the basis of the renowned Amylo process for saccharification of starchy materials prior to their fermentation for alcohol production. This process was developed in France, but is used most extensively in the Orient where sucrose is in short supply. The mass of mold growth and bran (*Rhizopus delemar*) is added to the heat-liquefied starch material in a tank (sweet potatoes in Japan), which is aerated for several hours during which the mold develops slightly but produces enough diastatic enzyme to convert the starch to fermentables sugars. The mass is then pasteurized, inoculated with yeast, and allowed to ferment anaerobically in the customary manner.

In the Orient, in the manufacture of numerous fermented foods and shoyu sauces from rice, soybeans, and wheat, a slurry of ground grain is treated with mold bran, "koji." Selected strains of *Aspergillus oryzae* are used. The pregrown fungus cells function mainly via their preformed content of various diastatic, lipolytic, and proteolytic enzymes, and also others liberated during autolysis (amino acid decarboxylases), and carry out desirable transformations in the substrate, principally in the absence of air. Little or no further growth of the mold occurs after the koji has been added to the substrate. The desirable flavor and aroma bodies are the result of autolytic enzymes and are generated over an incubation period of many weeks at relatively low temperatures. In its main aspects this process is quite analogous to the brewing of beer. Spoilage organisms are suppressed, and certain desirable air-borne bacteria and yeasts encouraged, by the relatively high sodium chloride content.

2. LIQUID CULTURES

a. Surface Growth

For ease of handling and setting up of large numbers of experimental treatments, the practice of cultivating molds as pads on the surface of liquid media traditionally has been the favorite method. Only in the past few years, and largely through the impetus of penicillin, has it been displaced by the more speedy, and generally more efficient, submerged or shake culture techniques (see p. 56). Much valuable information can be obtained by comparative studies of different organisms in stationary flask or bottle cultures or by comparing the effect of different treatments on any one organism. Frequently, as in the case of products of practical value, different media are tested in large numbers to find the optimum for production of the desired substance. The literature on mold metabolism is replete with experiments of this nature on the production of oxalic, citric, kojic, fumaric, and gluconic acids from carbohydrates. The same applies to penicillin production as well as to an imposing list of other antibiotic substances. Optimum conditions for the formation of these substances in the liquid portion of the culture have been carefully worked out. In some cases this has been done for the mold mycelium itself. Total weight, pigment formation, and fat content have been studied systematically in this manner.

Another kind of research utilizing surface growth on liquid is perhaps best exemplified by the scores of studies by Raistrick and coworkers in which the pure cultures of fungi were grown in one medium, usually Czapek-Dox, under standardized conditions for long periods of time, and the products of mold growth both in the filtrate and in the mycelium isolated, identified, and studied chemically. These studies make, for the most part, no effort to control or influence the course of metabolism, the mature cultures, including metabolism liquors and cell material, merely being worked up for whatever organic chemicals they would yield.

A third type of fruitful experimentation has been that dealing with the transformation of particular substances added singly to the media, usually for the purpose of identifying the product of conversion and thus elucidating the mechanism of its formation. The first substance usually is suspected to be a precursor of the second and the finding of the latter in substantial amounts often is presumptive, though by no means conclusive, evidence for that particular mechanism. This approach has been widely used in mechanism studies on the origin of acid production from carbohydrates (Bernhauer, Wehmer, Chrzaszcz, Butkewitsch) and in oxidation of organic acids by *Aspergillus niger*.

Further utilization of the surface growth techniques has been in the development of elegant methods for quantitative assay of various growth factors (Phycomyces and Neurospora), heavy metals (*A. niger*), available phosphorus and potassium in soils (Cunninghamella) and as an indicator of the presence of traces of inorganic arsenic (*Penicillium brevicaule*). This list is not at all complete, but gives an idea of the valuable applications evolved from surface cultures.

Detailed consideration of the circumstances at play and of the forces at work in surface cultures of fungi make it clear, as will be analyzed presently, that this system is hardly ideal for the study of the mold as a biochemical entity, and for revealing its true metabolic makeup.   Nevertheless, for preliminary characterization and survey studies, it can yield extremely valuable information.   Thus, the types of chemical substances the fungus is capable of utilizing as carbon and energy sources and also the relative availability of various forms of nitrogen, inorganic and organic, can be defined in comparative surface cultures, and provide valuable characterization of the physiological nature of the organism. Its rate of growth and total amount of cell material synthesized from various substrates reveal the efficiency of the organism in utilizing the substrates and this can be presented numerically as the "economic coefficient" $\left\{\dfrac{\text{grams cell material synthesized}}{\text{grams carbohydrate consumed}}\right\}$.   Similarly, a host of other features are easily capable of experimentation and contribute to the description of the organism's response by way of growth and metabolism.   Included here are effect of pH, temperature, oxygen tension, minerals including trace metals, neutralizing agents, poisons, organic substances, concentration of salts and other medium constituents, etc. Analysis of the culture fluids indicates qualitatively (at most) the general biochemical group to which the organism belongs.   Culturally, interesting data also are obtainable: nature and relative abundance of the vegetative mycelium, wrinkling, extrusion of droplets, pigments (insoluble and diffusible), color and abundance of sporulation, etc., are some of the observations commonly made.

Where the formation of a particular dissimilation product has been established, quantitative determinations (usually in the case of organic acids) of the product formed and of the amount of sugar consumed permit calculation of the conversion coefficient $\left\{\dfrac{\text{grams product formed}}{\text{grams sugar consumed}}\right\}$. Measurement of respiratory CO_2 during growth by aeration into standard alkali or into CaO (Ascarite) rounds out a study of the organism's biochemical behavior with respect to (1) production of cell material, (2) complete oxidation of substrate to CO_2, and (3) formation of known or unidentified metabolic products ("carbon unaccounted for").   If the last named fraction is high, follow-up isolation and characterization is indicated.

Results of biochemical activities of fungi in surface growth experiments are very much subject to influences by physical factors consequent to the type of vessel used for cultivation.   Thus, the wider the mouth of the vessel, and the looser the cotton plug, the more oxygen is available to the rapidly proliferating mold, and, as will be seen later, the oxygen

supply in the vessel is often the limiting factor in growth rates.   Cotton
plugs of any thickness or density are definite mechanical barriers to the
ingress of oxygen and the latter can easily fall behind the rate at which
the growing organism is able to consume oxygen.   Thus, the overall
incubation time may be appreciably shortened by having a cotton plug
as thin and as loose as is consistent with the maintenance of pure culture
conditions.   In certain cases, especially in synthetic media with inorganic nitrogen, and particularly where high initial acidity prevails as in
citric acid studies, cotton plugs can be abandoned altogether, inverted
beakers or similar contrivances over the mouth of the culture vessel
sufficing to prevent contamination in the principle of Petri plate tops.
The best indication as to whether the usual flask culture is limited by
aeration is to compare its rate of growth and/or any biochemical function
with those in replicate flasks having an aeration tube leading down to
within a centimeter or so of the surface of the liquid and maintaining a
steady flow of fresh sterile air during the whole incubation period.   The
complications arising from the accumulation of respiratory carbon
dioxide in the atmosphere above mold pads in surface cultures, and also
from that CO_2 resulting from neutralization in the case of organic acid
production when calcium carbonate is present, will be treated in the
next section.

In addition to being a limiting factor in physiological and biochemical
experiments on a laboratory scale, this problem of adequate gas exchange
in vessels with surface growth may have definite practical implications.
Thus, in the case of large-scale bottle plants for the production of penicillin, before this method was rendered obsolete by the tank process, the
available oxygen supply in the bottles could be shown definitely to be
limiting the rate of growth of *P. notatum*, and not only the rate, but the
total amount of penicillin produced.   A very practical means of minimizing this difficulty caused primarily by the slow rate of gaseous diffusion
through cotton plugs down to a region accessible to the organism, was to
induce the vessels to "breathe."   This was achieved by reducing the
sensitivity of the thermostat controlling the incubator temperatures, so
that fluctuations of a few degrees in temperature occurred regularly.
These changes in external temperatures set up slight pressure differences
between the inside and outside of the vessels, creating a pumping action,
thereby facilitating gaseous diffusion, and favoring growth and penicillin
formation.

It is evident from the foregoing that the shape and size of the culture
vessel may have a definite bearing on the nature of the results obtained.
This is also true of the depth of liquid in any one type or size of vessel.
Generally this is directly related to the surface area of the liquid, and the

whole complex usually expressed as an index, $\dfrac{\text{surface area (sq. cm.)}}{\text{volume (cc.)}}$. In general, the more shallow the level of medium in any given shape or size vessel, the more oxidative the conditions and consequently metabolic reactions dependent on oxidation predominate. Actually, a thin layer means less substrate to oxidize, and the oxygen in the gas phase goes further. Furthermore, the substrate is usually more rapidly and more completely consumed, for diffusion of residual sugar and other minerals is retarded in deeper layers of liquid. One finds, therefore, that in the case of the shallower levels, 1 sq. cm. of mold pad has much less sugar to turn over, and because of superior oxidation conditions, leads to higher concentration of metabolic products per milliliter of culture fluid, whether they be citric (*Aspergillus niger*) or fumaric (*Rhizopus nigricans*) acids or penicillin (*Penicillium notatum-chrysogenum*), streptomycin (*Streptomyces griseus*) or riboflavin (*Eremothecium ashbyii*). Concentration per milliliter is extremely important in the extraction and purification of substances produced in relatively small weight yields like penicillin or streptomycin. It is almost axiomatic that thinner layers of medium yield the highest concentration of oxidative (organic acids) or synthetic metabolic products per unit culture liquid. This does not hold true for ethanol, acetaldehyde, and other products of anaerobic metabolism. From the standpoint of commercial production in bottles or trays an economic balance is made between depth of liquid and *total amount* of product formed, as well as concentration, per unit of time. Up to a certain point, concentration can be sacrificed in favor of total conversion.

For the inoculation of media in vessels of large surface area, as trays or Fernbach flasks, the use of dry or "unwetted" spores is almost indispensable for rapid and complete pad formation. Such spores may be readily obtained from solid substrates as described above, and when present in sufficient numbers, because of the surface tension of the medium, tend to spread over the entire surface, giving a continuous mold pad instead of isolated patches. Ordinary air atomizers have proved effective for inoculation on a large scale by dispersing spores uniformly and extensively.

The use of calcium carbonate as a neutralizing agent in mold cultures is treated in detail in the next section. However, in connection with growth experiments it often is desired to have $CaCO_3$ present. The germination of spores of many fungi is inhibited if they are inoculated into a liquid sugar-containing medium in which $CaCO_3$ is present. This may be due to pH effects or to formation of toxic products by sterilizing the carbonate and sugar together. In any case the best practice is to sterilize the carbonate separately and add it carefully to the culture flask 1 or 2 days after the spore inoculum has germinated and produced a definite web of mycelial growth.   Since organic acid formation is extremely small in that time, the carbonate actually is not required earlier.

b. Replacement Cultures (Pilzdecke)

In the study of transformations and conversion of one substance into another, and this applies especially to dissimilation reactions, it is desirable to eliminate, insofar as possible, the growth or assimilatory reactions.   In this manner the substrate is not diverted into cell material, and the study of the fate and conversion of the particular substrate is not complicated by the assimilatory reactions.   Actually some assimilation does take place under these conditions and this is discussed on p. 50. The cell material performs the transformations essentially as an enzyme system.   This corresponds to the well-known "resting-cell" technique in bacteriology, and is an invaluable tool for mechanism studies, for it permits a particular metabolic process to occur independently of the myriad of other activities typical of growing cells.   One of the greatest advantages lays in the fact that it permits a more complete quantitative accounting of the products as definite identifiable and measurable substances, as contrasted, where growth takes place, with "cell material."

As the term connotes, replacement cultures are procured by first obtaining fully-grown pads or surface growth of fungus on a complete medium.   The culture fluid is then gently poured out of the vessel under aseptic conditions and in a manner that causes the fungus pad to rest flat and right side up against the bottom or side of the vessel.   The fluid may be saved for analysis or discarded.   An equal portion of sterile distilled water is then introduced aseptically so as to refloat the mold pad, and the cell material is washed free from adhering residual medium constituents by gently rotating the vessel vertically around its long axis. This wash water is then removed and replaced as before with a sterile solution of the substance under investigation.   The replacement liquid must be devoid of nitrogen and minerals, particularly phosphorus, for in their absence the organism is unable to divert large amounts of the carbon source for growth in the usual sense.   Therefore, the products of conversion accumulate in the medium, in high yields, thus expediting expression of the reaction as a chemical equation, with all components identified and measured.   Various modifications are, of course, possible, as the experimental approach warrants.   Thus, where carbohydrate is supplied as substrate, as for example, fumaric acid production from ethyl alcohol by *Rhizopus nigricans*, it is necessary to have a neutralizing agent present so as to prevent accumulation of acidic products to a stage inhibitory to continued normal action of the cells. Calcium carbonate usually is satisfactory for this purpose.

Trapping substances may be introduced to fix otherwise transitory intermediates in metabolism of the substrate. Thus, dimedon or sodium sulfite removes and fixes the acetaldehyde as an insoluble addition product. The normal reactions are diverted in this manner. Similar changes can be achieved by the presence of certain enzymatic inhibitors or poisons.

Unlike growing cultures, replacement cultures are very active in metabolizing the substrate, particularly carbohydrates, under anaerobic conditions, and comparative analysis of replicate cultures held anaerobically, and at different degrees of aerobiosis, yields valuable information as to the mechanism of the dissimilation reactions. This has found particular application in studies on alcohol production by Fusaria, and in fumaric and lactic acid formation from carbohydrates by species of Rhizopus. As in all experiments where mechanisms are being investigated, it is necessary to measure the carbon dioxide evolved during the experiment. Because of the relatively large mass of cell material usually present, the CO_2 evolution of control pads on water without substrate must be measured and deducted from the value in the substrate treatment. This control figure is apt to be rather large since active mold pads are rich in accumulated "reserve" substances which are respired to CO_2 in the absence of substrate. For this reason it is always desirable to have rather large amounts of substrate metabolized by the mold so that any CO_2 liberated from this reaction would not be obscured by the endogenous CO_2 of the mold material itself.

When $CaCO_3$ is present, rather frequent shaking, in a manner which does not wet the upper surface of the mold pad or injure the pad in any way, is necessary to bring the neutralizing agent into contact with the acidity that accumulates in the liquid contiguous to the cell material. Calcium carbonate is an extremely important accessory in bio-chemical experiments involving growing or replacement cultures where the incubation period usually lasts several days and where substantial amounts of substrate are being metabolized. If aeration conditions are at all suitable, one or more organic acids will almost always accumulate, and in varying amounts, all depending on the substrate, and this is especially true for carbohydrates. Also the organism, the medium on which the cell material was developed, and other special environmental conditions are effective in determining amount and nature of the organic acids produced. In many types of mold oxidations the presence of calcium carbonate leads to the accumulation of such large amounts of organic acids that the solubility of the calcium salts is exceeded and they crystallize out and accumulate in the medium. This always occurs in oxalic acid and can easily be demonstrated with lactic, fumaric, and gluconic acid-forming fungi. The crystallization with the latter can, under favorable conditions, become so complete as to cause the entire culture liquid to "set" in the form of a solid gel.

It is important to emphasize that although calcium carbonate favors increased acid formation in the case of those organisms prospering at pH ranges approximating neutrality, it does, on the other hand, have a decided inhibitory effect on the accumulation of citric and kojic acids by *Aspergillus niger* and *A. flavus*, respectively, because a low pH is optimum for the formation of these particular acids. Itaconic acid production by *A. terreus* is also favored by low pH.

Most carboxylic acids formed by molds are relatively weak acids. Small amounts do not dissolve $CaCO_3$ or do so only slowly notwithstanding the presence of excess $CaCO_3$ in the medium; neutralization may be made complete at the end of the experiment by boiling. Calcium in solution then becomes an index of the total acidity (carboxyl groups), including known and unknown acids. Calcium determinations as a measure of total acidity, combined with specific quantitative analysis for the known acids present, reveal how much of the total acidity is unaccountable as known acids. Rarely, from sugar at least, is only one organic acid produced by a mold although one may predominate, and identification and isolation of the unknown acids is prompted and facilitated by knowledge of their presence and concentration. Thus citric, gluconic and oxalic acids frequently occur simultaneously in *A. niger* cultures, fumaric, succinic and malic acids in cultures of various Mucorales and also in lactic acid-producing Rhizopus. As much as 20 per cent of the total acidity produced by the higher kojic acid-yielding strains of *Aspergillus flavus* consists of other organic acids.

In general, the relative proportion of the different acids formed by a fungus culture is inconstant, and the amounts depend on the strain of organism, nutrient medium, pH, temperature, degree of aeration, etc. In the technological utilization of molds, calcium carbonate is necessary for maximum yields of penicillin in corn steep liquor medium, and apparently is associated with maintenance of a favorable pH range for penicillin formation. Acid formation also results when many substrates other than sugars are metabolized by fungi.

In the industrial processes for the production of gluconic, fumaric, lactic, and oxalic acids by the submerged method, the necessity for using $CaCO_3$ instead of other (soluble) neutralizing agents has the inherent disadvantage of limiting the process through mechanical hindrance, diffusion limitations, and recovery problems due to crystallization in the culture fluid of the respective calcium salts. This necessitates the use of lower sugar concentrations or, where applicable, development of a means of preventing the crystallization of the calcium salts, such as in the case of calcium gluconate by the formation of soluble boron complexes, or by limiting the amount of $CaCO_3$ present. For unknown reasons, probably related to the cation, other neutralizing agents are not as useful as $CaCO_3$ in fungus cultures.

An important impression gained from biochemical studies with replacement cultures is that because the synthetic reactions characterizing growing cultures are absent, the physiological behavior of the organism appears much more uniform, reproducible, and less subject to variability and influences by other factors. For example, so long as nitrogen is lacking, the effect of mineral salts and heavy trace elements is small if effective at all.

Replacement cultures, because of the large amount of cell material, have the distinct advantage of speeding up experimental work, for they start acting vigorously on the substrate immediately and are able to metabolize appreciable quantities of substrate in from just several hours to a few days. Growing cultures metabolize appreciably less in that time. Preformed or resting cell material appears to be extremely hardy and can be "replaced" with fresh substrate many times and still be physiologically active. The best recorded example of this is the effective re-utilization of the cell material of A. niger for the semicontinuous production of gluconic acid (Porges et al., 1940). It is interesting to note, as an example of physiological hardiness of mold mycelium, that the rate at which the A. niger mycelium oxidized glucose to gluconic acid was only slightly less after the 13th glucose charge than it was with the first.

This would mean that vital growth factors, coenzymes, catalysts, etc., are not leached out of the cells, or can be synthesized in amounts sufficient to maintain physiological vigor. It is probable that under the condition of the experiments the cell membrane is not permeable to these substances. At mildly alkaline pH values cozymase is readily removed from yeast cells.

It was mentioned earlier that a feature of special value about replacement cultures is the elimination of competing synthetic reactions inherent to growing cultures, thus "channelizing" the metabolism of the fungus. This results in fewer products and makes possible a more complete accounting of the original substrate as specific chemical entities. Since growth in the usual sense is impossible, theoretically all of the consumed substrate can be accounted for as products in solution and as CO_2. While this is true in a general sense, and certainly comparatively so in relation to growth cultures, it is not strictly true because of the occurrence of "oxidative assimilation." Oxidative assimilation probably occurs universally in fungi under replacement culture conditions although this phenomenon has not often been considered in physiological studies with molds. Oxidative assimilation describes that as yet unclarified process whereby "resting cells" of microorganisms under aerobic conditions incorporate a portion of the substrate into cell material, meanwhile oxidizing the remainder to CO_2, although it is not necessary to assume that the oxidation should go to completion. The energy required for the assimilatory process, which is endothermic, is derived from the energy-liberating (exothermic) oxidation of the residual portion of the substrate.

Oxidative assimilation has been extensively studied for numerous different bacterial species, for yeast and for *Prototheca zopfii*, a chlorophyll-less alga. Invariably the amount of CO_2 produced by respiring bacterial cells bears a discrete simple fraction relation to the number of carbon atoms in the substrate undergoing oxidation, and since often no other metabolic products are detectable, the remainder of the substrate can only be converted into cell material, i.e., assimilated without corresponding increase in cell numbers. An increase in cell weight has been directly proved in a few cases (see Clifton, 1946 for review). These definite $\frac{CO_2}{substrate}$ ratios undoubtedly signify that a definite part of the carbon skeleton of each molecule is assimilated through a definite enzymatic mechanism, the rest going to CO_2. In this way the glucose molecule may be one-third or one-half assimilated, fumaric acid one-quarter or one-half, pyruvic acid one-third or two-thirds, etc.

The ultimate product of this assimilation or synthesis appears to be a reserve foodstuff, probably glycogen, starch, or a similar polysaccharide, presumably stored in vacuoles. The assimilatory mechanism can be poisoned with dinitrophenol, sodium azide, or sodium cyanide, under which conditions the entire substrate is oxidized to CO_2, since the assimilatory mechanisms are selectively inhibited. As stated above, oxidative assimilation has not often been studied in molds. In view of the conspicuous synthetic propensities of fungi it seems extremely likely that oxidative assimilation plays an important part in the metabolism of these organisms, and the few studies done in this regard bear out the fact that in the usual manometric approach up to two-thirds of the glucose may be assimilated (Foster, unpublished; Dorrell, 1948) and the same evidently applies to the utilization of amino acids (Schade, 1940).

The respiratory exchange of fungi is important under conditions of organic acid formation by the mycelium, that is, in relatively high concentrations of carbohydrate, namely, 2 to 10 per cent (see Chapter 4). While oxidative assimilation occurs to a conspicuous degree under the usual manometric conditions where a few hundredths of a millimole of substrate is furnished, it is doubtful that it occurs to the same degree when that amount of mycelium is turning over much higher concentrations of sugar, and forming acids. The total amount of assimilation here must be a much smaller proportion of the sugar consumed, if for no other reason than eventually the cell will be saturated with regard to assimilation potentiality.

c. Submerged Growth. Comparative Physiology of Surface vs. Submerged Growth

From much of the foregoing it is evident that for the most effective studies on mold physiology and biochemistry, none of the methods already described are completely adequate. Submerged growth cultures theoretically and practically afford the closest approach to the ideal method of studying mold metabolism. The principles involved in the technique, and the implications possible for the interpretation of physiological studies with fungi under different conditions were first clearly enunciated in 1933 in a classic paper entitled "Zur Methodik der Schimmelstoffwechseluntersuchung" from the renowned Laboratorium von Mikrobiologie at the Technische Hoogschule in Delft, Holland by Prof. A. J. Kluyver and his student and collaborator, L. H. C. Perquin. This and subsequent papers by these authors represent the first attempt to study mold metabolism systematically under strictly controlled conditions, and to elucidate some fundamental principles obtained thereby. The main feature of this method is the use of physiologically homogeneous cell material. As in the case of surface growth cultures, submerged cultures can be freed from the growth culture fluid, the cell matter washed, and fresh sterile substrate solutions introduced, and all the features discussed in relation to surface replacement cultures apply to the submerged. However, a number of special points in connection with the latter will be taken up in the subsequent discussion.

The vast majority of investigators on molds and those using molds as tools in the study of biochemical reactions have failed to appreciate the importance of employing physiologically homogeneous mold material. Only by doing so can conclusions have unequivocal quantitative value, and be duplicated at will. Any biochemical process known to occur in surface cultures can be induced to occur under the proper conditions in submerged culture with the same organism, or strains related to or derived from the particular organism.

Obtaining submerged mold material is an easy matter, but careful consideration of all factors is important, for all submerged cell material is not necessarily physiologically homogeneous. If the liquid medium inoculated with fungus spores is maintained in a state of mechanical agitation with or without supplementory aeration during the growth period, the growth will consist of individual discrete particles, not unlike small beads under certain conditions, circulating continuously through the culture liquid.   In young cultures, while the individual colonies are still quite small, the growth appears fine and of smooth texture, with no distinct particles evident to the eye.   No surface pad develops, although a thin ring of sporulating surface growth may occur around the upper reaches of the vessel above the liquid.   In the early stages the suspended growth is not unlike a bacterial turbidity.   Depending on the organism, the age of the culture, the nature of the medium, and other factors, the appearance of the suspension may vary from fine during the early stages to coarse in the older cultures.   Microscopically, the suspension will consist of minute colonies of fungus material, every colony having originated from a single spore or piece of mycelium in the inoculum.   While the colonies are still quite small the suspension remains homogeneously distributed throughout all parts of the liquid, but when they get larger they may agglomerate, and the suspension tends to lose its homogeneity. Later, as the culture passes its peak, autolysis sets in, and much of the cell material may dissolve leaving a thin liquid.

The principal feature about cell material cultivated in this fashion is that all cells of the culture are uniformly exposed to the environmental factors, both physical and chemical, during the growth period.   A stream of fine air or oxygen bubbles passing through the liquid simultaneously with mechanical agitation, results in the attainment of conditions fairly close to optimum for the most rapid growth of the fungus.   The small particles or colonies of cell material present a tremendously greater cell surface area for exchange of nutrients and waste products.   Aeration is enhanced by facilitating access of the cells to oxygen and removal of CO_2, and, if calcium carbonate is employed as a neutralizing agent, it is maintained in suspension and thereby continually neutralizes the acidic products of metabolism as soon as they are formed.   As a consequence of all these features, the rate of growth is greatly accelerated.   From the standpoint of the laboratory experimentalist, as well as the industrial microbiologist, the implications of this fact are self-evident.   The amount and nature of submerged growth depends, as might be expected, on the nature and concentration of the various nutrients, the rate of shaking, the gas supply, total volume of liquid in the culture vessel, amount of inoculum per unit volume of medium, etc.   These will be discussed below.

The best interpretation of the superior features of submerged growth for metabolic studies of molds comes from an analysis of the inadequacy of surface cultures, for, in all cases the limiting features of surface growth are circumvented by the very means of obtaining submerged growth. It is patently evident that the metabolism of any organism grown in the form of a surface pad on a liquid medium represents at best only a rough approximation of the overall reactions carried out by the mold, and, reveal little with respect to the ultimate biochemical potentialities of the organism. Data obtained by the surface method of cultivation represent only the overall result of the metabolic processes of an extremely heterogeneous mixture of physiological systems. They comprise the resultant of numerous and diverse processes.

Consider the usual mold surface pad. The mycelial or vegetative portion is variable in thickness, consisting of a dense mass of tightly intertwined and meshed hyphal cells. It is more than likely that a relatively small proportion of all the cells comprising the mold substance are in direct contact with the nutrient solution. The main body of the liquid remains quite clear and free of growth except for some particles of inoculum that may have dropped to the bottom and developed there slowly. Many fungi have the tendency to develop in the upper region of the liquid, but subsurface, and the growth material is wet, membranous, and slimy and may form little or no dry aerial mycelium. The lower portion of the mycelial mat is in direct contact with or even submerged in the nutrient liquid, and the upper half or so, constituting the more diffuse or aerial mycelium, is removed from the liquid, dry, and more or less exposed directly to the atmosphere. When a developing culture is removed for biochemical analysis after a period of, for example, 5 days growth, it is clear that the analytical data obtained on the culture fluid represent the averages of the metabolism of mold cells from the lower portion of the pad, from the middle or interior of the pad, and from the top or aerial region. This matter may be even more complicated because with some fungi, and under some conditions, the true aerial mycelium characteristically is not always necessarily developed at the same time. The aerial portion may be only one or two days old, or may not even be formed until the sixth or seventh day, so that analyses as a function of time again yield data from variable mycelia. The value obtained for residual sugar in the medium yields, by deduction from the value of an uninoculated control medium, the amount of sugar consumed by the fungus up to the time of analysis. As above, this value is merely an average value representing the sugar consumed by those lower cells bathed in the sugar solution and other nutrients and enjoying extreme luxury nutrition, by those cells in the dense middle interior region of the mold pad, which are not bathed in the medium and hence cannot metabolize sugar freely, and by the cells of the upper portion and aerial mycelium, which, being so far removed from the sugar and nutrient solution, probably are in a state of starvation or limited nutrition in view of the long and tortuous path of transport to them from the liquid through the interior of the mold hyphae. This movement, discernable under the microscope, is known as protoplasmic streaming. The validity of the figure for sugar consumption as applied to an understanding of the metabolism of the mold is, therefore, subject to serious question. A differential in the tolerance of aerial mycelium vs. the mycelium in contact with the culture liquid was noted for *Neurospora crassa* in connection with a respiratory poison, iodoacetic acid. This was explained on the basis of a lower iodoacetate concentration in the aerial hyphae tips, which are not exposed directly to the solution (Ryan *et al.*, 1944).

The same line of reasoning holds for any particular metabolism product being studied, citric acid, for example. Those cells bathed in sugar are exposed, of course, to the full osmotic concentration effect and excrete citric acid accordingly. The central cells certainly do not receive the benefit of the high sugar concentration present and consequently, if a certain concentration of sugar is optimum for acid formation, these cells are bound to produce little acid or will produce it inefficiently. It is extremely unlikely that the cells in the upper regions, including the aerial mycelium, make any acid whatsoever. Thus, the citric acid value is the resultant of many different rates and degrees of efficiency of formation of citric acid.

A similar reasoning applies to the gaseous environment. A proper supply of oxygen is required for the formation of this oxidation acid, and it would appear that the lower cell levels, which have an abundance of sugar, are limited in their ability to convert the sugar to citric acid, for want of oxygen which obviously has to diffuse down through the thickness of an actively respiring mold tissue. It is quite likely that oxygen is made available to the lower cellular levels by an intrahyphal protoplasmic streaming. As pointed out earlier, the oxygen in cotton-plugged flasks containing surface cultures diminishes rapidly. Carbon dioxide is simultaneously produced, and, being heavier than air, settles like a blanket over the mold mass. This (respiratory) carbon dioxide, together with that arising during the course of growth due to the neutralization of organic acids by $CaCO_3$, acts by a "sweeping effect" to limit the amount of oxygen that reaches the cells.

It is a common observation that in many mold processes, especially where the mold has low available sugar concentration, and where liberal aeration is provided, the organism tends to oxidize the substrate molecule to completion (CO_2 and H_2O), producing no acid, or reduced yields. Thus, in the ordinary mold cultures, the cells in the upper portion of the mold pad are highly aerobic, and the oxygen may even repress acid formation, even though other conditions were favorable. Cogent evidence of the activity of the fermentative or anaerobic processes functioning simultaneously with and independently of the oxidative processes, may be obtained from the fact that almost invariably in surface cultures of fungi growing on solutions containing sugar, even if the fresh air is passed above the surface of the growth, ethyl alcohol, always the product of anaerobic breakdown of sugar by molds, may be found in not insignificant amounts.

The very physical construction of the mold pad is not only inimical to the homogeneity of the metabolic activities of the organism but may actually be harmful. A layer of metabolic products that the mold has been forming during growth or, in the case of replacement cultures, during metabolism accumulates immediately under the surface pad of mold growth. In the metabolism of the organism these are excretion products. Their accumulation to a fairly high concentration in a stratum immediately adjacent to the cells tends to be repressive to growth, either through a specific toxic effect or through the building up of a high concentration of hydrogen ions due to unneutralized organic acids, or due to the retardation of penetration of fresh nutrients to the cells from the bottom layers of the culture liquid.

These effects are ascribable, of course, to diffusion limitations. Not only do excretion products accumulate contiguous to the cells, but the concentration of fresh nutrients in that region becomes depleted, thus limiting the rate of growth or reaction in spite of an abundance of available nutrients in the lower levels of the medium. Elimination of the diffusion barrier by agitation is at once manifested as an appreciable increase in growth rate or conversion of substrate. This holds for the usual surface growth, without having to resort to submerged growth, hence is a true diffusion effect. The following data from May *et al.* (1929) show how glucose oxidation to gluconic acid is accelerated in surface culture when diffusion limitations are obviated by keeping the liquid in motion through subsurface agitation by means of a slow-moving propellor under the mold pad.

Dextrose concentration	Gluconic acid yield %	
	Stationary	Agitated
10%	27.8	40.5
15	49.2	65.3
20	55.0	60.6

Actually this effect is accentuated much more markedly when diffusion is eliminated by means of shake or submerged cultures.

Thus, it cannot be emphasized too strongly that the findings obtained from stationary culture analyses represent the overall reactions of a heterogeneous mass of cells some of which, in the early stages of growth, are metabolizing actively, while others are not due to nutrient deficiencies, some of which have their metabolism deranged due to the accumulation of toxic products, and some of which are metabolizing aerobically while others, in the denser and lower portions of the mold mass are metabolizing anaerobically. It seems unavoidable to conclude that the majority of the early (and even current) work on molds is subject to re-interpretation on this basis and data obtained represent merely the composite of a number of different biochemical reactions functioning simultaneously. The true significance of some quantitatively minor, but qualitatively vital, action may be obscured by some other preponderant action occurring at the same time.

3. Techniques of Obtaining Submerged Growth

Several different means can be used for performing submerged growth experiments on a laboratory scale. Essentially they differ in the mechanics of the experimental setup. Not all provide the ideal conditions for submerged growth, and the relative merits and deficiencies of each will be discussed in connection with each method. In general the methods commonly employed fall into 2 groups; (1) those without mechanical agitation and (2) those with some form of mechanical agitation. The first group as a whole relies upon passage of air through the culture liquid for the setting up of vigorous currents in the liquid sufficient to prevent the formation of a surface pad and to maintain the growth particles in a constant circulation throughout the liquid. The advantages of this principle are its simplicity, ease of setting up in routine, and the suitability of small ordinary laboratory apparatus and equipment. For many types of preliminary or survey experiments, these methods are quite satisfactory. They all have the disadvantage, to various degrees, of not providing the optimum aeration conditions, this being primarily due to lack of mechanical agitation. The second group requires a complicated mechanical experiment setup where individual treatments are concerned, or a large and expensive piece of machinery generally known as a "shaking machine." As brought out in the previous chapter, a machine of this type should be part of the standard equipment of any microbiological laboratory interested in metabolic studies on microorganisms.

a. Submerged Growth without Mechanical Agitation

The simplest, but least efficient means consists merely of a tall narrow vessel tightly fitted with a rubber stopper through which pass inlet and outlet tubes for air. The inlet tube reaches to the bottom of the liquid and the outlet tube comes just past the bottom of stopper. The air is sterilized by filtration through tubes containing about 4 inches of sterile non-absorbent cotton. Aeration is secured either by application of positive pressure at the inlet or by suction at the outlet tube. The best churning effect of the liquid is secured by the fastest air flow consistent with harmless splashing and foaming. Despite the large excess of air passed through such cultures in this manner, all cells are not exposed to aerobic conditions because the air is not utilized efficiently. There is inadequate simultaneous distribution of the available air supply to all cells in all parts of the liquid. Invariably, cultures of this type have a strong alcoholic odor in the exhaust air, indicative of anaerobic sugar fermentation i.e., oxygen insufficiency. Another reason is that aeration of fungus cultures by air streams alone tends to cause growth to conglomerate into large clumps, making it impossible for cells in the interior of the clumps to obtain oxygen.

To facilitate better distribution of the air supply the air must be subdivided. This increases the amount of oxygen in solution through larger diffusion surface at air-liquid interphase and also aids in the spreading of smaller bubbles throughout the whole liquid. The degree of air comminution depends on the size, number, and total area covered by the holes in the air distributor. In order of ascending efficiency the ordinary laboratory aerating devices are (a) a bulb studded with holes at the end of the air tube, (b) a porous stone aerator attached to air tube, and (c) a sintered glass false bottom. Theoretically, fine porosity is the best, up to the point beyond which the force with which the divided air passes up through the liquid becomes so gentle that the desired vigorous mixing action is lost. Fine air bubbles tend to carry the growth to the surface of the liquid, and although it is constantly in a state of movement, the motion is localized in the upper portion.

Fine bubbles also cause foaming troubles, which, unless controlled, cause the culture liquid to overflow through the outlet tube and ultimately to get contaminated, if most of the culture is not lost first. Foaming is especially troublesome in media rich in natural materials, as yeast extract, corn steep liquor, or peptone, which tend to stabilize the foam. Furthermore, as mold growth proceeds, even in synthetic media consisting of inorganic nitrogen, salts, and carbohydrate, metabolic products, presumably higher fatty acids formed as a result of the synthetic activities of the organism, cause serious foaming difficulties. This is especially marked if the pH is near neutrality, due to soap formation between inorganic cations and the fatty acids. For this reason foaming is generally less in acid media, and antifoams work best on the acid side.

Foaming may be controlled in two ways:

(1) By the addition of foam-breaking substances known as antifoams. They apparently act by reducing the surface tension whereby the air-liquid emulsion is broken. They should be non-volatile. Generally effective antifoams are soybean oil, castor oil, sulfonated castor oil (turkey red oil), lard, mineral oil, and dioctyl phenyl phosphonide. Others are olive oil, higher alcohols such as octadecanol, Vegefat Y, lard oil and oleic acid. Other plant oils are useful. Mixtures of these are often more effective than one alone. Thus, lard oil containing 3 per cent octadecanol is greatly superior in penicillin production than either component separately. Antifoams may be very toxic to various organisms in the amounts required for effective suppression of foam, and preliminary toxicity tests must be conducted in the selection of any antifoam for use with a particular organism. The amount usually added to the medium before sterilization ranges from 0.1 to 0.5 per cent. Antifoam efficacies are compared on the basis of antifoam index, the best antifoam for use with a particular organism having the highest index. This is obtained under standardized aeration conditions from the following ratio:

$$\frac{\text{Minimum concentration antifoam inhibitory to growth of the organism}}{\text{Minimum concentration of antifoam effective in combatting foam}}$$

It is obvious that each organism may have a different index with any one antifoam agent.

Although foaming is controlled in the first stages of growth, it may get worse later. This may be due to the formation of foamogenic substances by the mold, necessitating the addition of more (sterile) antifoam, or it may mean that the antifoam itself is being destroyed by the growing mold. Many of the antifoam agents enumerated above are triglycerides of higher fatty acids, and many organisms have the ability to hydrolyze such substances by means of lipases.

(2) Foaming can be reduced or eliminated by a reduction in rate of air flow through the liquid, and as mentioned earlier, the tendency to foam may be somewhat controlled by the size of air bubbles. Air flow should be reduced only as a last resort, for by doing that, the very objective of the aerated submerged cultivation is defeated, i.e., the assurance of aerobic uniform conditions for all cells in the liquid at every instant. Concomitant with the reduced air flow are (a) reduced rate

and total amount of growth and (b) lower yields of oxidized metabolic products. Sugar consumption continues, only instead of being metabolized at maximum rate to oxidized products such as carboxylic acids, it is fermented to ethyl alcohol and CO_2. Sometimes the critical foaming period lasts only a certain period of time, and after nursing the culture through this period, the air flow can be increased to its original rate, without foaming. With culture media and organisms giving foaming difficulties regularly, it is good practice to charge the vessel only one-third to one-half, so as to allow ample volume for a "head" of foam in the vessel and thus retard or prevent its expulsion through the exit air tube.

b. Submerged Growth with Mechanical Agitation

Two types are used, (1) propellors and (2) shaking.

(1) *Propellors*. On a laboratory scale submerged growth setups involving propellor agitation are the more awkward, cumbersome, and difficult to operate. Usually a high speed motor turns the propellor, which maintains the culture liquid throughout the growth cycle in a state of more or less violent agitation. Theoretically this is the best way of securing efficient aeration, and most large scale industrial aerobic microbiological processes utilize the principle of propellor or impeller agitation. The main difficulty with laboratory-scale propellor agitation is the bearing by which the revolving propellor shaft enters the fermentation vessel, but it is possible to devise a satisfactory system that will not at the same time jeopardize the sterility of the medium and the purity of the culture during the growth period. Use of a propellor necessitates the use of a closed vessel, hence air must be introduced, either above the liquid level or below it. The former probably is satisfactory provided the amount of liquid being stirred is not too large, and provided that a sharp vortex is created whereby air is whipped into the liquid by the propellor blades. The theoretical objection to the idea of propellor agitation on the vortex principle is that air bubbles may be ejected from the liquid by centrifugal force. The particular advantage of high speed propellor agitation is that it prevents the mold mycelium from developing into large clumps, maintaining homogeneously distributed small particles, thereby ensuring optimum diffusion and aeration conditions with consequent maximum rate of metabolic transformations. Propellor agitation is not necessary for most laboratory investigations, but may be desirable in certain special cases, such as, for example, in so-called "stirred bottle" experiments where an attempt is made to reproduce on a small scale the conditions existing in large-scale production tanks, with the object of a systematic study of factors influencing the tank process.

(2) *Shaking Machines*. These are by far the most useful, simple to operate, and versatile methods of procuring submerged growth. This method has the extremely important advantage, one which none of the other methods possess, of providing a uniform and reproducible physical environment for large numbers of replicate cultures and different treatments during the whole course of any one experiment, and from experiment to experiment as well. This is the ultimate in standardization of the aeration-agitation complex, which, as has been emphasized throughout the foregoing, is so influential in the metabolic activities of mold cultures from all aspects. On any one shaker, large numbers of different medium constituents, different species and strains of organisms, and many other special experimental modifications in nutritional or biological factors may be compared and evaluated with full assurance that the results are directly those derived from the imposed treatments and not from a variable physical environment.

Two types of shaking machines are in general use: the rotary type and the reciprocal type. In the rotary machines, a shelf or tray, containing many flasks fixed in place by spring clamps or other devices, is rotated through a prescribed arc in a horizontal plane. This arc, or thrust, may be regulated by the degree of eccentricity of the drive powered by a motor located under the tray. Aside from the center bearing, the only guides are flexible ties at the four corners. Aeration is achieved by the fact that the liquid in the culture vessels is kept, through centrifugal force, in a thin and constantly changing film at the walls. Oxygen from the atmosphere inside the cotton plugged vessel dissolves in the liquid film. This, because of the changing and thin layers present, minimizes the limitations of diffusion in the solution of oxygen.

The reciprocating type of shaker depends for aeration on turbulence due to sloshing back and forth of the liquid and also due to droplet and spray formation. The shelf or tray holding the vessels is shaken with a reciprocating movement on a horizontal place. Both types of machines can be designed to accommodate any type vessel, and some have been constructed to hold several hundred 250-ml. Erlenmeyer flasks in double or triple tiers. The machine is located in a constant temperature room of the desired incubation temperature.

The degree of oxygenation of the culture liquid in shaker flasks is inversely proportional to the volume of liquid. The smaller the volume, the thinner the film, and every unit of liquid is directly exposed to the atmosphere a larger proportion of the incubation time. The effect of volume is striking, and results are directly dependent on the volume of medium. The full significance of this effect is self evident from the data in Table 1, dealing with riboflavin formation by the ascomycete

Eremothecium ashbyii. This effect is general for aerobic microbiological processes.

TABLE 1

VOLUME OF MEDIUM IN SHAKE CULTURES AND ITS EFFECT ON RIBOFLAVIN FORMATION BY EREMOTHECIUM ASHBYII[1,2]

Volume of medium	Riboflavin produced, μg. per ml. of medium after					
	2 days	3 days	4 days	5 days	6 days	9 days
800 ml.	39	49	89	95	132	158
400	46	84	100	110	195	179
200	89	198	216	253	336	358
100	200	384	490	565	685	660
50	195	395	526	605	680	759

[1] Unpublished data of E. O. Karow.
[2] Two-liter flasks used for each treatment; incubation on rotary shaker.

The optimum volume must be determined for each organism or process. The minimum is set by physical limitations: (1) evaporation during incubation periods of several days. Evaporation is accelerated by the moving liquid and results in concentration of the solutions, and in sampling difficulties. (2) When the volume is too small the heavy mold growth tends to migrate to the center of the vessel and agglomerate where it may not be totally submerged in the little liquid present there, since the centrifugal force collects the free liquid at the periphery of the flask. (3) Samples must be removed periodically for analyses. For most submerged growth experiments, 40 ml. of medium per 250-ml. Erlenmeyer flask is satisfactory. Foaming does not occur in rotary shaker cultures. However, as a point of practical interest, a few drops of a non-toxic antifoam in shake cultures usually exerts a beneficial effect on the growth and biochemical activities of molds, due presumably to a lowering of the surface tension so that exposure of the liquid to the atmosphere and subsequent oxygenation are enhanced. The rate of growth is accelerated so much in submerged shake cultures as compared to stationary cultures that the oxygen supply in the vessels may become depleted if the cotton plug is too tight or if it should get wet.

One of the best studies on the availability of oxygen to the fungus, and on the metabolic activity, under homogeneous physiological conditions is that on the production of gluconic acid by *Aspergillis niger* strain 67. Three critical factors and their interrelation were clarified: air flow, agitation, and air pressure. In every case maximum sugar utilization occurred at the highest rates of each, and since gluconic acid formation is a direct oxidation, maximum conversion yields occurred simultaneously with maximum glucose utilization. These features are detailed in Chapter 9.

INOCULATIONS

When shake cultures are inoculated with spores, from 18 to 36 hours elapse before significant growth and metabolic activity takes place, due to the germination period of the spores. This, on the whole, makes experimentation inefficient and slows up the execution of experiments and the flow of results. The lag period may be almost entirely eliminated by the use of pregerminated spores prepared by incubation on the shaker, for 1 or 2 days before inoculation of the main experiment, of a flask of medium made into a heavy suspension of spores. This fine, suspended young growth can be pipetted easily as inoculum for a number of flasks in a large experiment. The experimental flasks begin to develop almost immediately on the shaker.

Where the time factor is critical, as in development of industrial processes, vegetative inoculum, either submerged or surface type, is used. This starts the new culture with virtually no lag, or at least a greatly reduced lag. Since growth starts from each viable particle regardless of how small it is, a greater number of viable particles in any given volume of inoculum means a faster development, i.e., a shorter overall time for the process. Maximum efficiency in this regard is secured by using mycelium, either surface or submerged, homogenized in a Waring blender. This technique was first used by the USDA group on the gluconic acid process in 1937 (Moyer et al.) and has more lately been applied to other organisms (Dorrell and Page, 1947). In penicillin production, "blending" of Penicillium submerged mycelium, when diluted as much as 40,000 times, adequately substitutes for unblended submerged inoculum at a 1:10 seeding rate (Savage and Vander Brook, 1946). This technique does, therefore, make for an enormous increase in efficiency of inoculum, which also is easily handled by pipetting.

One of the most common faults in the submerged cultivation of fungi is the use of too small an inoculum. Development of the culture is delayed inversely as the amount of inoculum. Enough particles of inoculum should be introduced into a culture medium so that in effect it becomes a heavy suspension of spores, hyphae, or young mycelia. Best results are obtained when the culture is inoculated with 5 to 10 per cent of its volume of a heavy pregerminated culture or with the same amount of a fully grown vegetative submerged culture. When the number of viable cells becomes too small, the desired homogeneous suspended type of growth consisting of small individual colonies or clumps of mycelia fails to develop. Instead, the relatively few viable cells each develops into large individual colonies that are usually spherical and range in size from small peas to marbles or larger. The ambient liquid remains substantially clear. This type of growth arises where competition for the available nutrient is not great among the relatively few cells present, so that each particle of inoculum has sufficient nutrient to build a relatively massive colony. With mass inoculum all cells develop simultaneously, provided shaking is vigorous enough to prevent agglomeration, and the competition for the available substrate is great enough that each consumes only a small part of the total. The result is a myriad of small pellets or colonies down to microscopic size, giving in effect the uniform and homogeneous suspended type of culture.

The large spherical colony-type of growth is unsuited for metabolic studies, for much the same reasons that surface pads are unsuited. Only those cells at the periphery of the colony are exposed freely to nutrients and oxygen. The great majority of the cells in the interior obviously do not have optimum nutritional conditions. When these spongy spherical colonies are bisected the central portion has a strong alcoholic odor, indicating a lack of oxygen for the cells in the interior. Such cultures are very slow in transformation of substrate, and in fact, in growth itself.

The greatest tendency for the development of this large aggregate-colony type of growth appears when the nutrient conditions are unfavorable for rapid and abundant growth, and where agitation conditions are very mild, as in shake flasks with too deep volumes of liquid of very slow motion. Probably the most important single factor is the use of small numbers of inoculum particles. These conditions are most commonly met in the growth of fungi on synthetic media, with inorganic nitrogen source and where the chemicals are so pure that the content of "trace" elements is below the optimum, and often where low pH develops. Under such conditions even massive numbers of inoculum spores or hyphae tend to form the ball-like growth. Under the influence of gentle and continuous agitation, spores and pieces of hyphae in the inoculum tend to aggregate, and the larger the aggregate becomes, the more efficient it becomes in trapping additional free floating cells, germinated and ungerminated. One possibility is that spores germinate at different rates, and those germinating first and forming germ tubes and secondary hyphal branches probably trap other ungerminated or germinated spores encountered during the constant circulation and which stick together and form the nucleus of the large pellet type of colony. Particles of inert foreign matter may also function as a clumping nucleus. Not all the viable spores in the aggregate eventually germinate and contribute their mycelia to the colonial pellet.

In a microscopic study of pellet formation in *P. notatum* cultures, Bachus (personal communication) noted that the germinated spores in the center of the pellets have arrested germ tubes, with collapsed protoplasts, and that these cells are aborted and degenerate. Probably this state (autolysis?) is brought about by the inability of these cells to secure sufficient oxygen and nutrients, and represents the more advanced stage of those anaerobic conditions conducive to the formation of alcohol in the center, as mentioned earlier. This investigator observed that early in the stage of development (42–72 hours) a differentiation into three zones gradually took place: a rind area, a middle zone, and the core. The rind consists of youngest cells, branched and intertwined, whose cytoplasm is dense and granular, and this becomes progressively less towards the interior so that highly vacuolated degenerate cells and spore cases are encountered in the core.

Similar observations with numerous excellent photographs of the behavior of several different organisms are given by Burkholder and Sinnott (1945). These authors consider this to be morphogenesis, but as the curious growth pattern is not a fundamental link in the biological development of the organism but is largely a manifestation of a set of peculiar physical conditions, some question exists as to whether this phenomenon should be considered as morphogenesis.

ADAPTATION

The principle of adaptive enzyme formation, first clearly espoused by Karström, is a well-known and definitely established phenomenon among bacteria and yeasts (Karström, 1938). Fungi have been little investigated in this respect, but there are definite indications that in this group of microorganisms adaptation to the presence of specific ingredients in the medium may occur, and can exert a definite effect on the interpretation of the experimental results, depending on whether or not adapted inoculum was used in the experiment. This is particularly important where the rate of attack of a variety of different carbohydrates is being compared. The ultimate capacity of the organism to attack one carbohydrate may be fallaciously represented unless the inoculum is taken from an actively developing culture containing the identical carbohydrate. One instance of adaptation has already been mentioned in connection with the growth of *Streptomyces griseus* on rice bran and that this probably is not adaptive enzyme formation. Another example is the utilization of lactose by a penicillin-producing fungus. *Penicillin chrysogenum* X1612 was grown in shaker cultures for 48 hours in a basal corn steep liquor medium in two treatments: one contained 3 per cent lactose as carbohydrate; the other contained 3 per cent glucose. Both were separately used to inoculate corn steep liquor-lactose media, which then were incubated in the shaker; samples were removed periodically for lactose determination. The cultures that had received lactose inoculum began to utilize the carbohydrate in 26 hours whereas the culture with the glucose inoculum did not attack the lactose for 55 hours, and the penicillin activity reached was substantially lower than with an adapted inoculum (Foster *et al.*, 1946).

Several other instances of increased enzymatic powers of an organism, which may or may not be adaptative enzyme formation, have been reported. Thus, tannase production by *Aspergillus niger* is greatly enhanced by successive passage through media containing tannin, and the content of allantoicase in the dried mycelium of *Sterigmatocystis niger* is much greater if the organism is grown on uric acid or allantoin. The same holds for lipolytic enzymes, which are produced most abundantly when the fungi are cultivated on media containing pure fats and oils or mixtures of these, such as triolein, coconut oil and soybean oil. Media consisting of peptone, sucrose, or glycerol in the absence of fat are useless for lipase production by *A. niger*. According to Kertesz, the quantity of saccharase (invertase) formed by *Penicillium glaucum* is dependent on the concentration of sucrose in the medium.

Tannase and also pectinase production are two of the few enzymes, formed by fungi, which are strictly adaptive, since no tannase formation whatsoever occurs in the absence of the specific substrate although it is produced in abundance in the presence of gallins, tannins, and similar substances. The same applies to the pectin enzymes (see Chapter 18).

On the other hand, in certain cases the response of an organism to a specific substrate is peculiar and unpredictable. *Aspergillus niger* cell material grown on lactose media contains an enzyme that splits glucosides and galactosides, but when the fungus is grown on maltose the enzyme preparation splits only glucosides. Also, the content of inulase in the mycelium of *Penicillium glaucum* is greater when growth takes place on cane sugar than on inulin. Other instances of this type are saccharase (invertase) production by *Aspergillus flavus*, which was larger when potato butt instead of saccharose medium was used, and glucose oxidase, which was larger with sucrose as a carbon source than with glucose. For a more complete coverage of this particular phase of mold enzymes see Bernhauer and Knoblock (1941).

Two instances are known where successive transfers of fungi through carbohydrate media gradually led to considerably greater acid-producing powers. Fumaric acid production by what was originally a low-yielding strain was increased considerably (Bernhauer and Knoblock) and in the case of citric acid formation by *A. niger* the acidity produced in 14 per cent sucrose medium increased from a low of 0.2844 N to 0.8116 N, an increase of 286 per cent, during 18 transfers at weekly intervals. According to Doelger and Prescott the organism will continue to form increasing amounts of acid in each new fermentation up to a limit of 1.2 N (7.7 per cent) citric acid solution in 9 days' incubation. These are not adaptations in the sense of Karström, but either a selection, through successive transfers, of acid-tolerant progeny, or the accidental dominance of progeny characterized by higher acid-producing powers. More often successive vegetative transfers of fungi result in loss of, or reduction in, any particular biochemical function. This is called physiological degeneration, and is discussed in Chapter 5. In the absence of more definitive experiments it cannot be stated that true adaptation of all the vegetative cells present had occurred, as contrasted to selection and preferential development of certain of the cells capable of attacking the substrate more vigorously than other members of the population. Whatever the mechanism, the need for full consideration of this factor is evident in testing the utilization of various medium constituents.

UTILIZATION OF SUBMERGED GROWTH FOR SPECIAL PHYSIOLOGICAL EXPERIMENTS

The nicest and most elegant application of the principle of submerged growth to physiological experimentation with molds was made by Kluyver and Perquin in their classic paper on this subject in 1933. They emphasized the indispensability of using mold cell material of completely homogeneous makeup for physiological studies, and demonstrated the method for obtaining this by first cultivating good growth in submerged culture, aseptically removing and washing the cell material from aliquots by filtration, and resuspending the aliquots from the same lot of cell material in experimental nutrient culture fluids. Four major factors were elucidated as being vital in metabolic experimentation on dissimilation processes: (1) conditions under which the cells are grown prior to the replacement phase. Table 2 demonstrates this marked effect. A kojic acid strain of *Aspergillus flavus* (No. 3538) was grown for 48 hours on a shaker in three different media of the following composition:

Medium A	Medium B		Medium C	
Malt extract 15° Balling)	Glucose	200 g./l.	Glucose	100 g./l.
	NH₄NO₃	1.125	NH₄NO₃	0.563
	H₃PO₄	0.054	KH₂PO₄	1.0
	HCl	0.1	MgSO₄·7H₂O	2.0
	MgSO₄·7H₂O	0.5		

Medium B was previously developed (May *et al.* 1931) as being optimal for kojic acid formation by the same strain of *A. flavus*. Total dry weights of cell material obtained for 150 cc. medium were respectively 1.136 g., 0.192 g., and 0.308 g.

Washed cell material from each of the three media, equivalent to 150 mg. dry weight, was introduced aseptically into 150 ml. of the following medium contained in 500-ml. Erlenmeyer flasks and shaken for 24 hours: glucose, 5 per cent, H_3PO_4 0.500 g., KH_2PO_4 1.860 g. (pH 2.2).

The striking influence of the source of the mycelium on subsequent physiological activity of that mycelium is evident from the table. There is a remarkable variation in ability to utilize glucose and form kojic acid.

TABLE 2

EFFECT OF GROWTH MEDIUM ON METABOLISM OF WASHED MOLD MYCELIUM IN A FRESH REPLACEMENT MEDIUM[1]

Mycelium grown on	Glucose consumed, per cent solution	Kojic acid formed, per cent solution	Conversion yield[2] of kojic acid
Medium A..............................	0.49	0.06	15.5
	0.52	0.06	14.6
B..............................	0.06	0	0
C..............................	0.49	0.25	64.8
	0.48	0.23	60.5

[1] Kojic acid formation by *Aspergillus flavus*.   From Kluyver and Perquin (1933).

[2] Per cent of theory assuming 1 mole kojic acid from 1 mole glucose.

Obviously these deviations must be due to differences in composition of the cell material obtained from the different media. In view of recent findings on the constancy of the amino acid content of the protein of fungi grown in widely differing media (see Chapter 17) it is unlikely that gross changes were induced in the protein composition of the cell material. It appears rather that changes in the enzymic makeup were induced, since these might be so small quantitatively as to be an insignificant part of the total cell protein. Thus, they would not reflect a substantial change in the whole protein constitution of the mycelium, and yet, being catalytic, would exert profound changes in metabolic reactions.

(2) Influence of glucose concentration on rate of glucose consumption. This is a well known biological effect, and vital from the standpoint of working methods. All fungi have optimum sugar concentrations which, through osmotic effects or specific enzyme effects, are most favorable for consumption of the sugar. It is important to recognize that the sugar

concentration found to favor maximum rate of sugar utilization is not at all necessarily the best for rate of growth or maximum expression of other metabolic processes, such as organic acid formation. In general, the ordinary fungi are tolerant of relatively high ranges of osmotic pressure, especially of carbohydrates. This property explains their common association with spoilage of jams, jellies, and fruit preserves, which depend on high osmotic pressure of sugar to prevent microbiological spoilage. In physiological experiments 5 to 10 per cent generally is optimum. The following data exemplify the concentration influence in a submerged replacement experiment (Kluyver and Perquin, 1933)

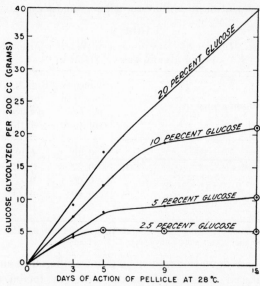

Fig. 1.—Influence of glucose concentrations on the rate of glycolysis by Rhizopus pellicles. Circles indicate that all the sugar has disappeared (from Waksman and Foster, 1938).

and Fig. 1 demonstrates the rather extreme differences in sugar utilization as a function of concentration and time in replacement surface pad cultures of a lactic acid-producing strain of Rhizopus. *Aspergillus flavus* mycelium grown on medium A and distributed for the secondary dissimilation experiment in 5, 10, and 20 per cent glucose solutions, consumed after 23 hours shaking, 0.96, 1.82, and 1.10 g. glucose, respectively. Similar data are available for most molds whose dissimilative processes have been studied, including fumaric, lactic, citric, oxalic, gluconic, and kojic-producing strains. As would be expected, there is a definite optimum concentration of carbohydrate for any organism or physiological process. In the case of *A. flavus* 20 per cent was definitely beyond the maximum, whereas this was not so for Rhizopus (Fig. 1). The full significance of concentration effects for physiological experiments is greater than might first appear, for obviously the concentration begins to change appreciably within a few hours after shaking begins and continues to change with prolonged incubation. However, as Kluyver and Perquin pointed out, if the experiments are relatively short-time ones, approximately 24 hours, conditions remain essentially homogeneous, although this should be ascertained for any particular experiment, particularly since a shorter time may be desirable or essential with lower sugar concentrations. Long-time experiments represent the nfluence of a whole range of constantly changing concentrations.

Glucose concentration leads to some other extremely important considerations in the dissimilation processes of fungi and their overall metabolism. These are discussed in Chapter 4.

(3) Influence of salts on dissimilation processes.

Minerals have long been known to exercise profound effects on metabolic processes of fungi, and implications of this effect are discussed in Chapters 3 and 7. The following data from Kluyver and Perquin exemplify the effect under washed cell replacement conditions with 10 per cent glucose, and make it obvious that the mineral content can profoundly alter the rate of sugar utilization and the fate of the sugar. Especially striking is the effect of trace elements on fungus metabolism, a subject covered extensively in Chapter 7.

Replacement medium	Glucose consumed, per cent	Kojic acid produced, per cent	Conversion yield of kojic acid, per cent
0.1% KH_2PO_4 0.2 $MgSO_4 \cdot 7H_2O$ 0.056 NH_4NO_3	1.12	0.18	20.4
0.1% KH_2PO_4 0.2 $MgSO_4 \cdot 7H_2O$	.60	0.18	38.0
No salts	.51	0.13	32.3

(4) Influence of oxygen on metabolic processes. This has already been treated in detail. In physiological submerged replacement experiments the optimum amount of cell material must be ascertained as a preliminary to subsequent experimentation. The rate of oxygen consumption by suspended cells is limited by the rate of solution of oxygen from the atmosphere. Too large an amount of cell material creates a biological oxygen demand exceeding the rate of solution of oxygen.

Accordingly, oxidative metabolism is reduced, resulting in an appreciable alteration in the nature of the dissimilation processes. Factors influential here are the relations between amount of cell material, volume of liquid, size of flask, and rate and degrees of shaking. The very volume and thickness of mold vegetative cells may be an obstacle to the complete fulfillment of oxygen requirements owing to the limited rate of oxygen diffusion from the surface of the cell to the active cytoplasm in the cell interior, and to the prior uptake of the oxygen by the layers of cytoplasm in the peripheral regions of the cell. One might expect this to be true particularly when the cells are coated with gummy or slimy polysaccharide materials. As a result, cytoplasm in the cell interior might become impoverished for oxygen, and anaerobic or fermentation metabolism would occur there. Such events might explain the formation of not inconsiderable amounts of ethanol by fungi in submerged cultures under conditions of high oxygenation (see Chapter 9).

RESPIRATION EXPERIMENTS

For the many reasons covered above, homogeneous cell material is indispensable and submerged growth is the best method of preparation. The suspended growth should be the very fine type, for even small pellets are not homogeneous enough for critical respiratory experiments. Very young cultures, taken before pellets develop or clumping occurs, are most suitable. The mycelia can be centrifuged, washed, resuspended uniformly by rapid passage in and out of a pipette, and aliquots pipetted into Warburg vessels much as bacterial suspensions are handled. Gould and Tytell (1941) and Semeniuk (1944) successfully utilized surface pad growths for study of respiratory and fermentative mechanisms. The washed pad was homogenized into active uniform suspension by shaking with glass beads, and the suspended material pipetted in aliquots to respirometers. Wherever it can be applied, the technique for homogenizing either surface or submerged mycelia described on p. 62 is probably the best single method for obtaining fungus cell suspensions. Experiments dealing with mechanisms of respiration of molds can easily be followed manometrically (Ryan et al., 1944).

In some ways mold cell material is not ideal for biochemical studies involving respiration in connection with dissimilation processes. First, the extremely high endogenous respiration makes interpretation of oxygen uptake and carbon dioxide formation from the oxidation of added substrate open to question since, in most cases, the amount of substrate is necessarily small in order that the potential gaseous exchange does not exceed the capacity of the respirometer. It is always difficult to decide whether the value for endogenous respiration is to be deducted from that for the substrate, i.e., does endogenous respiration proceed simultaneously with oxidation of the substrate, or does it, in the presence of a readily utilizable energy source, become suppressed? Until this can be settled, the validity of the quantitative interpretation is open to serious question, and it is incumbent on the investigator to decide this for the organism and type of problem concerned. Usually supplementary experiments permit a logical conclusion. (See Barker, 1936; Doudoroff, 1940; van Niel and Cohen, 1942; and Foster, 1944.) Secondly, dissimilation products such as organic acids are usually formed by fungi only when the substrate concentration is considerably higher than the respirometers could accommodate if the substrate were completely consumed, and the conversion yields are dependent on substrate concentration up to a certain optimum.

Thus, ideal respiration conditions where the biochemical transformations typical of the fungus occur in nearly maximum degree may be represented as follows: (1) Very short time experiments with optimum high substrate concentration, in which just enough substrate is utilized to produce gas changes within the maximum measurable by the respirometer. Under such conditions the characteristic dissimilation potentialities of the organism, such as the type and amount of organic acids it forms, are manifested. This means that a large part, if not most, of the substrate is unconsumed; but, by microanalyses, quantitative balances between the amount of substrate used, specific organic acids, CO_2 or other products formed, oxygen consumed, and increase in mycelial weight can be established. Complete balance data are essential for an interpretation of mechanism of formation of the various products of metabolism.

(2) Longer time experiments where substantially all the available substrate is metabolized and the CO_2 and O_2 exchange measured in specially-adapted apparatus. Thus, the use of very large vessels in manometers filled with mercury increases the capacity of Warburg type respirometers for many experiments of this type (Foster and Davis, 1948). Often oxygen measurements are not necessary in making carbon balances, and the CO_2 may be measured titrimetrically after trapping in NaOH or $Ba(OH)_2$ solution, or gravimetrically after absorption in ascarite tubes. Such experiments do not require respirometers, and the liquid or solid CO_2-absorbant system is attached to the exit air vent of the culture vessel, which may be an ordinary flask.

Respiration activities of the mold mycelium itself in the absence of added substrate (endogenous respiration, autorespiration) can be studied in the respirometer apparatus. From the respiratory quotient the nature of the reserve cellular materials undergoing oxidation can be studied, also the influence of growth conditions, effect of starvation, and other intrinsic respiratory characters of the mold (Dorrell, 1948).

Enzyme Preparations

Although little application to fungi has yet been made, the various methods so successful for securing active enzyme juices and preparations from yeast and bacteria would seem to offer great promise in mold biochemistry. These methods are reviewed by Umbreit *et al.* (1945a), Werkman and Wood (1941), and, especially for fungi, in Bernhauer and Knobloch (1941).

1. EXTRACTS FROM LIVING CELLS

This would correspond to the cell juice of yeast first obtained by Buchner, and to "maceration" preparations in which the living cells are disrupted and the juices liberated by various physical means. Gould and Tytell (1941) failed to obtain preparations from *Fusarium tricothecoides*, active in fermenting glucose, by various methods including grinding with sand in the cold with subsequent centrifugation, by freezing and grinding, and by pressing at very high pressures. However Semeniuk (1944) ground the mycelia of *Chaetomium funicola*, *Aspergillus niger*, *Fusarium lini*, *F. cubense*, and *F. nivium* with sand and the resulting minced preparations fermented glucose and actively respired. Mann (1944) succeeded in extracting a polyphosphatase with water from the pulp of ground *A. niger* mycelia. This enzyme, because of the ease with which it acted on metaphosphate, was named metaphosphatase. Muller (see Chapter 15) obtained very active glucose oxidase juices by grinding fresh *A. niger* mycelia in a mortar with sand and diatomaceous earth, followed by pressing out the juice from the pasty mass in a Buchner press under 300 atmospheres pressure. Other physical means of liberating cell juice may not be successful. The tissue homogenizer (Umbreit *et al.* 1945) led to loss of most of the activity of *Penicillium sp.* but may be applicable to other organisms. The spongy nature of mold mycelium, homogenized first in a Waring blendor, does not lend itself suitably to grinding with powdered glass in the grinding cones apparatus of Utter and Werkman (1942), because the liquid is expressed and the mycelial residue is stringy and curdlike, rather than pasty as necessary for the technique.

2. EXTRACTS FROM DEAD CELLS

Most often the cells are desiccated. A mild treatment like this is absolutely necessary to preserve the enzymes. This procedure is essentially that of preparation of the famous Lebedev juice from yeast wherein the cells are air-dried quickly in thin layers, then autolyzed in water (or glycerol) for a few hours at 37°C. This disrupts the cells and liberates the active enzymes in solution, which can be separated from the cell debris by filtration or centrifugation. This zymase solution may show a long induction period before it commences to ferment sugar and certain activating substances reduce the lag period appreciably (Neuberg and Lustig, 1942). The process is enhanced by grinding the dry cells with powdered glass or sand to disrupt them before autolysis. To prevent bacterial growth and destruction of the enzymes the solution must have an excess of a preservative such as toluene, benzene, or ether.

3. CRUDE CELL PREPARATIONS

Desiccated cells can be stored and will retain their enzyme activity for long periods of time. They may be used without any attempt to extract the enzymes from the cell mass, and are very active when placed in a suitable aqueous substrate at appropriate pH and temperature. These preparations are very useful for certain types of investigations. Desiccation is obtained by rapid air drying or *in vacuo* over P_2O_5 so as to reduce to a minimum destruction of the desired enzymes by other intracellular enzymes during the drying period. For this reason very thin layers of material are spread in glass plates or dishes and dried at room temperature or 30°C. under a current of air from an electric fan. When dry, the brittle mass is stored over $CaCl_2$, P_2O_5 or H_2SO_4 to remove the last traces of water. Fusarium cells prepared by this method were unable to ferment glucose, although the preparation had good carboxylase activity, which was stable even after long storage (Tytell and Gould, 1941). Similarly, mycelium preparations containing active glucosidase and allantoicase have been obtained by other workers.

Sometimes the desiccated mycelium is more active towards a substrate than the living fresh mycelium. This is true of oxalacetic acid decarboxylase in *Rhizopus nigricans* (Foster and Davis 1948) and these authors have also shown (unpublished) that the fresh mycelium of this organism is entirely inert towards succinate, yet clear-cut succinoxidase activity was displayed by mycelia desiccated over P_2O_5 *in vacuo*. This type of result appears best interpreted on the basis of membrane permeability. The selectivity of the cell is destroyed by drying, as it is by certain other treatments.

Desiccation is also frequently achieved by fat solvents, yielding products similar to the "zymin" of yeast. The fresh cells are added in small portions to a relatively large volume of anhydrous acetone and allowed to stand with frequent shaking for several minutes. Methyl alcohol or ethyl alcohol-ether mixture (2:1) can also be used. For 100 g. of moist pressed cells 2–2.5 liters solvent is used. The dehydrated cells are separated from the liquid, and treated with 2 successive portions of ether (200 ml.). The thoroughly dried cells are freed from ether by vacuum over $CaCl_2$ or $CaSO_4$, ground, tightly stoppered, and stored in the cold. In principle this corresponds to the classical Acetone-dauerhefe method for yeast, the preparation being known as zymin or zymase.

Theoretically the ideal manner of preparing crude cell enzymatic preparations with a minimum of destruction is by the "freeze-dry" process of vegetative cells, similar to the lyophil process for the preservation of stock cultures of various microorganisms. The mycelium is frozen rapidly in thin layers, preferably in thin layers on the walls of the vessel, by immersing in crushed dry-ice or mixture of dry-ice and acetone, ether or alcohol (approx. $-70°C.$), and placed under high vacuum so that the water evaporates without passing through the liquid state (sublimation). In case the vacuum is not sufficient to maintain the vessel contents frozen until dry, the vessel should be kept immersed in the freezing mixture during the entire drying process. The desiccated product is fluffy, and grinds readily. It is very hygroscopic and should not be exposed too long to the atmosphere. The whole dry powder could be used for experiments, or clear extracts prepared as above in water or buffer solutions.

There is no doubt that future progress toward the elucidation of the precise mechanisms of the various biochemical transformations effected by fungi depends to a large degree on the development of methods for securing and the utilization of enzyme preparations that contain non-viable cells or are cell-free. It is surprising that throughout the years this approach has not been applied to the study of various intermediary enzymes of the classical dissimilation process performed by molds (citric, oxalic, kojic, etc.).

4. EXTRACELLULAR ENZYME PREPARATIONS

These are well known and easily obtained, especially hydrolytic enzymes of the diastatic, proteolytic, and pectinolytic groups. Sometimes enzymes concerned with intermediary metabolism are excreted (or liberated by autolysis) into the medium by growing cultures, and can be obtained from the culture filtrate in cell-free condition and further purified. Glucose oxidase (glucose aerodehydrogenase) later "rediscovered" as the antibiotic notatin and penicillin B (see Chapter 15) is a notable instance of this type. Metaphosphatase can also be isolated from the culture fluid of *Aspergillus niger* (Mann, 1944) and several other examples are given at various points in this book.

REFERENCES

Barker, H. A. 1936. *J. Cellular Comp. Physiol.* **8**, 321–350.
Bernhauer, K., and Knoblock, H. 1941. Die Methoden der Fermentforschung. G. Thieme, Leipzig, Vol. 2, pp. 1303–1325.

Birkinshaw, J. H., Charles, J. H. V., Hetherington, A. C., Raistrick, H., and Thom, C. 1931. *Trans. Roy. Soc. London* **B220**, 55–92.
Booth, V. H., and Green, D. E. 1938. *Biochem. J.* **32**, 855–861.
Burkholder, P. R., and Sinnott, E. W. 1945. *Am. J. Botany* **32**, 424–431.
Clifton, C. E. 1946. *Advances in Enzymol.* **6**, 269–308.
Davis, H. 1948. Detection and Occurrence of Acid-Producing Fungi. Master's Thesis, Dept. of Bacteriology, Univ. of Texas.
Doelger, W. P., and Prescott, S. C. 1934. *Ind. Eng. Chem.* **26**, 1142–1149.
Dorrell, W. W. 1948. Oxidative Respiration of *Fusarium graminearum*. Ph. D. Thesis, Univ. of Wisconsin.
Dorrell, W. W., and Page, R. M. 1947. *J. Bact.* **53**, 360–361.
Doudoroff, M. 1940. *Enzymologia* **9**, 59–72.
Erb, N. M., Wisthoff, R. T., and Jacobs, W. L. 1948. *J. Bact.* **55**, 813–821.
Foster, J. W. 1944. *J. Bact.* **48**, 97–111.
Foster, J. W., and Davis, J. B. 1948. *J. Bact.* **56**, 329–339.
Foster, J. W., and Woodruff, H. B. 1945. *J. Bact.* **51**, 363–369.
Foster, J. W., Woodruff, H. B., Perlman, D., McDaniel, L. E., Wilker, B. L., and Hendlin, D. 1946. *J. Bact.* **51**, 695–698.
Gould, B. S., and Tytell, A. A. 1941. *J. Gen. Physiol.* **24**, 655–667.
Karström, H. 1938. *Ergeb. Enzymforsch.* **7**, 350–376.
Kluyver, A. J., and Perquin, L. H. C. 1933. *Biochem. Z.* **266**, 68–81.
LeMense, E. H., Corman, J., Van Lanen, J. M., and Langlykke, A. F. 1947. *J. Bact.* **54**, 149–159.
Mann, T. 1944. *Biochem. J.* **38**, 339–345.
May, O. E., Herrick, H. T., Moyer, A. J., and Hellbach, R. 1929. *Ind. Eng. Chem.* **21**, 1198–1203.
May, O. E., Moyer, A. J., Wells, P. A., and Herrick, H. T. 1931. *J. Am. Chem. Soc.* **53**, 774–782.
Moyer, A. J., Wells, P. A., Stubbs, J. J., Herrick, H. T., and May, O. E. 1937. *Ind. Eng. Chem.* **29**, 777–782.
Neuberg, C., and Lustig, H. 1942. *Arch. Biochem.* **1**, 191–196.
Porges, N., Clark, T. F., and Gastrock, E. A. 1940. *Ind. Eng. Chem.* **32**, 107–111.
Ryan, F. J., Tatum, E. L., and Geise, A. C. 1944. *J. Cellular Comp. Physiol.* **23**, 83–94.
Savage, G. M., and Vander Brook, M. J. 1946. *J. Bact.* **52**, 385–391.
Schade, A. L. 1940. *Am. J. Botany* **27**, 376–384.
Semeniuk, G. 1944. *Iowa State Coll. J. Sci.* **18**, 325–358.
Tytell, A. A. and Gould, B. S. 1941. *J. Bact.* **42**, 513–26.
Umbreit, W. W., Burris, R. H., and Stauffer, J. F. 1945. Manometric Techniques and Related Methods for the Study of Tissue Metabolism. (a) pp. 84–90, (b) pp. 92–94. Burgess, Minneapolis.
Utter, M. F., and Werkman, C. H. 1942. *Biochem. J.* **36**, 485–493.
van Niel, C. B., and Cohen, A. L. 1942. *J. Cellular Comp. Physiol.* **20**, 95–112.
Wagner, R. P., and Guirard, B. M. 1948. *Proc. Natl. Acad. Sci. U. S.* **34**, 398–402.
Waksman, S. A. 1947. Microbial Antagonisms and Antibiotic Substances. 2nd ed., Commonwealth Fund, New York.
Waksman, S. A., and Foster, J. W. 1938. *J. Agr. Research* **57**, 873–900.
Werkman, C. H., and Wood, H. G. 1941. Die Methoden der Fermentforschung. G. Thieme, Leipzig, pp. 1191–1214.
Wirth, J. C., and Nord, F. F. 1940. *Science* **92**, 15–16.
Woodruff, H. B., and Ruger, M. 1948. *J. Bact.* **56**, 315–321.

CHAPTER 3

CHEMICAL NATURE OF THE MOLD MYCELIUM

Fungi as a whole do not have a characteristic composition, either in respect to types of compounds, i.e., proximate analysis, or individual components, i.e., specific analysis. A number of different factors are responsible for this. There are literally thousands of different species of fungi, and it could hardly be expected that the composition of cell material would be constant through the great diversity of different species. According to Bessey (1935), over 35,000 Ascomycetes, 24,000 Basidiomycetes, and 25,000 Fungi Imperfecti were known up to 1925, and Smith fixes the total at 89,000 in 1938. Some 3,000 genera are involved. Variable amounts of aerial vs. submerged mycelium are produced, different degrees of sporulation are encountered, some grow extremely rapidly while others are notoriously slow growers.

Some tend to form dry, brittle surface pads, and are contrasted to the subsurface slimy growth of others. Different strains of the same species and even different daughter colonies of any single spore parent culture may and usually do vary within great inherent morphological, cultural, and physiological limits. All of these characteristics play a part in the quantitative distribution of the various cellular components, as well as the qualitative composition. As shown below, the age of the culture is an important aspect of cell composition, especially with respect to comparison of cultures, because the rates of growth of different organisms even under identical conditions make it evident that chronological age certainly is not equivalent to physiological age. As cultures age, autolysis sets in at various rates, and not only does this change the relative composition of the cell material, but it usually involves a marked loss in total weight of cell material. This process is continually taking place in a growing culture. The microscopic observation is frequently made that actively growing cells, such as the hyphae in the periphery of agar colonies, or the aerial mycelium in liquid surface culture, are packed with granular bodies of different sizes and that the whole filament is refractile, indicative of abundant cytoplasm. The same is true of cells in young submerged shake cultures. On the other hand, older cells, such as those in the interior of the surface pad, or those in the center of an agar colony, have large empty spaces, and generally have substantially less cell content. Such cells are often nearly devoid of cytoplasm; the cell consists essentially of the cell wall. These often are referred to as ghost or shadow cells. Tausson (1938) has made some quantitative studies of the numbers of living and dead cells in fungus cultures.

Analytical results, qualitative and quantitative, on surface-pad cultures of fungi are subject to the same criticisms and limitations discussed in the previous chapter in connection with the physiological activities of surface pads. Here, too, data represent the resultant of composition of cells under widely varying nutritional and metabolic circumstances in the same culture. As in the previous case, analysis of cultures of uniform cellular composition can be obtained only on growth under shake conditions. Shake cultures eliminate another complication, though probably of minor significance, since the cell material consists, except under very special conditions (Foster *et al.* 1945) of vegetative mycelium, to the exclusion of spores. Most analyses of surface pads have included spores and mycelium together.

As might be expected, the composition, qualitative and quantitative, of submerged mycelium and surface growth of any one organism may be quite different, because of the profound metabolic difference implicit between these conditions. It seems a reasonable assumption that the composition of uniform cellular material typical of submerged cultures most closely approximates the basic or vital makeup of molds, and comprises the least common denominator of composition for active living mold mycelium. If the words "typical" or "normal" are at all applicable, they could express quite closely the significance of the composition of submerged cell material for the latter are metabolically homogeneous.

Finally, the nature of the medium on which the organisms are grown is of paramount importance. Significant changes in the composition of the growth medium usually are reflected, in a rough way, in the makeup of the cell material derived from that medium. A medium high in minerals, in nitrogenous constituents, or in carbohydrates or non-nitrogenous substances, will affect the cell material content of each in a similar way respectively. This aspect will be treated in detail below. On the other hand, it is remarkable how successful fungi are in achieving the synthesis of the innumerable components of cell material from simple or complex nutrients alike, under greatly diversified nutrient conditions, and with such reproducibility as to eventuate as cell material from all cases.

PROXIMATE COMPOSITION OF FUNGI

Complete proximate analyses of fungi are very few. Usually one must piece together the information on special fractions, each obtained from different reports, in order to secure an overall picture of the cell material. It goes without saying that the group constituents characteristic of all living biological systems are found in fungi. Perhaps the most complete data of this type are those of Porges (1932) and of Schulz (1937), who not only fractionated the mycelium of *Aspergillus niger* but showed how the relative composition could be altered markedly by the cultural conditions. Especially emphasized was the heavy metal nutrition of the organism, with particular stress on the effect of zinc. The latter author used a different strain of *A. niger*, but otherwise attempted to reproduce the experiments of Porges as faithfully as possible, using the same medium composition, etc. He has compared his data with that of Porges. (See Table 1.) The specific analyses of the various fractions are included here because they illustrate the methods of a complete proximate analysis and also represent one of the most complete analyses of mold mycelium available. As might be expected, the strains used by these authors were physiologically different, indicated first by the economic coefficients (grams sugar utilized per gram cell material synthesized) and titratable acidity of the culture fluid due to organic acid formation. These strain differences are further strikingly manifest from the analytical data on the proximate analysis. Comparing the data in the "no zinc" columns, Schulz' organism was substantially richer in the fraction represented by alcohol extract, cold water extract, H_2SO_4 extract and total ash. On the other hand, Porges' strain was superior in the hot water extract and the residue therefrom, the HCl extract and residue, residue from H_2SO_4 and the "lignin" fraction. These strain composition differences are further sharply defined by the changes in the composition of each strain caused by the presence of 0.01 per cent ZnSO . The percentage change in each fraction, caused by zinc in relation to the "no zinc" controls, are listed in Table 1. Notable are the deviations in ether extract, alcohol extract, cold water extract, and hot water extract.

For the most part, the more resistant fractions, HCl extract and residue, H_2SO_4 extract and residue, and "lignin" fractions were affected alike in the two strains by the presence of zinc. Whether this is typical for other strains will have to await similar comparative data, but from experience with other aspects of mold physiology it would appear unlikely. Available evidence indicates that little uniformity indeed can be expected in physiological behavior between different strains of the same species. This holds true in regard to any one medium, and is further demonstrated by divergent responses to the same imposed cultural modifications.

The item listed as "nitrogen" under the various fractions was, for convenience, arbitrarily designated to represent the soluble nitrogenous

TABLE 1

PROXIMATE COMPOSITION OF TWO STRAINS OF ASPERGILLUS NIGER AND THE
INFLUENCE OF ZINC

	Porges' data			Schulz' data		
	No Zn	With Zn	Per cent difference	No Zn	With Zn	Per cent difference
Sugar consumed, g.[1]	49.5	77.9	+ 58	24.4	58.0	+124
Mycelium dry wt., g.[1]	9.26	20.65	+123	3.5	20.0	+470
Economic coefficient[2]	5.34	3.77	− 42	6.97	2.9	−140
Acid formed per gram dry mycelium, cc. 0.1 N	236	120	− 97	189	53	−256
	Per Cent of Dry Mold Material					
Ether extract	2.69	5.18	+ 93	2.99	7.47	+150
Alcohol extract	11.35	12.90	+ 14	29.79	20.04	− 33
Reducing sugars	1.54	1.54	0	4.22	0.85	− 80
Nitrogen	0.22	0.27	+ 23	0.37	0.40	+ 8
Ash	0.04	0.07	+ 75	0.58	0.42	− 28
Cold water extract	5.23	8.84	+ 69	8.30	9.18	+ 11
Reducing sugars	0.45	0.42	− 7	0.72	0.24	− 67
Reducing sugars after hydrolysis	......	......	.....	1.73	1.98	+ 14
Nitrogen	0.16	0.18	+ 12	0.15	0.20	+ 33
Ash	1.93	1.80	− 7	2.65	2.74	+ 3
Hot water extract	5.77	5.30	− 8	4.48	7.06	+ 58
Reducing sugars	0.35	0.29	− 17	0.54	2.83	+425
Reducing sugars after hydrolysis	......	......	.....	1.92	4.12	+115
Nitrogen	0.23	0.16	− 30	0.20	0.11	− 45
Ash	0.27	0.44	+ 63	0.42	0.40	− 5
Residue	68.81	66.07	− 4	53.75	59.60	+ 11
Dilute HCl extract	27.99	38.78	+ 39	20.61	31.14	+ 51
Hemicelluloses	21.14	31.28	+ 48	12.43	22.02	+ 78
Nitrogen	1.04	0.75	− 28	0.91	0.93	+ 2
Residue	40.82	27.29	− 33	33.14	28.46	− 14
80 per cent H_2SO_4 extract	15.15	13.00	− 14	18.88	22.48	+ 19
"Cellulose"	11.15	11.12	0	10.82	15.37	+ 42
Nitrogen	0.53	0.25	− 53	0.64	0.47	− 27
Residue	25.67	14.29	− 44	14.26	0.598	− 58
Nitrogen	1.06	0.85	− 20	0.53	0.29	− 45
Ash	0.04	0.08	+100	0.04	0.02	− 50
"Lignin"	18.98	8.92	− 53	10.91	4.15	− 62
Total nitrogen (sum of fractions)	3.27	2.52	− 23	2.80	2.41	− 14
Total ash (sum of fractions)	2.28	2.39	+ 5	3.69	3.58	− 3
Carbon content of mycelium	45.82	45.58				

[1] Per liter of medium. Seven days incubation at 30°C. 300 cc. medium per 2-liter flask.
[2] Grams sugar consumed per gram mycelium synthesized.

materials extracted by the particular treatment, and besides free and conjugated proteins, may consist of organic bases, such as purines and pyrimidines, free amino acids and peptides, nucleic acids, enzymes, certain vitamins, etc. The ether soluble fraction contains fats, higher alcohols, part of resins and waxes, free fatty acids, and some free carboxylic acids, phospholipides, and sterols. The alcohol fraction contains lipides and waxes insoluble or slightly soluble in ether, such as cerebrosides, resins, certain phospholipides, simple sugars, carboxylic acids, amino acids and peptides, quinones, pigments, polyhydric neutral substances, etc. In the cold water fraction are found simple substances of a non-lipide nature which are poorly soluble in ether and alcohol. Acids, amino acids, peptides, coenzymes, phosphorylated metabolites, and low molecular weight sugars would be included. High molecular weight sugars, starches, and other polysaccharides are dissolved in the hot water fraction, whereas the dilute HCl fraction measures the amount of polysaccharides and polyuronides partially or incompletely soluble in hot water, chiefly starches, hemicelluloses, and slimy substances consisting of mixed polymers, mucins, gums, glycogen, etc. It may be noted that such substances are also appreciably represented in the alcohol, cold, and hot water extracts as indicated by reducing sugars liberated by acid hydrolysis of these fractions. The resistant polymers, soluble only after hydrolysis in hot 80 per cent H_2SO_4, are celluloselike substances, and chitin or chitinosans. The chitins probably account for a good deal of the rather high nitrogen content of this fraction, and liberation and hydrolysis of protein from insoluble conjugated proteins also may contribute to the nitrogen content. The fraction insoluble in 80 per cent H_2SO_4 consists chiefly of the highly resistant lignins, characterized by high content of aromatic nuclei. In the case of polysaccharides determined after hydrolysis, the true value is only nine-tenths of the observed reducing sugar value due to water of hydration. Protein and lignin have a strong affinity for each other, forming highly resistant complexes known as ligno-proteins, and these make up the high protein content of the insoluble residual material left after hydrolysis with 80 per cent H_2SO_4 (Waksman, 1936).

The major constituents of the mycelium are polymerized materials of the easily-hydrolyzable polysaccharide (hemicellulose) and protein types, and the resistant materials like difficultly-hydrolyzable polysaccharides; the latter group comprise the structural or matrix portion of the cells and are associated chiefly with cell walls, and spores, and in some cases specialized bodies like chlamydospores, perithecia, etc. In view of the fact that the cellulose was not isolated and characterized as such, the fraction designated as cellulose by Porges perhaps should be considered as difficultly-hydrolyzable polysaccharides. The designation of lignin also is rather debatable, for the existence of true lignin in fungi is not yet unequivocal (see below); at least this fraction is "ligninlike." The hemicellulose fraction, together with the smaller lipide fraction constitute the rich and readily available reserve or storage energy supply of the organism. It is interesting to note that zinc, known to favor cell synthesis at the expense of organic acid production (Chapters 4 and 7), is especially effective in raising the content of these energy-rich materials, the lipide fraction by as much as 150 per cent and the hemicelluloses by 78 per cent. The remaining significant increase was in the cold water fraction consisting of sugars, polyhydric alcohols and amino acids, possibly the building blocks of the reserve materials. All these increases were made at the expense of resistant complex structural materials, which in the zinc culture were reduced to 47 and 38 per cent, respectively, of the value for the control cultures. As will be shown later, the lipide fraction is characteristically much higher in certain fungi, and moreover, can be varied within rather wide limits by cultural conditions. Schulz reported a number of other informative experiments.

Proximate analyses performed on the same organism under identical conditions, only cultivated at different times, yielded data in remarkably good agreement, both on the control cultures and in regard to the zinc effect. In general it is extremely difficult to reproduce physiological experiments with fungi quantitatively; Schulz' data indicate that rigorous control of conditions can lead to reproducible results.

The mycelium composition of the same strain grown on the following two nutrient solutions showed little difference; their differences were much less than between two different strains grown on the same medium (Table 1), but were larger than discrepancies obtained at different times using the same strain and the same medium. However, the effect of zinc on most of the various components of cell material was strikingly different in the two solutions (Table 2). Such a reaction is unexpected in view of the uniform results obtained in the "no zinc" solutions. The extreme variation in response is cogent testimony of latent physiological differences within strains of fungi morphologically indistinguishable and otherwise responding virtually identically on another medium, e.g., no zinc. The only similarity in the zinc cultures is that the increments made in the various fractions were made mainly at the expense of the "lignin" fraction, in agreement with the results in Table 1. While zinc usually evokes the greatest response in fungus growth in synthetic media, other heavy metals in trace amounts also produce similar, though smaller, effects especially when the basal medium is prepared from reagent- or chemically-pure-grade ingredients (Chapter 7). The data of Schulz reveal that the effects of cadmium, manganese, and iron, are of the same trend as zinc, although some quantitative discrepancies were observed, and in some few cases, decreases in certain fractions resulted as contrasted to increases in others.   Here again increased concentrations of other cell fractions due to the cadmium, manganese, and iron were at the expense of the very resistant lignin fraction.   The similarity of changes in cell composition is suggestive of similar metabolic functions of these trace elements.

TABLE 2

CHANGE, IN PER CENT OF CONTROLS, CAUSED BY ZINC IN DIFFERENT MEDIA[1]

	Solution 1	Solution 2
Fats, etc..................................	+150	− 40
Crude protein............................	− 15	+ 30
Reducing sugars..........................	− 28	− 80
Water soluble polysaccharides.............	+ 30	+115
Hemicelluloses...........................	+ 80	+ 25
"Cellulose".............................	+ 45	+150
"Lignin"................................	− 60	− 85
Ash......................................	− 3	− 60

Solution 1, g. per Liter	Solution 2, g. per Liter
Glucose 94	87
NaNO₃ 4	NH₄NO₃ 10
K₂HPO₄ 1	KH₂PO₄ 5
MgSO₄ 0.5	2.5

[1] From Schulz (1937).

Schulz further provides complete analytical evidence for very significant shifts in quantitative relations of the various mycelial fractions as a function of age of culture.   While this was strongly suspected from other isolated data, Schulz, by a complete proximate analysis on 7- and 16-day old cultures, provides clear-cut evidence for it in regard to every fraction making up the mold material.   Here again the zinc response was appreciably different at the two stages of development, with autolytic processes evidently playing an important role in the older cultures, and especially those containing added zinc (see autolysis, p. 87).   The changes with age would be expected in the case of the "no zinc" controls where the growth practically doubled between the seventh and sixteenth days.   Nevertheless, equally great changes in relative composition were observed in the zinc cultures notwithstanding the fact that growth was already at a maximum at the seventh day.   Evidence like this makes it very likely that in molds, as in other biological systems including higher animals, the various cellular constituents are in a dynamic state, undergoing continuous breakdown and resynthesis independent of growth in the usual sense of the term.   Otherwise it is extremely difficult to account for the large proportional shifts in relative composition observed by Schulz and others in physiologically old cultures.   This fits in well with the almost axiomatic variability of the enzymatic activities of different strains of fungi, on the same and different media and at different ages, and in regard to dissimilation processes, respiratory activities, and the synthetic powers of the cell in connection with any specific extracellular metabolic product.

It is regretable that no comparable analytical data are available for mold mycelia obtained under homogeneous physiological conditions, i.e. in submerged aerated cultures.   Considering the unpredictable factors influencing surface growth (Chapter 2), it seems not unlikely that comparative experiments may yield submerged cell material of considerably more uniform composition.

The phycomycete *Rhizopus japonicus*, together with *R. oryzae* of importance in various rice fermentations in Japan, has also been subjected to extensive chemical fractionation (Lim, 1935), with special emphasis on the individual components of the various fractions.   Unfortunately, because of different cultural conditions, analytical methods, etc., there is no basis for a comparative evaluation with the organisms of Porges and Schulz.   The various components isolated will be discussed in the appropriate sections later.

The data contained in Table 1 for nitrogen and carbon content of mold mycelium are quite typical.   Due to the high carbohydrate content of the medium the figure of 3.12 per cent is on the low side of the values, which in general may run between 3 and 6 per cent under the usual conditions of cultivation.   It should be pointed out that most analytical data have been obtained by the Kjeldahl method which fails to measure the nitrogen in certain resistant types of substances such as pyridines, pyrimidines, azo compounds, and in general unsaturated nitrogen-containing rings.   These, however, only comprise a small portion of the total N of the cells, never more than 10–15 per cent.   Combustion methods employed for N determinations (Dumas, ter Muelen) are most reliable, and are necessary where accurate N balances are desired.

The nitrogen content of fungi is variable and is directly dependent on the N content of the medium as well as the amount of readily utilizable carbon source.   Under conditions of nitrogen starvation, the N content of certain fungi may be as low as 1 per cent (Gerlach and Vogel, 1903); on the other hand the value may be extremely high during luxury consumption of nitrogen source, as in the early stages of growth, and in nitrogen-rich media, or in the absence of readily available carbohydrate (low C/N ratio). Thus, *Zygorhynchus mölleri* and *Trichoderma koningi* had 6.8 and 6.9 per cent N when grown on 1 per cent glutamic acid medium, but when 2 per cent glucose was also present the values were lowered to 4.6 and 5.3 per cent respectively (Waksman and Lomanitz, 1924). Apparently nucleoprotein and other vital nitrogenous compounds of the cell are actively synthesized during the early and rapid stages of growth, for progressively with age, reserve carbonaceous materials of a storage or fibrous cell-wall nature are laid down, resulting in overall reduction of the N content of the whole-cell material. This sequence is not unlike that in higher plants.

TABLE 3

N CONTENT OF ASPERGILLUS NIGER MYCELIUM ON ACID AND ALKALINE MEDIA[1]

Age, days	N content, per cent	
	Acid medium	Alkaline medium
4	6.21	3.46
6	4.75	
7		3.52
9	3.87	
10		3.83
14	3.63	3.98
26		4.12
29	3.25	

[1] From Behr (1930).

However, even this time-nitrogen relation is largely a function of cultivation conditions. Data in Table 3 show that whereas the N content of the mycelium of *Aspergillus niger* diminishes with age in $(NH_4)_2SO_4$ medium (physiologically acid, pH ~ 0.80) it may even increase when $NaNO_3$ serves as the N source (alkaline, pH ~ 6.0). Such results are explainable on the basis of differential autolysis occurring in the two media, nitrogenous compounds being more rapidly lost in the acid medium, and carbonaceous materials in the alkaline. The maximum dry weight of mold was reached on the sixth and seventh days respectively. Similar data in acid media are given by Takata (1929e) (see also Klotz, 1923). Hilpert *et al.* (1937b) demonstrated that the composition of the mycelium could be altered rather substantially by different concentrations of nitrogen source. Thus, in a typical experiment demonstrating the effect of high and low N nutrition of *A. niger* on the elementary composition of this organism, the data in the following tabulation were obtained.

Elementary analysis of mycelium	Medium containing	
	0.3 per cent NH₄Cl	.025 per cent NH₄Cl +.025 per cent (NH₄)₂SO₄
N	5.24	2.8
C	47.9	45.34
H	6.7	6.38
OCH₃	0.32	
Ash	1.58	

In addition to lowering the N content of the mycelium to one-half that in the high-N medium, the low-N medium caused an appreciable reduction in total carbon content of the mycelium. The N changes are strikingly brought out in these data (Hilpert *et al.*, 1937b):

Conc. in medium	Dry wt. of mycelium, g.	Per cent N in mycelium
0.05% (NH₄)₂SO₄	0.438	1.63
0.25% (NH₄)₂SO₄	1.349	3.51
0.5% (NH₄)₂SO₄	1.489	4.51
0.5% NH₄Cl	1.293	4.56

Values for the carbon content of the mold mycelium range from 45 to 55 per cent, the organism and cultural conditions deciding the value in any one case. Probably the carbohydrate concentration of the medium could increase or decrease this value between limits, but specific data are not available. Steinberg's abundant data (1939) on nitrogen utilization of *A. niger* in relation to sugar concentration indicate increased mycelial dry-weight synthesis with increasing sugar concentrations in media with the same initial content of NH_4NO_3 nitrogen, and otherwise identical. However, the N removed from the medium in these cases was much the same, regardless of the sugar concentration and the differential in cell material synthesized. Thus at a N level of 360 mg./liter the N uptake per culture in four days was: with 2.5 per cent sucrose, 15.4 mg.; with 5 per cent sucrose, 16.0 mg.; and with 7.5 per cent sucrose, 14.0 mg. Dry weight yield and N consumption in any given sugar concentration was virtually linear with respect to the N content of the medium ranging from 0 to 560 mg. N per liter as NH_4NO_3, NH_4Cl, or $NaNO_3$. At any given initial carbohydrate level, the N content of the mycelium was a function of the initial N content of the medium; the range extended from 2 per cent N in low-N media to 3 per cent in high.

An unexpected finding was that even where the N content of the medium was the limiting .factor in mycelial growth, the organism did not absorb all the available nitrogen from the medium.   In general, only 73 to 90 per cent of the nitrogen originally present was consumed, regardless of the initial content.   It may well be that the 10 to 27 per cent apparently unabsorbed actually was assimilated and excreted again as autolytic products or other complex nitrogenous excretion products of the synthetic activities of the organism.   Steinberg's data do not preclude the interpretation that this fraction actually was organic N.

PROXIMATE COMPOSITION OF SPORES

Some fungi are characterized by extremely abundant conidiospore formation, and under proper conditions sporulate so profusely that by suitable techniques masses of spores substantially free from vegetative mycelium and sporophores can be obtained.   It would not be too surprising if in some cases the actual dry weight yield of spores exceeds the mycelial dry weight of the same culture.   Quilico and Di Capua (1933) obtained a spore yield of 0.86 g./sq. dm. of *A. niger* surface area.   Table 4 shows the proximate composition of spores of *Aspergillus oryzae* harvested from washed soybean bran by shaking and sieving through silk to separate non-spore material (Sumi, 1928).   Large masses of spore material is obtainable in this way.

TABLE 4

PROXIMATE COMPOSITION OF CONIDIOSPORES OF ASPERGILLUS ORYZAE[1]

	Per cent		Per cent
Water......................	17.43	Water-soluble reducing sugar (as glucose).............	0.07
Crude fat (ether extract).....	0.88	Crude fiber................	11.21
Alcohol extract (after ether extract).................	23.25	Pentose and methyl pentose..	0.66
Total N....................	8.69	Glycogen.................	6.33
Protein N.................	3.64	Starch....................	No reaction
Protein (protein N $\times$ 6.25)...	22.75	Galactose.................	Neg.
Hot-water-soluble N.........	6.93	Ash.......................	5.33
Amino N...................	0.94	Total P in ash (P_2O_5).......	66.05
N in phosphotungstate ppt...	5.25	P in lecithin (P_2O_5).........	0.12
Ammonia N................	0.31	Lecithin..................	1.32
Carbohydrate (as glucose)....	9.00	Sterol (ergosterol)..........	0.08
Water-soluble carbohydrate (as glucose)...............	0.60		

[1] From Sumi (1928).

The following materials were isolated or identified in the alcohol extract: mannitol, 3.15 per cent of original whole spores; organic bases including volatile amines, purines, basic amino acids, betaine, and stachydrine. The residual material (300 g.) after successive extraction of the spores with ether, alcohol, and hot water, yielded 5 to 6 g. chitin. From the hot water extract uric acid was isolated in 0.6 per cent yield of the material extracted. Previously, Aso (1900) had isolated xanthin and other organic bases from *A. oryzae* spores. In studies of this kind the question always arises as to whether they represent decomposition or hydrolytic products liberated from more complex cellular components during the isolation procedures. The data of Aso show abnormally high water content in air-dry spores (42.5 per cent).

AUTOLYSIS. GENERAL CHARACTERISTICS OF GROWTH CULTURES

Actively growing fungus cultures reach maximum growth quickly under favorable conditions, followed by a decline in the dry weight of the solid growth material. Depending on the age and conditions, the rate of and total loss in weight (autolysis) may vary within wide limits, and is usually brought about by substantial depletion of nutrients or through inhibition of further development by creation of unfavorable growth environment. The latter may involve development of extreme acid or alkali conditions, accumulation of metabolic products in concentrations inhibitory to the mold producing them, diffusion limitations, etc.

The autolyzing mycelium is characterized by lack of turgor or rigidity; it becomes a soft, pulpy, slimy mass. The loss in dry weight is, of course, due to solubilization and release of cellular constituents into the surrounding medium through the cell membranes otherwise impermeable to this passage. In certain bacteria autolysis is marked by complete lysis of the cells, leaving a clear solution. This does not occur spontaneously among the filamentous fungi although in another filamentous group, the actinomycetes, the phenomenon of complete self-digestion and loss of cellular identity is old and well known (Katznelson, 1940; Krassilnikov and Koreniako, 1938).

A number of changes in the medium accompany the autolytic process. The medium gradually assumes a color similar to freshly prepared ordinary tea and at times may be a deep red-brown. This intrinsic dark brown coloration is ascribed to accumulation of resistant N-containing "humin," and it is especially characteristic of neutral or alkaline autolysates. Bortels (1927) observed a parallelism between autolysis and a violet-red coloration of the medium upon addition of alkali. The colored humin complex was ascribed to splitting of cyclic compounds from cell proteins and their condensation and catalytic oxidation by traces of copper present. Maximum humin formation coincided with depletion of sugar in the medium and NH_3 formation. Added tyrosine or tryptophane in the presence of sugar favored "humin" formation, presumably by virtue of their aromatic groups (Behr, 1930). Liberation of tyrosine may be used to follow protein digestion quantitatively (Anson, 1937). Metz (1930) also observed the correlation between autolysis and the dark red-brown color of the solution in a study of 13 different organisms. It was most marked in the presence of zinc and iron together.

Liberation of soluble nitrogen is an outstanding character of the autolytic process. Behr (1930) made extensive nitrogen balances on the autolysis of *A. niger* and examined the influence of imposed conditions on the process. Thus, autolysis as indicated by loss in mycelial weight and solubilization of cell nitrogen was much greater and more rapid in a physiologically alkaline medium (pH 6–7, $NaNO_3$ as N source) than in a physiologically acid medium (pH 1.0, $(NH_4)_2SO_4$ as N source) even though maximum growth was reached much earlier in the latter. By far the major portion of the soluble N was in the form of ammonia and the organic nitrogen fraction was two to three times greater in the acid medium than in alkaline. Conceivably, the rarity of proteolytic enzymes (pepsin?) in microorganisms active at pH 1.0 may account for the failure to break down the organic nitrogen to NH_3. The deaminase and deamidase of *A. niger* have been shown to have an optimum pH of 7 (Schmallfuss and Mothes, 1930). In view of the fact that all proteolytic enzymes, with the exception of pepsin, have an optimum pH in neutral or alkaline range, a logical explanation is apparent for the greatly accentuated autolytic processes in media near neutrality. pH 4–4.5 is optimum for liver autolysis (Bradley, 1938), an observation ascribable to the fact that the isoelectric point of the cell proteins, hence their susceptibility to digestion, corresponds to this pH range. Of the known proteolytic enzymes cathepsin acts optimally at pH 4–4.5. In Behr's experiments the percentage N content of the mycelium was fairly constant even up to 172 days, indicating that there was no selective liberation of cell protein but that other constituents were lost proportionally. A relatively small portion of the organic N in solution was accountable for as amino acids. (However, see Woolley and Peterson, 1937a, b, and c for aggravated autolysis.) Sixty per cent of the organic N was alcohol-soluble and this fraction appeared to consist of peptones and polypeptides. The alcohol-insoluble fraction gave a positive biuret test and hence presumably was proteinaceous in nature. As might be expected, the NH_3 content was roughly in inverse relation to protein and peptone N, the latter compounds accumulating during the early stages of autolysis and diminishing in the later stages, and vice versa for the NH_3. Amide nitrogen was little more than negligible. Of five different strains of *A. niger* compared, the autolytic process was characterized by high NH$_3$-low protein in three, and by low protein-high NH$_3$ in the other two strains. Woolley and Peterson observed that as much as 30 per cent of the mycelial N was converted to NH$_3$ during autolysis of *A. sydowi*.

As seen in the next section, the very high content of nitrogen-rich chitin could account for the existence of the normal N content of the autolyzed mycelium in acid media, but this could not be the whole explanation. In an alkaline media the chitin fraction decreases with age and is very low in the oldest cultures. Autolysis included chitin in this case, and it was destroyed at a faster rate than the other nitrogenous constituents. Apparently the mycelium here contains substantial amounts of an unidentified autolysis-resistant nitrogenous fraction. Evidence for such a resistant protein was provided from studies of the autolytic processes in *Aspergillus sydowi* (Wooley and Peterson, 1937a and b; Bohonos *et al.*, 1942). The most favorable condition for autolysis was to allow the ground dry mycelium to autolyze in the presence of thymol for 3–4 days. The initial pH was 7.0 and Na$_2$CO$_3$ had to be added periodically to neutralize the acidity that developed. From a beginning value of 1.53 mg. soluble N per ml., of which 0.7 mg. was amino-N, these values rose to 3.03 and 1.7 mg. respectively. Ammonia nitrogen finally was 0.4 mg. per ml. During autolysis, 63 per cent of the nitrogen of the mycelium became water soluble. Several free amino acids were liberated and could be recovered from the autolysate. An unautolyzable protein remained in the mycelium and could be extracted by 1 per cent NaOH. Eight grams of the resistant protein was isolated per kilogram of original dry mycelium.

The autolytic processes are accelerated by increased temperatures and may proceed concomitantly with the growth of the mold culture so that an actual increase in mycelial weight is observed despite unmistakable evidences of autolysis (Schmidt, 1936).

Autolysis obviously must be accompanied by the liberation of a host of other cell constituents in soluble form. This not only includes nitrogenous materials other than amino acids and their polymers and NH$_3$, but numerous other non-nitrogenous fractions, such as simple sugars, free and combined, organic acids, lipide materials, vitamins and coenzymes, and minerals, free and combined. With few exceptions the literature is extremely scanty on these points in relation to fungi. It is well known from extensive studies on autolytic processes involving animal tissues (see Haehn, 1936 and Bradley, 1938) that the cell constituents undergo drastic changes. Thus, because fungi are notorious carbohydrate metabolizers, it is to be expected that phosphoric acid would accumulate in mold autolysates due to its enzymatic liberation from the organic phosphate reservoirs of the cell, mainly intermediate phosphate carriers, nucleic acids, nucleotides, and phospholipides. Sufficient free H_3PO_4 may be liberated to effect a distinct change in pH toward the acid side, if events comparable to those in autolyzing liver take place in molds. In liver as much as 300 mg. inorganic P per 100 g. tissue may be liberated in 6 days (Bradley, 1938). The liberation of magnesium during autolysis of *A. niger* in acid medium was found (Rippel and Behr, 1930) to occur at a lower rate than that of total ash constituents; with progressive age the ash of the mycelium became richer in its magnesium content. Thus at maximum growth (7 days) the mycelium contained 4.26 and 0.16 per cent ash and MgO, respectively, whereas after 160 days the figures were 0.92 and 0.10.

The pH of the medium has no significant effect on the total ash of *A. niger* mycelium until autolysis sets in, when marked differences result, as is evident in Table 5.

TABLE 5

ASH IN MYCELIUM OF ASPERGILLUS NIGER IN ACID AND NEUTRAL CONDITIONS[1]

	Age, days							
	3	5	7	18	24[2]	33	61	160
Acid..................	4.93	4.65	4.26	1.89	2.25	1.75	1.44	0.92
Neutral...............	6.45	4.31	4.27	4.36	8.04	7.85	9.05	5.39

[1] From Rippel and Behr (1930). Figures represent per cent.
[2] Conspicuous autolysis at this time in neutral cultures.

In acid medium ash constituents are lost proportionally more rapidly than organic constituents in the autolytic process, but the situation is reversed in neutral medium.

A large proportion of the organic sulfur of the mycelium of *A. niger* becomes liberated as soluble organic sulfur compounds during autolysis (Rippel and Behr, 1936).

CHEMICAL NATURE OF THE CELL WALL OF FUNGI

1. CHITIN

When dried fungus material is extracted with a fat solvent and saponified with alcoholic NaOH to remove all lipides, and then exhaustively extracted with hot 5 to 10 per cent NaOH, a colorless, more or less friable mass is obtained. This resistant fraction comprises the cell walls, structural membranes, and skeletal material of the fungus mycelium. It consists of chitin and other non-nitrogenous polymerized substances of polysaccharidic and possibly lipoid nature. After hydrolysis for 3 hours in concentrated HCl (or H_2SO_4), removal of the (HCl) acid, and concentration under reduced pressure, crystals of hexose amine (glucosamine or 2-amino glucose) separate out. Hexosamine is the primary unit of chitin and chitosan and is the ultimate hydrolytic product of these substances. Liberation of acetic acid always accompanies hydrolysis of chitin, and, if the hydrolysis is carried out under milder conditions (70 per cent H_2SO_4), the degradation is incomplete and N-acetylglucosamine can be isolated, proving the linkage of the acetyl group to the amino group of the sugar residue. N-acetylglucosamine may, then, be considered as the true building unit of the chitin molecule. There is one acetyl group for each glucosamine residue in chitin. On the other hand, if the chitin is treated with 40 to 60 per cent alkali, or fused with solid alkali at 160°C., chitosan, consisting of an aggregate of four glucosamine residues, can be isolated in crystalline form; for each molecule of chitosan, two moles of acetic acid are liberated. Complete acid hydrolysis of chitosan results in the liberation of four moles of glucosamine and two more acetic acids molecules. Chitin, then, is made of secondary chitosan units, which in turn are made of the primary units, of which two are acetylated. Chitin is a polymer of anhydroacetylglucosamine. The degradation may be represented as follows:

$$(C_{32}H_{54}N_4O_{21})x + 2x\ H_2O \xrightarrow{\text{Conc. KOH}} x(C_{28}H_{50}N_4O_{19}) + 2x CH_3COOH$$

Chitin   Chitosan   Acetic acid

$$C_{28}H_{50}N_4O_{19} + 3H_2O \xrightarrow[\text{Hydrolysis}]{\text{Mild HCl}} 2C_6H_{11}O_5(NH{-}COCH_3) + 2C_6H_{11}O_5(NH_2)$$

Chitosan N-Acetylglucosamine   Glucosamine

$$\bigg\downarrow \begin{array}{l}\text{Conc. HCl}\\(+2H_2O)\end{array}$$

$$2C_6H_{11}O_5(NH_2) + 2CH_3COOH$$

Glucosamine   Acetic acid

The hydrolysis conditions may have a destructive effect on the products of hydrolysis; thus, glucosamine is 25 per cent destroyed by prolonged boiling under hydrolysis conditions, and glucose completely destroyed, so that theoretical yields of glucosamine and hexoses are not obtained from the *Penicillium javanicum* alkali-resistant fraction, which amounted to 25 per cent of the defatted mycelium (May and Ward, 1934).

Van Wisselingh (1898) devised a qualitative microchemical test for the identification of chitin in microscopic preparations, and this test has been widely used in studying the occurrence of chitin in various microorganisms. The test is based upon conversion of chitin to chitosan by alkali fusion at 160–180° for 1 hour, dilution, and neutralization with H_2SO_4. The residue is then treated with KI—I_2 and dilute H_2SO_4, and the preparation takes on a strong violet color if chitin was originally present. About one hundred different fungi, including all the major groups, were examined for chitin and cellulose by color tests and both were never found to occur together. Only in certain intermediate groups of organisms, namely *Didymium squamulosum*, a myxomycete, and in the groups Peronosporae, *Pythaceae*, and *Saprolegniae* in the oomycete group of Phycomycetes lacked chitin. (See also Schmidt, 1936; Von Wettstein, 1921.) Zygomycetes show positive chitin tests and a negative cellulose reaction.

The existence of the alkali-resistant fraction in higher or fleshy fungi was discovered in 1811 by Braconnot who called it "fungin."

Most of the early work on chitin isolation dealt with fleshy fungi belonging to the Basidiomycetes and Ascomycetes (see Winterstein, 1893; Gibson, 1895), but the occurrence of chitin in lower filamentous fungi has been amply established in recent years. The most extensive study was made by Schmidt (1936), who isolated chitin in yields ranging up to 4 per cent of dry mycelial material from seven different species of the Mucorales group, three Basidiomycetes, two species of Oidium, and three mycelial yeasts. Chitin could not be isolated from the one oomycete tested, *Pythium de baryanum*, thus confirming the qualitative tests of earlier workers on this group, and it was absent in bacteria, Actinomycetes and true yeasts. The chitin content decreased with the age of the culture, an effect said to be associated with autolysis.

Von Wettstein (1921) developed the interesting idea, later espoused by Nabel (1939) that phylogenetic relations between groups of fungi, especially Phycomycetes, are apparent on the strength of the possession of chitin or of cellulose in the cell walls as determined by staining procedures. In other words, the composition of the cell wall is an important criterion for group relations. In general, all Eumycetes have chitinous cell walls with the exceptions of Saccharomycetes and Laboulbeniales in the Ascomycetes, and Oomyceteae and Monoblepharideae in the Phycomycetes, in which cases the cell walls are chiefly cellulose. These latter four groups are therefore considered to be relatively young phylogenetically as compared to the chitin-bearing fungi, and are thought to be recent evolutionary offshoots from the corresponding algal forms.

Nabel's results with a large number of different organisms indicated that in all Chytridiaceae and Blastocladiaceae the membranes consist of chitin, whereas all other Oomyceteae contain no chitin, but cellulose instead. These results were considered as linking the class Myxomyceteae to the class Phycomyceteae, the Chytridiaceae being a family in the former class and the Blastocladiaceae a family in the Oomycetes of the latter class. A newly-described member of the Chytridiaceae, *Rhizidiomyces bivellatus*, contains both chitin and cellulose and is therefore believed to be evidence for an evolutionary sequence from the Chytridiaceae *via* Blastocladiaceae to the Oomycetes. This organism had an inner chitin membrane covered by a cellulose membrane. The chitinous membrane tended to dissolve and disappear naturally as the culture developed, leaving only the cellulose in the mature organism.

According to Garzuly-Janke (1940) all of 67 different filamentous fungi had chitinous cell walls chiefly, but no mannans, whereas 72 yeasts and yeastlike fungi (Saccharomycetes and Pseudosaccharomycetes) had little or no chitin but definitely had mannans in the cell membranes. Two exceptions in the latter were *Nadsonia fulvescens* and *Rhodotorula* (two species). This author concluded that an apparent antagonism exists between mannan and chitin produced by fungi, but this generalization seems premature and rather ill-founded in view of the fact that certain Penicillia were already known to synthesize mannans (see Chapter 16).

Like all other biochemical aspects of fungi, the chitin content of any one organism is subject to conditions of cultivation, and, in one of the few complete experiments dealing with the formation of chitin as a function of physiological conditions, the chitin content of *Aspergillus niger* changed strikingly as a function of pH of the medium and age of the culture (Behr, 1930). Table 6 shows that the chitin content of the mycelium is markedly greater when the organism is grown on acid medium and that the chitin content increases progressively with age, whereas the converse is true in alkaline medium. Similar results have been obtained for all filamentous fungi, particularly *Cunninghamella elegans* (Schmidt, 1936). In the acid medium there was no loss in mycelial weight with age, indicating little autolysis; yet there was an absolute increase in chitin yield with time, indicating an active chitin synthesis in the older cultures. This chitin synthesis may mask autolytic activity involving non-chitinous fractions, since it is hardly to be expected that cultures 36 to 170 days old did not undergo some autolysis. Marked autolysis did occur in the "neutral pH" medium and this was accompanied by an even greater loss, proportionally, in the chitin yield. It amounted to 91 per cent against a corresponding reduction of 59 per cent in mycelial weight. From such results it is evident that analytical data at random on a culture has only qualitative significance and is of little aid in characterizing the organism. As Schmidt (1936) has pointed out, temperature is a vital factor in autolysis, and the reduction in chitin content of mycelium occurs much faster at slightly elevated temperatures.

The alkali-resistant fractions from different fungi vary rather significantly in their N contents, indicating lack of uniformity. Thus, the value for the fraction from *Aspergillus fischeri* was 3 per cent (Norman and Peterson, 1932) and 6.37 per cent for *A. oryzae* (Takata, 1929f). Similarly, the alkali-stable fractions obtained from fleshy fungi almost always contain less than 4 per cent N, although after special treatment chitin of high N content has been obtained from Boletus, Agaricus and Polyporus (Proskuriakow, 1926) and in one case chemically pure chitin

TABLE 6

INFLUENCE OF pH OF MEDIUM AND AGE OF CULTURE ON CHITIN CONTENT
OF ASPERGILLUS NIGER

Physiologically acid medium, $(NH_4)_2SO_4$ as source of N

Age, days	pH	Mycelial wt., g.	Chitin		
			Yield, g.	Per cent	N content
3	1.18	....	.....	9.20	6.59
10	0.92	1.70	0.20	11.62	6.58
36	1.06	2.10	0.28	13.27	6.51
48	1.09	2.10	0.29	14.56	6.49
170	1.30	2.00	0.42	21.20	6.48

Physiologically alkaline medium, $NaNO_3$ as source of N (neutral pH)

Age, days	pH	Mycelial wt., g.	Chitin		
			Yield, g.	Per cent	N content
3	4.31	....	.....	4.13	5.94
10	5.37	2.30	0.107	4.64	6.01
36	6.73	1.20	0.059	4.95	5.90
68	6.50	0.95	0.012	1.30	6.00
170	6.60	0.94	0.010	1.04	6.00

[1] From Behr (1930).

was isolated (*Boletus edulis*) (Scholl, 1908). Generally the yields of purified chitin from fleshy fungi range from 3 to 5 per cent. The fact that other nitrogen-free substances occur in some form of combination with chitin in the cell membranes of fungi has long been suspected from the fact that yields of glucosamine and N content considerably lower than theoretical were obtained after hydrolysis of the alkali-resistant fractions. Since pure chitin contains 6.9 per cent N, where the N content of the alkali-resistant mycelial fraction is significantly less than that, it is evident that non-nitrogenous substances accompany the chitin. These associating substances are of the hemicellulose type and can be selectively destroyed by oxidation, leaving the chitin intact (Scholl, 1908). This is accomplished by making a thin slurry of the mold material in 1 per cent

$KMnO_4$, allowing it to stand until the $KMnO_4$ is completely converted to MnO_2. The liquid is filtered off and the brownish mass warmed with very dilute HCl (1:40) to dissolve the MnO_2. The liquid is removed, and the pulp washed with water and dried with alcohol and ether. The N content of this preparation approaches that of chitin, and further proof of its chitinous nature may be obtained by recovery of glucosamine hydrochloride quantitatively after drastic acid hydrolysis. In addition, chitosan can be obtained by the alkaline fusion procedure. Schmidt (1936) modified this isolation procedure to make it faster and less expensive.

In the case of *Aspergillus fischeri*, 20 per cent of the dry mold weight was alkali insoluble, only 35 per cent of which could be accounted for as glucosamine. On the basis of differential rates of hydrolysis it was concluded that two component polymers were present, one containing hexosamine, glucose, and acetyl residues, and the other, more readily hydrolyzed, glucose residues alone. Cellulose could not be detected. Unless one assumes free glucose to have arisen from glucosamine in the first polymer, this would not be typical chitin. Glucose can be isolated from a hydrolysate of *Boletus edulus* "fungus cellulose" (alkali-resistant fraction) (Winterstein, 1893) indicating that glucosans are of widespread occurrence in the cell walls of fungi. The total alkali-resistant cell wall material of higher fungi, *Agaricus campestris, Lacterius volemus, Armillaria mellea*, and *Polyporus betulinus*, comprises 20 to 44 per cent of the dry organisms (Proskuriakow, 1926), but after destruction of the non-chitin fractions by oxidation, the yields were only 2.8 to 5.5 per cent. In the case of *P. betulinus*, 3 per cent yield of a preparation containing only 1 per cent N was obtained, 78 per cent of which consisted of a difficultly hydrolyzable (70% H_2SO_4) polysaccharide composed of glucose residues. In the case of *Lacteria volemus* two polysaccharides composed of glucose residues were found, one easily hydrolyzable by 3 per cent H_2SO_4 and the other difficultly hydrolyzable, requiring 75 per cent H_2SO_4. A chitin preparation called "mycetin" was isolated in a less drastic fashion from *Boletus edulis* and contained 2.1 per cent N, and also a difficultly hydrolyzable carbohydrate (Dous and Ziegenspek, 1926). After acid hydrolysis, the hexosamine was isolated in crystalline form and found to be different from glucosamine in solubility properties; it was named "mycetosamine," as contrasted to the similar product from animal chitin, called "chitosan." Deamination of these products yielded different sugar residues, proving that chitin and fungus mycetin are not identical. From chitin the sugar chitose (an anhydro sugar, $C_6H_{10}O_5$), was obtained, and from mycetin a methyl pentose, which was not rhamnose or fucose, and which was named "mycetose." The presence of acetic acid in the molecule was not ascertained.

Infiltrating Materials

It seems probable that different fungi synthesize different chitins or chitinlike substances, and that these never exist alone in the membranes and cell walls of fungi, but in more or less firm chemical association with other non-nitrogenous materials, similar, for example, to the association of xylans, cellulose, and lignin in the cell walls of higher plants. The fibrous nature of the microscopic construction accounts for the structural rigidity of fungus hyphae and fruiting structures (Fig. 1).

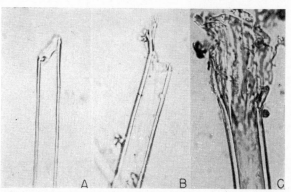

FIG. 1.—Broken conidiophores of *Aspergillus niger* × 700.   A, Conidiophore showing clean break suggesting a glass tube.   B, Broken conidiophore showing fibrous wall structure.   C, Portion of conidiophore crushed and further revealing the fibrous structure of the wall (from Thom and Raper, 1945).

Savulasku (1935) and Thomas (1930) found the resistant polysaccharide "callose" associated with chitin in the membranes of Nigrospora and Sclerotina respectively.   (Cf. Rhizidiomyces and cellulose, Nabel, 1939.)

Fungus hyphae are notoriously difficult to stain and generally are inert to solvents, dyes, alkalies, acids, and special staining reagents.   In 1890 Mangin attributed this to the presence in the cell wall of resistant substances that prevented the penetration of the reagents to the main "cellulose" portion of the membrane.   This thin cellulose membrane was itself considered to be protected by a layer of fatty acid, which in turn was covered by a protein-carbohydrate mixture.   Extraction of the fatty acid was necessary before the cellulose could be stained.   Oxidation of the fatty acids with bromine also facilitates removal of the carbohydrate material.   Similar results were obtained by Thomas (1930) for several species of Sclerotina in which the outer covering was the resistant polysaccharide callose impregnated with fatty acids.   The hyphae can be resolved into their component parts by extracting the fatty substances with alcoholic alkali and ether, and the carbohydrate with subsequent cold aqueous alkali. Alternate treatments are best. The residual hyphal material now exhibited the typical staining reactions for chitin, and glucosamine was isolated from the acid hydrolysate. Lecithin was found in the fat extracts. Callose is an acidic carbohydrate by virtue of its content of ethereal phosphate. It yields glucose upon hydrolysis. Callose is slightly soluble in water and dilute acids, but not dialyzable. It is doubly refractive and is readily soluble in weak alkali, concentrated solutions of calcium chloride, stannous chloride and sulfuric acid. It is soluble in alkali carbonates and it swells, forming a gelatinous mass, in ammonia. Its acidic properties account for its ability to fix basic stains such as aniline blue, resorcin blue, and benzidine and toluidine dyes. Callose is wide spread in the plant kingdom. In the fungi it has been found in various Peronosporaceae and Saprolegnaceae and different Ascomycetes and Basidiomycetes. It was not detected in Uredinales, but is present in many of the Mucorales, including the spores (Mangin, 1899). Chlamydospores also contained this carbohydrate. It occurs in lichens, algae, and, in higher plants, is a constituent of pollen grains, pollen tubes, phloem cells, and root hairs.

In 12 species of Fusaria examined (Thomas, 1928) the hyphal walls consisted of an outer covering of a protein-pectin complex, next a cellulose-fatty acid complex and finally the basic skeleton of chitin. Here also, in order to detect the cellulose and chitin, it was necessary to carry out drastic extractions to remove the external coatings.

2. CELLULOSE

The existence of true cellulose in certain fungi is beyond reasonable question, despite the fact that the majority of investigations have employed qualitative staining reactions for the demonstration, that thorough-going chemical analyses for cellulose in fungi are very rare, and that quantitative data are lacking almost entirely. Whereas cellulose in higher plants exists in close association with lignins, the latter are said not to occur in fungi and are replaced by other infiltrating complexes such as fats and fatty acids, other polysaccharides of a hemicellulose nature, pectin substances, proteins, and possibly cutinlike materials. As brought out above, unless drastic chemical action is taken to remove the associated complexes, they may be and usually are present in sufficient quantity to mask entirely the presence of the cellulose in qualitative staining tests by preventing the penetration and access of the reagents to the inner cellulose layers. De Bary was apparently the first to obtain good evidence for the presence of cellulose in many different species of fungi covering several major groups, by obtaining a blue color with iodine and sulfuric acid after removal of alkali-soluble constitutents. The cellulose fraction was soluble in ammoniacal copper hydroxide (Schweitzer's reagent). De Bary (1887) named this material "fungus-cellulose," a term still commonly used although his description does not exclude chitin. In several papers Mangin (1899) reported extensive experiments along this line with various Mucorales. Cellulose, callose and cutin were found in all cases. The cellulose in young hyphae and in young sporangia was associated with pectin compounds which at maturity disappeared naturally, leaving a preponderance of nearly pure callose. Mangin was probably the first to recognize the complexity of the structure of the fungus cell wall and to appreciate the protective influence of some constituents on others sought by staining reagents. On this line of reasoning he proposed that the many different kinds of cellulose reported up to that time only appeared different due to infiltrated materials, and that the many different terms be abandoned in favor of cellulose.

The next important studies on cellulose in fungi came almost 40 years later. Thomas (1928) made an extensive chemical fractionation of the mycelium of 12 species of Fusaria. The fresh mycelium gave negative tests with the classical cellulose reagents, I_2-KI solution and chloro-zinc iodide. However, after successive chemical treatments to remove pectin proteins and fatty acids, the free cellulose could be dissolved in Schweitzer's reagent and recovered as a precipitate of pure cellulose upon neutralization of the ammoniacal copper solution. The precipitate gave the typical blue staining reaction for cellulose with I_2-KI solution and H_2SO_4. Upon hydrolysis, glucose was liberated.

The tenacity with which the various cell wall components may be associated with each other is exemplified by the fact that after the first cellulose extraction with Schweitzer's reagent, more cellulose could be extracted if a layer of proteinaceous material was first removed by boiling with 10 per cent alkali. After removal of all the cellulose, the hyphae and septa were still structurally intact, indicating a highly resistant fraction. This was shown to be chitin.

A fatty acid fraction amounting to 8.3 per cent of the dry weight of the mycelium was extractable with hot alcoholic potash and it was suggested that the fat fraction accounts for resistance of Fusaria hyphae to the action of strong acids and other reagents. However, from this experiment, it is not certain that the fat did not originate from the protoplasm of the hyphae rather than from the cell walls.

The work of Farr and Eckerson (1934) purporting to show cellulose in several species of Aspergillus has been sharply criticized by Castle (1945). The former demonstrated by staining procedures and birefringence studies that cellulose occurs in the sporangiophores only. Further claimed was the demonstration of visible anisotropic crystalline cellulose particles of uniform size, in the cytoplasm, each surrounded by a pectic layer. The particles are deposited as a lining to a pectic membrane in the cell walls in linear fibrillar arrangement in spirals. The process was said to be similar to the deposition of cellulose in cotton fibers. Castle could not confirm these findings, and concluded that chitin is the main structural material of Aspergilli. Birefringence in a fungus cell wall does not, according to Castle, necessarily mean cellulose is present, as other materials display this characteristic.

3. LIGNIN

Information on the occurrence of lignin in fungi is exceedingly scanty and it may be stated that definite proof of the presence of true lignin in fungi is not available. *Klein's Handbuch der Pflanzenanalyze* states categorically that lignin is absent in fungi and bacteria (Zetzche, 1932). Because lignin of plant origin is resistant to 80 per cent acid, residues obtained in this way from fungi have rather arbitrarily been considered as lignin, without specific chemical data. Lignins are characterized by high carbon and methoxyl content (typical analysis: C, 64 per cent; H, 6; O, 30: OCH_3, 21), and it would be of interest to ascertain the nature of the acid-resistant fraction from fungi, since it constitutes such a large portion of the cell material.

It seems probable that substances do exist in fungi which are not chemically identical with the lignin of higher plants and yet which have general properties sufficiently in common to be considered as ligninlike. It is believed that several different lignins exist among the higher plants. For example after strong acid hydrolysis the "lignin" fraction of *Polyporus fomentorius* represented 25 per cent of the original material, yet it contained no methoxyl groups, which generally are considered typical of lignin (Kalb, 1932). Similarly, extremely high amounts of ligninlike materials were found by Thom and Phillips (1932) as the fractions resistant to boiling fuming HCl in certain fungi as follows: *Alternaria*, 17.25 per cent; *Epicoccum*, 20.3; *Sclerotinia liberiana*, 7.85; *Cladosporium*, 29.27; *Hydnum caput-ursi*, 2.65; *Polyporus sulphureus*, 3.40; *Trametes pini*, 54.08; *Fomes igniarius*, 36.95.

On the other extreme, Hilpert *et al.* (1937a) maintain that lignins in higher plants and fungi are artifacts arising during their chemical preparation and extraction as a result of the action of strong acids on carbohydrates, especially methylated sugars, originally present in the natural material. In the fungi, the virtually negligible OCH_3 (methoxy) content of the "lignin" fraction was interpreted as evidence supporting this view, but this would not necessarily follow if, as mentioned above, this lignin fraction differed from the typical plant kind by lack of methoxy. The extreme chemical resistance of this fraction would appear to favor its consideration as "ligninlike" until specific evidence to the contrary is provided.

NITROGENOUS COMPONENTS OF THE CELL MATERIAL

As might be expected, the major portion of the nitrogen content of mold protoplasm is in the form of protein. Little can be said as to the specific nature of the proteins of fungus tissue. The nucleated character of the mold cells means that nucleoproteins, presumably of the desoxy-ribose type, are certainly present. Other proteins must make up the general cytoplasmic structure. In addition, the proteins in the form of cellular enzymes might well account for a significant portion of the total proteins, considering the remarkable rate at which cell synthesis proceeds under favorable conditions, and also keeping in mind the innumerable different constituents of the cells all undergoing synthesis and, to some extent breakdown, through the agency of enzymes. The enzyme proteins must indeed be relatively high in certain fungi that are highly selected and cultivated especially for their ability to produce large amounts of proteolytic, diastatic, lipolytic, or pectinolytic enzymes for industrial purposes.

Outstanding as a feature of most molds is their rapid synthesis of protein (as cell material) in high conversion yields from inexpensive and crude nutrients. Under conditions of protein shortages for animal feed, sooner or later attention is focused upon processes for the microbiological production of protein in the form of mold mycelia or yeast cells from cheap or waste carbohydrote sources and inorganic nitrogen such as NH_4NO_3 or urea. During World War I the Germans developed this process utilizing cellulosic materials like wood, straw, etc., after prelim-inary hydrolysis to the utilizable simple sugars. Animals were fed straw that was heavy with mold growth due to treatment with inorganic nitrogen (Pringsheim and Lichtenstein, 1920). (See review on protein from mold by Toursel, 1942.)

From 100 kg. dry wood, yeast yields of 21–31 kg. dry weight have been obtained, yielding 12–16 kg. raw protein. One cubic meter of waste sulfite liquor yields 10–12 kg. dry yeast. Within the last five years considerable attention has been given to the remarkably efficient protein synthetic powers of the moldlike yeast, *Torula utilis*. The British government has constructed a plant in Jamaica where molasses as a carbohydrate source is extremely cheap. This partially fills the prophecy of the distinguished biochemist T. Robertson (1920) that one day in the future proteins obtained from microorganisms grown on cheap carbohydrate and minerals and inorganic nitrogen would provide a major source of food for the human population. Protein yields in excess of 50 per cent of the cell dry weight, and 60 per cent conversion yields of cell material from the consumed carbohydrate are reported. Details of this process using *Torulopsis utilis* are given by Thaysen and Morris (1947). Under optimum aeration conditions, in the logarithmic phase, the generation time of the organism is 100 minutes, i.e., the weight of yeast doubles every hundred minutes. This protein is intended for human consumption and is used in England to fortify bread and possibly other food products.

For a high rate of protein synthesis, it is obvious that a readily utilizable carbohydrate must be available because proteins contain approximately 50 per cent carbon. The nutritional aspects of yeast protein are treated at length in a recent monograph (Somogyi, 1946). (See also Fink, 1942; Brewer, 1943.) According to Peukert (1943), mold protein cultivated on waste sulfite liquors are palatable and contain appreciable amounts of diamino groups usually lacking in plant proteins. Lechner and associates have studied, in a series of papers, the factors influencing protein synthesis by *Torula utilis*, especially on the sugars generally made available from wood hydrolysates. Especially significant was the wide range of cell protein content, which varied according to cultural conditions. The cell contains many nitrogenous substances besides proteins, and in bulk, these may collectively make up a good part of the total. Included are chitin, nitrogen-containing lipides, amino sugars, coenzymes, vitamins, amino acids, purine and pyrimidine bases, and special synthetic products as penicillin, gliotoxin, etc. These latter are specific to certain organisms and will be treated in a separate chapter.

1. PROTEINS AND AMINO ACIDS FROM MOLDS

Due probably to difficulties in completely extracting the protein from the mold mycelium, no precise data on the protein content are available. Almost invariably protein values are calculated on the conventional N × 6.25 basis. It is obvious that this may lead to results considerably too high for molds where a good portion of the nitrogen is non-protein, as seen above. Furthermore, in many proteins the N content is not 16.5 per cent. Nevertheless, taking this means as the only one available, it is safe to state that, like all other characteristics of molds, the protein content varies within extremely wide limits between different organisms and between different cultural conditions for any one organism. Among 24 different species of Aspergilli and Penicillia cultivated under identical conditions on inorganic medium, the crude protein ranged from 13.7 to 43.7 per cent with an overall average of 31.6 per cent (Pruess *et al.*, 1934). Every one of these same organisms cultivated on an organic medium (glucose-malt sprouts), had a substantially lower protein content with an overall average of only 22.5 per cent. In some cases, the deviation was extremely great. For example, in the synthetic medium *Penicillium chrysogenum* had 43.7

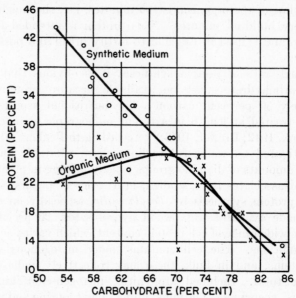

Fig. 2.—Relation between protein and carbohydrate content of mold mycelium cultivated on organic vs. synthetic medium (from Pruess *et al.*, 1934).

per cent protein and only 15.0 per cent in the organic medium. In the synthetic medium the crude protein content stood in a straight-line inverse proportion to the carbohydrate content of the mycelium (Fig. 2). This held true only within a narrow range for the organic medium. In other words, in mycelia grown in synthetic media carbohydrate replaces protein, whereas this is true only to a certain extent in organic media. As will be seen later, fat replaces proteins to a large extent in the organic medium-grown mycelium.

It is important to bear in mind that these considerations are in actuality dealing with total N content, not true protein. Considering the high content of chitin attainable in some organisms, to mention only one nitrogenous constituent, it is apparent that the arbitrary figure of N × 6.25 is fallaciously employed in determining the protein content of the mold mycelium. The figure 6.25 is a conversion factor for the N content of the *isolated protein*, and must be used only very conservatively in cases like cell material where only a fraction of the total N actually is protein. In view of this fact, and because the protein content (N $\times$ 6.25) varies greatly according to the strain and cultural conditions, and moreover, because there are numerous reports giving the N content of the mycelium, the above data of Pruess *et al.* (1934) are considered typical, and inclusion of other data on this point is unnecessary. The important conclusion to be made is that, as in every other aspect of mold metabolism, the protein content and synthesis is not constant, but fluctuates within wide limits, even for a single mold strain, according to the cultural conditions imposed during growth.

2. PROTEINS OF MOLD MYCELIUM

Here also the information is scattered, fragmentary, and incomplete.

One of the earliest chemical studies on mold protein (Thomas and Moran, 1914) recognized the existence of more than one protein in *Aspergillus niger* and in yeast. A phosphoprotein and a coagulable albumin were demonstrated, and the former was considered to be split off from its native nucleoprotein combination in the intact cells. This protein gave qualitative tests for glucosamine, a finding amply confirmed by later workers. Nelson (1933) describes a globulin in the protein fraction of *Fusarium lini.*

One of the more thorough attempts toward fractionation of the nitrogenous portion of mold mycelium, especially in relation to protein content was that of Gorcica *et al.* (1934) on *Aspergillus fischeri* in the Wisconsin laboratories. The best extraction of the nitrogenous components was obtained using fresh untreated mycelium. It was mill-ground to a paste in the cold and extracted three successive times with ice water, this fraction amounting to 17 per cent of the original N. The dry powder left after removal of lipides from the filter cake (alcohol-ether, 1:1) was reextracted with water, yielding 12 per cent of original N. Neither water extract gave any test for protein, and 3.9 per cent of the N in the first extract was as urea. Presumably other small molecular weight substances like amino acids, peptides, bases, vitamins, etc. were included in the aqueous extract. The main portion of the nitrogen of the mycelium, 40 per cent, was obtained in the next step, extraction with 1 per cent KOH for 2 days at room temperature. Following this, 13 per cent N was recovered in the hot 4 per cent KOH after boiling the residue for 1 hour. The residual nitrogen after this treatment was mainly chitin. The cold alkali fraction gave positive tests for protein and in addition contained considerable carbohydrate. In fact, no preparation procedure gave a protein fraction free from sugar. Two proteins were present, one precipitatable by acid and the other soluble. The acid-soluble fraction could be precipitated with $CuSO_4$ at pH 6.2–6.5, whereas the acid-insoluble protein, which could be dissolved in dilute alkalies, was precipitated by mineral acids and reduced Fehling's solution after hydrolysis. The following tabulation summarizes other data obtained on these two proteins:

	Acid soluble, per cent	Acid insoluble, per cent
N	12.3	11.8
P	2.4	0.4
Ash	12–37	1.2
Basic N, per cent of total N	38	22.8
Monoamino N, per cent of total N	36.5	60.2

The 50 per cent more basic N in the acid soluble protein as well as the high P content, was interpreted as being due to the presence of nucleic acids or nucleoprotein in this fraction, but no further evidence was adduced.

Eight years later, in a continuation of the Wisconsin studies on the constitution of the mold mycelium, Bohonos et al. (1942) isolated from *Aspergillus sydowi* after extensive autolysis a protein soluble in 1 per cent NaOH which had resisted digestion during the prolonged autolysis of the cell material. The protein was precipitated by adjustment to pH 4.85 but would not redissolve at a lower pH, as would protein extracted from unautolyzed mycelium. Yields were about 8 g. of unautolyzable protein per kilogram of dry mycelium. The isolated protein had the unique property of resistance to digestion by proteolytic enzymes including pepsin, papain, pancreatin, trypsin, ficin, and an enzyme preparation from a strongly proteolytic *A. parasiticus*. The N content was rather low (11.3 per cent average on an ash-free basis) and acid hydrolysis of various preparations released an average of 9.1 per cent reducing sugar, 3.5 per cent hexosamine, 1.9 per cent ash, 0.7 per cent phosphorus, and 0.5 per cent purine-N. From hydrolysates of the protein histidine, arginine, lysine, tyrosine, aspartic acid, leucine, and proline were isolated. Tryptophane was detected by the Hopkins-Cole test. A large amount (30 per cent) of humin was formed during the acid hydrolysis. Variable analyses on different preparations make it likely that several proteins were present rather than a single homogeneous entity. The phosphorus and polysaccharide were firmly bound in the protein and probably comprise a portion of the protein molecule.

The alkali-soluble protein of *Aspergillus oryzae* was studied by Takata in one of a long series of papers on the composition of *Aspergillus oryzae* mycelium from the standpoint of human food material (Takata, 1929c). The protein thus extracted was insoluble in water and alcohol, partly soluble in 10 per cent NaCl solution, and contained 14.78 per cent N, 1.77 per cent P, 2.66 per cent ash, and a trace of S. Similar to that from *A. sydowi*, the protein is considered a phosphoglucoprotein on account of its bound P and 4 per cent reducing sugars, mostly glucosamine, in acid hydrolysates.

Another protein in the mycelium, left after alkaline extraction, differs from the resistant protein of Bohonos *et al.* in that it could be liberated from the residual mycelium by pepsin digestion. The product obtained was not, of course, true protein; it had the properties of a large peptone and was considered to have been present in the original mycelium in complex combination as glucoprotein. This pepsin-liberated fraction contained 17.02 per cent N of which 10.1 per cent was free amino-N, 0.59 per cent ash, a trace of S, and no P. The van Slyke N distribution of the original mycelium, the isolated protein and the peptone were as follows:

	Per cent		
	Mycelium	Protein	Peptone
Total N	5.77	15.19	17.02
HCl-insol. N	2.10	1.80	0.17
NH₃ N	14.31	10.53	4.06
Humin N	2.43	3.01	1.12
Basic N	23.45	29.11	32.84
Arginine N	9.16	14.96	15.16
Histidine N	5.90	10.61	10.01
Lysine N	6.88	3.65	6.76
Cystine N	1.51	trace	trace
Monoamino N	52.65	54.21	60.04
Amino N	42.24	50.07	56.04
Non-amino N	10.32	4.14	4.00
Losses	5.15	1.14	1.77
Tyrosine	2.32	10.50	10.53
Cystine	0.36	0.12	0.12
Tryptophane	0.00	2.05	2.07

Behr (1930) isolated a protein from *A. niger* by first boiling the mycelium with 2 per cent HCl to remove binding materials and conjugates, then extracting with cold 2 per cent NaOH, followed by neutralization, and precipitation with copper sulfate solution on the alkaline side. The dry material was then put in form of a suspension and the copper separated by treatment with H_2S, leaving the free protein, as confirmed by formol titration.

Another phosphoprotein, isolated from *Rhizopus japonicus* (yield, 29.7 g. from 1 kg. dry mycelium), was given the name Rhizopenin (Lim, 1935). It was insoluble in H_2O, NaCl solution, and alcohol, easily soluble in alkali and precipitated by acid, and analyzed as follows: N, 15.25 per cent; H, 8.75 per cent; C, 53.23 per cent; S, 0.21 per cent; P, 1.29 per cent. It was rich in basic amino acids, tyrosine, and tryptophane. The ratio of cystine S to total S was 1:18 and the isoelectric point was pH 2.95–3.02.

In a study of culture filtrates from Fleming's original penicillin-producing strain of *Penicillium notatum* and *P. chrysogenum* Clutterbuck *et al.* (1932) found a protein, obviously synthesized by the mold from synthetic media containing an inorganic nitrogen source and excreted into the culture solution. In view of the long incubation period, 21–28 days, it is quite likely that the solubilized protein was largely a consequence of autolytic processes. It is unlikely that such a high molecular weight substance would pass through the living cell membranes. The protein was separated by acid precipitation and freed from the alcohol- and ether-soluble yellow pigment, chrysogenin, the principal impurity. From 38 liters of filtrate 4.1 g. purified protein was isolated. It analyzed as follows: C, 51.64 per cent; H, 6.90 per cent; N, 12.85 per cent; S, 1.34 per cent. The protein was easily hydrolyzed by enzymes and acids and the following N fractionation was obtained on the hydrolysate:

N fraction	Mold protein, per cent
Total N	12.95
NH_3 N	6.69
Melanin N	4.46
Arginine N	8.22
Histidine N	8.51
Cystine N	3.51
Lysine N	2.07
Monoamino N	62.09
Non-amino N	5.33

These figures bear a close resemblance to those for the alkali-soluble protein of alfalfa leaves, it was pointed out.

3. NUTRITIONAL VALUE OF FUNGUS PROTEIN

Mold proteins are apparently inadequate to satisfy the protein requirements of animals wholly. At best they can serve as supplements to feeds containing other proteins relatively rich in other necessary amino acids or peptides, thus enabling a reduction in their content in the feed. Dried *A. oryzae* mycelium containing 38 per cent protein was deficient as a sole protein source for albino rats, although good growth was made and the protein was 80 per cent digestible (Takata, 1929c). The principal difficulty encountered in animal experiments is that to cover the protein requirements of animals the mold mycelium must make up about 50 per cent of the feed. This high content means that a high content of other mycelial constituents must also be ingested and these generally lead to unpalatability and can cause sickness. For example *Penicillium notatum* mycelium from surface production of penicillin gives rats a severe diarrhea. *Aspergillus sydowi* mycelium is toxic to rats (Woolley *et al.*, 1938), but the toxicity could be overcome by other complex nitrogenous feed supplements. These factors would, of course, vary according to the mold species used and probably according to its cultivation conditions. With respect to nutritional deficiency of the protein of any one mold, it seems not unlikely that a systematic survey would reveal other fungi whose proteins contain the factors in question and that these molds could then be fed jointly or even cultivated jointly in mixed culture. The studies of Skinner *et al.* (1933) are the most complete of those dealing with the nutritional value of mold mycelium for rats.

Mycelia from *A. fischeri*, *A. oryzae*, *P. chrysogenum*, and *A. sydowi* as the sole nitrogen source, and comprising 50 per cent of the feed, did not permit growth of rats, and deaths occurred after a few weeks. One strain of *A. fischeri*, cultivated on organic media in contrast to inorganic media for the other fungi, led to an even more rapid weight loss in the animals. Supplemented with casein or yeast, the mold mycelium diet gave good growth, indicating lack of toxicity. The utilizability of the fungus protein was demonstrated by the favorable effect on growth when added to an otherwise low nitrogen diet. Similar results, supplementing mold protein with casein or corn gluten, had previously been obtained by Skinner (1924) with *Penicillium flavo-glaucum*. Skinner concluded that the inadequacy of this mold protein was due to a low cystine content because gelatin, containing no cystine, was ineffective as a supplement, whereas cystine-containing casein or gluten was.

Fusarium lini mycelium supplemented with adequate amounts of thiamine was found to be a satisfactory source of protein and other vitamins for normal growth, reproduction, and lactation in mice. *F. graminearum* mycelium, on the other hand, was satisfactory only if supplemented with multiple B vitamins (Vinson *et al.*, 1945).

No data on the use of mold mycelia or proteins in human nutrition have come to the author's attention.

4. AMINO ACIDS

There is no reason for not believing that fungi synthesize all the known amino acids although the possibility exists that when thorough amino acid analyses of mold mycelium are applied to more of the vast number of fungi known, some may be found to lack certain of the so-called "recognized" amino acids. Precedence for the absence of amino acids in the protoplasm (protein) of biological systems is provided by the absence of the amino acids methionine, tyrosine, lysine, and arginine in algae low in the phylogenetic series, these absences diminishing in algae higher in the evolutionary sequence (Mazur and Clark 1939; 1942). In view of the fact that isolation methods were employed for amino acids, and that such results contradict the general belief of the essentiality of all the amino acids in the makeup of a living cell, it would be well to re-examine these systems with the very highly sensitive and specific microbiological analytical methods. It is, of course, likely that certain amino acids may not be contained in specific proteins, but the idea that they are totally lacking in the cell has yet to be rigorously proved. The formation of special low molecular-weight amino acid-containing compounds may also be mentioned, as, for example, fumaroalanide by *Penicillium resticulosum* (Birkinshaw *et al.* 1942).

Amino acid data on molds has been handicapped due to tedious and insensitive analytical methods and lack of attention because of their practical unimportance. Thus, all work until very recently dealt with isolation of amino acids, either free or as standard derivatives, from acid hydrolysates of the mold material, or by inference from Van Slyke N distribution analysis, or by qualitative color tests for their presence. The recent advent of microbiological methods of assay for amino acids, and their great reliability in the majority of cases, together with the quickness with which many results can be obtained, would at once seem to render many other approaches to amino acid studies obsolete, except for specialized objectives. These advantages are also characteristic of paper chromatography methods.

Isolation experiments date back to 1905 when glycine, alanine, leucine, glutamic acid, and aspartic acids were isolated from *Aspergillus niger* grown on three different nitrogen sources, $NaNO_3$, glutamic acid, and glycine respectively (Abderhalden and Rona, 1905). No tyrosine or phenylalanine could be isolated, a surprising thing because usually tyrosine is so insoluble that it readily crystallizes directly from concentrated protein hydrolysates, except when present in too low concentration. Woolley and Peterson (1937a, b, and c) have isolated a total of 13 different amino acids from *Aspergillus sydowi*, and they point out that deductions made regarding the presence of amino acids from nitrogen distribution experiments or from color tests may be fallacious due to interferences of other materials in complex extracts or hydrolysates, and that physical isolation is the only certain proof for the presence of any amino acid. In a chemical sense these observations hold true, but the remarkable proved specificity of most of the microbiological assay methods has made them of indisputable value in such work, and especially in the case of amino acids present in relatively low concentrations where isolations become exceedingly difficult. In any case, there is now universal agreement that the only feasible methods for precise quantitative studies on amino acid content of mold protein are microbiological assay procedures, and paper chromatography (see Chapter 19).

The presence of certain amino acids in various fungi has been reported from time to time, but most complete studies have been made on *Aspergillus oryzae*, *A. sydowi*, *Rhizopus japonicus* (Lim 1935, see protein section), *R. nigricans*, *Aspergillus niger* and *Penicillium notatum*. The first three were investigated mainly with chemical isolation procedures; they refer to certain other works in the literature of less complete nature. In a protein isolated from the first-named organism, Takata demonstrated six amino acids by Van Slyke's distribution method. Woolley and Peterson (1937a, b, c) have made exhaustive amino acid isolations from *Aspergillus sydowi*, and have obtained the following 13 amino acids: lysine, arginine, histidine, leucine, isoleucine, serine, valine, threonine, tyrosine, proline, tryptophane, aspartic acid, and glutamic acid. With the exception of arginine these were all isolated from well-autolyzed material. Autolytic enzymes rapidly destroy the arginine, liberating ammonia, and make it necessary to employ fresh mycelium for this isolation. Amino acids may, of course, be constituents of more than one protein in any organism; witness that seven were also isolated from the unautolyzable protein of this organism (Bohonos *et al.*, 1942). The 13 amino acids amounted to 17.1 per cent of the total N of the mycelium, but this figure is a minimum due to losses encountered in isolation work of this kind. The high content of the hydroxyamino acids, threonine and serine, was especially noted. The presence of phenylalanine, glycine, and hydroxyproline could not be detected even by sensitive color reactions, which indicated their absence although they may have been destroyed during autolysis. The presence of active deamidases in mold tissues has already been noted.

The synthesis of the aromatic amino acids, tryptophane and tyrosine, from inorganic N by *A. niger*, *Trichoderma koningi*, *Zygorhynchus moelleri*, *Penicillium sp.*, *A. oryzae*, *A. terreus*, and *P. flavo-glaucum* has been established by colorimetric tests (Skinner 1924).

TABLE 7

AMINO ACID COMPOSITION OF REPRESENTATIVE MICROORGANISMS[1,2]

Organism[3]	Nitrogen	Histidine	Arginine	Lysine	Leucine	Isoleucine	Valine	Methionine	Threonine	Phenylalanine	Tryptophane
					Per cent of dry weight						
Rhizopus nigricans	5.80	0.98	1.21	1.59	1.46	0.98	1.05	0.33	0.96	0.81	0.25
Penicillium notatum	6.13	1.67	1.40	1.53	2.1	1.22	1.51	0.39	1.37	1.16	0.49
Aspergillus niger	5.21	0.90	1.04	1.04	1.48	0.88	1.09	0.22	1.11	0.85	0.25
A. niger mycelium											
Before sporulation	7.61	1.20	2.6	2.7	2.6	1.41	1.83	0.52	1.67	1.48	0.52
After sporulation	4.99	1.53	1.40	1.19	1.30	0.70	0.95	0.22	0.93	0.77	0.31
Spores	5.54	0.54	1.19	1.33	1.75	0.99	1.29	0.23	1.27	1.01	0.33
Staphylococcus aureus	10.75	0.72	2.3	5.2	3.4	2.8	2.4	0.81	2.0	1.84	0.23
Escherichia coli	13.19	1.26	4.3	4.5	6.4	3.8	4.5	1.7	3.2	2.7	0.79
Bacillus subtilis	10.07	0.87	2.4	3.4	4.8	3.0	3.5	1.08	2.2	2.2	0.38
Streptomyces griseus	9.09	0.85	2.9	2.2	3.8	1.63	3.5	0.56	2.4	1.65	0.68
Saccharomyces cerevisiae	8.94	2.7	2.4	3.1	3.8	2.5	2.8	0.65	2.4	2.1	0.59
Rhodotorula rubra	6.95	1.99	3.7	3.0	3.3	2.1	2.5	0.53	1.79	1.72	0.45

[1] From Stokes and Gunness (1946).
[2] Nutrient broth-dextrose medium.
[3] Incubation period: fungi 5 days, yeasts 2 days, bacteria 1 day.

Comprehensive quantitative data on several microorganisms including bacteria, yeasts, actinomycetes, and fungi were provided by Stokes and Gunness (1946) by means of microbiological amino acid assays on acid- or alkali-hydrolyzed cell material. These studies were limited to the so-called amino acids "essential" to animal nutrition, for which a single assay organism, *Streptococcus lactis* R is required, and deal with the influence of cultural conditions on the quantitative content of these 10 amino acids. Cultivation of a fungus under identical conditions but at different times yielded highly reproducible amino acid contents. Table 7 gives the comparative data for three fungi and the analyses on two yeasts; one actinomycete and three bacterial species are included for comparative purposes. In the case of the fungi, although differences are apparent for each amino acid, the values are all in the same range. The lower amino acid content of the fungi as compared to the other groups of organisms is ascribed to the substantially lower protein content of mold mycelium (see total N column), but there are no outstanding differences in relative abundances of any of the amino acids among the four groups of organisms. Calculated on the basis of total protein (N × 6.25), the fungi contain, with the exception of tryptophane, less of the amino acids than the bacteria. It is to be noted that phenylalanine, previously not detected in fungi, has been found in the three fungus species tested and in all the other cultures as well. Tryptophane is uniformly present in lowest amounts. Taken as a whole, the amino acids in microbial cells are quite similar in composition to plant and animal proteins. It is important to bear in mind that one cannot say microbial proteins, for several proteins may exist in the microbial cell, each deficient in certain amino acids yet yielding the total overall figure given in Table 7. Data on plant and animal proteins generally are obtained on the separated protein, not the whole plant, as in this case.

The data in the lower portion of Table 7 on sporulation indicates that before sporulation the mycelium is relatively rich in all the amino acids, and that the spores deprive the mycelium of about half its content of all the amino acids except histidine, a small amount of which went into the spores. The mycelium thereby becomes enriched in this compound after sporulation. In general, the spores and their mycelium have comparable amino acid compositions. Clear-cut evidence is provided that the amino acid composition of molds is variable and changes as a result of the nature of the medium and aeration conditions (submerged vs. surface growth). Figure 3 charts the results obtained with *Penicillium notatum* under four different cultivation conditions. The differences in analytical figures are not great except perhaps in the case of histidine, but they are nevertheless significant, especially in relation to the idea of the inconstancy of the composition of mold mycelium.   In eight of the ten amino acids studied, stationary corn steep cultures had the highest content.   Other data of Stokes and Gunness indicated that the bacteria and actinomycetes also are subject to rather wide fluctuations in composition as a result of different cultural conditions.

5. NUCLEIC ACIDS

The importance of nucleic acids relates to nucleoproteins and nucleotides, which function as catalysts in intermediary metabolism, e.g., adenosine-triphosphate, di- and triphosphopyridine nucleotide (coenzymes I and II) and flavin-adenine nucleotide.   Study of these compounds in

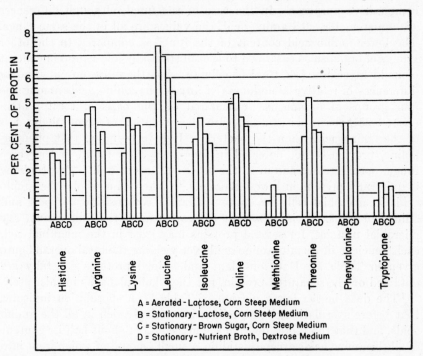

FIG. 3.—Effect of cultural conditions on the amino acid content of *Penicillium notatum* (from Stokes and Gunness, 1946).

fungi has scarcely been touched.   The intriguing possibilities in relation to the genic desoxyribonucleoproteins and the frequently occurring mutations encountered in fungi should be evident from the demonstration of McCarty (1946) that isolated nucleic acid is the mutating transforming agent in the pneumococcus (see Chapter 6).

Japanese investigators have isolated nucleic acids from *Aspergillus oryzae* (Takata, 1929d) and *Penicillium glaucum* (Akasi, 1939).   The nucleic acid content of the Aspergillus, calculated from the purine base N of the mycelium, was 6.31 per cent, i.e., 15.8 per cent of the total N of the mycelium was nucleic acid N. The preparation contained N, 13.16, and P, 7.01 per cent, and was free of amylose and protein. The bases adenine, hypoxanthine, and uracil were isolated from hydrolysates. The yield from *P. glaucum* was much smaller, 0.9 per cent of purified nucleic acid from the mold mycelium, and was identical with yeast nucleic acid.

6. OTHER NITROGENOUS SUBSTANCES

Nitrogen-containing lipides are discussed under the section on that subject. (See also chitin.) Certain other nitrogenous materials have been isolated in small yields from the mycelium (Takata, 1929a), as, for example, betaine, $(CH_3)_3N(OH)CH_2COOH$, and the derived stachydrine, n-methylproline methylbetaine,

$$
\begin{array}{cc}
H_2C\!\!-\!\!-\!\!-\!\!-CH_2 & \\
| & | \\
H_2C & CH\!\!-\!\!CO \\
\diagdown & | \\
N\!\!-\!\!-\!\!-\!\!-O \\
\diagup \diagdown & \\
CH_3 \quad CH_3 &
\end{array}
$$

Others bases, obviously derived from nucleic acid breakdown, including adenine, xanthine, hypoxanthine, cytosine, and guanine have been demonstrated in various fungi. These substances are doubtless of universal occurrence in fungi. Hypoxanthine or guanine are growth factors for *Phycomyces blakesleeanus*, the two being interchangeable (Robbins and Kavanagh, 1942).

A photosensitive compound, $C_{17}H_{12}N_2O_2$, m. 220°, decomp., was isolated from the mycelium of *Penicillium puberulum* in which it did not appear until the age of 5 weeks. It contains two enolic groups, gives a blue-violet fluorescent solution, and has characteristic absorption bands at 243 and 374 μ. The substance has antibiotic properties (Campbell et al., 1945).

Cyclic choline sulfate, $(CH_3)_3NCH_2CH_2OSO_2$, was isolated from ⌊————O————⌋ *Aspergillus sydowi* mycelium in yields of 0.26 per cent (Woolley and Peterson, 1937d). Losses in isolation procedure indicate a substantially higher content of this material in the original mycelium. This compound hitherto had not been known to occur naturally. Uric acid has been isolated in small amounts from *A. oryzae* spores (Sumi, 1928).

Two different colorless crystalline nitrogen-containing compounds from the fungus mycelium were reported by Oxford et al. (1935). One, from *Penicillium griseo-fulvum*, m. 165°, decomp.; the other, from *P. brefeldianum*, m. 132–135°.

LIPIDES IN THE MOLD MYCELIUM

Microscopic examination of the cells of a rapidly growing fungus culture, especially with a high sugar concentration in the medium as an energy source, reveals the presence of numerous refractile globules ranging in size from those very conspicuous down to those indistinguishable from minute granules. These accumulations of fatty or lipide materials can be observed in almost any organism, but in some they are of extraordinary magnitude, amounting to one-third and almost as much

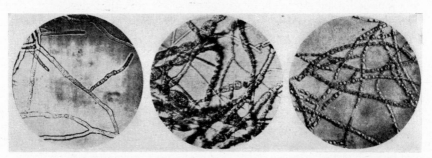

FIG. 4.—Fat globules in submerged Fusarium mycelium at different stages of growth. (a) Fat formation just beginning, (b) good fat formation, (c) maximum fat formation. Note how the large fat globules virtually fill the hyphae (from Damm, 1943).

as one-half the dry mycelial weight in certain instances. They may appear as giant globular bodies, giving the hyphae the appearance of a string of beads. These globules occupy almost all the space in the cells, and increase in size from minute granules in young cultures to the large globular state in older cultures high in fat synthesizing capacity (Figs. 4 and 5). Superficial drying of the cells tends to cause the small fat droplets to coalesce into larger globules (Lindner, 1922a). These fatty materials are not pure or homogeneous by any means, as chemical analysis has demonstrated the presence of as wide a variety of components in the lipide fraction as occurs in other biological systems. While the major deposits of fat obviously are in vacuolar globules, some lipide material undoubtedly does exist in the cytoplasm proper, and it has already been pointed out that fatty materials are laid down in the cell wall of fungi.

These accumulations of fat globules are generally described as reserve or storage products, built up under conditions of favorable nutrition. Supporting this idea is the fact that optimum conditions invariably involve the surfeiting of the organism with energy-rich food in the form of high concentrations of carbohydrate, thus enabling conversion of a large portion of this energy source into high-energy-content fats (but see Chapter 4).

In line with the idea of fat as reserve storage material one would expect to find that they diminish or disappear under unfavorable nutrient conditions leading to starvation. This observation has been made repeatedly with bacteria, particularly in relation to carbohydrate storage products and also granules of volutin, the nucleoprotein reserve material of many bacteria. Perrier (1905) considered the fat to be a reserve

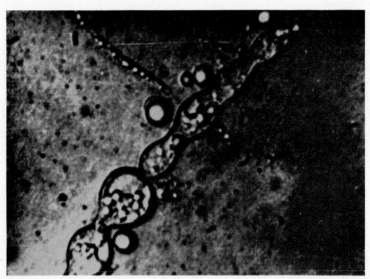

FIG. 5.—Fat globules in *Endomyces vernalis*. Note globules outside the cells, probably liberated by rupture of other cells (from Reichel and Reinmuth, 1938).

material and later workers (Belin, 1926; Prill *et al.*, 1935; Fink *et al.*, 1937b) subscribe to this idea in showing that fat content of *Aspergillus niger*, *A. fischeri* and *Oospora lactis* mycelia diminished markedly upon prolonged inanition. Belin classified the fat of molds and other living systems into "*élement constant*" and "*élement variable.*" The "*élement constant*" was considered to be the vital lipide material intimately a part of protoplasm, presumably phospholipides and lipoproteins, and not reducible below a certain minimum value. For *A. niger* this was 1.37 per cent. "*Élement variable*" was that reserve or stored fat subject to great quantitative variation and not truly a part of protoplasm. These terms are still employed in animal and human physiology. Prill *et al.* (1935) demonstrated that the absolute amount of fat in *A. fischeri* began to decrease after the tenth day and decreased more rapidly than the rest of the mycelial components until about the fortieth day, after which the decreases were almost the same.   Thus, the fat content dropped from 23.3 to 11.6 per cent and then remained constant.   This is fairly good evidence for the interpretation as utilization of the stored fat by the mold in the absence of other energy sources.   The possibility of autolytic lipolytic enzymes solubilizing some of the fat and thus its being lost in the culture filtrates also exists.

In one instance (Kordes, 1923) microscopic examination showed that the hyphal fat globules persisted during prolonged starvation, when no other energy source was available, leading to the conclusion that the fat was not a reserve storage product but rather a waste excretory product; this idea is supported by studies on *Oospora wallroth*, in which maximum fat content occurs only after 70–100 days, and where the globules of fat in the mycelium are considered to be the result of degenerative changes in the protoplasm (Geffers, 1937) and not useful to the organism.

As in virtually every biochemical activity of molds, the degree to which fat synthesis proceeds is a function of two main determinative factors (1) strain specificity, or the genetic capacity for synthesis and (2) cultural conditions.   These are discussed later.

An abundant literature has been accumulated on fat synthesis by fungi, relatively far out of proportion in respect to other components of the cell material which may be considered as the "vital" materials of protoplasm.   Two explanations may account for this emphasis: (1) analyses of total fat contents are extremely easy to make in routine—by simple ether or other fat solvent extraction of dry mycelium and (2) the potential practical implications of fat synthesis by selected strains of fungi from cheap carbohydrates and minerals.   During wartime or in other periods where critical shortages of fats and oils develop, and thus where economic considerations are not limiting, the prospects for large-scale fat manufacture become more feasible.   This situation has its analogues in the production of glycerol by yeast fermentation by the Germans in World War I, and in the microbiological synthesis of proteins for human and stock feeds during World Wars I and II.

Fat shortages were most acute in Germany during both wars, and as a result a tremendous amount of study has been devoted in that country to the development of practical processes for fat production using microorganisms; consequently, virtually all published developments are of German origin.   Microbiological fat production was pioneered by P. Lindner (1922a, b), and the famous *Endomyces vernalis* process was developed by him and his associates during the first world war after a study of numerous other organisms including fungi, yeasts, and bacteria.

It has been further studied extensively by Fink and coworkers (1937a, b), who also developed a process using *Oospora lactis* growing in milk whey. In the latter process the fat content of the dry mycelium approximated 22 per cent, with a fat coefficient of 12 to 14. Fourteen grams of fat could be obtained per square meter of *O. lactis* mycelium in the shallow pan process. The term fat coefficient was introduced by Rippel (1940) to evaluate the specific organisms as agents for the conversion of carbohydrate to fat, and is the number of grams of crude fat synthesized by the organism during the consumption of 100 g. of substrate carbohydrate. On the basis of maximum mycelial weight yields obtained under optimum conditions, and from calorimetric studies, Rippel concluded that a fat coefficient of approximately 15 is the theoretical maximum, and it is of interest to note that while many organisms approach this figure, it has never been exceeded. Since a mycelial weight yield (economic coefficient) from 100 g. carbohydrate would at most be 50 g., with the highest fat content running 50 per cent of that figure, one might theoretically expect a fat coefficient of 25. However, fat is considerably higher in energy content than carbohydrate (9.3 Cal./g. vs. 4.2) so that a large portion of the energy of the consumed sugar is converted into fat, and extra energy is required as well for the endothermic process of the chemistry of fat synthesis. Calorimetric studies on the energy inevitably lost as heat during growth of the organisms (entropy) indicate that the energetics of the system is quite satisfactory for the synthesis of 15 g. fat from 100 g. carbohydrate.

These microbiological processes were carried out mainly in 2 ways: (1) the floor process and (2) the shallow-pan process. The floor process is essentially the bran process described in Chapter 2, only instead of being conducted in sterilized drums, it was done on the open floor, and periodically turned over physically to facilitate aeration. Like the fate of Wehmer's original Citromyces process for citric acid production, contaminations proved to be the undoing of these floor processes, and soon after the war forced the closing of the one plant utilizing this process. The Oospora process was believed to be especially resistant to contaminating organisms and thus was adapted to the tray process. In the case of the floor process, separation of the fat from the bulk of material was an added problem. Fat synthesis by the surface process using *Oospora wallroth* on milk whey gave yields of 3 to 5 kg. fat per 1000 liters of milk whey, and with 10–12 kg. dry mycelium, although in a time so long as to be useless for practical production (Geffers, 1937).

A complete coverage of the details of the Endomyces process is given by Fink, *et al* (1937b). Two main carbohydrate sources were used: waste sulfite liquor and molasses, both requiring supplementary mineral and nitrogen sources, inorganic or organic. Rapid growth with little fat synthesis took place during the first 2 or 3 days; this phase was called "protein generation." The stage of "fat generation" developed from the third to about the eighth day, when the fat content of the mycelium was at maximum. Typical performance of Endomyces on waste sulfite liquor containing approximately 3 per cent sugar was 4.51 kg. fat from 10.08 kg. dry mycelium harvested from 1000 liters of the liquor medium. This made a surface area of microbial growth of 5667 sq. meters (Lindner, 1922b).

From 12 kg. molasses diluted to 4–6 per cent sugar content in the final medium and incubated 7 days in shallow layers 1–2 cm. in depth, amounting to 278 square meters surface mycelium area, 6.6 kg. fresh weight Endomyces mycelium was harvested. Upon drying, 2.2 kg. mycelium was obtained, yielding 1.0 kg. oil. Calculated differently, 100 kg. molasses containing 46 kg. sugar yields 7.9 kg. oil (Fink, et al., 1937b). The cells of the dried mycelium must be ruptured by grinding with sand to liberate the fat. The oil resembled olive oil and rapeseed oil in composition. Agitation and aeration markedly depressed the fat yields by these organisms, and because of mechanical and contamination problems the processes have been inefficient to operate, if successful at all.

During World War II when fat shortages again prevailed in Germany, a new successful submerged process for fat production was developed by H. Damm. While the patents on the process include Ascomycetes and Phycomycetes of the genera Rhizopus, Mucor, Mortierella, and Gibberella (Damm, 1944) grown in submerged molasses cultures and giving fat yields in excess of the corresponding surface cultures, the most successful results and developments were made with a species of Fusarium especially selected for fat-synthesizing abilities (Damm, 1943). The organism reaches maximum growth and fat content in 40–48 hours, a great improvement over the surface process, and can utilize a variety of substances as carbon source for fat synthesis: glucose, fructose, organic acids, acid amides, disaccharides, and pentoses although the latter are utilized more slowly. The mycelium rich in fat globules (Fig. 4) is collected by centrifugation and dried. The dry weight amounted to 35 per cent of the moist mycelium. In one experiment in a 50 per cent sugar solution, the fat amounted to 50 per cent of the mycelial weight and yields of 12–15 kg. fat per cubic meter (12–15 g./l.) were obtained. The Fusarium oil is quite similar in chemical constants to peanut oil and olive oil, and is said to be useful wherever these are employed, both for human consumption and in industry.

1. GENERAL ASPECTS OF LIPIDE SYNTHESIS IN FUNGI

Special emphasis will be given here to the chemical nature of the lipides of fungi, with only limited treatment of conditions conducive to high fat synthesis, because, except for a few points to be mentioned, the cultivation conditions are highly specific to the organisms concerned, and what applies to one does not have general application. Such details can be obtained in the original papers.

Much of the lipide material in microorganisms is not free, and for this reason values for lipide contents are generally higher after some pre-treatment to liberate the fatty materials. The forms in which lipides are found are not known but lipoproteins are a good possibility, and combinations with carbohydrates and sterols have also been suggested. Lecithoproteins are known. Doubtless others exist. Generally a mild hydrolysis is successful in liberating extractable fat. A striking instance is provided by Starkey's (1946) experiment on a yeast, which contained 53.3 per cent lipide on the basis of dry cell weight. The first three successive extractions, ether, chloroform, and boiling 50–50 ether and ethanol extracted only 11.0 per cent. The main portion, 42.3 per cent, was obtained in a fourth extraction, with ether, after liberation of the fat by hydrolysis of the cell material with hot 2 per cent HCl. The possibility also exists that fat globules are surrounded by a membrane whose chemical nature is such that it is not soluble in fat solvents, thereby protecting the globular contents from solution. Possibly a protein film similar to that surrounding fat globules in homogenized milk is present. The acid treatment would destroy this membrane. Petroleum ether also is a satisfactory fat solvent. The choice of solvent has a significant quantitative bearing on lipide contents. A comparison of acetone, alcohol, chloroform, ethyl ether and isopropyl ether led to the choice of isopropyl ether (Pruess et al., 1934) for three reasons: (1) it is inexpensive, (2) it extracted maximal quantities of true fatty material, i.e., material soluble in ethyl ether, and (3) the fat it extracted was cleanest in appearance with the exception of that extracted by ethyl ether. Ethyl ether itself extracted the least amount of lipide whereas alcohol and acetone removed appreciable quantities of non-lipide materials; chloroform was eliminated because it extracted higher alcohols and waxes. Petroleum-ether is also a useful fat solvent. It should be mentioned that mild acid hydrolysis prior to extraction might have altered this picture somewhat.

The lipide content of filamentous fungi ranges between the extremes of 1 and 50 per cent. These figures are probably minimal due to incomplete extraction, especially of bound lipides. In the neighborhood of 100 different fungi have been examined for total lipide content, and the few highest ones have been further studied in detail as to the cultural conditions favoring high fat yield and also as to the chemical nature of the fatty material produced. Almost all the studies are limited to the genera Aspergillus and Penicillium, a total of 85 members having been surveyed by Ward *et al.* (1935) and Pruess *et al.* (1934). The former probably represents part of the 120 cultures tested for fat by Lockwood *et al.* (1934) and covered 39 Penicillia and 22 Aspergilli; they list only the 10

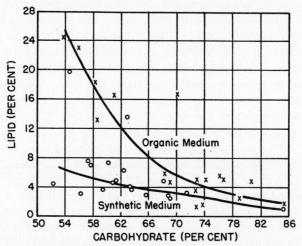

Fig. 6.—Relation between lipide and carbohydrate content of mold mycelium cultivated on organic vs. synthetic medium (from Pruess *et al.*, 1934).

species with ether-soluble fat content greater than 15 per cent, six of which ranged from 20.2 to a high of 28.5 per cent. Nine of the 10 highest organisms were *Penicillia*. The six high organisms were in order *Penicillium flavocinerium, P. piscarum, P. oxalicum, P. roquefortii, P. javanicum,* and *P. soppi.* The remaining 51 organisms were not named.

Pruess *et al.* (1934) compared nineteen Aspergilli, four Penicillia and one Paecilomyces on two media, one glucose-salts, the other glucose-malt sprouts. On the synthetic medium lipide values ranged from 1.1 to 19.9 per cent, with an average of 6.0 per cent; on the organic medium the range was 1.5 per cent to 24.4 per cent, averaging 8.8 per cent, i.e., 50 per cent higher fat content than on synthetic media. There was considerable free fatty acids in the fats calculated as oleic; these values ranged from 8.0 to 70.0 per cent, without any correlation with the total fat content of the organisms. The above data are typical for molds, although by no means complete, for numerous data on single or a few organisms are available in the literature, but they are in line with the above figures.

When lipide content was plotted against the carbohydrate content in the mycelia of the 24 different fungi studied, the interesting relations brought out in Fig. 6 were obtained. On synthetic media the lipide percentages are relatively low but there is a definite trend toward an inverse relation between lipide and carbohydrate content. In the organic media there was a pronounced inverse relation between these two components of the mycelium. This apparently means that the individual organisms have a tendency to synthesize one or the other constituents to a more or less marked degree, but not both, so that the higher the capacity for one, the lower it is for the other.

One will recall from Fig. 2 on p. 102 that the inverse ratio between carbohydrate and protein did not hold on organic medium. From Fig. 6, it is evident that the inverse relation holds for lipide, and protein.

2. FACTORS INFLUENCING TOTAL LIPIDE SYNTHESIZED

The innate, lipide synthesizing ability of a particular species is evident from the forgoing. The particular strain of a particular species is also a crucial factor. For example, nine different strains of *A. fischeri* ranged from 10.9 to 18.3 per cent of fat in the mycelium (Pruess *et al.*, 1934). Another instance is the extreme variation in fat content observed in 50 different strains of *Oidium lactis* (*Oospora lactis*) tested for usefulness in a technical microbiological process for manufacturing fats from carbohydrates in whey, supplemented with urea- or $(NH_4)_2SO_4$- N (Fink, *et al.*, 1937a); a similar situation was encountered by Geffers for *O. wallroth*. For detailed treatment of strain specificity in general see Chapters 5 and 6.

Organisms which have been studied in detail regarding cultivation conditions for maximum fat content are *Aspergillus fischeri* (Prill *et al.*, 1935), *Penicillium javanicum* (Lockwood *et al.*, 1934) and *Oidium lactis*.

3. CARBOHYDRATE CONCENTRATION

As indicated before, the maximum capacity of an organism for fat synthesis is strikingly a function of initial carbohydrate concentration. The highly unphysiological conditions of sugar contents greater than 20 per cent are required, and, in the case of *A. fischeri*, fat content was progressively increasing even through 70 per cent sugar solution in the synthetic mineral medium, the highest content tested (Table 8). The mold mycelium was analyzed just at the time of complete sugar utilization at each concentration, thus eliminating secondary autolytic and starvation processes.

TABLE 8

FAT CONTENT OF ASPERGILLUS FISCHERI AS A FUNCTION OF SUGAR CONCENTRATION[1]

Glucose Added to 100 ml. Solution, g.	Fat in Dry Mycelium, Per Cent
1	10.4
3	11.8
5	10.8
10	13.1
15	15.6
20	18.0
30	23.3
40	28.1
55	33.3
70	36.0

[1] From Prill et al. (1935).

Actually, a very high C/N ratio in the medium is equally important, for as it decreases for any given concentration of sugar, the fat synthesis falls off markedly, presumably because the carbohydrate is diverted to protein synthesis. The growth of most other fungi is inhibited by sugar concentrations exceeding 30–40 per cent (Lockwood et al., 1934), but up to the point of diminishing growth, fat content invariably is a direct function of available carbohydrate concentration, assuming the bulk of the sugar is consumed (Belin, 1926; Bohn, 1931; Terroine and Bonnet, 1927). The last-named authors observed that for every 10.69 calories the mold Sterigmatocystis nigra (A. niger) stored as fat, 12 calories had been supplied by the carbohydrate which was consumed—an extremely efficient energy conversion of practically 90 per cent, considering the fat is the product of synthetic metabolism.

In this sense fat accumulation as a product of carbohydrate metabolism may be considered analogous to formation of high yields of organic acids, a manifestation of shunt metabolism, in this case insoluble shunt products. This idea is discussed in detail in Chapter 4.

Several different sugars are known to function as starting materials for fat synthesis by molds; these include glucose, mannitol, sucrose, levulose, xylose, arabinose, and glycerol, which indicates that all are probably broken down to a common intermediate through which fat synthesis then proceeds (see later). Fat synthesis was never observed when the energy source of the mold was protein, regardless of concentration (Belin, 1926).

A number of other empirical factors have crucial significance insofar as high fat content goes; the data pertaining to them indicate once more how flexible the biochemical activities of these organisms are. They stress further the contention that the true potentialities of an organism can be evoked from the latent stage only by a systematic, largely empirical, examination of the ordinary factors known to influence microbiological development and activities. Thus, a powerful control over the ultimate amount of fat synthesized by fungi has been demonstrated for such simple factors as the source of nitrogen in the medium and the degree of acidity in the medium. The latter factor may develop physiologically through selective ion utilization and/or organic acid formation from the carbohydrate, as well as by adjustment of the initial pH of the medium (Pontillon, 1930a; Prill et al., 1935; Lockwood et al., 1934). Neutral or alkaline pH values are highly favorable; with A. fischeri, use of $CaCO_3$ in NH_4Cl medium gave a fat content of 23.2 per cent as compared to 9.0 per cent in the control, and in another experiment an initial pH of 2.0 yielded 19.2 per cent fat, increasing regularly to 37 per cent at pH 8.0, the highest pH value tested. The quality of the fats also are subject to appreciable change, as is brought out below.

Mycelia from cultures of different ages may have different fat contents. The percentage of fat rises to a peak, remains constant for several days (in surface culture), and then falls off.

Temperature and increased aeration of surface cultures are without significant effect on total fat content although striking modification in the composition of the fats obtained have been noted (see below). The profound influence of trace elements in the medium, notably zinc, manganese, iron and cadmium, on the composition of the A. niger mycelium, especially in stimulating the synthesis of the lipide fraction at the expense of the lignin fraction, has already been treated in detail (Porges, 1932; Schulz, 1937). Similar results have been obtained for Rhizopus nigricans and Aspergillus flavus (McHargue and Calfee, 1931) with manganese, copper, and zinc.

Lockwood et al. (1934) tested fifty-two metal ions of which four, molybdenum, tungsten, colombium, ferric and chromic ions, stimulated fat synthesis. Increased air pressure reduced fat content, and the surface-volume ratio of the culture vessel had an important influence: the lower the ratio the smaller the fat content. Thus, with a surface-volume ratio of 0.413, 19.3 g. glucose was required to produce 1 g. fat, while at a ratio of 0.103, 31.1 g. glucose was required.

4. COMPOSITION OF MOLD LIPIDES AND THE INFLUENCE OF CULTURAL CONDITIONS

Since the terms fat and lipide have a generic connotation, it might be expected that individual components of the numerous members of the lipide fraction would not be affected alike by cultural conditions and that their relative quantitative amounts might be subject to considerable fluctuation. This is all the more likely from the diverse chemical natures of materials in the lipide fraction (see below), which after all, are similar only in their solubility characteristics. The situation is not at all unlike the shifting ratios of gluconic, citric, and oxalic acid produced from carbohydrates by a single strain of Aspergillus or Penicillium under varied growth conditions; or of fumaric, succinic, and lactic acids by species of Rhizopus; or in the synthesis of vitamins and of antibiotic substances, which all are chemically diverse but have, in a general way, similar biological properties. Indeed, the enhancement of one type of chemical substance generally leads to a reduction of others in the same group, and this also holds for the components in the fat fractions.

TABLE 9

INFLUENCE OF pH ON VARIOUS FAT FRACTIONS OF ASPERGILLUS FISCHERI[1]

Initial pH	Fat in mycelium, per cent	Percentage of fat		
		Fatty acids	Unsapon. matter	Sterol
2	19.2	64.5	15.7	10.3
3	17.0	66.5	14.6	11.3
4.6	19.5	59.0	12.9	8.6
6	23.9	78.5	6.7	4.6
8	37.0	76.5	2.9	1.8

[1] From Prill et al. (1935).

The best studies of this nature are on A. niger (Pontillon, 1930a and b) and A. fischeri (Prill et al., 1935) in which the changing composition of the fat as a result of cultural conditions was followed by analyses on the extracted fat for the following components: fatty acids, iodine number, unsaponifiable matter, sterol, phosphorus, and nitrogen. The P and N data indicate the amount and nature of the phospholipides present. In several experiments dealing with effect of N source, pH, etc., the higher the total amount of fat, the higher was its content of fatty acids, which made up the bulk of the mold fat. Fatty acids comprised up to 85 per cent of the total fat in one treatment (Prill et al., 1935). Higher fatty acids always meant a drop in the content of unsaponifiable matter, including sterols and lipides; and the evidence was that the increment of fat consisted almost entirely of glycerides. Thus, the conditions for synthesis of fatty acids are the converse of those for other components of the fat. This effect is exemplified in Table 9 dealing with different initial pH values.

In 1928 work from two laboratories furnished evidence for an interesting effect of temperature of growth on the chemical nature of the fatty acids of the fat fraction.   Thus, with two fungi, *A. niger* and *Rhizopus nigricans*, and also for the timothy bacillus, the iodine numbers (degree of unsaturation) of the lipide fatty acids were low when the organisms were grown at high temperatures, and high when grown at reduced temperatures (Pearson and Raper, 1927; Terroine *et al.*, 1927).   For example, the iodine number of *A. niger* fat grown at 18°C. was 194; at 25°, 129; at 35°, 95.   For *Rhizopus nigricans* the values were 88 at 12° and 78 at 25°.   While these results seemingly had generalized significance, the Wisconsin laboratories could not confirm them with *A. fischeri*.   An extended review of lipides in relation to all kinds of fungi is given by Pontillon (1932–1933) and the most recent review of the subject is by Bernhauer (1943).

5. CHEMICAL COMPOSITION OF FATS SYNTHESIZED BY FUNGI

From the foregoing it is evident that an analysis of the fat from any one strain of mold cultivated for a certain period of time on a special medium is not an absolute quantitative representation of the fat composition of that species.   The lack of uniformity in analytical approaches to the make-up of mold fat makes it impossible to make comparative studies.   Data in Table 10 provide, however, a good basis for judgment of the general chemical nature of mold fats.   In every case surface culture mycelium was used.

The data in Table 10 indicate that the bulk of the lipide fraction consists of glycerides of the commonly occurring C_{16} and C_{18} saturated and unsaturated fatty acids, especially palmitic, stearic, oleic, and linoleic.   Small amounts of a C_{24} acid (N-tetracosanic) and a C_{26} acid (cerotic) have been isolated from certain fungi.   Short-chain acids, caproic (C_6), also occur in molds.   Barber (1929) states he had evidence for the presence of a unique C_{19} fatty acid in *Penicillium sp.* (see also Bernhauer and Potzelt, 1937; Ruppol, 1937).   Ninety per cent of the fatty acids of *Fusarium lini* consisted of palmitic, 19.8%; linoleic, 32.9%; and oleic, 37.3% (Fiore, 1948).

New fatty acids discovered in fungi are shown below.   The first two are produced by *Penicillium spiculosporium* (Clutterbuck *et al.*, 1931) and the last two by *P. minioluteum* (Birkinshaw and Raistrick, 1934).   Spiculosporic acid has also been isolated from *P. crateriforme* (Oxford and Raistrick, 1934).   The relation between the first two acids is evident from the fact that oxidation of spiculosporic acid with potassium permanganate in acetone solution gives almost quantitative yields of γ-ketopentadecoic acid.

$$
\begin{array}{ccc}
CH_3 & CH_3 & CH_3 \\
| & | & | \\
(CH_2)_9 & (CH_2)_9 & (CH_2)_9 \\
| & | & | \\
CH \cdot COOH & CH_2 & CH\text{———}CO \\
| & | & | \\
CH\text{———} & CO & HO \cdot C \cdot COOH \\
| \quad | & | & | \\
CH \cdot COOH \quad O & CH_2 & CH\text{———}O \\
| \quad | & | & | \\
CH_2CO\text{—} & CH_2COOH & COOH
\end{array}
$$

Spiculosporic acid   γ-Ketopentadecoic acid   Minioluteic acid

The lipides of pathogenic fungi are covered by Peck (1947).

TABLE 10

PHYSICAL CONSTANTS AND CHEMICAL COMPOSITION OF SIMPLE LIPIDES OF SOME FUNGI[1]

	Penicillium javanicum	A. niger	A. sydowi	P. aurantio-brunneum	A. citromyces	Fusa-rium	A. oryzae
Solidification temp., °C	6–7						
M.p., °C	~15						
Sp. g.	0.9145	......	0.9198				
Refractive index	1.468						
Acid No.	10.6	71.2	43.4	....	....	0.5–4	60
Ester No.	....	97.8	126.1	....	....	192	
Saponification No.	191	169	169.5	....	....	190–196	186.5
Iodine No.	84	95.1	114.4	....	....	79–90	124.3
Reichert-Meissl No.	0.3	0.99					
Acetyl No.	10.7	......	....	51			
Total fatty acids, per cent	91.6	67.5	80.8	85.4			
Volatile acids (as butyric)	....	......	0.46				
Caproic acid (C_6)	....	......	....	....	+[3]		
Saturated acids, per cent	30.8	13.0	22.6	....	....	....	1.4
M.p. of Saturated acids, °C.	52.5						
Mean mol. wt. of Saturated acids	272						
Palmitic acid (C_{16}), per cent	21.4	7.1	8.8	8.6	+		
Stearic acid (C_{18}), per cent	8.6	0.9	11.0	5.3			
N-tetracosanic[2] acid (C_{24}), per cent	0.8	1.8	0.9	0			
Cerotic acid (C_{26}), per cent	....	......	....	....	+		
Unsaturated acids, per cent	60.8	45.4	52.9	....	....	....	98.5
Oleic (C_{18}), per cent	31.7	21.5	29.6	40.2	+	....	72.4
Linoleic (C_{18}), per cent	29.1	23.9	16.3	31.2	+	....	12.4
Linolenic (C_{18}), higher acids, per cent	....	......	1.7	0		....	13.7
Unsaponifiable, per cent	2.0	12.0	8.18	4.5	10	....	8.01
Sterols, per cent	....	......	5.36	....	....	....	8.7
Ergosterol, per cent	....	1.4	+	1.9	+		
Glycerol, per cent	....	6.2	4.2	3.1	+		
Ceryl alcohol (C_{26}), per cent	....	......	....	....	+		

[1] Collected from various literature sources in the text. Data on *P. javanicum* from Ward and Jamieson (1934).

[2] Also called lignoceric acid.

[3] + = present.

6. MECHANISM OF FAT SYNTHESIS IN MOLDS

Considerable experimental evidence on this point has accumulated in recent years, stimulated no doubt by the availability of high fat-yielding organisms, notably *Endomyces vernalis*, although ordinary yeast *Saccharomyces cereviseae* has also been used extensively in these studies. It was early recognized that fats originated from carbohydrates. The origin of the glycerol moiety of the glycerides is not in question, being formed through the reduction of triose(phosphoglyceraldehyde) as clarified by the Embden-Meyerhof-Parnas scheme of yeast fermentation.

The main problem has been the mechanism whereby the long chain fatty acids are built up by fat-synthesizing organisms. Emil Fischer believed that hexose sugar chains simply condensed to form (in the case of three hexoses) a C_{18} chain which then, through reduction of hydroxyl groups, ended up as fatty acids. To form a C_{16} acid, two pentose and one hexose molecule would combine. There has never been any evidence to support this idea and the fact that no C_{15} fatty acids ever arise from three pentose molecules further weakens the idea; moreover, the origin of C_{14}, C_{20}, C_{22}, etc. acids is difficult to explain. Fischer's idea is purely of historical significance though his view was supported by Smedley-McLean and Hoffert as late as 1926.

Most modern ideas are based on a direct condensation of sugar split-products, instead of the sugars themselves. Without going into details of animal fat synthesis it is enough to say that the evidence, in particular that obtained with isotopic elements on animals, is overwhelmingly in support of the idea of condensation of sugar split-products, especially acetaldehyde, to long chain acids. Further, in the field of bacterial metabolism the evidence of analogous syntheses, namely C_4- and C_6-fatty acids, is clear-cut with respect to their origin from C_2 condensations.

In experiments with the high-fat synthesizer *Endomyces vernalis* acetaldehyde is considered the initial intermediate in fat acid synthesis. Haehn and Kintoff (1923, 1925) found that acetaldehyde clearly stimulated fat synthesis, even in protein media with no sugar. They further observed that abundant carbon dioxide formation took place during fat synthesis from sugar and pointed out that this indicated a simultaneous origin of acetaldehyde, the reaction being presumably the decarboxylation of pyruvate. The same observations and interpretations were made in connection with the mechanism of fat synthesis by *Sterigmatocystis nigra* (*A. niger*) (Terroine and Bonnet, 1927). Weiss *et al.* (1947) found that *Fusarium solani* synthesized more fat from acetate than from glucose, implicating C_2 building blocks. Fat synthesis in Fusarium has been treated in many papers from F. F. Nord's laboratory during the past several years. A purple Fusarium pigment is said to influence fat synthesis in this fungus (Nord *et al.*, 1948). Haehn and Kintoff found that fat could also be formed from substances giving rise to acetaldehyde during attack by the fungus: lactic acid, pyruvic acid, ethanol, aldol, and glycerol. The fat globules in the cells increased from practically nothing until they occupied one-half to three-quarters of the cell volume when the organism was supplied with alcohol or glycerol. Acetaldehyde could be trapped by sulfite during action of the mold on sugar, and the fat content of the mycelium was reduced in this case. Acetaldehyde was considered to be the key intermediate in fat synthesis by *Endomyces vernalis* through condensation and oxido-reduction processes. The reduction of unsaturated intermediate aldehydes is coupled with the oxidative dehydrogenation of glyceraldehyde to pyruvate via glyceric acid, which then enters the cycle by generating more unsaturated aldehydes through formation of more acetaldehyde.

$$CH_3COCOOH \rightarrow CO_2 + CH_3CHO$$

Pyruvic acid   Acetaldehyde
(from carbohydrate)

$$2CH_3CHO \xrightarrow[\substack{Aldolase \\ (carboligase)}]{} CH_3 \cdot CHOH \cdot CH_2 \cdot CHO \xrightarrow{-H_2O} CH_3 \cdot CH{=}CH \cdot CHO$$

                               Aldol   Crotonaldehyde

$$\begin{array}{c} CH_3 \cdot CH{=}CH \cdot CHO \\ + \\ R \cdot CHO \\ \text{Triose} \end{array} \quad \overset{H_2}{\underset{O}{+ \Big|}} \rightarrow \begin{array}{c} CH_3 \cdot CH_2 \cdot CH_2 \cdot CHO \\ \text{Butyraldehyde} \\ + \\ CH_3COCOOH \\ \text{Pyruvic acid} \end{array}$$

(phosphoglyceraldehyde)

$$CH_3 \cdot CH_2 \cdot CH_2 \cdot CHO + CH_3CHO \rightarrow CH_3 \cdot CH_2 \cdot CH_2 \cdot CHOH \cdot CH_2 \cdot CHO \xrightarrow{-H_2O} H_2O$$

$$\begin{array}{c} CH_3 \cdot CH_2 \cdot CH_2 \cdot CH{=}CH \cdot CHO \\ \alpha,\beta\text{-Hexylenaldehyde} \\ + \\ R \cdot CHO \\ \text{Triose} \end{array} \quad \overset{H_2}{\underset{O}{+ \Big|}} \rightarrow \begin{array}{c} CH_3 \cdot CH_2 \cdot CH_2 \cdot CH_2 \cdot CH_2 \cdot CHO \\ \text{Capronaldehyde} \\ + \\ CH_3 \cdot CO \cdot COOH \\ \text{Pyruvic acid} \end{array}$$

(phosphoglyceraldehyde)

The capronaldehyde was believed to give rise to the common C_{18} fatty acids by either of two processes:

(a) Further addition of acetaldehydes as above until oleic and palmitic acids are reached.

(b) Three molecules of capronaldehyde (or hexadienal) may condense to oleic or stearic acids. Oxidation to the saturated acid is represented as:

$$\begin{array}{c} R \cdot CH{:}CH{:}CHO \\ + \\ +H \quad H \quad O \end{array} \rightarrow R \cdot CH_2 \cdot CH_2 \cdot COOH$$

The first possibility, namely building up through successive C_2 addition, was considered the more likely manner of synthesis. Other experimental observations match the theoretical considerations. During active fat synthesis, and in the absence of growth, an average of 40 per cent of the sugar consumed was lost as carbon dioxide, and about 30 per cent converted to fat (Haehn and Kintoff, 1925). These yields are consistent with the following scheme, which is based on acetaldehyde as intermediate:

$$C_6H_{12}O_6 \rightarrow 2CH_3 \cdot CHO(-H_2O) + 2H_2 + 2CO_2$$
$$180 \qquad\qquad 88$$

$$C_{15}H_{31}COO \cdot H_2C$$
$$\qquad\qquad\qquad\qquad |$$
$$15C_6H_{12}O_6 \rightarrow C_{15}H_{31}COO \cdot HC + 5C_3H_8O_3 + 21H_2O + 24CO_2$$
$$\qquad\qquad\qquad\qquad |$$
$$C_{15}H_{31}COO \cdot H_2C$$

Theoretical CO_2 according to these equations is 39.11 per cent and the fat (as tripalmitin) is 29.8 per cent, both values in good agreement with the observed figures.

This problem has been further studied by Reichel and Reinmuth (1938), Reichel and Schmid (1939) and Reichel (1940). They are in accord with a synthesis by condensations of acetaldehyde but their theory differs from that of Haehn and Kintoff after the crotonaldehyde stage. Their proposed mechanism is based on the following evidence: octylaldehyde and decylaldehyde were oxidized to the corresponding acids by *E. vernalis*. Hexadienal supplied to the organism was converted into an acid with an equivalent weight of 307, which indicates a condensation of three molecules of the six-carbon unsaturated aldehyde. Octatrienal yielded an acid of equivalent weight of 266, an indication of condensation of two molecules of this aldehyde. Evidence was obtained that crotonaldehyde and acetaldol were condensed to higher fatty acids consisting respectively of four molecules of each aldehyde. These condensations all were considered to be effected by the enzyme aldolase. It must be pointed out that in each case the acid equivalent weights were made by titration of petroleum ether extracts of culture filtrates 5 to 7 days old, and the amounts of extracts titrated and from which the values were computed were extremely small, ranging from 1.2 to 19.4 mg. With such small quantities the question might be raised as to the contribution of fat acids to the petroleum ether extract by the mold cell material itself, making a mixture and thus obscuring the results. The following steps were proposed on the basis of the observed facts:

[A] $2CH_3CHO \rightarrow CH_3 \cdot CH{=}CH \cdot CHO + CH_3CHO \rightarrow CH_3 \cdot CH{=}CH \cdot CH{=}CH \cdot CHO$
Acetaldehyde   Crotonaldehyde   Acetaldehyde   Hexadienal

Hexadienal may form C_{18} unsaturated acids by condensation according to three possibilities:

(a) $3CH_3 \cdot CH{=}CH \cdot CH{=}CH \cdot CHO \rightarrow CH_3 \cdot (CH{=}CH)_8 \cdot COOH$
        Hexadienal   Octadeca-octanol acid

or (b) $3CH_3 \cdot CH{=}CH \cdot CH{=}CH \cdot CHO \xrightarrow{H_2} 3CH_3 \cdot CH_2 \cdot CH_2 \cdot CH{=}CH \cdot CHO \rightarrow$
        Hexadienal   Hexylenaldehyde

$$CH_3 \cdot (CH_2 \cdot CH_2)_3 \cdot (CH{=}CH)_5 \cdot COOH$$
$$C_{18} \text{ Unsaturated acid}$$

or (c) $3CH_3 \cdot CH{=}CH \cdot CH{=}CH \cdot CHO \rightarrow \text{Unsaturated } C_{18} \text{ acid}$
        Hexadienal

The C_{18} unsaturated acids from reactions (a), (b), and (c) $\xrightarrow{+H_2}$ Oleic acid $\xrightarrow{H}$ Stearic acid.

Another possibility is pointed out in which crotonaldehyde may condense directly to C_{16} compounds:

[B] 1. $2CH_3 \cdot CH{=}CH \cdot CHO \rightarrow CH_3(CH{=}CH)_3CHO$
or 2. $CH_3 \cdot CH{=}CH \cdot CH{=}CH \cdot CHO + CH_3 \cdot CHO \rightarrow CH_3(CH{=}CH)_3CHO \rightarrow$ Hexa

decenic acid $\xrightarrow{H_2}$ Hexadeca-heptanol acid, palmitic acid, or as above, b, c.

The idea of a C_2 origin of fatty acids is further borne out by an experiment of Jacquot and Raveaux (1943) where a concomitant increase in alcohol and lipide production occurred with *A. niger* as a function of increased carbohydrate concentration. This could easily be interpreted as excessive formation of acetaldehyde from pyruvate resulting from forced carbohydrate metabolism, and further disposal of the accumulated C_2 by different enzyme systems available in this organism, namely (a) reduction to alcohol and (b) condensation to long chain fat acids.

The elaborateness of the theories of Haehn and Kintoff and of Reichel given in detail above should not misguide the student as to their soundness. They can only be regarded as speculations, and lack sufficient critical evidence to warrant designation as hypotheses. Perhaps the only feature of the theories considered proven is the role of a C_2 fraction (acetaldehyde) as the primary building block of fatty acids.

7. BARKER'S THEORY

Evidence obtained by Barker and coworkers in recent years (Bornstein and Barker, 1948; Barker, 1947) relative to the synthesis of short chain fatty acids by the anaerobic spore-forming bacterium *Clostridium kluyveri* give a more specific insight into the mechanism of synthesis which may well have general biological applicability, if one subscribes to the doctrine of comparative biochemistry. *C. kluyveri* converts ethanol and acetate under anaerobic conditions almost quantitatively to *n*-butyrate, *n*-caproate, and hydrogen. Similarly, it converts ethanol and propionate to acetate, *n*-butyrate, *n*-valerate, *n*-caproate, *n*-heptanoate, and hydrogen. There is good evidence for the following reactions:

$$CH_3COOH \xrightarrow{C_2H_5OH} CH_3(CH_2)_2COOH \xrightarrow{C_2H_5OH} CH_3(CH_2)_4COOH$$
Acetic acid   Butyric acid   Caproic acid

Barker (1947) suggests that the key C_2 compound in fatty acid synthesis is not acetaldehyde, as traditionally supposed, but acetic acid and acetylphosphate, a biologically important intermediate in metabolism that has been extensively investigated by its discover, F. Lipmann (1941). Barker postulates the following mechanism for the above reactions:

$$CH_3CH_2OH + K_2HPO_4 \rightarrow CH_3COOPO_3K_2 + 4H$$
Acetylphosphate

$$CH_3COOPO_3K_2 + CH_3COOH + 4H \rightarrow CH_3CH_2CH_2COOH + K_2HPO_4 + H_2O$$
Acetylphosphate   Butyric acid

Radioactive carbon isotopic experiments support this hypothesis in which the long chains are built up by successively compounding acetic acid with fatty acid phosphates.   Thus, caproate synthesis now involves condensation of butyrylphosphate and acetic acid:

$$CH_3CH_2CH_2COOPO_3K_2 + CH_3COOH + 4H \rightarrow CH_3(CH_2)_4COOH + K_2HPO_4 + H_2O$$
Butyryl phosphate   Acetic acid

Odd number carbon chain fatty acids are synthesized via this model reaction:

$$CH_3CH_2COOPO_3K_2 + CH_3COOH + 4H \rightarrow CH_3(CH_2)_3COOH$$
Propionyl phosphate   Acetic acid n-Valeric acid

This system is an oxido-reduction cycle.   The generation of acetyl phosphate from ethanol is an oxidation (dehydrogenation), liberating 4H per mole.   These 4H, presumably via coenzyme I, are used as a reducing agent in the synthetic reactions.   The formation of butyryl phosphate, etc. is assumed to occur by a transfer of the phosphate group from acetyl phosphate to butyric acid, a known enzymatic reaction (Koepsell, et al., 1944).

The primary condensation of $C_2 + C_2 \rightarrow C_4$ is believed to form the corresponding β-keto acid, which then is reduced by the 4H to the fatty acid.   Thus in the case of $C_2 + C_2$ condensation, the β-ketoacid is assumed to be acetoacetic acid,

$$CH_3COCH_2COOH \xrightarrow{+4H} CH_3CH_2CH_2COOH$$
Butyric acid

Acetyl phosphate may be generated in various ways according to the enzyme makeup of the organism: oxidation of alcohol, and oxidative decarboxylation of pyruvic acid (see Chapter 9).   Kleinzeller (1948) has the most recent review of the biosynthesis of fats.

8. STEROLS

For some time, a few years back, special impetus was given to the study of the content in mold mycelium of one component of the fat fraction, namely the sterols, especially ergosterol. This substance is converted into antirachitic vitamin D_2 by ultraviolet irradiation, and with the artificial enrichment of foods and pharmaceuticals with this vitamin, and the discovery that fungi synthesize appreciable amounts of ergosterol, studies toward increasing the sterol content of this natural source of ergosterol were of obvious importance. In the early days of vitamin D manufacture and enrichment the bulk of ergosterol used for this purpose was extracted from the waste *Aspergillus niger* mycelium of the large scale manufacture of citric acid by the mold process. Today the most economic source is reported to be waste brewers yeast.

As pointed out earlier the discovery of certain sterols as precursors of vitamin D stimulated search for natural sources of these materials in view of the impossibility of their chemical synthesis, at least on an economical scale.

Sterols of various kinds probably are universally distributed in fungi, if not in all living organisms, with the possible exception of bacteria. Their function in the cell is unknown, and there appear to be mixtures of several sterols, only one of which has been identified with certainty in the filamentous fungi. Most emphasis has been placed on ergosterol, the specific irradiation precursor of calciferol, vitamin D_2. Ergosterol was first isolated from the ergot fungus *Claviceps purpurea* on grain (ergot) (the term fungisterol has been loosely applied to mean any sterol occurring in these organisms), hence its name. Actually, fungisterol was the name given to a new sterol, different from ergosterol, isolated from ergot and other fungi by Tanret in 1908. Sterol fractions and pure ergosterol have been isolated from a large number of different species and genera of filamentous fungi, and conditions for their formation established. A review of isolations made until 1930 is given by Pruess *et al.* (1931).

In keeping with our ideas of strain specificity different stock strains of the same species may vary substantially in the sterol content of the mycelium (Pruess *et al*, 1931), and even the single spore isolates made from one parent culture of *A. fischeri* varied between the limits of 0.73 and 1.48 per cent of the dry mycelium as sterol, some exceeding and some falling short of the sterol content of the parent culture (Wenck *et al.*, 1935b). Fifteen strains of *A. niger* varied from 0.23 to 1.16 per cent sterol (Bernhauer and Potzelt, 1935).

Detailed studies of the usual microbiological, cultural, and environmental factors on sterol content of mold mycelium have been made for several organisms. Pruess *et al.* (1931) studied 23 different organisms under various conditions and found alcohol-soluble sterol contents ranging from 0.1 to 1.0 per cent of the fungus material, with up to 0.4 per cent remaining bound in the mycelium. Selected organisms were irradiated with ultraviolet light and found to exhibit antirachitic activity in rats. Increased sugar concentrations appreciably reduced the sterol content of the several fungi tested, and this appears to be a general effect. In a later paper (Pruess *et al.*, 1934) 23 species of Aspergilli and Penicillia and one Paecilomyces were found to have sterol contents ranging from 0.26 per cent to 1.70 per cent, with a general average of 0.77 per cent. The average figure did not change between inorganic and organic media, although inconsistent individual deviations were noted.

More extensive studies yet were by Pruess *et al.* (1932) where 30 Aspergilli, 20 Penicillia and 15 assorted species were examined for total sterol content. The range was 0.17 to 1.70 per cent of the dry mycelium, *Paecilomyces varioti* No. 1 having the highest figure, when grown on malt-sprout glucose medium. Total sterol produced, 32.9 mg. per 100 ml. culture liquid, was, however, highest in *Aspergillus sydowi* owing to the more extensive growth made by this organism. Sterol synthesis was doubled in neutralized media ($CaCO_3$) as against unneutralized.

Wenck *et al.* (1935a) showed that, for *A. fischeri*, sterol content dropped progressively from 1.16 per cent with a 10 per cent glucose medium to 0.67 per cent with 40 per cent glucose. An inverse ratio between sterol content and initial pH of the medium was observed: at pH 2.0, 1.98 per cent sterol; at pH 8.0, 0.66 per cent. Highest sterol yields (2.23 per cent) were obtained in a medium with a low urea content (0.5 per cent) adjusted initially to pH 2.0 and incubated at 37°. This medium also gave the highest weight yields of sterol (134 mg.) per 100 ml. medium, and the highest yield per gram of carbohydrate consumed (6.7 mg). The C/N ratio of the medium played an important role, maximum sterol content occurring at a glucose/urea ratio of 20/1.

A large number of other factors, such as temperature, nitrogen source, incubation time, carbon source, neutralizing agents, etc. were studied by the above authors as well as many others (Prickett *et al.*, 1930). According to Bernhauer and Potzelt (1935) trace elements may promote sterol content in one strain of an organism, and produce the reverse effect in other strains. Doubtless this would apply to other cultural influences. Mold spores also contain sterols. From 1 kg. of *A. oryzae* spores, Sumi (1928) isolated 0.8 g. crude ergosterol; the purified material had the empirical composition $C_{27}H_{42}O$ (Sumi, 1929). Pure ergosterol is $C_{28}H_{44}O$, so the spore sterol may not be identical with ergosterol.

The actual content of ergosterol in dried mycelium has been ascertained in only a few cases, mainly with penicillin-producing species of Penicillia, where, by spectrographic analysis as well as by isolation, the content was 1.1 to 1.3 per cent of the surface-grown mold mycelium (Cavallito, 1944). From *P. notatum* submerged mycelium no ergosterol could be isolated and only traces were detectable spectographically. Total sterols comprise as much as 13.5 per cent of the total lipide fraction (Prill *et al.*, 1935). Ergosterol has been isolated from species of *Fusarium* (Fiore, 1948).

Sterols exist in both free and bound state in the cells. One of the more common forms is as an ester with palmitic acid, ergosterol palmitate. This compound has been isolated in crystalline form from the mycelium of 14 out of 15 strains of *Penicillium brevi-compactum* and from *P. italicum* and *P. aurantiogriseum* var. *Poznaniensis* (Oxford and Raistrick, 1933) and from *A. fumigatus* mut. *helvola* (Wieland and Prelog, 1947). Also isolated from the latter was ergosterol peroxide, which has a double oxygen bridge across the second benzene ring between carbon atoms 5 and 8. Since the peroxide forms easily in the light in the presence of sensitizers it may be a secondary, and not primary, product of the mold.

Terroine and co-workers (1927) pointed out that high sterol content of *Sterigmatocystis nigra* and certain high-fat seeds does not coincide with high content of simple lipides and that the sterols probably are formed at the expense of simple fats, i.e., when sterol synthesis is high, simple fat synthesis is reduced. This idea seems borne out strikingly in the experiments of Prill *et al.* (1935) on total fat and sterol content of *A. fischeri* under a number of different cultural conditions, which evoked large fluctuations in fat content, and in general there was an inverse relation between total fats and sterols (Table 9). On the other hand, in animal organs, fat and sterol increases are parallel, which has been cited as evidence for common origin-carbohydrates.

If this relation is true, it would suggest that both kinds of lipides have a common precursor, and that in fungi, diversion of the precursor to synthesis of one form of the lipide retards the synthesis of the other.

9. MECHANISM OF STEROL SYNTHESIS

The origin of sterol in the animal body has been the subject of considerable debate and is beyond the scope of this treatment. Carbohydrates, oleic acid, and squalene all have been proposed as the main building blocks. Isotopic experiments with animals indicate that C_2 compounds are involved in compounds of the cyclopentanoperhydrophenanthrene type, to which class sterols belong. The evidence already clearly indicates C_2 building blocks for simple fats, so this interpretation may be based on fact. In bacteria, acetate is considered to be the precursor of the fatty substances of the cell (Guirard *et al.*, 1946). Interestingly, ethyl alcohol has been found to promote the highest sterol content of the mycelium in comparison to other carbon sources. Succinic acid, conceivably a source of C_2, also was favorable (Bernhauer and Potzelt, 1935; Wenck, *et al.*, 1935).

Serious studies on the mechanism of sterol formation in fungi appears to have been made only by the Roumanian investigators Vanghelovici and Serban (1939–40; 1941) working with *A. niger*. Bernhauer and Potzelt (1935) previously had speculated as to the biosynthesis of sterols from crotonaldehyde even though this substance was toxic for the fungus. To circumvent this obstacle carboxy precursors (α-keto acids) of crotonaldehyde and methyl crotonaldehyde were pictured as condensing as follows, on purely speculative reasoning:

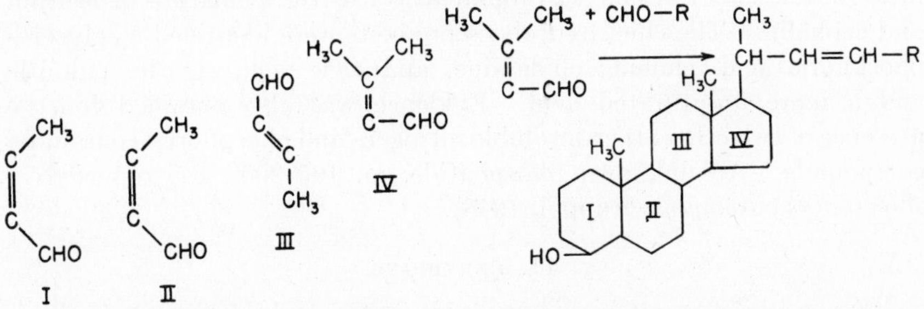

The Roumanian investigators concluded that sterol synthesis must pass through small carbon chain fragments, inasmuch as sterols are formed from C_2 to C_6 substrates. Evidence for the participation of aldehydic compounds was gained by inhibiting sterol synthesis in *A. niger* when sulfite ions were present (trapping experiment). Fatty acids were considered to be the raw material for sterol synthesis, the first step being their conversion to unsaturated acids. Yields of sterols were at a maximum just at the beginning of autolysis, and other unidentified sterols were present besides ergosterol.

10. PHOSPHOLIPIDES

While much is known about the phospholipides (phosphatides) of plant and animal tissues, and especially of yeast and certain bacteria, in particular the tubercle bacillus, this subject has been scarcely touched in the case of filamentous fungi. Lecithin and phosphatide fractions have been reported in various fungi (Thomas, 1930; Aso, 1900) but detailed chemical studies on phosphatides appear to have been made only on two fungi, *Aspergillus oryzae* and *A. sydowi*.   Takata (1929b) isolated three phosphatides from 2 kg. dried *A. oryzae* mycelium:

(1) A diaminomonophosphatide, soluble in hot alcohol, precipitating out in the cold, insoluble in ether and acetone; P = 2.27 per cent, N = 2.12 per cent, P:N = 1:2.06. This compound contained about 20 per cent carbohydrate.

(2) A monoaminomonophosphatide soluble in ether, precipitating out with absolute alcohol; P = 4.44 per cent, N = 2.10 per cent, P:N = 1:1.05.

(3) Soluble in ether and absolute alcohol, insoluble in acetone.

The yields of these three phosphatides on the basis of dry mycelium were respectively 0.74, 1.15, and 0.28 per cent. Sumi (1928) isolated lecithin from spores of *A. oryzae*.

Woolley *et al.* (1935) obtained yields of 0.43–0.73 per cent of mycelium as an ether-soluble, acetone-insoluble phospholipide with an N:P ratio of 1. This fraction was found to consist of a mixture of lecithin and cephalin. The chief hydrolysis products were identified as glycerophosphoric acid, choline, cholamine, and oleic acid, stearic, palmitic and a more unsaturated acid. Evidence was also obtained for the presence of two other ether-insoluble nitrogen- and phosphorus-containing compounds. An unknown phosphatide, m. 195–200° was reported in *Aspergillus citromyces* (Ruppol, 1943).

11. CEREBRINS

One cerebrin, a nitrogen-containing compound of long-chain fatty acids occurring in the lipide fraction has this structure:

$$C_{15}H_{31} \cdot CHOH \cdot CH \cdot CHOH \cdot CH_2 \cdot CH_2OH$$
$$\underset{\text{Fungus cerebrin}}{HN \cdot CO \cdot CHOH \cdot C_{24}H_{49}}$$

It was first isolated from the poisonous mushroom *Amanita muscaria* by Zellner in 1904 and named "fungus cerebrin," and since then has been isolated from many fleshy fungi and also from yeast. The only record of its occurrence in lower filamentous fungi was its isolation in crystalline form from dried mycelium of *Aspergillus sydowi* in 0.1 to 0.4 per cent yields (Bohonos and Peterson, 1943). It was obtained by ether extraction of the mycelium remaining after autolysis and alkali extraction, and exists in the bound form in the mycelium, as it could not be obtained from unautolyzed mycelium.

Ruppol (1943) studied the cerebrins of *A. citromyces* and isolated two: (1) a cerebrin of the cerebronylsphingosine type, m. 108–110°, containing 1.93 per cent N; (2) a similar compound, m. 147–9°, containing 1.79 per

cent N.   Hydrolysis by dilute H_2SO_4 gave cerebronic acid and sphingosine.   No cerebrosides were found.

12. RESINS

Pontillon (1929) provides evidence, by rough chemical tests, for the
presence of resinous substances in *A. niger* mycelium.

CARBOHYDRATES PRODUCED BY FUNGI

This subject is considered in detail separately in Chapter 16; some
discussion is included also in the paragraph heading "Infiltrating Materials" above.

ASH

Basic information on the mineral nutrition of fungi was already
provided some eighty years ago by the researches of Pasteur's student,
Raulin (1869) which established the fact that common fungi have
extremely simple nutritional requirements, including, besides a carbohydrate source of energy, and inorganic nitrogen, K and P, in the form
of potassium phosphate and $MgSO_4$ a source of Mg and S.   He also
recognized the need for iron and zinc.   Actually, Raulin's medium was
unnecessarily complicated even though it consisted of simple chemicals,
and Pfeffer simplified it in his well-known medium consisting only of
sucrose, NH_4NO_3, KH_2PO_4 and $MgSO_4 \cdot 7H_2O$, and many modifications
have since been made (Czapek's especially).   However, Pfeffer over-
simplified the medium and it is now known that additional nutrients are
required for mold growth over those listed in Pfeffer's solution, and the
only reason growth does occur in Pfeffer's medium is because it contains
as impurities in the ingredients, water, glassware or inoculum, the other
essential mineral nutrients which happen to be required in minute or
"trace" amounts, but which nevertheless have to be considered as true
nutrients as the salts required in much larger amounts.

It goes without saying that every one of the so-called biological
elements may be found in the ash remaining after ignition of mold
mycelium.   Indeed, fungi can accumulate certain mineral ions in their
mycelia which, when absent, apparently permit just as much growth as is
obtained when they are present.   It follows that physical phenomena
like membrane permeability and ionic equilibria must play a role in the
absorption of mineral constituents from nutrient media.   A further
expected result is that the mineral content of fungus cell material of any
organism may be subject to great fluctuations quantitatively, and in
special cases even qualitatively.   This is actually the case, and the
mineral content of mycelium, collectively and individually, depends on
the cultural conditions at any one time, and of course, on the mineral

nutrition in particular.   Deviations may be so significant that it cannot be said of fungi that they possess a typical mineral composition.   Any analytical data simply reflect the results obtained with mold material cultivated under a specific set of conditions, and need not, and probably do not, represent the mineral composition of mycelium in general, or even of other organisms cultivated on the same medium.   Unfortunately, comparative data of this kind for difference organisms is lacking.   This lack of uniformity in mineral composition of fungi is not a new idea— the same thought has been emphasized repeatedly in connection with all the other cellular components already discussed.

In this section the functions (where known), of various minerals in the mold mycelium and the transformations inorganic elements undergo through the agency of molds will not be discussed.   They are treated elsewhere in this book.   In addition, the whole subject of trace elements is given separate consideration.   Included here will be certain quantitative analytical data on the composition of the ash of mold mycelium, and special emphasis is given to influences which can alter both the total ash content and its composition.

Japanese investigators, in different experiments, have given the composition of the ash of *A. oryzae* spores and mycelium plus spores as in the following tabulation:

	Per cent of total ash	
	Spores[1]	Mycelium[2] plus spores
K_2O	45.9	28.16
Na_2O	4.1	11.21
CaO	1.0	1.95
MgO	4.4	3.88
Fe_2O_3	4.9	1.65
P_2O_5	39.6	48.55
SO_3	2.0	0.11
SiO_2	0.41	
Cl	Present	0.07

[1] From Aso (1900).
[2] From Takata (1929f).

One of the most comprehensive studies on mineral metabolism of fungi was made by Rennerfelt (1934) using *A. niger*.   The distribution of several minerals between the vegetative mycelium and spores is given in Table 11.   The spores stored minerals to an extent greater than three times the mycelium, every element with the exception of calcium being more concentrated in the spores.   Calcium was believed bound in the mycelium as calcium oxalate, thus preventing its migration to the spores. The high mineral content in the spores may be interpreted as a storage process in anticipation of spore swelling and germination under favorable conditions. The storage of magnesium in the spores is noteworthy, whereas the phosphorus value is unexpectedly low in view of the fact that one might expect to find energy-rich phosphate esters accumulated in spores.

TABLE 11

MINERAL CONTENT OF ASPERGILLUS NIGER MYCELIUM AND SPORES[1]

	Millimoles per gram dry weight						
	Total ash, per cent	K	Mg	Ca	Mn	Na	P
Mycelium.............	1.84	0.067	0.014	0.114	0.005	0.007	0.034
Spores...............	5.77	0.328	0.098	0.007	0.011	0.016	0.047
Spores/mycelium......	3.13	4.9	0.1	0.062	2.1	2.3	1.4

[1] From Rennerfelt (1934).

Like all other components of mold cell material, the ash composition can be greatly altered by conditions of cultivation, mainly mineral nutrition. The presence of certain individual minerals in the medium can have a big influence on the uptake of the other ions by the organism. Thus, the presence of 1.0 mg. Fe per flask increased the uptake of K from 0.21 to 0.35 m Mole per gram dry mycelial weight, and meanwhile reduced the P uptake 50 per cent from the control of 0.26. Total ash content was unchanged by the Fe.

Naturally the amount of an element absorbed per gram dry weight mycelium parallels the concentration of that element in the medium from zero up to a definite maximum. The following summary from Rennerfelt's data shows the wide range encountered in the content of four elements in the mycelium in this respect.

CONTENT OF ELEMENTS IN DRIED MYCELIUM, m MOLE/G.

	Mycelium grown on media in which the concentration of the particular element was	
	Smallest	Highest
K	0.073	0.27
Ca	0.0012	0.139
Mn	0.007	0.172
P	0.014	0.120

1. CALCIUM

Even when not required for growth, addition of any element to the medium leads to abundant accumulation in the mycelium. Thus, calcium is generally considered unnecessary for growth of fungi (Buromsky, 1913; Steinberg, 1919; Mann, 1932; but see Chapter 7), yet, when present in the medium, calcium ion is absorbed by the mycelium and may comprise a substantial portion of the ash, depending on the medium concentration (see above tabulation; also Rippel and Stoess, 1932). Extremely large amounts of calcium may be absorbed by the mold. From a medium saturated with $CaSO_4 \cdot 2H_2O$ ($\sim$ 100 mg. Ca per 250 ml.) *A. niger* absorbed 80 mg. of Ca. Small amounts of Ca in the medium had no effect on mold growth; larger amounts (50–100 mg. Ca per 250 ml. medium) caused a 10–17 per cent increase in mold dry weight. This increment was shown to be due entirely to the calcium oxalate deposits in the mycelium, resulting from the high Ca content and from oxalate formation from sugar (Robert, 1911, 1912). Even when efforts are made to exclude Ca or any other of the so-called unessential elements, they are usually present in minute amounts as impurities in the medium ingredients, glassware, etc., so that they are absorbed into the cell material and are demonstrable there. Mann (1932) obtained excellent growth of *A. niger* in a medium which, by chemical tests, had less than 1 part Ca in 25 million parts medium (the limit of chemical sensitivity) yet spectrographic analysis of the mycelial ash showed its presence together with other so-called "absent" elements, iron, manganese, lead, aluminum, and sodium. Doubtless any element added to the medium will be found in the ash of the organism.

In general, of all the cations analyzed, potassium is present in mold cells in highest quantities, followed by magnesium and sodium. Phosphorus is, however, present in amounts larger than any other single mineral element.

2. PHOSPHORUS

Phosphorus relations between the mold mycelium and the medium are of special interest because of the numerous key functions and compounds in which this element participates: coenzymes, phosphoproteins, phospholipides, etc. This point is discussed in Chapter 9. This accounts for the high P content of mold mycelium, which in Schnüche's (1924) experiments ranged from 1.0 to 3.0 per cent of dry mycelium, expressed as P_2O_5. In Rennerfelt's experiments increasing medium content of KH_2PO_4 progressively raised the ash content of the mycelium from 1.78 to 5.25 per cent. This increase was due not only to increased P content of the mycelium, but, similar to the effect of iron mentioned above, also to concomitant increases in the other major ash constituents, namely, K, Mg, and Na. Thus, phosphate seems to exert a favorable influence on the transport of other ions. Young mycelium is richest in P, doubtless a result of the role of phosphorus compounds in active synthesis of cell material.

Compounds of phosphorus other than those of known composition and significance in metabolism have been isolated from fungi. Of special significance are the polymers of phosphoric acid, metaphosphates $(HPO_3)_n$, whose isolation in pure form from a natural source appears to have been done for the first time by Mann (1944) from *A. niger* and confirmed by Ingelman (1948). Mann suggests this structure as a possibility for his metaphosphate:

$$
\begin{array}{ccc}
\text{OH} & & \text{OH} \\
| & & | \\
\text{O=P—O—P=O} \\
| & & | \\
\text{O} & & \text{O} \\
| & & | \\
\text{O=P—O—P=O} \\
| & & | \\
\text{OH} & & \text{OH}
\end{array}
$$

It is possible this is a fragment of the polymetaphosphate type compound isolated by Ingelman from *A. niger* mycelium. This substance is a high molecular weight compound and is non-dialyzable, i.e., an inorganic colloid. It contained 25 per cent P and small amounts of organic impurities. Demonstrated in both cases were metaphosphatases, enzymes breaking down the metaphosphates liberating orthophosphate (phosphoric acid).

The metaphosphates are distinct from the inorganic pyrophosphate $(H_2P_2O_7)$ also isolated by Mann from *A. niger* mycelium.

$$
\begin{array}{ccc}
\text{O} & & \text{O} \\
\| & & \| \\
\text{HO—P—O—P—OH} \\
| & & | \\
\text{OH} & & \text{OH}
\end{array}
$$

Cocarboxylase and adenosine diphosphate are well-known organic pyrophosphates in cells. Pyrophosphate is split by a specific enzyme pyrophosphatase, which does not attack metaphosphate. Metaphosphatase splits both pyrophosphate and metaphosphate. The function of these compounds is unknown, but because they form stable complexes with cationic metals it is possible they prevent loss of metals from the cell by simple permeability.

A curious organic phosphorus compound, monoallylphosphite, $CH_2:CHCH_2OPO_3H_2$, has been isolated from *A. niger* mycelium by the

Japanese, Baba, (1943). The compound is soluble in ether, and is a solid, melting at 172–5°. The mold autolysate, and takadiastase also, contains a phosphatase which hydrolyzes the compound.

3. MAGNESIUM

According to Rippel and Behr (1930), acid extraction of the mycelium of *A. niger* removes 97 per cent of the mycelial magnesium in soluble form. The Mg is precipitable directly from the extract by phosphate in ammoniacal solution, hence exists either in inorganic or loose organic combination. No magnesium-containing material was soluble in organic solvents. The MgO content in mycelium harvested from neutral pH medium was about double that from acid medium (0.17 per cent vs. .35 per cent) and a similar relation held for the MgO as percentage of total ash.

4. POTASSIUM

Rippel and Behr (1934) describe some interesting physiological effects of potassium ion, an element usually taken for granted in nutritional work and considered to influence the amount of growth a fungus makes but not usually influencing metabolism. Molliard (1920) had already reported that *A. niger* produced more oxalic acid in K-deficient media than with an abundance of this element. Table 12 shows that growth is severely limited in a K-deficient medium, but, gram for gram, the K-deficient mycelium produced much more oxalic acid than the K-containing control. This effect possibly can be interpreted along the lines of shunt metabolism described in Chapter 4.

TABLE 12

POTASSIUM DEFICIENCY IN A. NIGER[1,2]

Potassium present	Mycelial dry wt., g.		Oxalic acid produced per g. mycelium	
	+	–	+	–
Incubation, 4 days..............	1.12	0.05	0.005	0
7..................	1.78	.08	.030	0.157
13..................	2.20	.13	.031	.142
28..................	2.27	.22	.018	.205
41..................	2.18	.25	.003	.237
58..................	2.13	.32	.0	.439

[1] From Rippel and Behr (1934).
[2] In 75 ml. 10 per cent sugar medium.

This is further borne out by the following data which show that the economic coefficient of K-abundant cultures is considerably superior.

	Potassium	Economic coefficient[1]
High N medium..................	Abundant	0.30
	Deficient	0.16
Low N medium..................	Abundant	0.25
	Deficient	0.11

[1] G. mycelium per g. sugar consumed.

Table 13 shows the alterations in chemical composition of mycelium induced by K-deficiency.

TABLE 13

POTASSIUM DEFICIENCY AND CHEMICAL COMPOSITION OF A. NIGER DRY MYCELIUM[1]

	Myc. wt.	pH	K$_2$O	Na$_2$O	Total N	Protein N	NH$_3$-N	Protein N in per cent of total N
Potassium abundant..	1.50 g.	3.71	1.33%	0.57%	3.86%	2.83%	0.27%	73.3
Potassium deficient...	0.25	4.14	0.08	0.35	5.44	2.68	1.47	49.3

[1] From Rippel and Behr (1934).

There was considerably more ammonia in the K-deficient mycelium, due probably to the inability to synthesize cell material, yet meanwhile reducing the NO$_3$—N source to ammonia, which, as the data show, piles up. Of the total nitrogen in the mycelium, the K-abundant cells were able to convert appreciably more to protein than the K-deficient cells (last column, Table 12).

The potassium content of mycelium grown in K-abundant medium varies with the strain of fungus, the range being 0.62 to 2.44 per cent K$_2$O for the several strains studied by Rippel and Behr. The interesting correlation was made that strains with the highest K$_2$O content produced the most oxalic acid. Thus, a good oxalic acid strain of A. niger would have twice the K$_2$O content of poor ones.

5. SODIUM

Sodium is unessential for mold growth, so far as is known. However, mold mycelium invariably will absorb available sodium from the medium. The mycelial ash always shows some sodium.

REFERENCES

Abderhalden, E., and Rona, P. 1905. *Z. physiol. Chem.* **46**, 179–186.
Akasi, S. 1939. *J. Biochem. Japan* **29**, 21–29.
Anson, M. L. 1937. *J. Gen. Physiol.* **20**, 565–574.
Aso, K. 1900. *Bull. Coll. Agr. Komaba Tokyo Imp. Univ.* **4**, 81–96.

Baba, S. 1943. *Proc. Imp. Acad. Tokyo* **19**, 70–79.

Barber, H. H. 1929. *Biochem. J.* **23**, 1158–1164.

Barker, H. A. 1947. *Antonie van Leeuwenhoek* **12**, 167–176.

Behr, G. 1930. *Arch. Mikrobiol.* **1**, 418–444.

Belin, P. 1926. *Bull. soc. chim. biol.* **8**, 1081–1102, 1120–1150.

Bernhauer, K. 1943. *Ergeb. Enzymforsch.* **9**, 297–360.

Bernhauer, K., and Potzelt, G. 1935. *Biochem. Z.* **280**, 388–393.

Bernhauer, K., and Potzelt, G. 1937. *Biochem. Z.* **294**, 215–220.

Bessey, E. A. 1935. Textbook of Mycology. Blakiston, Philadelphia, pp. 129–130.

Birkinshaw, J. H., and Raistrick, H. 1934. *Biochem. J.* **28**, 828–836.

Birkinshaw, J. H., Raistrick, H., and Smith, G. 1942. *Biochem. J.* **36**, 829–835.

Bohn, P. R. 1931. *Compt. rend.* **193**, 441–442.

Bohonos, N., and Peterson, W. H. 1943. *J. Biol. Chem.* **149**, 295–300.

Bohonos, N., Woolley, D. W., and Peterson, W. H. 1942. *Arch. Biochem.* **1**, 319–324.

Bornstein, B. T., and Barker, H. A. 1948. *J. Biol. Chem.* **172**, 659–669.

Bortels, H. 1927. *Biochem. Z.* **182**, 301–358.

Braconnot, H. 1811. *Ann. chim. phys.* **79**, 272–282.

Bradley, H. C. 1938. *Physiol. Revs.* **18**, 173–196.

Brewer, G. 1943. *Z. Volksernähr.* **18**, 138.

Buromsky, J. 1913. *Zentr. Bakt. Parasitenk. Abt II* **36**, 54–66.

Campbell, A. H., Foss, M. E., Hirst, E. L., and Jones, J. K. N. 1945. *Nature* **155**, 141.

Castle, E. S. 1945. *Am. J. Botany* **32**, 148–151.

Cavallito, C. J. 1944. *Science* **100**, 333.

Clutterbuck, P. W., Lovell, R., and Raistrick, H. 1932. *Biochem. J.* **26**, 1907–1918.

Clutterbuck, P. W., Raistrick, H., and Rintoul, M. L. 1931. *Phil. Trans. Roy. Soc. London* **B220**, 301–330.

Damm, H. 1943. *Chem. Ztg.* **67**, 47–49.

Damm, H. 1944. U. S. Patent No. 2,346,011.

De Bary, A. 1887. Comparative Morphology and Biology of the Fungi Mycetozoa and Bacteria. Oxford, pp. 8 and 13.

Dous and Ziegenspek. 1926. *Arch. Pharm.* **264**, 751–753.

Farr, W. K., and Eckerson, S. H. 1934. *Contribs. Boyce Thompson Inst.* **6**, 189–203.

Fink, H. 1942. *Forschungsdienst* **16**, 724–738.

Fink, H., Haehn, H., and Hoerburger, W. 1937a. *Chem. Ztg.* **61**, 689–693, 723–726, 744–747.

Fink, H., Haenseler, G., and Schmidt, M. 1937b. *Z. Spiritusind.* **60**, 74, 76–77, 81–82.

Fiore, J. V. 1948. *Arch. Biochem.* **16**, 161–168.

Foster, J. W., McDaniel, L. E., Woodruff, H. B., and Stokes, J. L. 1945. *J. Bact.* **50**, 365–368.

Garzuly-Janke, R. 1940. *Zentr. Bakt. Parasitenk. Abt. II* **102**, 361–365.

Geffers, H. 1937. *Arch. Mikrobiol.* **8**, 66–98.

Gerlack, M., and Vogel, I. 1903. *Zentr. Bakt. Parasitenk. Abt. II* **10**, 636–643.

Gibson, E. 1895. *Ber.* **28**, 821–822.

Gorcica, H. J., Peterson, W. H., and Steenbock, H. 1934. *Biochem. J.* **28**, 504–511.

Guirard, B. M., Snell, E. E., and Williams, R. J. 1946. *Arch. Biochem.* **9**, 361–379.

Haehn, H. 1936. *Ergeb. Enzymforsch.* **5**, 117–154.

Haehn, H., and Kintoff, W. 1923. *Ber.* **56**, 439–445.

Haehn, H., and Kintoff, W. 1925. *Chem. Zelle u. Gewebe* **12**, 115–156.

Hilpert, R. S., Becker, D., and Rossée, W. 1937a. *Biochem. Z.* **289**, 179–192.

Hilpert, R. S., Friesen, G., and Rossée, W. 1937b. *Biochem. Z.* **289**, 193–197.

Ingelman, B. 1948. *Acta Chem. Scand.* **1**, 776–777.

Jacquot, R., and Raveaux, R. 1943. *Compt. rend.* **216**, 318–319.

Kalb, L. 1932. Klein's Handbuch der Pflanzenanalyse Springer, Berlin, Vol. 2, pp. 191, 201.

Katznelson, H. 1940. *Soil Sci.* **49**, 83–93.

Kleinzeller, A. 1948. *Advances in Enzymol.* **8**, 299–341.

Klotz, L. J. 1923. *Ann. Missouri Botan. Garden* **10**, 299–368.

Koepsell, H. J., Johnson, M. J., and Meek, J. S. 1944. *J. Biol. Chem.* **154**, 535–547.

Kordes, H. 1923. *Botan. Arch.* **3**, 282–311.

Krassilnikov, N. A., and Koreniako, A. I. 1938. *Microbiology USSR* **7**, 829–837.

Lechner, R. 1940. *Vorratspflege u. Lebensmittelforsch.* **3**, 220–240.

Lim, H. 1935. *J. Faculty Agr., Hokkaido Imp. Univ.* **37**, 165–209.

Lindner, P. 1922a. *Z. angew. Chem.* **35**, 110–114.

Lindner, P. 1922b. *Chem. Ztg.* **46**, 855–856.

Lipmann, F. 1941. *Advances in Enzymol.* **1**, 99–162.

Lockwood, L. B., Ward, G. E., May, O. E., Herrick, H. T., and O'Neill, H. T. 1934. *Zentr. Bakt. Parasitenk. Abt II* **90**, 411–425.

McCarty, M. 1946. *Bact. Revs.* **10**, 63–71.

McHargue, J. S., and Calfee, R. K. 1931. *Botan. Gaz.* **91**, 183–193.

Mangin, L. 1890. *Compt. rend.* **110**, 644–647.

Mangin, L. 1899. *J. Botany* **13**, 209–216, 276–287, 307–316, 339–348, 371–378.

Mann, M. L. 1932. *Bull. Torrey Botan. Club* **59**, 443–490.

Mann, T. 1944. *Biochem. J.* **38**, 345–351.

Mazur, A., and Clark, H. T. 1938. *J. Biol. Chem.* **123**, 729–740; 1942. **143**, 39–42.

May, O. E., and Ward, G. E. 1934. *J. Am. Chem. Soc.* **56**, 1597–1600.

Metz, O. 1930. *Arch. Mikrobiol.* **1**, 197–251.

Molliard, M. 1920. *Compt. rend.* **170**, 949–951.

Nabel, K. 1939. *Arch. Mikrobiol.* **10**, 515–541.

Nelson, C. I. 1933. *J. Agr. Research* **46**, 183–186.

Nord, F. F., Fiore, J. V., and Weiss, S. 1948. *Arch. Biochem.* **17**, 345–358.

Norman, A. G., and Peterson, W. H. 1932. *Biochem. J.* **26**, 1946–1953.

Oxford, A. E., and Raistrick, H. 1933. *Biochem. J.* **27**, 1176–1180.

Oxford, A. E., and Raistrick, H. 1934. *Biochem. J.* **28**, 1321–1324.

Oxford, A. E., Raistrick, H., and Simonart, P. 1935. *Biochem. J.* **29**, 1102–1115.

Pearson, L. K., and Raper, H. S. 1927. *Biochem. J.* **21**, 875–879.

Peck, R. L. 1947. Biology of Pathogenic Fungi. Chronica Botanica, Waltham, Mass., pp. 167–189.

Perrier, A. 1905. *Compt. rend.* **140**, 1052–1054.

Peukert, M. 1943. *Cellulosechemie* **21**, 32–34.

Pontillon, C. 1929. *Compt. rend.* **188**, 413–415.

Pontillon, C. 1930a. *Compt. rend.* **191**, 1148–1151.

Pontillon, C. 1930b. *Compt. rend.* **191**, 1367–1369.

Pontillon, C. 1932–1933. *Rev. gén. botan.* **44**, 417–449, 465–483, 526–560; **45**, 20–52.

Porges, N. 1932. *Botan. Gaz.* **94**, 197–205.

Prickett, P. S., Massengale, O. N., Cox, W. M., and Bills, G. E. 1930. *Proc. Soc. Exptl. Biol. Med.* **27**, 701.

Prill, E. A., Wenck, P. R., and Peterson, W. H. 1935. *Biochem. J.* **29**, 21–23.

Pringsheim, H., and Lichtenstein, S.   1920.   *Cellulosechemie* **1**, 29–39.
Proskuriakow, N. J.   1926.   *Biochem. Z.* **167**, 68–76.
Pruess, L. M., Eichinger, E. C., and Peterson, W. H.   1934.   *Zentr. Bakt. Parasitenk. Abt II* **89**, 370–377.
Pruess, L. M., Gorcica, H. J., Greene, H. C., and Peterson, W. H.   1932.   *Biochem. Z.* **246**, 401–413.
Pruess, L. M., Peterson, W. H., Steenbock, H., and Fred, E. B.   1931.   *J. Biol. Chem.* **90**, 369–384.
Quilico, A., and Di Capua, A.   1933.   *Atti accad. Lincei* **17**, 93–98.
Raulin, J.   1869.   *Ann. Sci. Nat. 5th Ser. Botan.* **11**, 93–299.
Reichel, L.   1940.   *Angew. Chem.* **53**, 577–579.
Reichel, L., and Reinmuth, W.   1938.   *Biochem. Z.* **299**, 359–362.
Reichel, L., and Schmid, O.   1939.   *Biochem. Z.* **300**, 274–283.
Rennerfelt, E.   1934.   *Planta* **22**, 221–239.
Rippel, K.   1940.   *Arch. Mikrobiol.* **11**, 271–284.
Rippel, K., and Behr, G.   1930.   *Arch. Mikrobiol.* **1**, 271–276.
Rippel, K., and Behr, G.   1934.   *Arch. Mikrobiol.* **5**, 561–577.
Rippel, K., and Behr, G.   1936.   *Arch. Mikrobiol.* **7**, 584–589.
Rippel, K., and Stoess, U.   1932.   *Arch. Mikrobiol.* **3**, 492–506.
Robbins, W. J., and Kavanagh, F.   1942.   *Proc. Natl. Acad. Sci. U. S.* **28**, 65–69.
Robert, Mlle.   1911.   *Compt. rend.* **153**, 1175–1177.
Robert, Mlle.   1912.   *Compt. rend.* **154**, 1308–1311.
Robertson, T.   1920.   Principles of Biochemistry.   Lea and Febiger, Philadelphia.
Ruppol, E.   1937.   *J. pharm. Belg.* **19**, 63–68.
Ruppol, E.   1943.   *Bull. soc. chim. biol.* **25**, 57–66.
Savulesku, T.   1935.   Cited in Nabel (1939).
Schmallfuss, R., and Mothes, K.   1930.   *Biochem. Z.* **221**, 134–153.
Schmidt, M.   1936.   *Arch. Mikrobiol.* **7**, 241–260.
Schnüche, R.   1924.   *Biochem. Z.* **153**, 372–423.
Scholl, E.   1908.   *Monatsh.* **29**, 1023–1036.
Schulz, G.   1937.   *Planta* **27**, 196–218.
Skinner, C. S.   1924.   *J. Bact.* **28**, 95–106.
Skinner, J. T., Peterson, W. H., and Steenbock, H.   1933.   *Biochem. Z.* **267**, 169–178.
Smedley-MacLean, I., and Hoffert, D.   1926.   *Biochem. J.* **20**, 343–357.
Smith, G. M.   1938.   Crytogamic Botany. I. Algae and Fungi.   McGraw-Hill, New York, p. 8.
Somogyi, J. C.   1946.   Die Ernährungsphysiologische Bedeutung der Hefe.   Beihefte zur Zeitschrift für Vitaminforschung. Nr. 4, Medizinischer Verlag Hans Huber, Berne, 114 pp.
Starkey, R. L.   1946.   *J. Bact.* **51**, 33–50.
Steinberg, R. A.   1919.   *Am. J. Botany* **6**, 330–372.
Steinberg, R. A.   1939.   *J. Agr. Research* **58**, 717–732.
Stokes, J. L., and Gunness, M.   1946.   *J. Bact.* **52**, 195–207.
Sumi, M.   1928.   *Biochem. Z.* **195**, 161–174.
Sumi, M.   1929.   *Biochem. Z.* **204**, 412–413.
Takata, R.   1929a.   *J. Soc. Chem. Ind. Japan* **32**, 155–158B (Suppl. binding).
Takata, R.   1929b.   *J. Soc. Chem. Ind. Japan* **32**, 169–172B (Suppl. binding).
Takata, R.   1929c.   *J. Soc. Chem. Ind. Japan* **32**, 243–244 (Suppl. binding).
Takata, R.   1929d.   *J. Soc. Chem. Ind. Japan* **32**, 245 (Suppl. binding).
Takata, R.   1929e.   *J. Soc. Chem. Ind. Japan* **32**, 308 (Suppl. binding).

Takata, R.   1929f.   *J. Soc. Chem. Ind. Japan* **32**, 497–510, 544–557.

Tanret, C.   1908.   *Compt. rend.* **147**, 75–77.

Tausson, V. O.   1938.   *Microbiology USSR* **7**, 75.

Terroine, E. F., and Bonnet, R.   1927.   *Bull. soc. chim. biol.* **9**, 588–596.

Terroine, E. F., Bonnet, R., Kopp, G., and Vechot, J.   1927.   *Bull. soc. chim. biol.* **9**, 678–691.

Thaysen, A. C., and Morris, M.   1947.   *Antonie van Leeuwenhoek* **12**, 204–214.

Thom, C., and Phillips, H.   1932.   *J. Wash. Acad. Sci.* **22**, 230–239.

Thom, C., and Raper, K. B.   1945.   A Manual of the Aspergilli.   Williams & Wilkins, Baltimore, p. 222.

Thomas, P., and Moran, R. C.   1914.   *Compt. rend.* **159**, 125–127.

Thomas, R. C.   1928.   *Am. J. Botany* **15**, 537–547.

Thomas, R. C.   1930.   *Am. J. Botany* **17**, 779–787.

Toursel, O.   1942.   *Forschungsdienst* **16**, 736–738.

Vanghelovici, M., and Serban, F.   1939–1940.   *Bull. sect. sci. acad. roumaine* **22**, 287–292.

Vanghelovici, M., and Serban, F.   1941.   *Bull. sect. sci. acad. roumaine* **23**, 431–445.

Van Wisselingh, C.   1898.   *Jahrb. wiss. Botan.* **31**, 619–687.

Vinson, L. J., Cerecedo, L. R., Mull, R. P., and Nord, F. F.   1945.   *Science* **101**, 388–389.

Von Wettstein, F.   1921.   *Sitzber. Akad. Wiss. Wien Math.-naturw. Klasse I* **30**, 3–20.

Waksman, S. A.   1936.   Humus. Williams and Wilkins, Baltimore.

Waksman, S. A., and Lomanitz, S.   1924.   *J. Agr. Research* **30**, 263–281.

Ward, G. E., and Jamieson, G. S.   1934.   *J. Am. Chem. Soc.* **56**, 973–975.

Ward, G. E., Lockwood, L. B., May, O. E., and Herrick, H. T.   1935.   *Ind. Eng. Chem.* **27**, 318–322.

Weiss, S., Fiore, J. V., and Nord, F. F.   1947.   *Arch. Biochem.* **15**, 326–328.

Wenck, P. R., Peterson, W. H., and Fred, E. B.   1935a.   *Zentr. Bakt. Parasitenk. Abt II* **92**, 330–338.

Wenck, P. R., Peterson, W. H., and Greene, H. C.   1935b.   *Zentr. Bakt. Parasitenk. Abt II* **92**, 324–330.

Wieland, P., and Prelog, V.   1947.   *Helv. Chim. Acta* **30**, 1028–1031.

Winterstein, E.   1893.   *Ber. deut. botan. Ges.* **11**, 441–445.

Woolley, D. W., Berger, J., Peterson, W. H., and Steenbock, H.   1938.   *J. Nutrition* **16**, 465–476.

Woolley, D. W., and Peterson, W. H.   1937a.   *J. Biol. Chem.* **114**, 85–90.

Woolley, D. W., and Peterson, W. H.   1937b.   *J. Biol. Chem.* **118**, 363–370.

Woolley, D. W., and Peterson, W. H.   1937c.   *J. Biol. Chem.* **121**, 507–520.

Woolley, D. W., and Peterson, W. H.   1937d.   *J. Biol. Chem.* **122**, 213–218.

Woolley, D. W., Strong, F. M., Peterson, W. H., and Prill, E. A.   1935.   *J. Am. Chem. Soc.* **57**, 2589–2591.

Zetzche, F.   1932.   Klein's Handbuch der Pflanzenanalyse. Springer, Berlin, Vol. 3, No. 1, 264–269.

CHAPTER 4

GENERAL CONSIDERATIONS OF MOLD METABOLISM

EFFICIENCY OF CELL SYNTHESIS AND FATE OF SUBSTRATE

Given the right conditions, filamentous fungi are, as a rule, extremely efficient in their ability to convert substrate into cell material. In general, a rich medium, containing complex organic nitrogenous sources and an abundance of minerals, especially trace elements, and excess availability of oxygen to all cells, is most favorable for rapid and abundant growth, and at the same time, efficiency of cell synthesis. On the other hand, with the proper balance between nutrients, high capacity for conversion of carbohydrate to metabolic products other than cell material is possible. Most available data refer to growth on synthetic media, where analysis for amount of substrate (carbohydrate) metabolized is direct and unequivocal. Interpretation of utilization of complex materials such as corn steep liquor, yeast extract, and peptone is questionable due to analysis difficulties. Efficiency, or economic coefficient, is the ratio of dry weight of mold mycelium to the amount of carbohydrate consumed. It is commonly expressed in percentage.

As a class, fungi under optimum conditions are more efficient synthesizers of cell material than most bacteria. Under optimum conditions yeasts and actinomycetes are about equivalent to fungi. Unless one specifies the experimental conditions, efficacy data on fungi are almost meaningless. When carbohydrate is consumed by a growing fungus, it undergoes three metabolic fates. It is converted into cell substance, carbon dioxide, and accumulations of various products derived from the sugar, such as soluble organic acids, alcohols, etc. excreted into the medium, and fats, complex aromatic compounds, etc. deposited in the mycelium. It is obvious that for a certain amount of carbohydrate consumed, suppression of either CO_2 or dissimilation products must lead to an increase in cell material. One can do little about the CO_2 for it is linked inseparably to growth of molds, but one can alter profoundly, and at will, the amounts of accumulated dissimilation products, and consequently the efficiency of synthesis. If carbohydrate is diverted to excretion products such as organic acids, obviously that much less of the carbohydrate is converted into cells, and the efficiency is lowered. Available data indicate that under conditions where carbohydrate is

148

not diverted to waste metabolic products, and where growth is relatively rapid on synthetic media, fungi in surface cultures may convert 25 to 50 per cent of the carbohydrate into dry cell substance; usually, unless special conditions are created, the figure is much less and occasionally figures exceeding 50 per cent are reported.

Two of the most important factors affecting the economic coefficient are those directly affecting the amount of waste products formed, i.e., carbohydrate concentration and trace elements, notably zinc. An interpretation of these effects is given in Chapter 7, but Table 1 shows clearly how markedly they influence efficiency of cell synthesis. In zinc-containing cultures, glucose utilization is greater at all three sugar concentrations and conversion efficiency to fumaric acid is considerably less than in the zinc-deficient cultures. With the exception of the 10 per cent concentration the growth efficiency is correspondingly greater. In the zinc cultures sugar concentration had a profound effect on growth efficiency, which is inversely proportional to the concentration of sugar. Thus from a high of 40 per cent in 2.5 per cent glucose, the growth efficiency was halved in 5 per cent glucose and dropped to a low of 6.3 per cent in 10 per cent glucose.

TABLE 1

EFFICIENCY OF CELL SYNTHESIS OF R. NIGRICANS IN RELATION TO CARBOHYDRATE CONCENTRATION AND ZINC[1]

Glucose concentration	Glucose consumed[2]		Fumaric acid conversion		Economic coefficient of cell synthesis[3]	
	Zn absent	Zn added	Zn absent	Zn added	Zn absent	Zn added
per cent	g.	g.	per cent	per cent	per cent	per cent
2.5	3.41	4.14	45.9	2.5	14.1	40.0
5.0	5.31	7.79	38.3	23.2	13.9	21.3
10.0	5.08	12.97	31.9	21.9	16.0	12.5

[1] From Foster and Waksman, 1939.
[2] Per 200 ml. in surface cultures after 7 days.
[3] $\dfrac{\text{Cell substance}}{\text{Glucose consumed}} \times 100$.

The fumaric acid-forming efficiency was just the reverse. With the lowest glucose content it was 2.5 per cent whereas with 5 per cent glucose it was 23.2 per cent. The disparity in fumaric acid conversion between no zinc and the zinc cultures was striking, especially in the low sugar range. It is apparent that fumaric acid formation took place at the expense of growth, i.e., growth efficiency is best when acid formation is lowest. In the absence of zinc, fumaric acid formation is high at all

sugar concentrations, and consequently growth efficiency is uniformly
low. The zinc effect is typical of many different metabolic types of
fungi (see pp. 167 and 273) and is named the "zinc shunt."

Not always does formation of small yields of end products reflect to
the advantage of cell synthesis, for the consumed carbohydrate can end
up in the third of the metabolic fates already mentioned: viz. carbon
dioxide. Heavy metals, minerals, and organic impurities exert effects
of this kind on the growing fungus. Most experiments in the literature are not sufficiently complete to demonstrate this important physiological effect but the data in Table 2 serve to exemplify it. In this
experiment sucrose and molasses are compared as substrates for a citric acid-producing strain of *Aspergillus wentii* under submerged conditions in an atmosphere of streaming pure oxygen on a rotary shaker.

TABLE 2

METABOLIC FATE OF PURE SUCROSE AND SUCROSE IN MOLASSES BY A. WENTII[1]

	Sugar consumed		Citric acid[2] conversion		Cell substance dry wt.		Growth efficiency[3]	
	4 days	8 days	4 days	8 days	4 days	8 days	4 days	8 days
	g.	g.	per cent	per cent	g.	g.	per cent	per cent
Molasses.......	9.45	13.93	2.9	3.9	1.69	2.34	17.7	16.8
Cane sugar.....	4.87	8.44	27.7	50.0	1.06	1.22	21.8	14.5

[1] From Karow (1942).

[2] $\dfrac{\text{Citric acid formed, g.}}{\text{Sugar used, g.}} \times 100.$

[3] $\dfrac{\text{Cell substance, g.}}{\text{Sugar used, g.}} \times 100.$

Direct measurements of CO_2 production were not made, but since citric
acid was the only dissimilation product in solution, the only other
metabolic product besides the cell substance must have been carbon
dioxide. At both incubation periods, namely 4 and 8 days, the acid
yields were very low in the molasses cultures and high in the cane sugar
cultures, yet the efficiency of cell synthesis is about equal in all cases.
The plausible explanation for the differential in acid yields is that a large
portion of the carbohydrate consumed in the molasses cultures was converted to the ultimate end product of aerobic metabolism, carbon
dioxide. Similarly, a large portion of the consumed sugar goes to carbon
dioxide, concomitantly reducing gluconic acid yields by *A. niger* when
the pH of the medium is low, as when only a small amount of $CaCO_3$ is
used as a neutralizing agent (May *et al.*, 1934). Buromsky (1913)
observed that up to seven times as much CO_2 could be formed by *A.*

niger than cell material was produced, although on the average this ratio $\left(\dfrac{CO_2}{\text{mycelium wt. yield}}\right)$, the respiratory coefficient (not to be confused with respiratory quotient, $\dfrac{CO_2}{O_2}$), was only 3 to 4.

An example of the extreme rapidity of growth of which fungi are capable is given by the rate of growth of *Penicillium chrysogenum* under good aeration and agitation conditions and in a very rich nutrient medium. These ideal environmental circumstances are most nearly approximated during the production of penicillin on an industrial scale, and in a typical production medium consisting of 2 per cent corn steep liquor solids, 3 per cent lactose and 1 per cent $CaCO_3$, the weight yield of dry cell material is high, amounting to 23 g./liter (Tanner *et al.*, 1945). This is about the average in the penicillin industry. In other cases, with *P. notatum* 832 the exceptionally high dry weight yield of 48 g./liter has been achieved in a corn steep medium containing readily available carbohydrate. Growth becomes so thick that the whole culture becomes virtually jellylike. Further increase in dry weight is almost impossible because of the mechanical difficulty of making oxygen accessible to the cells throughout the gruel-like mass, even if excess nutrients are available. It is very likely that this figure is very near the maximum possible in submerged fungus cultures. Most other mycelial weight yield figures in the literature are much lower, having been obtained in experiments which were not favorable to most efficient growth and were obtained incidental to the study of certain biochemical processes, usually organic acid formation. Generally these have been in synthetic carbohydrate-mineral medium, without complex mixtures of natural organic materials; as seen above, this usually means relatively restricted growth, especially where high yields of acids are involved. For example, under good aeration conditions, the cell material synthesized in submerged production of lactic acid by *Rhizopus oryzae* was 5.9 per cent of the sugar consumed (Ward *et al.*, 1938), of gluconic acid by *A. niger*, 7.1 per cent (Moyer *et al.*, 1937). By far the larger amount of the sugar consumed in these cases was converted to organic acids. Physical and nutrient environment conducive to maximum cell material synthesis are just as specific as those for the production of a particular metabolic product, but apparently no experimentation has been directly concerned with the specific objective of maximum mycelial weight yields such as has been done with food yeast.

In surface cultures, regardless of the medium and other physical conditions, the weight yields per volume of liquid obviously depend on the surface-depth distribution of the culture liquid. Theoretically the thinnest liquid layer will give the highest yields, at least in the shortest time. Shallow layers reduce diffusion limitations and anaerobic metabolism, and lead to maximum conversion of substrate carbohydrate into mold surface growth. With any given liquid depth and culture vessel, the mycelium yields will vary with the nutrient conditions, and in general are subject to the same influences typical of submerged cultures. Under the usual conditions of laboratory cultivation where liquid depth runs between 2 and 4 cm., surprisingly high conversion efficiencies and high weight yields per liter of medium are obtainable. The average yield of twenty-four species of Aspergilli and Penicillia was 24.1 g./liter of synthetic medium, with a high of 40.4 g. in the case of *Aspergillus carbonarius* (Pruess *et al.*, 1934), while in a glucose-malt sprout medium the average was 29.2 g./liter with a high of 50.3 g./liter for *A. carbonarius*.

In shallow pans (56 × 91.5 × 5 cm.) 41.5 g. of *Penicillium javanicum* per liter of 20 per cent glucose medium was obtained with sugar consumption of 1830 g., a conversion efficacy of 24.2 per cent. This compares favorably with conversion efficiencies of submerged cultures, but of course the time is much longer. A clue to the high yields may be obtained from the fact that only 8.0 per cent of the sugar consumed was diverted to citric acid, the only organic acid produced (Ward *et al.*, 1935). The surface growth (dried) from a square meter of medium in a shallow pan weighed approximately 800 g.

Currie (1917) studied the fate of sucrose in surface cultures of citric acid-producing strains of *A. niger* as represented by CO_2, oxalic and citric acids, and mycelium produced. Particularly striking from his data is the large proportion of the sucrose converted into CO_2 by the six different strains studied, and under all the different nutrient conditions. In most of the cases 30 per cent of the sucrose-C consumed could be accounted as CO_2—C, and in one case the value was 50.8 per cent. A high of 52 per cent in growth efficiency has been achieved with *A. niger* in an optimal mineral solution, particularly with respect to trace metals (Steinberg, 1942a). This appears to be about the highest recorded. In all likelihood there appears to be no great difference in growth conversion efficiencies of fungi in surface and in submerged cultures under optimum conditions, although in the latter all processes are greatly accelerated.

In another of Currie's cultures 0.4 g. dry mycelial weight was obtained from 1.41 g. sucrose, a growth conversion efficiency of 33.8 per cent. The CO_2—C produced in this case corresponded to 38.3 per cent of the sucrose-C, and as one might expect, total organic acids formed was among the lowest of the twenty treatments studied. In a parallel culture the CO_2—C amounted to only 12.4 per cent of the sugar carbon used. The data provide striking exemplification of the fact that the end-products of metabolism, namely organic acids, CO_2, and cell material can be varied at will, within wide limits, by strain selection and cultural conditions. It should be remembered that total weight yields of all the products of metabolism always will exceed the amount of sugar consumed. This is because nitrogen and other minerals are utilized in addition to sugar and converted into cell material, and furthermore because molecular oxygen is utilized in the oxidation processes involving CO_2 and carboxylic acids.

CARBON BALANCES

Balances between substrate consumed and products formed are best expressed in terms of carbon content of the respective substances. A detailed carbon balance for a high-yielding citric acid strain of *A. niger* gives (Wells *et al.*, 1936) the following typical figures: growth efficiency (economic coefficient), 6.6 per cent; CO_2—C from glucose——C, 12.4 per cent; weight conversion yield of citric acid from glucose, 73.0 per cent. The amount of CO_2 produced has an important bearing on the theoretical aspects of the mechanism of citric acid formation (see Chapter 12).

Steinberg (1942b) coined the term "carbon utilization factor" to express efficiency of utilization of substrate. It is the dry weight mycelium yield per gram of carbon in the substrate supplied. Obviously, unless it is ascertained that all the substrate is consumed, or a measure made of the amount consumed, this factor is a fallacious criterion of efficiency; an organism may use only a small portion of the substrate, but very efficiently, and would have therefore a low carbon utilization factor. On the other hand it is a useful overall expression of the relative utilizability of various substrates under one set of conditions. Of 120 different carbon compounds tested on *A. niger*, all were poor sources of carbon supply except the following (with carbon utilization factors): D-glucose, 1.43; D-mannose, 1.46; D-fructose, 1.38; L-sorbose, 1.26; and D-xylose.

The most detailed and comprehensive carbon balance yet made on fungi, including methods of analysis, are those of Birkinshaw *et al.* in Raistrick's monograph (1931). Table 3 contains samples of analyses made, selected from some 240 different fungi belonging to the following genera: Aspergillus (46 species), Penicillium (44 species), Gliocladium, Scopulariopsis, Paecilomyces, Fusarium (23 species), Sordaria, Chaetomium, Botrytis, Ustilago (2 species), Eidamia (2 species), Sporotrichum (2 species), Trichoderma (2 species), Cephalothecium, Cladosporium (5 species), Helminthosporium (6 species), Heterosporium (2 species), Alternaria (3 species), Fumago (2 species), Clasterosporium (2 species), Rhacodium, Stysanus, Epicoccum (2 species).

Every organism, save two, converted more carbon of the glucose

TABLE 3

Carbon Balance Sheets for Selected Fungi[1]

	Penicillium chrysogenum Ad 11	P. pfefferianium series Ad 74	P. spiculosporium [Ad 101]	Aspergillus clavatus Ac 86	Fusarium solani var. minus Ag 83	F. sambucinum Ag 70
Incubation, days...........	47	77	24	41	51	45
Carbon balance sheet						
Carbon in solution (start)....	4.952	4.944	4.851	4.901	4.901	5.018
Carbon in H₂SO₄.............	0.001	↓0.002	0.022	0.022	0.005	0.034
Carbon in CO₂.............	1.675	......	1.638	1.913	1.204	1.617
Carbon in mycelium........	1.024	0.887	0.181	0.347	0.430	0.208
Carbon in solution (end)...	2.176	1.655	2.757	2.512	3.175	2.974
Carbon accounted for........	4.876	......	4.598	4.796	4.814	4.883
Carbon accounted for per cent	98.5	......	95.7	97.8	98.2	96.3
Analysis of Solution						
Carbon in residual glucose....	0.069	0.252	0.134	0.009	1.948	0.129
Carbon in CO₂ in solution....	nil	nil	0.020	0.007	0.005	0.013
Carbon in volatile acids......	nil	0.002	nil	0.009	0.212	0.032
Carbon in non-volatile acids..	0.560	0.937	0.094	0.089	0.067	0.125
Carbon in volatile neutral compounds.............	0.004	0.036	2.381	2.064	0.488	2.464
Carbon in synthetic compounds[2]	0.089	0.212	0.003	0.151	0.144	0.104
Total carbon accounted for...	0.682	1.439	2.632	2.329	2.864	2.867
Total carbon in solution.....	2.176	1.655	2.757	2.512	3.175	2.974
Carbon unaccounted for[3].....	1.494	0.216	0.125	0.183	0.311	0.107
Residual glucose						
Glucose (by polarimeter) per cent...................	0.060	0.099	0.060	0.004	1.040	0.029
Glucose (Shaffer-Hartman) per cent.................	0.035	0.126	......	0.005	0.974	0.064
Glucose (Wood-Ost) per cent.	......	......	0.067	......	1.052	
Glucose (by alkaline iodine)..	0.091	0.144	0.146	0.087	1.035	
Acids						
Titration (N/1 acid) ml......	8.2	29.1	1.5	2.6	4.8	1.9
Volatile acids (N/1 acid) ml..	nil	0.17	nil	1.23	9.07	1.52
Barium salts (weight) g......	0.018	0.029	0.064	0.134	1.089	0.133
Calcium salts (weight) g......	1.803	3.474	0.398	0.332	0.329	0.689
Volume of oxygen absorbed ml......................	2.851	......	7.69	1.445	1.557	0.641
Respiration coefficient.......	1.10	......	4.03	2.48	1.45	4.74
Mycelium(weight) g........	2.151	1.726	0.392	0.649	0.849	0.375
Mycelium (carbon) per cent..	47.6	51.4	46.2	53.9	50.6	55.3

[1] From Raistrick *et al.* (1931).

[2] Non-volatile neutral compounds, such as proteins, peptones, etc.

[3] Non-volatile neutral compounds, such as polyhydric alcohols and majority of non-volatile neutral compounds.

substrate into carbon dioxide than they synthesized into cell material. *Penicillium spiculosporium* was the highest in this respect, producing 13.9 times as much CO_2 carbon as mycelium carbon, and for the majority (64 per cent) of the organisms studied, the ratio was greater than 2. The low exceptions were *Aspergillus nidulans* Ac9 and *A. sydowi* Ac29, having ratios of 0.81 and 0.99 respectively.

In general the highest CO_2 ratios are associated with high respiratory quotients $\left(\dfrac{CO_2 \text{ produced}}{O_2 \text{ uptake}}\right)$ and with a high carbon content in the "volatile neutral compounds" fraction. This relationship between the latter two fractions is logical and is based upon the production of ethanol and CO_2 simultaneously by the well-known mechanism of decarboxylation of pyruvic acid without, however, the absorption of oxygen usually accompanying respiration and growth. Consequently, as Table 2 in Chapter 9 shows, the relative magnitudes of the carbon in the volatile neutral fraction (ethanol) and the respiratory quotient parallel one another. Various Fusaria, generally known to be active alcohol producers, are characterized therefore by the highest R.Q's, the highest being 6.45.

Carbon balances can characterize the general type of metabolic activity of a fungus, especially in relation to assimilation (mycelial synthesis), CO_2 production, and types of metabolic products. Table 3 illustrates how helpful analyses of this kind can be in the preliminary estimation of the fate of the consumed substrate in different fungus cultures. The data for the two Fusaria exemplify the main biochemical characteristic of all members of this genus in producing large amounts of ethyl alcohol (neutral volatile fraction), and, concomitantly, relatively large amounts of CO_2, resulting in respiratory quotients substantially greater than unity. On the other hand, this character is also shown by organisms of other genera, ordinarily not associated with alcohol production, namely, *Penicillium spiculosporium* and *Aspergillus clavatus*, which, as judged from the neutral volatile fraction, are as active in this respect as most Fusaria. *Fusarium solani* var. *minus* is distinguished from *F. sambucinum* by the high volatile acid fraction, also reflected in the high yield of calcium salts obtained by precipitation with 80 per cent ethanol. *Penicillium chrysogenum* is given as an example of a culture whose products are not chiefly the usually encountered volatile neutral compounds, volatile acids, or non-volatile acids, but which produces large amounts of substances in the "carbon unaccounted for" fraction. Often this fraction contains substantial amounts of polyhydric substances like mannitol, glycerol, polysaccharides, etc.

It is evident that carbon balances make possible the characterization of the general qualitative metabolism of a fungus. Unless provided for, interpretation of results must always be conditioned by the fact that the data obtained represent the activities of only a particular strain, and at one stage of incubation, and on one medium and under one set of environmental conditions. One of the most important principles of mold metabolism is the inconstancy of the metabolic activities of fungi, and this inconstancy is predicated upon those very four factors: namely, marked alterations can be induced at will by different strains of the same species or even among progeny in one culture, by variations in the medium composition, by environmental circumstances, and by analyses obtained at different stages of growth.

A true biochemical evaluation of a particular fungus can be secured only by study of its metabolism under different conditions. A few selected key conditions, preferably the extremes and one intermediate of any one factor, are sufficient to picture the mold as a metabolic entity. For example, the nitrogen source and the trace element nutrition can induce such extremes in the metabolism of a fungus that examination of the data would prejudice the observer against associating the two sets of data with one organism. Again, it is a common experience that metabolic products formed and accumulating during the early stages of growth are later destroyed or further transformed, and that the metabolism and products of an organism while nitrogen and minerals are abundantly available, as during the early stages of growth, are quite different from the later stages when the medium becomes depleted in these elements.

ENERGETICS OF MOLD METABOLISM

Thermodynamically, growth of fungi, like other biological systems, is exothermic in an overall sense. The phrase "in an overall sense" is used advisedly, for simultaneous with the exothermic reactions are endothermic reactions, i.e., those requiring energy in order to take place. Such reactions are classified roughly as "synthetic" reactions, or rather, the reactions of synthesis. In general, exothermic reactions in biology are of two types: oxidation and hydrolysis by phosphatases. They are the degradative reactions. The energy liberated by the exothermic reactions meets two fates. A portion is furnished to motivate the endothermic reactions, and because the efficiency in this transfer is imperfect, some energy is always converted into the second form, i.e., is lost as heat (entropy).

The latter is an invariable accompaniment of physiological processes, including microbial growth, and under some conditions is dramatic. In ordinary laboratory work, the small size of the culture vessels rapidly dissipates the heat to the atmosphere and heat generation is rarely noticed. Where heat transfer is slow, as in the huge volumes of culture handled in tanks in industrial fermentations of all kinds, the heat evolution from exothermic reactions would raise the temperature of the tanks to a point where the process eventually would be self-pasteurized, were it not for artificial cooling. Another conspicuous example is the self-heating of manure or moist hay or other decomposing organic matter (composts) stacked in piles. The organic matter itself is a good insulator and the heat generated by microbial activity in the interior of pile (within a few inches of the surface) accumulates till it is virtually self-sterilizing at 70–80°C., where only thermophiles can survive. The accumulated heat in the interior may burn a person's hand if it penetrates deep enough. Some of the heat does, of course, escape, and the hot air, being virtually saturated with moisture, creates the steam seen rising from such piles on cold days; the cold air condenses the hot water vapor.

As mentioned on the first page of this chapter, the economic coefficient, (first formulated by the plant physiologist W. Pfeffer) is often used as a criterion of an organism's efficiency of utilization of substrate. It is strictly a weight conversion, and to a considerable extent it is empirical in that it is based solely on the main carbon source, usually glucose or sucrose, and does not allow for the entrance into the mold mycelium of nitrogen, other minerals, chemical uptake of water and of oxygen during respiration. The economic coefficient has been found in the case of *A. niger* to be independent of growth temperature over the range 22–38°C., the value remaining an average of 0.44 (Terroine and Wurmser, 1921). Tamiya (1932) formulated the "synthesis quotient" as a measure of conversion efficiency $\left(\dfrac{\text{g. mycelium}}{\text{g. C source respired to } CO_2}\right)$.

A much more accurate representation is that of thermodynamic efficiency, which is based on the actual calorific changes involved, i.e., how much of the energy (calories) in the substrate actually ended up as mold mycelium. These values can be obtained directly by combustion in a calorimeter. Energy lost as heat during growth can be measured by cultivating the organism in a calorimeter or by combustion measurements at the point of maximum growth: heat cals. = cals. in uninoculated medium minus (cals. in mycelium + cals. in culture filtrate).

The principal investigations along these lines with molds have been by the French investigators, Terroine and Wurmser (1921; 1922a, b, c; and the Japanese Tamiya (1932, 1933). They brought these thermal ideas, developed many years earlier by the physiologist Max Rubner, to bear on mold metabolism and adopted the Rubner coefficient:

$$\frac{\text{Heat of combustion of mycelium synthesized (g.} \times \text{kcals./g.)}}{\text{Heat of combustion of total carbon source consumed (g.} \times \text{kcals./g.)}}$$

This expression connotes conversion of the carbon source into mycelium and CO_2 exclusively. Tamiya (1932) determined this energy coefficient for *Aspergillus oryzae* cultivated on a variety of different carbon sources:

Rubner Coefficient

Glucose	0.48
Sucrose	.48
Dihydroxyacetone	.43
Glycerol	.37
Ethyl alcohol	.28

Terroine and Wurmser (1922b) found that glucose, levulose, sucrose, maltose, arabinose, and xylose all were utilized with about the same efficiency, namely in the range 0.41–0.46, and that different amounts and kinds of nitrogen in the medium did not alter the efficiency very greatly. In an extension of this work to additional carbon sources (Terroine and Bonnet, 1930), of the different 3-carbon compounds tested, dihydroxy-acetone was utilized most efficiently and though this was ascribed to the presence of a carbonyl group, it must be borne in mind that this substance and its equilibrium product, glyceraldehyde, are key intermediates in intermediary metabolism and may well therefore be assimilated directly and therefore more efficiently than compounds like glycerol and lactic acid.

One notices that the fewer the carbon atoms in the substrate, the less efficient its utilization, and this is a general phenomenon. This is due in large measure to the fact that some of the molecules have to be oxidized entirely to provide energy for assimilation of others, or intermediate building blocks (Bausteine) derived from them. In the case of longer carbon chains, particularly hexoses, the energy-liberating oxidation processes actually generate the intermediate blocks to be assimilated later.

The heat of combustion of a gram of mold mycelium runs in the neighborhood of 5 kcals. This figure naturally is subject to appreciable variation depending on the composition of the mycelium, which, as shown in Chapter 3, is subject to wide fluctuations. For example, a mycelium high in lipide content will have a higher heat of combustion because of the high calorie content of fats (9.3 kcals./g.). Terroine and Wurmser, and Tamiya use 4.8 kcals./g. to represent the average heat of combustion of mycelium obtained in the ordinary manner for common strains of fungi. That is, mycelium was harvested when all the sugar was consumed; cultivation in excess sugar would lead to high lipide mycelium.

Because the specific calorie content of mold mycelium (4.8 kcals./g.) is higher than the glucose from which it is derived (3.76 kcals./g.) the efficiency of energy utilization will always be appreciably higher than the economic coefficient. Thus where the latter figure was found to be 0.44 (Terroine and Wurmser, 1922a) the efficiency utilization of the available energy in 1 g. of glucose was $\dfrac{0.44 \times 4.8 \text{ kcals.} \times 100}{3.76 \text{ kcals.}} = 56$ per cent. Even this is not the true value because it assumes perfect conversion of the gram of glucose into mycelium and CO_2. As a matter of fact, in this experiment combustion of the medium revealed that small amounts of soluble products were present so that on the basis of carbon source actually consumed by the fungus (i.e., which disappeared from solution) the efficiency of energy utilization is raised to 59.4 per cent. Tamiya (1932) gives figures of 1 g. *Aspergillus oryzae* mycelium synthesized from 1.467 g. glucose, or $\dfrac{4.8 \text{ kcals.}}{1.467 \times 3.76} \times 100 = 87$ per cent thermodynamic efficiency, which in reality probably should be a little higher yet because combustibles in solution were not included. This figure appears exceptionally high and warrants confirmation before one unreservedly accepts the possibility of such high efficiency, especially since Molliard's (1922) value of 55.2 per cent checks that of Terroine and Wurmser. For ethyl alcohol the figures were 0.986 g. → 1 g. mycelium: $\dfrac{4.8}{0.986 \times 7.08 \text{ kcals./g.}}$ $\times 100 = 69$ per cent. This bears out the observation made above, that the organism utilizes alcohol considerably less efficiently than sugars.

The above data based on rather complete combustion facts, in themselves still do not represent the absolute efficiency of the organism in relation to the synthesis of cell material, for, as Terroine and Wurmser (1922a) stressed, the energy which the organism makes use of is not devoted wholly to synthesis of mycelium. A part of the energy is consumed in the maintenance of the mycelium already synthesized. The relative amounts directed through these channels varies according to conditions but, in general, the proportion utilized for synthesis of mycelium depends on the rate of growth; for maintenance energy the value is proportional to the amount of mycelium at any given time. According to these French authors the true efficiency coefficient is independent of maintenance energy. The energy value expended on synthesis alone is obtained by subtracting the kcals. of maintenance energy from the kcal. differential between the substrate consumed and the combustion value of all products (mycelium and soluble products). The expression for the absolute efficiency of the organism is therefore:

$$\text{Absolute efficiency} = \frac{\text{Energy in mycelium formed}}{\text{Energy expended for synthesis of mycelium}}$$

and it connotes the energy yield going into growth only. In the above cited experiments of Terroine and Wurmser for *A. niger*, the absolute efficiency was 68 per cent, a rather high degree of efficiency but of the same order of magnitude as that found for the growth of hogs. The remaining 32 per cent of the energy is, of course, dissipated as heat.

Tamiya has proposed that the measure of this heat energy under controlled conditions is indicative of the relative efficiencies of utilization of various substrates. This expression, which he calls "trophic heat coefficient" is the amount of heat (kcals.) liberated during the synthesis of 1 g. of mycelium under good aerobic conditions. (Anaerobiosis leads to incomplete utilization of carbon source.) In the case of glucose and alcohol cited above, the trophic heat coefficients were 0.72 and 2.18 kcals. respectively:

Glucose consumed = 5.52 kcal.	Alcohol consumed = 6.98 kcal.
1 g. mycelium = 4.8	1 g. mycelium = 4.8
Trophic coefficient 0.72	2.18

Terroine and Wurmser calculated the maintenance energy from the amount of respiratory CO_2 liberated: ml. $CO_2 \times 0.005$ = kcal. of glucose respired. In five experiments an average of 8.2 ml. CO_2 was liberated per gram dry weight mycelium per hour. They also give mathematical formulas to derive values for energy of synthesis vs. energy of maintenance.

According to Tamiya (1933), most of the energy in young growing cultures is devoted to synthesis, gradually going over to maintenance energy with age. Thus, during the active development of *Aspergillus melleus*, 85 per cent of the liberated energy was directed to synthesis, whereas in a 50 hour-old culture 40 per cent of the energy liberated by respiration was devoted to synthetic reactions and 60 per cent to maintenance. In still older cultures all the energy went for maintenance and none for synthesis. From data of Terroine and Wurmser, Tamiya computed that 80 per cent of the energy liberated by a surface pad of *A. niger* went to synthesis, and 20 per cent for maintenance. This subject is treated in further detail by Tamiya and Yamagutchi (1933), who point out that growth is closely linked with aerobic respiration, hence calculations based on CO_2 evolution are subject to some error.

RESPONSE VARIATION

The unique and tremendous response differences, both quantitative and qualitative, obtainable with any single fungus culture as a result of imposed cultural conditions are common experiences and well known to the microbiologist. This subject has been touched upon earlier in this chapter. It is not worthwhile going into specific details here, for numerous examples are available elsewhere in this book, and in this chapter it is more the fundamental cause we are concerned with than the effects. However, for the reader's orientation there may be cited biochemical characters such as amount and composition of cell matter synthesized, formation of extracellular enzymes, production of low molecular weight synthetic compounds (e.g., antibiotics, vitamins, pigments, etc.), accumulation of sugar split products (carboxylic acids), carbon dioxide evolution, and so on. Generally all of these are in balanced interrelation, a change in one usually being reflected by changes in others.

The alterations in cultural conditions which can induce most significant metabolism changes are often so slight that they are exceedingly difficult if not impossible to control fully, despite rigorous precautions. This accounts for the difficulties in reproducibility of results between laboratories employing identical cultures, and even between different trials in the same laboratory.

This type of physiological variation is to be distinguished from the genetic variation causing physiological differences between different individual cultures (discussed in Chapter 5). It relates to the extreme susceptibility of the physiological potentialities of any one fungus culture or spore population—which because of the enormous number of cells, may be considered collectively to function as an individual—to relatively slight alterations in environmental factors. We may designate this as "response variation," of which several instances are included above. The term "physiological variation" is often employed, but it does not have the connotation that the former term does in excluding genetic phenomena and in limiting the meaning to environmental sensitivity.

EFFICIENCY OF CELL SYNTHESIS OF MOLDS IN RELATION TO NATURAL ENVIRONMENT

It has already been amply demonstrated that the metabolism of any given mold culture is dependent upon environmental conditions, and that it can be made to fluctuate between extremely wide limits so that the change may actually take on the appearance of a qualitative difference. Indeed, it is a common event to have an organism produce no detectable single metabolic product, and yet with different cultural conditions, produce that very substance abundantly. Finally, there is the situation in which, on the one hand, one kind of product is produced, and, on the other, a totally different product.

What is the explanation of such behavior? While no single interpretation may provide the full story, it seems as though sufficient experimental and circumstantial evidence is available to provide a start on this intriguing question. One of the major metabolic differences between molds and bacteria is that there are no anaerobic molds, either obligate or facultative. Indeed, there is general concurrence with the idea that molds are highly oxidative organisms. This is not to say that molds will not metabolize carbohydrates anaerobically (fermentation), but rather that this is accomplished by preformed cell material and growth at the expense of fermentative metabolism exclusively apparently does not occur. In this connection see Istin (1947) on yeast and Emerson and Cantino (1948) on the mold Blastocladia. It is questionable if molds can develop (*i.e.*, *grow*) at a significant rate in the complete absence of molecular oxygen.

The possession of strong glycolytic mechanisms by many molds is, as seen below, the outstanding metabolic characterization of many of these organisms. On the other hand, possession of strongly aerobic metabolism has a profound implication for the economy of the mold organism insofar as utilization of its available energy source goes. It means that innately the organism has the ability to utilize its substrate for growth and cell synthesis, more efficiently due to the fact that aerobic respiratory processes are the most efficient for liberating and utilizing the energy of the substrate (which we shall assume is carbohydrate) for multifarious cellular activities. Considering the conditions prevailing in nature, such as those in the soil, the natural habitat for molds, the idea of organisms possessing a type of metabolism which enables them to utilize substrate efficiently and build up as much cell material as possible seems not unlikely.

Due to the rather frugal and precarious nutritional environment prevailing in this natural habitat of molds, it appears not unreasonable that they have become adapted to survival and existence under threshold nutritional conditions by their high efficiency of utilization of the limited energy source available.

The nutritional level of the soil must at most times be very low, except during those relatively isolated and sporadic periods when fresh plant or animal residues are available. Even then in neutral soils the fast-growing bacterial, and to some extent actinomycetal, population accounts for the utilization of the bulk of the readily decomposable organic materials. The fungi come in, then, as secondary invaders, utilizing the more resistant components of the organic matter and the remains of other microbial cells. Thus, through the competition with the rest of the soil population for available foodstuffs and the slow utilization of resistant organic fractions in the soil, the molds may be thought of as having become adapted through natural selection (probably preceded by mutation) to a highly effective economy in their prevailing environment, e.g., a low level or marginal nutritional state with respect to available energy and carbon source. Such an effectively economic metabolism might account for the survival of and the high number of fungi occurring in normal soils. This superior character could, then, be interpretable as a consequence of the failure of the organisms to waste energy in the form of products of anaerobic or aerobic metabolism, giving the efficient molds survival advantage over inefficient ones, which eventually would become extinct.

The important consequence of the efficiency concept is that maximum efficiency of energy utilization by the mold is attained only when the substrate is converted entirely into only two products, namely, the components of protoplasm and the inevitable CO_2. There is no evidence that molds form any dissimilation products under normal soil conditions, and in line with the foregoing, the only reasonable conclusion is that molds in soil oxidize these substrates entirely to CO_2 and H_2O, aside from that relatively high fraction converted into cell material. This concept probably has general application to the majority of aerobic microorganisms under the nutritional conditions prevailing in soils most of the time—complete conversion of substrate to CO_2, H_2O and cell material. Exceptions would be those relative few cases where split products of certain complex naturally-occurring compounds would accumulate. Such substances could not be attacked by the organism under any circumstances, and are not to be considered as dissimilation products, inasmuch as usually they consist of unchanged portions of the substrate molecules, rather than products arising from the substrate through transformation brought about by intermediary metabolism; in most cases they resemble the original substrate molecule. As an example, one might cite the oxidation of the side chain of an aromatic compound, leaving the ring structure intact. In any case some organism is certain to be found which would decompose the compound completely.

The inefficiency of anaerobic organisms in the utilization of substrate is a consequence of their always leaving a portion of the substrate in the form of metabolic reduction products, or, expressed differently, they leave the major portion of the energy of the substrate in the form of organic metabolism products. Obviously, with less energy obtained, the growth efficiency is reduced. The same line of reasoning holds true in the case of metabolic products produced by molds as a result of aerobic consumption of carbohydrate, namely, organic acids and other excretion products. Energy left in the form of accumulated products of any kind, actually means reduced efficiency of energy utilization up to that stage. In most cases the products may be further attacked after the original substrate is depleted, and their energy utilized (see page 182).

OVERFLOW AND SHUNT METABOLISM

Why then do molds produce large amounts of metabolic products other than cell material and CO_2 from sugar, namely, organic acids, carbohydrates, etc., when cultivated under laboratory or industrial conditions? The best explanation seems to be that the metabolism of the organism becomes deranged. It becomes, so to speak, pathological. This pathological behavior is a direct result of the influence of abnormal environmental conditions.

Of greatest importance is the carbohydrate concentration. Invariably laboratory media for cultivation of fungi contain carbohydrates in concentrations far exceeding those the organism ever would encounter in nature and to which the mold is adapted for maximum efficiency of utilization. This luxury of excess sugar sets off a chain of events culminating in faulty metabolism of the sugar as indicated by only partial utilization of the sugar molecule, leaving incompletely oxidized products accumulating in the medium, usually indicated as organic acids, although other products may also accumulate outside and inside the cells. It would appear that the enzyme mechanisms normally involved in complete oxidation of the substrate become saturated, and the substrate molecules then are excreted and accumulate as such, or they are shunted to secondary or subsidiary enzyme systems which are able to effect only relatively minor changes in the substance, which then accumulates in its transformed state. The latter mechanism is by far the most common. The limiting or bottleneck enzyme systems are never those concerned with the initial stages of carbohydrate dissimilation, but are those which act on the substrate only after it has been brought through the stage of split products. When the rate of utilization of the original sugar is limiting, obviously subsequent enzymes in the chain can accommodate all the raw product available to them in the normal way; no diversion results, and no accumulation of dissimilation products ensues. However, when the rate of splitting the carbohydrate chain into smaller split products proceeds faster than the subsequent enzymes can handle them, a metabolic shunt occurs, resulting in accumulation of products, or increase in other products produced only in small amounts normally. The inability to metabolize intermediates rapidly, which then are diverted through abnormal channels, has many analogies in general biochemistry. For example, in yeast fermentation the enzymes normally giving rise to ethanol can, by chemical treatment, be made limiting or inoperative so that triose from sugar is diverted to glycerol instead of ethanol. In animal as well as microbial metabolism, carbohydrate nutrition above that required for basal metabolism is divered to fat, which represents deposits of condensed sugar split products which accumulate as fat when the normal oxidation enzymes are surfeited.

In fact, the probability is good that metabolic shunts actually are the basis of the widespread practice of securing increased intensity of certain biochemical properties on the part of various organisms through mutation techniques, irradiation, chemical, etc. Especially has this objective been sought in connection with biosynthesis of industrially important compounds—penicillin, streptomycin, itaconic acid, and others. Spectacular success has been achieved with penicillin, and some moderate success with itaconic acid. A logical interpretation for these yield increments is that genetically controlled enzyme systems active in normal cells, and which offer an outlet for some of the intermediary compounds of the cell, are eliminated in the mutants, making proportionally more of the intermediates available to the other intact enzyme mechanisms, one of which, on a random basis, happens to be of interest to the investigator (see Chapter 6). It would be difficult to account for increased synthetic powers on any other basis.

The best evidence in support of metabolic shunts is that, other factors remaining constant, the enzyme saturation can be demonstrated simply by increasing the concentration of carbohydrate. In dilute sugar media (from 0 to 0.5–2.0 per cent sugar depending on conditions) molds usually will yield no organic acids whatsoever during the phase of active growth. This is an experiment approximating the nutrition of molds in their natural surroundings: adequate minerals of all kinds, sufficient utilizable N, and a very low C/N ratio due to very low carbohydrate supply. Results from such experiments may be adduced as comparable to the happenings in soil environment. Next comes a sugar concentration range where very small amounts of metabolic products will accumulate, and this becomes larger in proportion to increased sugar concentration up to a maximum of 8 to 15 per cent for most fungi. This parallel accumulation of acids usually is interpreted simply as the effect of carbohydrate concentration. Actually it is more a measure of sugar split products in excess of those required to saturate the enzyme systems involved in synthesis of protoplasm and in the oxidation to CO_2. Essentially it is "overflow" metabolism.

It is evident that the metabolism of the mold in a culture may be quantitatively as well as qualitatively different as the sugar concentration falls during consumption. The final balance of products merely represents the resultant of all the changing processes. The validity of Kluyver and Perquin's (1933) observation that clearcut biochemical evaluation of a mold can be made only in a high sugar concentration and for such a short time that the sugar concentration does not change materially is still a fundamental of mold metabolism.

If conditions are now imposed which alter the content of or capacity of the bottleneck enzymes, it might be expected that corresponding alterations in the amount of split products diverted through shunt reactions would take place. This is actually the case, and experimentally it is possible to vary the intensity of the shunt reactions within wide limits, by controlling key enzyme systems. The effect of sugar concentration has already been discussed, and other evidence supports the idea.

An easy demonstration of these points involves the so-called resting cell technique, also referred to as replacement method (Pilzdecke), incidentally, first used by Pasteur. For example, under certain conditions of cultivation where low sugar concentration is present in the medium, *Rhizopus nigricans* or almost any other mold, will grow rapidly and synthesize an abundance of cell material and form much CO_2. Careful tests on the culture filtrate fails to reveal the presence of even traces of organic acid. If this "pregrown" mycelium is now placed in a solution containing the same concentration of sugar as originally present in the medium but, except for some $CaCO_3$ as a neutralizing agent, containing no other nutrient material, large quantities of an organic acid, in this case fumaric acid, are formed quickly and accumulate in amounts comprising a substantial portion of the sugar consumed. That is, the identical cells which formed no acids from sugar during growth now form acids abundantly. The situation here is a logical development of the theme given above. During the growth stage, with an abundance of all nutrients essential for the building up of cell substance, the sugar split products are combined with nitrogen, sulfur, and minerals and built up into larger structural and functional components of cell material. In the replacement experiment with sugar solution, the sugar split products cannot be further converted into protoplasmic materials in conjunction with nitrogen, sulfur, and minerals because the latter are absent. Unable to be consumed through normal synthetic or growth channels, the split products are diverted and partially oxidized through supplementary enzyme systems, which happen to give rise to organic acids and, as seen later, possibly other materials. Some CO_2 also is always formed, and doubtless some is converted to intracellular carbohydrate or its equivalent via oxidative assimilation.

One recalls in this connection that the amount of organic acid formed per gram of carbohydrate consumed during the early stages of growth of molds always is less than that formed in a corresponding period during later stages of incubation. Generally, only near the end of maximum growth, i.e., when cell synthesis begins to slow down, are maximum conversion yields obtained, due to diversion of carbohydrate dissimilation through acid formation channels.

A further striking example in support of the metabolic shunt is provided by the elegant experiment of Mitchell and Houlahan (1946) in which the enzyme normally acting upon a metabolic intermediate is removed entirely by destroying the gene responsible for synthesis of that enzyme, i.e., creation of a mutant differing from the normal parent only by lack of one specific enzyme. A mutant strain of the mold *Neurospora crassa* was obtained which could not synthesize adenine due to lack of the enzyme essential for the conversion of adenine precursor to adenine. Blocked in its normal outlet, the precursor is now disposed of in a manner apparently totally foreign to a normal strain—it undergoes polymerization to form a purple pigment which accumulates in the mycelium and medium. To all appearances the organism has acquired a character, yet in reality it is merely forced to use an otherwise latent enzyme system.

Based on the foregoing, one of the best ways to test the latent ability of an organism to accumulate dissimilation products, is to provide it with excess sugar or other substrate and deprive it of one or more other nutrients essential to growth. This applies, of course, only to preformed vegetative cell material. Starting from spores, no growth would occur if an essential element were omitted. One might accomplish similar results by providing only limited amounts of a certain supplementary nutrient so that it quickly becomes exhausted during early growth, then forcing sugar metabolism through the accessory metabolic channels.

Another interesting demonstration of this idea centers around the catalytic effect which trace elements exert on the efficiency of utilization of available carbohydrate by molds. Notable in this respect is zinc, and to a lesser extent iron, manganese, and copper, and possibly others. The exact mechanisms by which these elements participate in mold metabolism are not known, but their overall effects have been established many times as catalyzing the conversion of substrate into cell material (see p. 149; also Chapter 7). If a few p.p.m. zinc are added to one flask of a zinc-deficient 2 per cent carbohydrate-complete-mineral medium, another no-zinc flask of the same medium inoculated with any acid-forming mold, and the cultures analyzed after a suitable growth period of 5 to 10 days, some profound differences are apparent. The zinc-containing culture will have synthesized an abundance of mycelium meanwhile producing no organic acid, or, at most, very small amounts. The no-zinc culture gives the reverse picture, much smaller mycelium development and substantial accumulation of organic acid in the culture filtrate. Also, in the zinc culture, an appreciably large percentage of carbohydrate carbon ends up as CO_2 as compared to the no-zinc control.

The explanation of these striking differences lies in the role of zinc, presumably functioning as a coenzyme, in catalyzing the more complete oxidation and conversion of the carbohydrate into cell material. Remembering that this conversion necessitates utilization of sugar split products, it is evident that zinc functions in some way as a mediator of enzymes involved in the transformation of split products to protoplasm and that the presence of the right amount of zinc is the governing factor in these transformations. In the zinc-deficient culture the transformation enzymes can operate only inefficiently, hence the split products are diverted to organic acid-forming enzymes, i.e., the "zinc shunt" acts.

However, the fully efficient zinc enzymes, of sufficient catalytic power to handle the split products from a 2 per cent sugar medium completely, can themselves become saturated by the split products from a higher sugar concentration (5 to 10 per cent), so that overflow metabolism sets in, and considerable organic acid accumulation takes place in the presence of an amount of zinc-enzyme sufficient to repress acid formation from lower sugar concentrations.

Further experimental confirmation of the metabolic shunt origin of products in mold cultures involves artificially supplying a dose of the precursors of a particular end product during the stage of enzyme saturation, i.e., during active utilization of supra-minimal sugar concentrations. Ciusa and Brüll (1939) did this experiment, adding to cultures of *A. niger* equimolar quantities of malic and glycolic acids as citric acid precursors in accordance with one of the current schemes for the biological synthesis of citric acid, namely condensation of C_4 and C_2 acids. In every case increased citric acid yields were obtained, as high as 9.28 times the amount formed from the sugar alone, when obviously the citric acid-forming enzymes were still unsaturated and were acting on split products or derivatives diverted from other saturated oxidation or synthetic mechanisms.

Several other examples of shunt metabolism could be cited. The well-known practice of employing poisons for specific enzymes is one. This technique is such a common one that details will not be given except to emphasize that when a poison shifts the balance of products formed by a microorganism, it is in principle, effecting shunt metabolism. Normal enzymes are inhibited and subsidiary enzymes then come into play with greater intensity than otherwise. One may cite the accumulation of reduced metabolic products as an aerobic organism is deprived of oxygen. In molds the reduced product generally is ethanol, while under conditions of aeration it is not formed, or, more, often, in smaller quantities.   In the presence of oxygen, C_2 split products, if formed at all, are oxidized *in situ* to CO_2 and H_2O via flavoprotein and the cytochrome hydrogen transport system.   Deprived of this pathway, in absence of oxygen, C_2 split products function not as hydrogen donors for oxygen, but as hydrogen acceptors from triose, and become reduced to ethanol.

It is understood that shunt reactions are in reality paired reactions which depend not only on a saturated and overloaded enzyme system, but also on a second enzyme system, normally latent or subdued, whose activity becomes manifest or accentuated through the availability of overflow intermediates.   It would not be unexpected, then, to find instances where the latter enzyme system is lacking and, as a consequence, the overflow intermediate is not metabolized through a diversionary route.   One would look for the hypothetical intermediate to accumulate, inasmuch as there is no other way out.   Several examples of this type could be given.   A fine instance of this simplest kind of metabolic block occurs in a strain of *Fusarium lini* in which an induced cocarboxylase deficiency results in a retarded rate of pyruvate decarboxylation as compared to the rate of formation of this acid from carbohydrate, the pyruvate accumulating and being easily isolated from the medium. Addition of thiamine to the culture medium restores the cocarboxylase level essential for maximum efficiency of carboxylase activity, thereby eliminating the enzyme bottleneck so that pyruvate no longer piles up in the culture fluid (Wirth and Nord, 1941).

From all the foregoing it is evident that the ability to form dissimilation products is intimately linked with the processes of cell synthesis and carbon dioxide production.   Resolved into mechanisms, the final balance depends on the capacity of the oxidative and cell synthesizing enzymes in relation to the load of carbohydrate split products they have to carry.

MECHANISMS AND POSTULATED INTERMEDIATES

One of the most favored and time-honored approaches to the problem of intermediary metabolism is to feed a biochemical system a series of chemicals postulated to occur somewhere between the breakdown of the substrate and the formation of the particular end product.   If the system utilizes the added compound and produces the identical end product formed from the original substrate in reasonable yield, the added substance is considered to be a normal precursor of the endproduct in the pathway from the original substrate.   Extensive use has been made of this technique in mold metabolism, particularly in relation to mechanisms of formation of organic acids.   Almost invariably the technique has been to employ the supposed intermediate as the only source of carbon in an otherwise complete medium, inoculate the organism and test for the particular end-product in question after suitable incubation times. Generally preferred is the technique of using washed, preformed mycelium furnished with the suspected compounds alone or with accessory nutrients.

It is not the purpose of this discussion to judge the general validity or acceptability of this kind of evidence in biochemical work. However, in mold metabolism the situation is such as to warrant a few theoretical observations specificially applicable to this field. Despite rather general use of this approach in the study of any one product, be it oxalic acid, kojic acid, citric acid or others, the results so far available are diverse and so conflicting that with few exceptions it is impossible to draw decisive conclusions as to the true mechanisms in question. For example it is, on the surface, astonishing that such opposing data have been obtained pertaining to the single process of oxalic acid formation in fungi, all with the "added intermediate" technique. Thus some authors get abundant oxalate formation from acetate, others insignificant yields. Some find and propose glycolic and glyoxylic acids as midway between acetate and oxalate especially on the strength of some conversion of these two acids to oxalate. Others maintain oxalate results from a hydrolytic split of oxalacetic acid, the latter resulting from acetate condensation through the C_4-dicarboxylic acid system. Careful experiments by a different worker fail to reveal any oxalate when oxalacetate is fed to the organism; this worker excludes acetate from any role in the process and postulates instead of hydrolytic fission of 2-keto gluconic acid to yield oxalate. Others believe that acetate is split out of initially formed citric acid, and next are the experiments in which oxalate is formulated as originating by dehydrogenation of two moles of formic acid. Finally no one has offered any mechanism for the extraordinarily high yields of oxalate obtainable from peptone solutions. One must remember, too, there is considerable arbitrariness as to whether a yield of the endproduct is of sufficient magnitude to warrant assertion that the tested substance actually is a precursor. In some cases conversion yields of only a few per cent have sufficed to incriminate certain precursors, and yet other workers believe that the bulk of the precursor should eventuate as the product, else the reaction is a secondary side one.

Controversial results like these typify other branches of mold biochemistry. It is illogical, mainly on the basis of comparative biochemistry, to assume the existence of so many different mechanisms for the formation of a single organic acid resulting from carbohydrate breakdown. There must be a flaw in the experimental approach, and a likely one stems from the concept of shunt metabolism.

Worth reiterating here is the view expressed and implicit in the previous section that an organic acid (for example) is formed in quantity from carbohydrate only after the organism has satisfied its primary assimilatory requirements.   The precursors of organic acids are surplus over those requirements.   Now when a fungus is furnished a hypothetical precursor as the sole carbon source, the likelihood is an exceedingly strong one that a significant portion, if not the bulk of the precursor, goes into the now unsaturated assimilatory and/or respiratory channels, in which situation the precursor is no longer surplus.   And since precursors generally are compounds that would yield integral assimilation building blocks only inefficiently, a large amount of these compounds would undergo consumption and combustion to fulfill these primary needs of the organism, leaving little chance for direct conversion of precursor to product.   In such circumstances an actual precursor might be erroneously eliminated from consideration.

It is entirely conceivable that differences in results obtained hitherto by various workers may be explained by the use of different strains of A. niger, or other organisms, which, on account of strain specificity, vary quantitatively if not qualitatively in the degree and efficiency to which their assimilatory and respiratory requirements are saturated.   Strain specificity doubtless explains the prevailing confusion.

To put the experimental method on a basis consistent with theoretical concepts one must perform such experiments under conditions where the complicating assimilatory and respiratory processes are, so to speak, presaturated, and hence minimize the importance of these phenomena in the independent conversion of precursor to product.   The most logical and efficient way of doing this is to have the organism actively metabolizing carbohydrate before and during the presence of the added precursor. Consumption of precursor now should theoretically be largely via conversion to end-product.   Obviously, optimum conditions would be those where the assimilatory reactions are saturated, and the system forming the particular end-product unsaturated, so the latter can accommodate added precursor.   Hence the carbohydrate concentration should be sub-optimal for maximum product formation when tested alone; indeed, that concentration just beginning to manifest overflow metabolism by the appearance of small or moderate yields of product might be the best one to employ for the precursor additions.

Adoption of such a technique, or at least the principles involved, might provide the means for obtaining more consistent results and in stabilizing what is presently a decidedly unsettled field.   Incidentally, it might be pointed out that on theoretical grounds at least one other possibility exists for eliminating the interference of assimilatory mechanisms in preformed mycelium, namely, by selective inhibitions by poisons.

Main Pathways of Carbohydrate Metabolism in Molds

This heading is intended to present a rationale which, in a general way, will serve to coordinate what appear on the surface to be a host of complex and unrelated types of metabolism in the numerous molds so far studied in some detail.   If one invokes the precepts of "comparative biochemistry" first enunciated and brought to bear on microbiology in 1925 by the eminent Dutch microbiologist in Delft, A. J. Kluyver (1926, 1931), and since continuously espoused in this country by Kluyver's disciple and former student and associate, C. B. van Niel, one finds it possible to discover a certain uniformity throughout the field of mold metabolism.   The very numerous different principal metabolic activities of molds can be looked upon as manifestations of a few main types of metabolic activity.   The great majority of them can be considered merely as extensions of the preceding ones so that gradually a series is built up, with comparatively simple examples on one end compounding successively to extreme complexity on the other.   Ramifications branch off the main series, to account for the extreme diversity of metabolic types encountered.   Viewed in this way, one perceives, in essence, what possibly might be considered as an evolutionary development from simple to complex metabolism, especially since in many cases the logical intermediate steps in the development of the series are known.   Or maybe (more likely!) the simple are derived from the complex through successive loss of function or of enzyme systems.   No argument is made that the schemes to be presented are evolutionary.   The main value of this idea is that it provides a foundation on which the principles of mold metabolism can be resolved into orderliness.

It is emphasized at this point that this discussion deals with the biochemical origin in molds of the main kinds of organic compounds generally known to be formed from carbohydrate in pure cultures of the organisms growing on media of relatively high carbohydrate content. Commonly they are referred to as "waste" or "excretion" products, though, as seen later, this need not be the correct interpretation.   Not included here is the mechanism of formation of vital components of the cell, i.e., protoplasm, nor the mechanism by which CO_2 originates from sugar, except where it has a bearing on other points under consideration. Under scrutiny here is the third of the three main fates of carbohydrate, namely, metabolic products, the other two being cell material and CO_2. Only generalized concepts will be given; the various processes are treated in detail in other chapters devoted to the individual processes.

The object of the following schematic presentation is to bring out the logical relations which exist among the main products of mold carbohydrate metabolism, and, where possible, to indicate that many of them have intermediary synthetic steps in common. In several instances a product accumulated by one organism represents a simple further transformation of a product formed characteristically by another mold. In the latter, the substance accumulates, due to inability of the fungus to effect further conversion quickly. The further conversion is effected in the former, hence the first substance does not accumulate, but a second one does. In this way it is possible to visualize a common metabolic channel for most fungi, any one differing from others by its ability to carry out one or more additional simple, single step reactions.

It is to be expected that in the more complex of metabolic systems, evidence for intermediates and transformations common to the simpler metabolic system would exist. Wherever investigated, this has been found to be true.

Not only can one find this kind of stepwise metabolic sequence among closely related organisms, but there are numerous instances of the same or similar sequences between distantly related organisms. Seemingly this points to a certain unity of biochemical actions throughout the whole of this group of organisms, a conclusion entirely compatible with Kluyver's generalized concept. There appears to be no general pattern relating taxonomy to biochemical potentialities within the fungi, and this could mean that metabolic offshoots evolved independently of structure. On this basis it is therefore in agreement with expectations that the same major types of biochemical activity are found to occur among widely unrelated groups of fungi.

Thus, most of the Mucorales, and certain Penicillia and Aspergilli have a preponderant C_2 metabolism, producing from hexose ethanol, acetic acid, with or without oxalic acid. Others carry this C_2 stage through the C_4-dicarboxylic acid stage only, producing mainly fumaric, malic, and succinic acids, and this is typical of the genera Rhizopus and Fusarium also. C_2 fractions can always be found as intermediates in these processes. In still other Mucors, Aspergilli, and Penicillia, as well as other fungi, these C_2 and C_4 compounds are used as precursors of citric acid, which accumulates in large quantities. Yet the C_2 and C_4 intermediates can usually be detected in the medium, accompanying, in small amounts, the major end product, namely citric acid. Though little experimental evidence is available, it is likely that in certain other Aspergilli, *Aspergillus itaconicus*, for example, the citric acid functions only as an intermediate, not accumulating but being further converted through a simple step into itaconic acid by decarboxylation. This is the most logical account of the accumulation of itaconic acid by these organisms.

One is also reminded by this line of reasoning of the simple chemical relations between the five-membered ring acids produced by *Penicillium charlesii* as revealed by the Raistrick school. These are γ-methyltetronic acid, carolinic acid, carlic acid and carlosic acid. In addition, ethylcarolic acid (terrestric acid) is formed by *Penicillium terrestre*, and the latest stage in the picture as it exists today is the synthesis of ascorbic acid by *Aspergillus niger* (Geiger-Huber and Galli, 1945). All these compounds are differently substituted tetronic acid derivatives, the relation of ascorbic acid to tetronic being as follows:

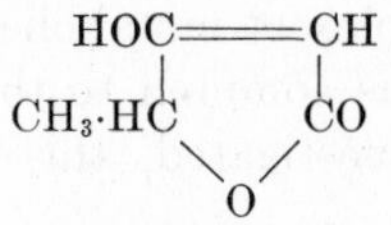

HOC=====CH   HOC=====COH

CH₃·HC   CO   CH₂OH·CHOH·HC   CO

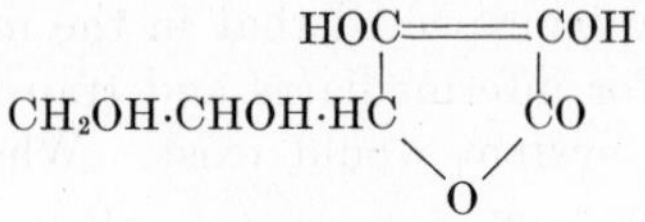

\\   /   \\   /

O   O

γ-Methyltetronic   Ascorbic acid

acid

In these cases, it appears that the metabolism is common, the organisms differing in their ability to carry out the final simple transformations. In the case of *P. charlesii* the synthetic sequence is also carried out by a single organism, but the other species mentioned can carry out modifications of this sequence.

Analogous systems exemplifying this principle may be found in the formation of 3,5-dihydroxyphthalic acid and three other derivative acids (C_{10}) by *Penicillium brevi-compactum*, and in the formation of different chemically homologous anthraquinone pigments by different species of Helminthosporium (Clutterbuck, 1931).

The main theme of the following scheme centers around the formation of split products from carbohydrate, and the type and fate of those split products. Based on this idea the following groupings are possible:

(A) No split products formed during sugar (hexose) utilization. In all these reactions the carbon skeleton of the carbohydrate is left intact.

(1) Gluconic acid and other sugar acids from aldosugars by oxidation of the aldehyde group, including galactonic acid, mannonic acid, xylonic acid, arabonic acid, etc.

(2) Uronic acids, in which the secondary alcohol group is converted to a carboxyl: glucuronic acid, etc.

(3) Dicarboxylic sugar acids resulting from oxidation of both the aldehyde and primary alcohol carbons to carboxyls: saccharic acid, mucic acid, etc.

These processes may be represented as follows:

$$
\text{CH}_2\text{OH(CHOH)}_4\text{CHO}
\begin{cases}
\longrightarrow \text{CH}_2\text{OH(CHOH)}_4\text{COOH} \rightarrow \\
\qquad\qquad \text{Gluconic acid} \\
\longrightarrow \text{COOH(CHOH)}_4\text{CHO} \longrightarrow \\
\qquad\qquad \text{Glucuronic acid} \\
\longrightarrow \text{COOH(CHOH)}_4\text{COOH} \leftarrow \\
\qquad\qquad \text{Saccharic acid}
\end{cases}
$$

Glucose

(B) Split products formed during sugar utilization.

In common with that of all other living systems the dissimilation of hexose sugars by molds follows uniformly the well-known mechanism of sugar breakdown through the triose or pyruvic acid stage, here referred to as C_3 compounds. And, as in the case of bacterial metabolism where many and diverse metabolic end products are encountered, the nature of the end products depends on how molds dispose of the intermediate C_3 compounds, this in part being a function of the enzyme makeup of any particular organism. In view of the easy transition from C_3 and its extremely important metabolic significance, acetaldehyde (C_2) may also be considered with C_3 for the moment. Just as in the case of all other living systems, C_3 and C_2 are the key intermediates in the formation of almost all mold metabolic products. The other main influence on the disposition of the C_3 and C_2 is the degree of anaerobiosis vs. aerobiosis, or in effect, the availability of oxygen.

Since the origin of C_3 and C_2 compounds lies in dismutation reactions independent of oxygen, the ultimate metabolic products may be considered to have passed through two stages of metabolism, the initial stages, anaerobic or fermentative, and the final, either a continuation of anaerobic reactions or the participation of aerobic reactions, depending on the compounds. Often, for the second stage, a mold may possess enzymes capable of effecting both anaerobic and aerobic transformation. In such cases, and similar to most normal cells, the availability of oxygen generally suppresses the anaerobic reactions, though not always, viz., lactic acid formation by certain of the Mucorales.

In addition to the above aspects of the fate of the C_3 and C_2 intermediates are two other main features:

(1) These fragments are transformed in various ways without changes in the carbon chain and are left finally still as C_3 and C_2 compounds.

(2) The fragments undergo condensation reactions leading to the accumulation of more complex compounds of higher molecular weight.

The condensation may be pure, involving only C_3 and C_2 compounds, or, as is likely in some cases, may be mixed, in which C_3 and C_2 compounds may combine with the other or with condensation products of the other. The condensations may be simple, involving only two or three molecules, or it may be highly multiple, leading to very complex high molecular weight compounds.

I. C_3 split products

(a) Simple conversion: lactic acid, glycerol, pyruvic acid.

(b) Condensation:

Two molecules → Kojic acid, hexose sugars, single ring compounds.
Many molecules → Complex ring compounds, pigments, including anthraquinones. Many compounds isolated by Raistrick school.

Of the condensation reactions only kojic acid and hexose sugars have experimental evidence in their support. On the basis of the ring synthesis in kojic acid, the idea is extended to include polycyclic compounds, although no evidence whatsoever is available on synthesis of these compounds. It should be emphasized that kojic acid is a C_5 ring, whereas many benzene ring-type compounds are known to accumulate in mold cultures.

II. C_2 split products

(a) Simple conversion: acetaldehyde, ethanol, acetic acid, ethylacetate, oxalic acid.

(b) Condensation:

Two molecules → (C_4) succinic acid, malic acid, fumaric acid, oxalacetic acid, and some others.

$$C_4 + C_3 \rightarrow C_7 \underset{\text{or}}{\Big\rfloor} {-CO_2}$$
$$C_4 + C_2 \longrightarrow \text{Aconitic acid}$$
$$\downarrow \uparrow$$
$$\text{Citric acid}$$
$$\downarrow {-CO_2}$$
$$\text{Itaconic acid}$$

8–9 Molecules C_2 → Higher fatty acids: stearic, oleic, palmitic, etc.

Several molecules $\overline{C_2}$
    +   → Complex high molecular weight pigments, and other synthetic compounds.
Several molecules C_3

Worthy of mention in connection with the condensation reaction in this section is that products of primary condensation, which are excreted and accumulate in cultures of some organisms, may, in other organisms, participate in further condensation reactions leading to larger molecular weight compounds. In the above listing citric acid originates from the

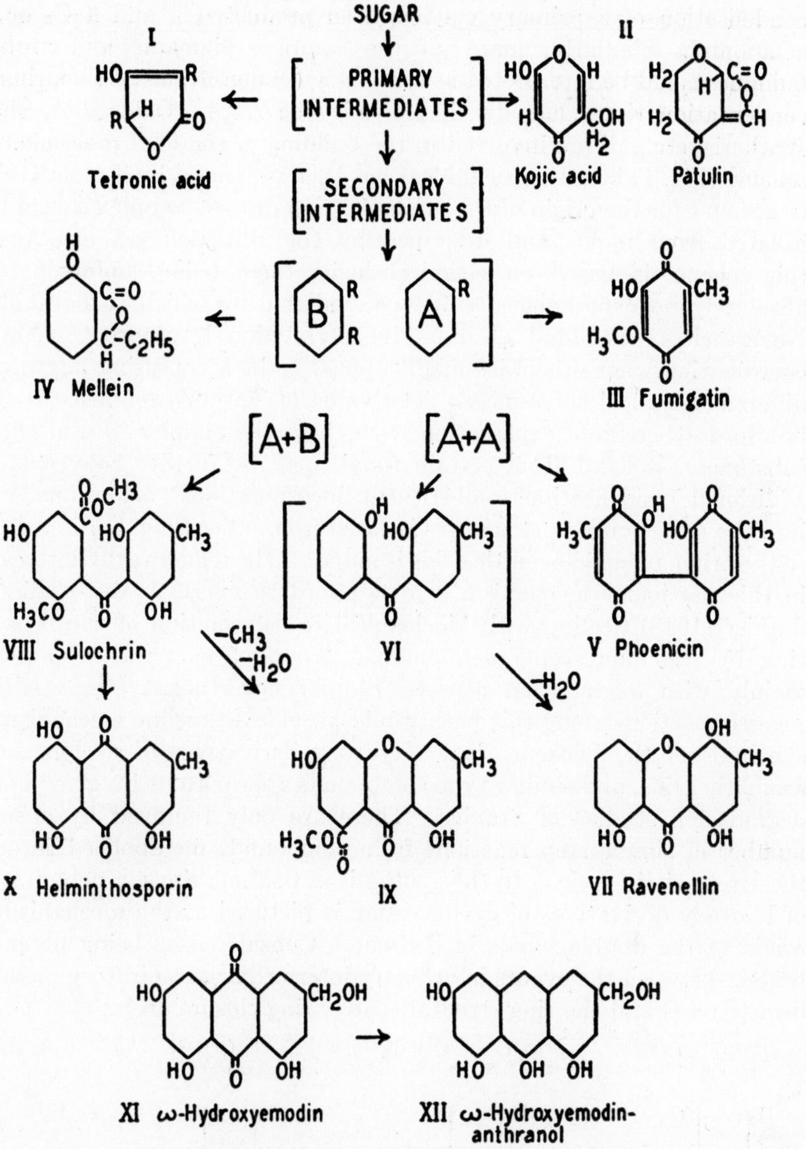

FIG. 1.—Hypothetical relations in biosynthesis of complex ring-type mold pigments (from Tatum, 1944).

condensation of a primary condensation product, C_4, and a C_3 or C_2 compound. Similarly, many of the complex pigments and anthraquinones could be interpreted as secondary condensations of the primary condensation rings, namely simple unicyclic rings. Oxidations, chain synthesis, etc., all are involved in the building of the final molecule. A scheme (Fig. 1) based on such ideas has been presented by Tatum (1944) to account for the origin of the numerous and diverse complex substances isolated from molds and described by the Raistrick school. Again, this scheme is based on chemical logic, there being, unfortunately, absolutely no experimental evidence available by which to be guided. Nevertheless, this kind of inductive correlation is of great value in coordinating what otherwise might appear to be a confusing mixture of different chemical substances. The value of Tatum's sequence is that it affords a credible explanation as to how the simpler of Raistrick's substances, isolated from certain fungi, may be further converted by additional condensations, substituent incorporations, oxidations, etc., into the more complex structures isolated from other fungi. An analogy to the origin of citric-aconitic acids is noted. The reader really interested in this particular mechanism cannot afford to overlook the studies of Stanier (1948) dealing with biochemical transformation of the benzene ring by the fluorescent pseudomonad group of bacteria. Concerned mainly with degradation aspects, Stanier nevertheless suggests that reverse reactions along this path would provide a possible mechanism of synthesis of the benzene ring. Hydroxy derivatives of cyclohexanol, aromatic acids, and similar type compounds appear to be involved in the degradation studies of Stanier. These are only removed by a small number of simple step reactions from compounds metabolized through the Krebs citric cycle. In the synthesis of benzene rings, a dehydration of hydroxy derivatives of cyclohexanol is pictured as the mechanism of origin of the double bonds in benzene. Considered as being potential bridges between the events in ordinary intermediary respiratory metabolism (Krebs) and the ring structures after ring closure are:

Citric acid   Quinic acid   Shikimic acid   p-Hydroxybenzoic acid

Quinic acid can be chemically oxidized to citric acid.

Returning to split products it will be noted that there are two mechanisms for synthesis of C_4 compounds: $C_2 + C_2$ and $C_3 + C_1$. Probably another mechanism, yet to be demonstrated in molds, is their origin from α-ketoglutaric acid (C_5) by decarboxylation, $C_5 \xrightarrow{-CO_2} C_4$.

1. CARBON SKELETON TRANSFORMATIONS INVOLVING C_3 COMPOUNDS

(a)

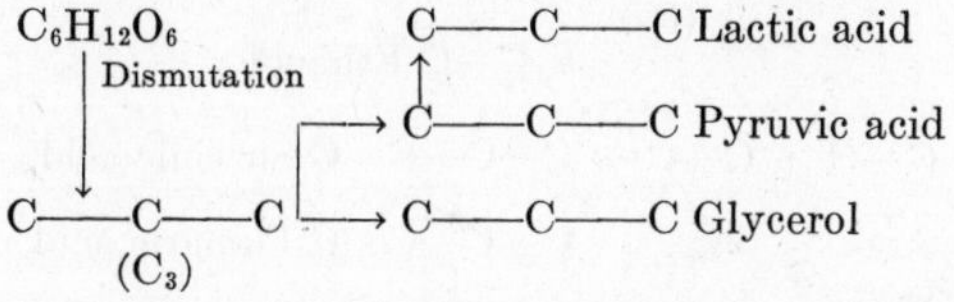

$C_6H_{12}O_6$

Dismutation

C——C——C Lactic acid

C——C——C Pyruvic acid

C——C——C Glycerol

C——C——C
(C_3)

(b)   C—C—C + CO_2 → C—C—C—C   Oxalacetic acid

(c)   C—C—C + C—C—C → C—C—C—C—C—C → (C—C—C—C—C—C)$_n$

                                          Polysaccharide

(d)

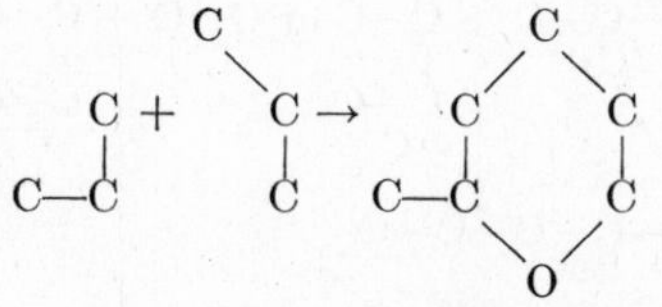

Kojic acid

(e)

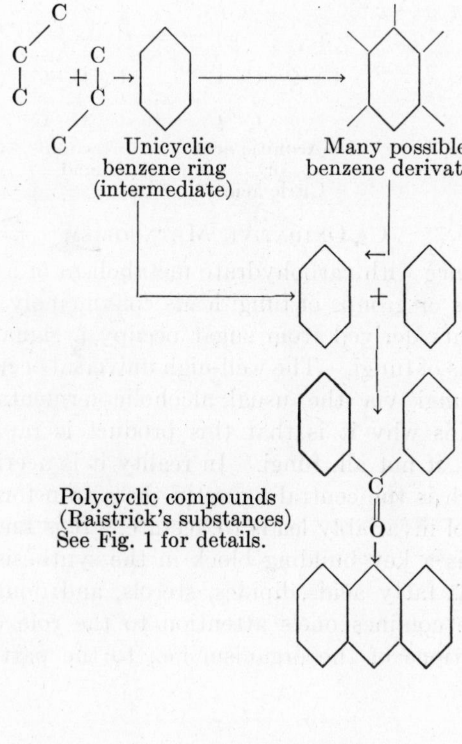

Unicyclic
benzene ring
(intermediate)

Many possible
benzene derivatives

Polycyclic compounds
(Raistrick's substances)
See Fig. 1 for details.

2. CARBON SKELETON TRANSFORMATIONS INVOLVING C_2 COMPOUNDS

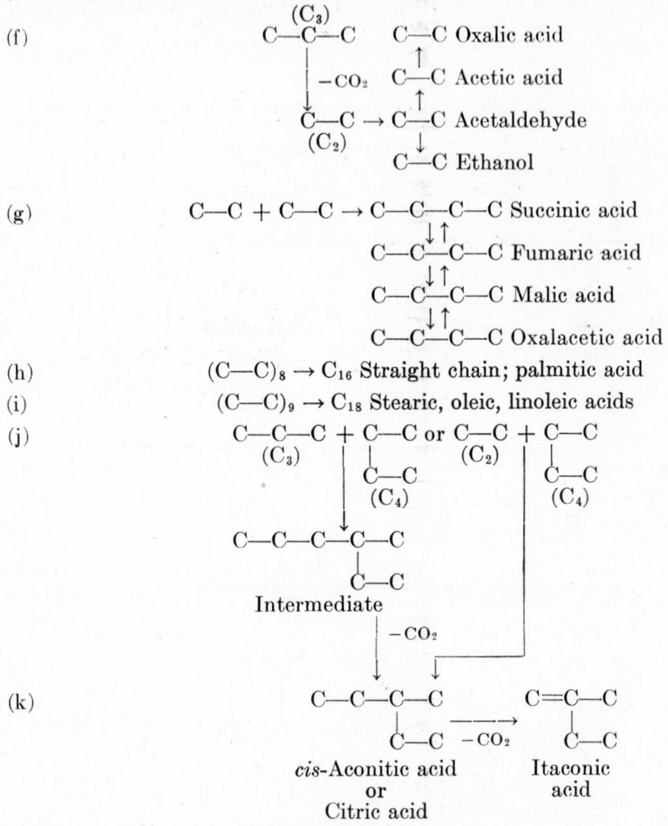

(f)

$$
\begin{array}{l}
\overset{(C_3)}{C-C-C} \qquad C-C \text{ Oxalic acid} \\
\quad\Big| \quad -CO_2 \quad C-C \text{ Acetic acid} \\
\quad\downarrow \\
\underset{(C_2)}{C-C} \rightarrow C-C \text{ Acetaldehyde} \\
\qquad\qquad C-C \text{ Ethanol}
\end{array}
$$

(g)

$$
\begin{array}{l}
C-C + C-C \rightarrow C-C-C-C \text{ Succinic acid} \\
\qquad\qquad C-C-C-C \text{ Fumaric acid} \\
\qquad\qquad C-C-C-C \text{ Malic acid} \\
\qquad\qquad C-C-C-C \text{ Oxalacetic acid}
\end{array}
$$

(h) $(C-C)_8 \rightarrow C_{16}$ Straight chain; palmitic acid

(i) $(C-C)_9 \rightarrow C_{18}$ Stearic, oleic, linoleic acids

(j)

$$
\begin{array}{l}
\underset{(C_3)}{C-C-C} + C-C \text{ or } \underset{(C_2)}{C-C} + C-C \\
\qquad\quad \underset{(C_4)}{C-C} \qquad\qquad \underset{(C_4)}{C-C} \\
\\
C-C-C-C-C \\
\qquad\quad C-C \\
\text{Intermediate} \\
\qquad\quad \Big| \ -CO_2
\end{array}
$$

(k)

$$
\begin{array}{ll}
C-C-C-C & C=C-C \\
\quad C-C \ \xrightarrow{-CO_2} & \quad C-C \\
cis\text{-Aconitic acid} & \text{Itaconic} \\
\quad\text{or} & \text{acid} \\
\text{Citric acid}
\end{array}
$$

C_2 OXIDATIVE METABOLISM

An aquaintance with carbohydrate metabolism of a great number of unrelated species or groups of fungi leads convincingly to the viewpoint that C_2 fragments derived from sugar occupy a signal position in the metabolic actions of fungi. The well-nigh universal occurrence of alcohol formation in fungi via the usual alcoholic fermentation mechanism doubtless explains why it is that this product is rapidly metabolized further by most, if not all, fungi. In reality it is acetic acid, or acetyl phosphate, which is the central figure in these transformations, but the attack on alcohol invariably leads to acetate. It is known that acetate (or its radical) is a key building block in the synthesis of cellular constituents such as fatty acids, lipides, sterols, and doubtless other substances. If one confines one's attention to the role of acetate in the respiratory reactions of the organism i.e., to the part it plays via its oxidation in the accumulation of extracellular products of carbohydrate metabolism, it is evident that here too acetate plays a versatile role, its exact fate depending on the particular organism.

The central role of acetate in the dissimilatory or oxidative aspects of mold metabolism may be conveniently represented by the following scheme. Details of each particular reaction or transformation will be found in the appropriate chapter in this book.

Thus, four main pathways are evident:

(1) Breakdown of the C_2 chain and oxidation to CO_2 and H_2O. This may take place via pathway 4 and the aerobic tricarboxylic respiratory cycle, (2) oxidation of the C_2 chain as such, i.e., to glycolic acid, (3) condensation of two C_2 chains to C_4-dicarboxylic acid, i.e., to succinic acid, and (4) condensation of C_2 with C_4 from the previous condensations to yield C_6, i.e., citric acid. In reality each of these transformations is a means of acetate oxidation, with different degrees of intensity. Each condensation reaction is a one-step oxidation, i.e., single dehydrogenation. Each of these primary oxidation reactions sets the stage for subsequent reactions as seen below:

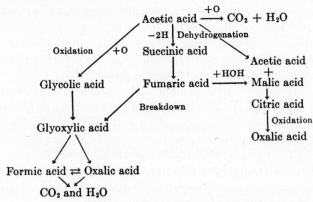

RESERVE STORAGE MATERIALS?

It is obvious that throughout the infinite variety of molds studied, on account of their diversified enzyme makeups, the products of overflow or shunt metabolism will be equally diverse. Not unexpected is the finding that some are water insoluble, or are non-diffusible through the cell membranes, and, consequently, are deposited within cells and accumulate there in substantial quantities, amounting in some cases up to 50 per cent of the total weight of the cell material. Considered in this light, metabolically speaking, there are two main types of metabolic shunt products, those soluble and diffusible in water, and those which are not. Lipides, polysaccharides, complex pigments, and compounds of the Raistrick type which are deposited in and accumulate in mycelium are insoluble shunt products, whereas organic acids, alcohols, pigments, and other low molecular weight compounds are soluble shunt products.

There is no more reason for considering fat and polysaccharide depositions as reserve or storage products, than the carbohydrates and organic acids formed and which accumulate outside the cells. One might even include the complex benzenoid pigments found by the Rais-trick school to comprise 30 to 40 per cent of the cell material. The principal arguments advanced in support of the "reserve material" hypothesis are two: they are laid down during luxury carbohydrate nutrition of the organism, and they disappear, by cellular oxidation, during starvation conditions, supposedly serving as a source of energy and carbon for maintenance metabolism (endogenous metabolism).

The first argument is equally true of virtually all products, including organic acids, accumulated by molds, either within or outside the cell. There is ample evidence also that the second argument is not peculiar to the intracellular accumulations. The observation is a rather general one that extracellular accumulations also tend to be utilized by the organism after exhaustion of the primary energy source, namely car-bohydrate. Yields of most, if not all, organic acids tend to fall after reaching a maximum coinciding with depletion of the sugar. Just as fat disappearance is slow and gradual, so is the attack on the initially accumulated soluble organic acids and carbohydrates.

In the final analysis this is simply a reflection of a statement made earlier in this chapter, that fungi can eventually oxidize completely the original available substrate to CO_2 and H_2O, and besides can syn-thesize cell material. So long as the organism is surfeited with easily consumed carbohydrate, the attack on shunt byproducts is deferred. Relieved of their saturation by the preferentially decomposed sugar, the dismutation enzymes now proceed with the slower degradation of the initially formed products of deranged metabolism.

Actually, the rate at which accumulated fats are attacked by the mold is so slow that it is difficult to see how it could be of value to the organism as a "reserve product" alternative to simple carbohydrates. No evidence is available, but it seems also possible that intracellular accumulations of the complex compounds, pigments, benzenoid com-pounds, etc., also might be further attacked and slowly consumed, pro-vided an abundance of oxygen is available. Functionally speaking, these compounds could very well be considered in a class with other mold products. Thus, extracellular accumulations of metabolic products would have to be considered as storage or reserve products by the same interpretation that intracellular materials are so considered. Such a conclusion seems untenable.

The ideas presented above, which lead to the conclusion that all such compounds happen to be subject to degradation by the mold irrespective of their location, are more acceptable. A water soluble, diffusible compound is by ordinary concepts just as available to the cell as insoluble fat in a vacuole. The attack and consumption of these accumulated products probably never begins until the organism exhausts its more easily attacked and preferred energy source—carbohydrate.

REFERENCES

Buromsky, I.   1913.   *Zentr. Bakt. Parasitenk. Abt II* **36**, 54–66.
Ciusa, R., and Brüll, L.   1939.   *Ann. chem. applicata* **29**, 3–11.
Clutterbuck, P. W.   1936.   *J. Soc. Chem. Ind.* **55**, 55T–66T.
Currie, J. N.   1917.   *J. Biol. Chem.* **31**, 15–37.
Emerson, R., and Cantino, E. C.   1948.   *Am. J. Botany* **35**, 157–171.
Foster, J. W., and Waksman, S. A.   1939.   *J. Bact.* **37**, 599–617.
Geiger-Huber, M., and Galli, H.   1945.   *Helv. Chim. Acta* **28**, 248–250.
Istin, M.   1947.   *Rèv. can. biol.* **6**, 496–543.
Karow, E. O.   1942.   Ph. D. Thesis.   Rutgers Univ.
Kluyver, A. J.   1931.   Chemical Activities of Microorganisms.   Univ. of London Press, 190 pp.
Kluyver, A. J., and Donker, H. J. L.   1926.   *Chem. Zelle u. Gewebe* **13**, 134–190.
Kluyver, A. J., and Perquin, L. H. C.   1933.   *Biochem. Z.* **266**, 66–81.
May, O. E., Herrick, H. T., Moyer, A. J., and Wells, P. A.   1934.   *Ind. Eng. Chem.* **26**, 575–578.
Mitchell, H. K., and Houlahan, M.   1946.   *Federation Proc.* **5**, 370–375.
Molliard, M.   1922.   *Compt. rend. soc. biol.* **87**, 219–221.
Moyer, A. J., Wells, P. A., Stubbs, J. J., Herrick, H. T., and May, O. E.   1937.   *Ind. Eng. Chem.* **29**, 777–782.
Pruess, L. M., Eichinger, E. C., and Peterson, W. H.   1934.   *Zentr. Bakt. Parasitenk. Abt II* **89**, 370–377.
Raistrick, H. *et al.*   1931.   *Trans. Roy. Soc. London* **B220**, 1–367.
Stanier, R. Y.   1948.   *J. Bact.* **55**, 477–494.
Steinberg, R. A.   1942a.   *J. Agr. Research* **64**, 455–476.
Steinberg, R. A.   1942b.   *J. Agr. Research* **64**, 615–633.
Tamiya, H.   1932.   *Acta Phytochim. Japan* **6**, 265–304; 1933.   *ibid.* **7**, 27–41.
Tamiya, H., and Yamagutchi, S.   1933.   *Acta Phytochim. Japan* **7**, 43–64.
Tanner, F. W. Jr., Pfeiffer, S. E., and Van Lanan, J. M.   1945.   *Arch. Biochem.* **8**, 29–36.
Tatum, E. L.   1944.   *Ann. Rev. Biochem.* **13**, 667–684.
Terroine, E. F., and Bonnet, R.   1930.   *Bull. soc. chim. biol.* **12**, 10–19.
Terroine, E. F., and Wurmser, R.   1921.   *Compt. rend.* **173**, 482–483; 1922a.   *ibid.*, **174**, 1435–1437; 1922b.   *ibid.*, **175**, 228–230; 1922c.   *Bull. soc. chim. biol.* **4**, 518–567.
Ward, G. E., Lockwood, L. B., May, O. E., and Herrick, H. T.   1935.   *Ind. Eng. Chem.* **27**, 318–322.
Ward, G. E., Lockwood, L. B., Tabenkin, B., and Wells, P. A.   1938.   *Ind. Eng. Chem.* **30**, 1233–1235.
Wells, P. A., Moyer, A. J., and May, O. E.   1936.   *J. Am. Chem. Soc.* **58**, 555–558.
Wirth, J. C., and Nord, F. F.   1941.   *J. Am. Chem. Soc.* **63**, 2855.

CHAPTER 5

NATURAL VARIATION

Some two hundred years ago, it is said (Ingold, 1946), Albrech von Haller, the famous Swiss scientist, described fungi as "a mutable and treacherous tribe." Time and mycologists have amply confirmed the incessant tendency of filamentous fungi toward spontaneous change, and this mutability has become recognized as one of the outstanding traits of this group of organisms. Doubtless such mutability holds also for all microorganisms. Its recognition first in the fungi probably has two explanations: the gross size of these organisms in culture makes changes easily discernible, and structural differentiation of the organism into diverse morphological parts greatly increases the chances for visible deviation from parent cultures or from the norm.

The main objective of this chapter is to analyze the events behind this mutability and to place the phenomenon on an intelligible basis, but first it is timely to examine the implications of mutability both for these organisms as they exist in nature and as the microbiologist is concerned with them.

If one considers the morphological and cultural aspects of a given fungus species, one recognizes definite minor structural differences which plague the mycologist in ascertaining the identity of a new fungus culture and in establishing a workable taxonomic system. Thus, it is known that fungi possessing major structural features in common are not fully identical in every respect, but that considerable variation exists among individuals placed without question in a single species. In the main, all the organisms in one species have characters distinct from those in another species. This is especially true when a new species is established, for usually only one (or a few members) of the new species is studied. However, as more and more members of the species are collected, it becomes evident that within the species itself there is an extensive gradation comparable to that described below with biochemical activities, and furthermore that some of the more extreme forms in one species have structural similarities with organisms on the fringe of another species.

In other words, not only are there gradations within the species, but the species themselves grade one into the other. Sometimes the bridging

184

organisms are lacking, or rather, not known, but the continuous relation between species is a well-recognized fact today, especially among the multispecied genera in the Fungi Imperfecti, if not in all major groups of fungi. In fact, in numerous cases it is difficult to decide just where one species ends and the next one begins. Recognition of this species gradation has led to the abandonment of the rigid classical botanical concept of the "species" in favor of the idea of "species groups" or biotypes, in which all the organisms are more closely related than those in another species group, and that the two groups merge, theoretically at least, imperceptibly into each other. The overlapping of species and the merging of the species groups so that placing of intermediate transitional forms is a formidable decision is nicely exemplified in Thom and Raper's manual on the genus Aspergillus (1945). A similar analysis has been made on the genus Fusarium (Snyder and Hansen, 1940). In the words of one authority " . . . the number of strains within the species is nothing short of astounding and would be almost unbelievable unless a person had had direct experience with them" (Stakman, 1940). Finally is an example of an intergeneric series, between *Aspergillus sydowi* and *Penicillium restrictum* (Thom and Steinberg, 1939).

It was probably applied microbiology that was largely responsible for the emergence of the idea that in fungi there exists a biochemical mutability of even greater range and diversification than that observable by gross or microscopic inspection. Detailed studies through the years on organisms of potential practical interest from the standpoint of their metabolic ("fermentation") activities or their pathogenicity have led to what may be considered axioms in microbial metabolism, and especially in relation to filamentous fungi.

1. The individual progeny from any culture of single spore origin may vary within wide limits in regard to the performance of any given biochemical activity, despite the fact that for all practical purposes all may be morphologically indistinguishable. This phenomenon, already mentioned several times in this book, and known as strain specificity*

* Incidentally, it may be pointed out that this observation, like so many "new" concepts and ideas in microbiology, and other sciences as well, turns out to be merely a rediscovery of a feature first recognized by a past master. In this case it was the genius of Pasteur who in 1876 fully perceived, appreciated, and even defined strain specificity, only he called it "le polymorphisme physiologique" (Pasteur 1876a). "On pourrait croire que toutes les variétés de *mucor* sont propres à donner le genre de levûre dont nous venons de parler. II n'en est rién. C'est encore une preuve frappante des différences physiologiques profondes que peuvent offrir des formes de végétation pourtant si voisines que les classifications botaniques sont contraintes de les rapprocher autant qu'il est possible. Déjà les *mycoderma vini* et les levûres alcooliques proprement dites, si semblables de formes et de développements qu'on les

is not, with relatively few exceptions (as for example, pigment formation), evident from simple inspection, but is revealed only by biochemical analysis. The degree to which this kind of mutability is fundamental in theoretical and practical microbial metabolism is emphasized by the consideration that, in addition to the range occurring with any one function, it must also occur individually with respect to every one of the host of biochemical reactions the organism is capable of effecting. Thus the cells in any one culture are far from being homogeneous physiologically.

With such differences possible within the progeny of any one culture, it scarcely needs to be emphasized how great the differences are that may be expected between morphologically indistinguishable strains of diverse origins, such as isolates from natural sources, or from different stock culture collections. Apart from quantitative differences, these often are even qualitatively different.

This type of strain specificity is much more extensive than is commonly thought, and it is not an exaggeration to say that of a collection of scores of different strains of a given fungus species emanating from various natural and laboratory sources, no two will behave exactly alike with respect to a number of common biochemical activities. Some will exhibit extreme differences in certain biochemical characters, seemingly making the organisms quite unrelated were it not for their morphological identity, and numerous others will be intermediate between the extremes. If enough strains are tested, more and more transitional forms will be found, each differing from the next ones to a minor degree, but still differing markedly from the extremes. It is evident then that an entire biochemical series exists in this group of strains, whose individuals may be thought of as grading one with the other.

2. In addition to the above, there is another kind of variation in progeny, this being merely an extension of the foregoing Axiom 1, and this is latent. Two morphologically indistinguishable strains, compared metabolically under any one set of conditions, may respond nearly alike or so resemble one another that they may be considered physiologically indistinguishable, or related. Yet, tested together under another set of conditions, gross differences in metabolic behavior may become evident. The data of Schulz (1937) make a neat instance. The proximate chemical compositions of the cell material of two different strains of *A. niger* were virtually indistinguishable when cultivated on a certain basal medium. The addition of a few parts per million of zinc ion to this medium caused marked changes in composition of the mycelium of both organisms (Chapter 3), but the changes were strikingly different

jugerait identiques, au moins dans l'état de nos connaissances, et si differents physiolgiquement, donnent de ce fait un exemple extraordinaire." (Pasteur 1876b.)

in the two organisms, so that there was no question that two different biochemical individuals were involved.

3. The above two axioms of variation are based on differences inherent between different fungus individuals, and there is good reason for believing that they are of genetic or nuclear origin. This, then, is genetic variation. The third axiom is predicated on a different kind of variation, one quite apart from genetic differences between individuals. Our only purpose in mentioning it in this chapter is to contrast this axiom (discussed in detail in Chapter 4) with the two above with which we are concerned. This is called "response variation" and involves the changes in response of any one individual culture to different cultural conditions— a situation obviously distinct from the problem of different individuals discussed above.

PHYSIOLOGICAL DEGENERATION

When, in any one fungus culture, progeny with a weaker power to effect a given biochemical function get the upper hand in the initially potent culture, as they may in the course of numerous consecutive transfers, the ultimately weakened culture is said to have undergone "physiological degeneration." Viewed in this way, the physiological potentialities of any culture are always changing during periods of active growth. This is probably the most telling testimony of the continuous changeability of the fungi, and its universality is best indicated by the fact that all investigations dealing with specific metabolic functions of a fungus sooner or later encounter physiological degeneration manifested by progressive loss of the function of particular interest.

Numerous examples of physiological degeneration are available in the literature, dealing with virulence and with production of various organic acids, antibiotic substances, pigments, etc. It is of major concern to the industrial microbiologist who must prevent this run-down of the culture, and every large-scale fermentation process adopts special precautions to minimize this hazard. To the plant pathologist interested in the relation of phytopathogenic fungi to virulence, this problem is paramount in importance. Another instance demonstrating the crucial significance of physiological degeneration relates to the discovery of unique processes in organisms which, upon reinvestigation years later, cannot be repeated even with authentic direct-line progeny of the original tube culture on which the first observation was made. A classical example is the change of Wehmer's *Aspergillus fumaricus* from an extraordinarily high yielder of fumaric acid exclusively, to a mixed acid fermentation, mainly gluconic, and to the virtual exclusion of fumarate (see Chapter 11). Apart from applied microbiology, the academic importance of this intense biochemical function would be unique were it possible to study it today. Thus physiological degeneration may actually cause important biochemical processes to be unavailable indefinitely, pending rediscovery in another organism.

The change in the organism that leads to physiological degeneration is in the final analysis, of genetic origin, the change being an inherent feature of the subculture. Some organisms are much more unstable than others, degenerating much more rapidly than others, and this instability is in itself an inherent character. Actually, radical changes in the cultural aspects of the organism are also encountered. Changes in growth rates, amount of mycelium, pigmentation, sporulation, aerial mycelium, etc., may be observed. In the final analysis these are the results of biochemical alterations. The reader further interested in this cultural aspect of spontaneous mutability will find several excellent photographs in Raper and Alexander (1945b) that demonstrate the radically different morphological and cultural types of progeny obtainable with various Penicillia under normal cultivation conditions.

One of the best detailed analyses of physiological degeneration is given by Whiffen and Savage (1947) for penicillin production by *Penicillium notatum*, and this work demonstrates a number of points discussed previously (see also Raper and Alexander, 1945b). In five to seven generations penicillin yields dropped from 140 units per ml. to 50. The surface pads of the degenerated cultures were much heavier, tougher, and more rigid, with faster and heavier sporulation than the parent. In general the lower-yielding strains rapidly outgrew the high yielders. Inoculum for these cultures was obtained from serially transferred spores. On the other hand, when the inoculum was prepared so as to exclude spores rigorously, and thus consisted of vegetative mycelium only, the penicillin potency remained undiminished even after the inoculum had been serially transferred fifty consecutive times; furthermore, no morphological variants were revealed by plating out the vegetative cells. Thus the process of genetic change leading to variation in progeny, is inescapably associated with the process of spore formation in this fungus strain. The nuclear phenomena characteristic of the vegetative mycelium and the conidiospores are responsible for this behavior. This is one aspect of a generalized natural phenomenon in fungi, known as natural variation, to be discussed separately below.

1. PREVENTION OF PHYSIOLOGICAL DEGENERATION

Because degeneration takes place only as a result of the nuclear phenomena associated with growth and reproduction, carrying cultures with a minimum of transfers, i.e., minimum of growth, is the means of preserving the potency of a culture. Inoculum taken for test from this preserved culture will show a satisfactory constancy of biochemical performance so long as the culture remains viable. Actually, if only a few survivors were present so that only one or a few spores were used, some differences might eventuate, for an inoculum large enough to represent the homogeneous parent culture must be used.

If on the other hand the parent culture is maintained in the stock culture collection in the traditional manner by transferring the culture to a fresh medium after a period of several months or a year, and repeating the process from the younger culture, the culture may, to be sure, be maintained in a viable state, but with altered physiology. The true original biochemical activities of this culture may be considered to have been discarded when the old tube is discarded after the subculture developed.

To eliminate degeneration, modern microbiologists carry stock cultures in a state which maintains viability indefinitely without the need for transfers for a period of several years at least. It cannot be emphasized too strongly that spore viability is not the only factor involved. As seen below, in the only study of its kind available, physiological degeneration occurs as a result of the use of spore inoculum, whereas spore-free vegetative mycelium maintains the culture in a state of undiminished vigor indefinitely. Three general approaches to culture preservation are employed:

(1) The preservation of cultures in a desiccated state. The drying is accomplished while the spores are held in the frozen state in the suspending fluid, which may be a protective colloidal material such as blood serum, skim milk, or gelatin. The tube is sealed and may be stored indefinitely. When used, the culture is of course as closely akin to the original as possible. The procedure, called lyophilization, and the apparatus used, is described in detail by Raper and Alexander (1945a). Also given are viability tests on some 170-odd different fungus cultures preserved in this manner for 20 to 24 months, and some preserved for $3\frac{1}{2}$ years. With few exceptions all Aspergilli, Penicillia, Mucorales, and Hyphomycetes were successfully preserved, whereas members of the Entomophthorales did not survive. In some instances the number of viable spores was considerably less than at the beginning of the test.

(2) Preservation in soil cultures. This technique is simple, requires no special apparatus and in preparation efficacy is as good or even superior to the lyophilization process; judging from present indications, it is the preferred method. Tubes of air-dried sieved loam soil are sterilized by prolonged autoclaving or dry heat until sterility tests are negative. About $\frac{1}{10}$ volume of a heavy spore suspension is then added and mixed

by shaking.   The soil tubes may then be desiccated in a vacuum desiccator, and stored in a cool dry place.   Another possibility is to incubate the inoculated soil for a few days at 25-30° whereupon some limited growth of the fungus occurs, followed by sporulation.   The culture may be stored in a cool place as is, or mechanically desiccated.   The principal value of soil tubes is that transfers from these master or stock cultures can be obtained innumerable times, over a period of years if necessary, the inoculum thus obtained being indentical each time.   All subsequent work then is on a uniform basis; or at least the inoculum may be eliminated as a variable in experimental work.   The prolonged usefulness of a single tube is due to the fact that a single tube contains 10 to 15 ml. of soil and each transfer requires only a loopful or a small clump to generate a new laboratory culture.

(3) Preservation in mineral oil slant cultures (Buell and Weston, 1947).   This involves the addition of sterile, heavy mineral oil to mature slant cultures of the fungi to a depth about 1 cm. over the uppermost portion of the agar or growth in the tube.   If the oil is in too deep a layer, the organism "smothers"; if too shallow, evaporation of the culture occurs.   The oil functions by (1) preventing evaporation of water from the culture and (2) by decreasing the metabolic rate of the fungus to a low steady state.   In practice this preservation procedure for stocks in a collection is probably the simplest of all methods and has the following practical advantages: (a) it is a highly simple procedure, (b) cultures are easily transferred merely by fishing some of the immersed mycelium and/or spores, (c) spores are not essential, and (d) it controls mites, which frequently are pests in fungus collections, penetrating the cotton plugs and contaminating cultures.   (The lyophilization process is effective only with organisms forming some kind of resistant bodies.)   Some 1800 cultures including Basidiomycetes, Ascomycetes, Phycomycetes and Sterilia Mycelia were successfully preserved up to 24 months, with a single exception.   This was the longest period tried.   Other workers have proved viability of 6-year-old cultures with this method.   Doubtless this method will receive wide spread use as more laboratories become acquainted with its desirable features.   The tubes with oil require no special storage conditions, the usual cotton plugs being adequate.

Age is not the sole factor in limiting the viability of ordinary slant cultures of fungi, and, on account of the enormous diversity of fungi, different factors are encountered for the various organisms or groups. Probably the only report available dealing with the maintenance of stock culture collections of agar slants and based on actual experience is the illuminating narration of J. Westerdijk (1947), fungus curator at the international "Central Bureau voor Schimmelcultures" at Baarn,

Holland, which the student should read. Viability may be considerably extended by controlling the pH in the stock culture tube against harmful changes due to acid or alkali formation during growth. Other factors also seem indicated.

Often, especially in industrial fermentations, it is essential to prepare numerous vessels of inoculum at frequent intervals. It is not essential to go back to the master soil culture each time, for experience has shown that serious degeneration does not set in until after several consecutive transfers; at least this is true of numerous different penicillin and streptomycin producing organisms. Consequently, a single loopful of soil culture may function as the progenitor of large numbers of parallel cultures, each one, at time of use in fermenters or in other biochemical use, no more than a definite number of transfers from the master soil tube, this number having a predetermined immunity to degeneration. This system is almost universally employed in industrial fermentations and may be represented schematically as follows:

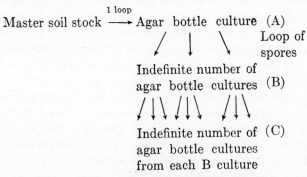

FIG. 1.—Scheme for uniform inoculum buildup.

After sporulation the numerous B cultures can be stored indefinitely in the cold until the next one is required to generate innumerable C cultures, ready for fermenter inoculation or biochemical experimentation. Thus all C cultures, though prepared at different times from different B cultures are only three transfers away from the parent stock, and make reproducibly uniform inoculum.

2. RESTORATION OF CULTURES AFTER DEGENERATION

As stated above, a degenerated culture does not consist exclusively of changed progeny; they are only present in more or less greater numerical frequency, and the culture, if not degenerated too far, still contains progeny typical of the original undegenerated parent and even superior in certain cases. These may be re-isolated by routine plating procedures.

In spontaneously degenerating cultures the tendency to form all different kinds of morphological and cultural variants concomitantly with biochemical variants has not, so far as is known, led to any absolute correlation between the ability to effect a biochemical function and cultural appearance. However, in some cases a rough artificial association is made, mainly for the convenience of the investigator. In this connection it may be noted that in a well-known case of induced mutation, a cultural feature, purple pigmentation, is specifically allied with loss of a biochemical function, i.e., conversion of adenine precursor to pigment (see Chapter 6).

If a biochemical function is involved, routine tests of numerous colony isolates should reveal one or more characteristically like the original parent, which then may be isolated and handled subsequently as a stock strain.

Sometimes slant cultures of heavy sporulating organisms, particularly of the Aspergilli and Penicillia, show isolated cottony, white patches of asporogenous mycelia. In transferring, these should be avoided; they are aberrations, possibly arising from secondary germination of already formed spores and are usually asporogenous.

In *Penicillium notatum* Hansen and Snyder (1944) concluded this mycelial type (M) to be a true genetic mutant arising in old cultures, even though of single spore origin (see also Foster *et al.*, 1943). Doubtless this is an instance of mutation and selection, the M type arising from the only spores germinating under conditions that are adverse for the vast majority of spores present (i.e., mutant spores). The M type is characterized by low penicillin yields and high production of yellow pigment, and breeds true. The rest of the conidia are normal in cultural and penicillin-producing characteristics. This is known as the C (conidial) type and, though pure young C cultures tend to remain free of interference by the M type, both types can be isolated from the apparently normal culture by single spore isolations. On account of the two contrasting types the term "dual phenomenon" was applied, but as seen later, multiple types may be involved in this kind of transformation. Whenever the M type is inoculated with C type, penicillin yields are reduced and pigmentation is more intense.

This situation is not contradictory to the data of Whiffen and Savage. It is merely one special case of the overall physiological degeneration where the low-producing variant happens to be morphologically distinct. In the other instance the physiological variants are morphologically identical and it is certain that the C type of Hansen and Snyder corresponds to Whiffen and Savage's culture in respect to physiological heterogeneity of the conidia, although it must be remembered that this heterogeneity is much more marked in some cultures than others (unstable vs. stable), this very difference in itself apparently being genetically controlled.

MECHANISM OF NATURAL VARIATION

This is known variously as saltation, mutation, dissociation, discontinuous variation, dual phenomenon ("Dauermodifikation"), and by other, lesser-known designations.   In connection with plant pathogens this feature is often referred to as "physiologic specialization" and the individual strains as "physiologic races."   It is evident that the numberless strain specificities of organisms isolated from nature, manifested by the diverse virulence, biochemical, cultural, and morphological characters distinctive of each strain, must have had their origin in nature in a fashion similar to the origin of the diverse progeny one finds in physiologically degenerated artificial cultures.   Other forces are at play, especially in selection in nature, but the underlying phenomena must be essentially the same.   Two main types of mechanisms are involved; in importance in the order named, at least in nature, they are (1) those in which the transformations result from the activities of genetically different nuclei, and (2) those in which the transformations result from mutation, i.e., a sudden change in the genetic makeup of a nucleus, and hence its progeny.

The whole subject of mutations is reserved for discussion in the next chapter, and only the first of the above two groups will be discussed here.

1. SEXUAL REPRODUCTION AS A MEANS OF GENERATING VARIANTS

This basic phenomenon in the so-called "perfect" fungi is too well known and so adequately covered in the standard treatises on mycology that the cytology and other details would be superfluous here.   However a model sexual cycle in an ascomycete, one of the three major classes of perfect (sexual) fungi, is given for reference purposes in the next chapter. The main point for our purpose is that each genetically different conidiospore gives rise to a mycelial colony that is different from the others. These genetically distinct organisms, all the same species, may appear different on account of morphological appearance, cultural aspects such as pigmentation, growth rates, or in certain biochemical activities revealed only upon analysis.   In the final analysis the first-named changes obviously are a consequence of biochemical differences.

In perfect fungi when hyphae of opposite mating types meet, terminal hyphal fusion takes place and nuclei of opposite sexual types combine to form the fusion nucleus or zygote.   In general, this undergoes two to three divisions, generating four or eight sexual haploid spores which occur in lineal arrangement in the ascus; several of these are present in a specialized fruiting body. The ordinary Mendelian pattern of segregation is obeyed and the individual spores will be similar to either of the two parent types, with respect to any given gene character.

Sex itself is a gene character that segregates randomly during reduction division, generating sexual spores of both sexes in a 1:1 ratio, as in the case of any other gene character. Since each of these ascospores can undergo an independent vegetative cycle in which the gene recombination is now evident, organisms different from the parents have been evolved. Thus, if the colorless (albino) male (+) strain is crossed with the normal colored female (−) strain, the progeny will consist of both (+) and (−) albinos and (+) and (−) colored. In reality, biochemical variants have been produced because pigment formation is a biochemical function, manifested as a cultural change. Actually, this system is similar to the situation in higher plants and animals.

In haploid fungi each genic character of the chromosomes in the sexual fusion nucleus will manifest itself in the first generation progeny, and incidentally, each genic character will demonstrate itself theoretically in one-half the progeny. As other genic characters distribute themselves similarly among the progeny, but in different members to comprise half (random assortment), as many different combinations are possible as 2^n, and $\dfrac{2^n}{2}$ expresses the number of possible combination of n pairs of factor differences for any one gene. Phycomycetes and most Ascomycetes are haploid.

In the Basidiomycetes and some Ascomycetes the situation in the mycelium is somewhat different. When individual basidiospores germinate, a haploid mycelium consisting of uninucleate spores is formed. When this mycelium meets a similar mycelium but of another mating type (several different mating types are known), i.e., when the mycelia of heterothallic strains meet, anastamosis occurs and the fusion cell now becomes binucleate with a member from each thallus. It is to be noted that the nuclei do not fuse at this point as in the formation of a fusion nucleus. When nuclear fusion does take place normal reductive division occurs during two divisions, generating four haploid basidiospores. This occurs after numerous conjugate nuclear divisions in which each nucleus divides independently during hyphal cell formation and, by means of the well-known clamp connection mechanism, each cell remains binucleate with a nucleus from each parent. Since each binucleate cell contains a complete chromosome pair, one in each nucleus, the mycelium is said to be diploid or dicaryotic. In smut fungi (Ustilaginales) the two sex-type nuclei remain associated throughout development in the host plant.

Fusion and formation of the diploid nucleus occurs only during chlamy-dospore formation.

The significance of diploidy in connection with natural variation lies in the fact that the phenomenon of genetic dominance and recessiveness comes into play, since each gene locus will be present twice in each cell. If monocaryotic mycelia differing in one or more non-sex contrasting (unit) characters, i.e., alleles, are crossed, the F_1 dicaryotic progeny will all show only one of the characters of each contrasting pair, it being dominant; the other, being recessive, shows up only in the progeny from a cross of two F_1 members, i.e., in the F_2 generation. Thus, strains are obtained that differ according to whether the unit character is mani-fested as dominancy or whether the recessive character appears. In other words, two different organisms are obtained from what seemingly was one type, but which bore the latter type as a recessive gene. Several examples of this phenomenon are known with respect to morphological and cultural characters, especially in Basidiomycetes, but the instances where this has been worked out for specific physiological or biochemical functions are rare. Plant pathologists have, however, provided excellent examples with reference to the property of pathogenicity (Craigie, 1940). Thus, the F_1 hybrid from crossing two races of wheat stem rust (*Puccinia sp.*) Nos. 9 and 15, each pathogenically distinct, proves to be identical in pathogenicity with the Race 9 parent, this character being, therefore, dominant to the Race 15 type pathogenicity. That the genes governing pathogenicity conform to the true Mendalian principle of inheritance is also demonstrated through the F_2 generation by crossing Races 9 and 36; the F_1 hybrid No. 17 results. No. 17 was selfed, yielding 126 second generation cultures (F_2) which were distinguished on the basis of types of pathogenicities and were distributed in seven races. The observed pathogenicity frequencies check very well with the theoretical Mendelian ratios of $27:9:9:9:3:3:3:1$ (Table 1). Different contrasting pairs are

TABLE 1

SECOND GENERATION FREQUENCIES OF PATHOGENICITY TYPES[1]

Pathogenicity race No.	17	1	36	11	15	85	57	
Observed frequencies	69	22	14	15	1	4	1	0
Calculated frequencies	54	18	18	18	6	6	6	2

[1] From Craigie (1940).

of course undergoing random assortment simultaneously, and after segregation numerous different combinations of these gene characters are possible, each combination in essence comprising a new genetic strain. Each of these is then theoretically capable of mating with the others, etc. In general, recessiveness in fungi involves characters unsuited for survival, because there is a selection for dominance. Such organisms generally are characterized by cultural abnormalities manifested as a weakness, and in low synthetic, metabolic, and growth vigor. Such cultures can be generated artificially by constant inbreeding, for recessive characters can appear only in the homozygous state, this condition being realizable only by careful laboratory selection of parental breeding types. In nature the prospects for homozygosity with respect to recessiveness are almost nil, owing to the infinite numerical superiority of normal wild types. These, by crossing with the abnormal strains, cause the abnormalities to disappear under the influence of the dominant allele in the wild type. When one considers that in sexual hybridization of fungi, all the other genetic phenomena known for higher plants and animals, for example crossing over, lethal factors, sex-linked characters, deficient chromosomes, linked characters, suppressors, etc., are found to occur, the opportunities for the origin of diverse races or strains are indeed self-evident. As innumerable spores generally are formed on a single thallus, the proximity of heterothallic fungi is conducive to a plethora of nuclear crosses and the creation of variants. Obviously the different mating type hyphae of a single thallus in the case of a homothallic organism are in such proximity that opportunities for genetic interaction are multifarious wherever vegetative growth takes place.

These ideas are no longer theory. They have been demonstrated to apply to the living world in general. Possibly the best known example of the Protean potentialities of fungi is the case of the cereal crop pathogens, the smut fungi. Studies on ninety monosporidial progeny isolated from chlamydospores from an interspecific cross between *Sphacelotheca sorghi* and *S. cruenta* exemplify the remarkable creative power of gene recombinations and segregation in fungi (Rodenhiser, 1940). Only two of the ninety progeny lines appeared identical with the *S. sorghi* parent, and one with *S. cruenta*. The others differed in one or more of the following visible colony characteristics: color, topography, surface, consistency, margin, rate of growth, and tendency to mutate. One can well imagine the heterogeneity that must have existed regarding physiological and biochemical properties, which would be detectable only by chemical testing. The genetic factors governing any one of the above cultural characters segregated independently of the others and of those determining sex. Compounding the multifariousness of this system is the discovery that eighty-one of the progeny lines had various tendencies to mutate spontaneously whereas neither parent had ever demonstrated this feature. This is probably due to the heterozygosity of the hybrid progeny as compared to the relative homozygosity of the parents.

The main contributors to this extensive field of mycogenetics are Blakeslee, Dodge, and Lindegren and for more details the reader is referred to the many publications of these authors. The principal point to be made here is that sexual reproduction in fungi perpetuates the genetic makeup of perfect fungi in a continually dynamic state, consequently affording opportunity for the origin in nature, or artificially through gene recombinations, of numerous different physiological and morphological strains or races. As each of these two aspects of the fungi ultimately depends on biochemical reactions, each of which is controlled by an individual gene, the basis for the genetic dependence of physiological and morphological features becomes clear.

To epitomize the foregoing, new genotypes are created by sexual processes, and the terrific spread of these genotypes is accomplished by the asexual processes of reproduction.

2. GENERATION OF VARIANTS IN IMPERFECT (ASEXUAL) FUNGI

The frequency significance of this type of non-nuclear fusion variation is possibly greater than in the case of perfect (sexual) fungi; or rather, variation caused by non-sexual processes is a more extensive source of variants in both perfect and imperfect fungi than is the sexual process itself in the former group. When done artificially, however, breeding new strains via the sexual cycle can be done on a predictable basis, whereas in the former it is largely at random unless individual gene markers are being followed. This type variant (hybridization) was well recognized long before the genetics of fungi was worked out and very extensively developed in relation to certain groups of fungi, mostly plant and animal pathogens, the organisms of disease importance. In the latter group the dermatophytes have received most attention, whereas in the former possibly the rusts and smuts have received most study. Rather full treatment of variation in plant pathogenic fungi, especially the rusts (*Puccinia graminis*), the smuts (*Ustilago zeae*) and others has been compiled in 1940 by Rodenhiser, Christensen, and Craigie in the volume *Genetics of Pathogenic Organisms*. In this same volume, Stakman has examined this problem with an interesting philosophical slant. The experiences and principles expounded for the much worked-on plant disease fungi are identical with those of all other fungi. Extreme variations in morphological and cultural characteristics and virulence have been obtained almost in every organism studied in these respects. It is impossible to cover all the studies in this field and the interested reader will find a list of selected representative references on the subject in the second edition of Henrici's *Molds, Yeasts, and Actinomycetes* (Skinner *et al.*, 1945) (see also Wolf and Wolf, 1947). However, the principal underlying mechanisms of these variations are fairly well known, or at least are on an intelligible basis, and have been found applicable in such a wide variety of different organisms that there is no question that a fundamental phenomenon independent of nuclear fusion is almost universally at play in the fungi. For the plant pathologist especially, the implications of this profuse asexual variation become all too quickly apparent after the crop geneticist has developed a crop plant supposedly resistant to the ravages of a particular species of parasitic fungi. The dynamic aspects of this problem have been marshalled in a recent treatise by Stakman (1947) and are exemplified by the title "Plant Diseases are Shifty Enemies."

HETEROCARYOSIS

This is the phenomenon mainly responsible for asexual variation and refers to the condition where genetically dissimilar, but similar mating-type nuclei exist in the same cell, but do not undergo fusion. This situation appears to prevail as discussed above in the binucleate hyphae of certain of the Basidiomycetes for variable periods of time, but eventually the sexual fusion of the different mating type nuclei occurs, so it is not heterocaryosis. Up to that time the nuclei multiply by simple mitosis. In the case of true heterocaryosis, however, the various nuclei in a single cell are not different mating types, though they are genetically different. Each divides mitotically, and the daughter nuclei do likewise. As a rule the genetic characters of the different types of nuclei making up the cells manifest themselves in the cultural and biochemical nature of the adult organism, but each type of nucleus retains its original genetic integrity. As it is evident that a non-sexual cross has in effect been obtained, the organism is considered a cytoplasmic hybrid. It is essential to distinguish this type of hybrid from those resulting from crosses between homothallic or heterothallic organisms, i.e., where true fusion nuclei are involved. This latter is called heterosis. The heterocaryotic state is attained by the intertwining of hyphae or germ tubes, resulting in fusion of two different hyphae and of more or less considerable interchange of the cell contents. Most imperfect fungi are multinucleate and many nuclei may be exchanged along with the cytoplasmic environment. The narrow fusion bridge known as anastomosis, through which the exchange occurs, may constrict, separating the two hyphae, or it may even branch to give a typical hypha. This phenomenon was described in 1884 by the great botanist, DeBary, in his classic book (De Bary, 1884). Excellent photomicrographs of this process in *Botrytis cinerea* are given by Hansen and Smith (1932) and reproduced in Fig. 2. The exchanged nuclei divide and the mycelium continues to grow as usual, finally forming conidia.

When mycelia originating from different conidia are placed under conditions suitable for fusion it is observed that some show a marked tendency to fuse with each other, others show a diminished tendency, and in others anastomosis is not demonstrable at all. Similarly, in a mycelium of single spore origin, adjacent hyphae may fuse readily, whereas in the mycelium from a sister spore few or no hyphal fusions take place. This behavior is reminiscent of the behavior of mating types in fungi with perfect stages, but nothing further can be said of this rela-

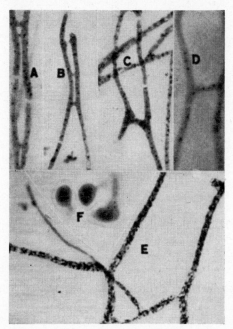

FIG. 2.—Anastomosis in *Botrytis cinerea* (from Hansen and Smith, 1932).

tion with certainty. In addition to hyphal fusion, the heterocaryotic condition can more rarely be initiated within a monocaryotic organism by a spontaneous mutation of one of the nuclei, which from that time on makes the mycelium heterocaryotic (Hansen, 1942).

The detailed mechanism of heterocaryosis in fungi, its manifestations, and its significance from the standpoint of the biology and the variability of Fungi Imperfecti were first clearly advanced by Hansen and Smith in the above paper and later developed for many different genera of fungi (Hansen and Smith, 1935; Hansen, 1938; Snyder and Hansen, 1940). Not only were heterocaryotic crosses obtained between different strains of the same species, but also between different well-characterized species

(*Botrytis allii* and *B. vicini*), yielding progeny resembling both parents, but also yielding progeny decidedly different from either parent, and to all appearances representing new species types. Figure 3 graphically portrays the principles of the work of these authors, as observed on *B. cinerea*, an imperfect fungus. A brief summary of these results is desirable because they represent the essence of asexual variation in fungi, although of course it may and does express itself in an infinite variety of ways. The following simple example affords a model of the working of this mechanism.

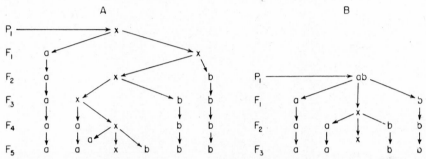

Fig. 3.—A. Behavior of the progeny of a single heterogenic conidium of *B. cinerea* through five single-spore culture series, showing the separation of the homotypes *a* and *b* from the heterotypes *x*. The chart represents a total of 650 single spore cultures.

B. Behavior of the progeny of the combination culture of homogenic strains *a* and *b* of *B. cinerea* through three single spore series, showing the production of heterotypes *x* and the subsequent reappearance of homotypes *a* and *b*. The chart represents a total of 1,180 single spore cultures (from Hansen and Smith, 1932).

Among *B. cinerea* conidia (which are multinucleate) is an inconstant type designated as *x*. From the individual conidia of this type three cultural types of the fungus are obtained: Constant type *a*, constant type *b* and the inconstant type *x*. Each of these types shows clearcut morphological and cultural differences from the others. It is well to bear in mind that the same holds where the differences are physiological or biochemical. Constant vs. inconstant refers to the stability of the agar slant cultures as visible from simple inspection. Constant type *a* subcultures true, yielding only type *a* through continued serial transfer. The same is true of constant type *b*. Type *x* always gives rise to all three types, *a*, *b*, and *x*. Hansen and Smith showed that this behavior is due to the fact that the fungus mycelium contains two types of nuclei, *a* and *b*, genetically different. The *x*-type mycelium contains both *a* and *b* and is heterocaryotic, and is obtained when pure types *a* and *b* are cultivated together, but not otherwise except from another *x*.

The origin of the three conidial types from a single *x* type conidium has a simple explanation. During conidiospore formation in x mycelium, the nuclei are constricted into spores, each spore containing small numbers of nuclei. By random assortment all the nuclei in one spore may be of one genetic type, and this spore is then pure type a or b. Chance also results in the inclusion in one spore of genetically different nuclei, that is, both a and b types, and the distinctive culture obtained from this spore is the inconstant type x. This is a general method for resolving heterocaryons. The ideal situation for resolving a heterocaryon obtains, of course, when the asexual spores are uninucleated.

It is obvious that in artificial culture and in nature, infinite numbers of such combinations and recombinations with regard to extremely complex types of genetic makeups are possible, and are doubtless occurring continuously. The existence of innumerable closely related, but different, fungus types in nature and the spontaneous changes occurring in "pure" cultures of single-conidium origin is now understandable; and the phenomenon of strain specificity and the dynamic physiological and cultural properties of fungi are interpretable on a rational basis.

Hansen (1938) established the universality of this phenomenon, finding it in thirty-two of thirty-five genera of Fungi Imperfecti tested. It also has been shown to account for the mycelial vs. spored type and the well-known "pleomorphic overgrowth" in dermatophytes (Wilhelm, 1947). Being mainly interested in the mycological aspects of fungi, Hansen dealt exclusively with a single genic character, namely that in which the culture forms a profusion of mycelium with relatively few spores vs. the limited formation of mycelium but with abundant spores. As all variants were hybrids of these two pure types he named this subject "dual phenomenon," designating mycelial and conidiospore strains as M and C types respectively, and hybrids as MC. A strain pure with respect to M or C is homogenic and a hybrid is heterogenic. Because this heterogenic situation doubtless exists for countless other genetically controlled cultural and physiological or biochemical characters of fungi, it would appear that the designation "dual phenomenon" in the "limited sporulation" sense that Hansen applied it is not adequate to describe the great multiplicity of effects embraced by this heterocaryotic behavior. Furthermore, mixing numerous different strains may yield a multiple heterocaryon. In fact, even in the case of conidiospore formation itself the problem is considerably more complex, for Lindegren (1936) has shown the existence of ten different mutants in *Neurospora* characterized by the loss of ability to produce conidia; and all ten were non-allelic. However, used in the sense of Hansen to connote the appearance of the two gross mycological stages of fungi, mycelial vs. conidial, the term "dual phenomenon" is of value.

Hansen proved what might be expected in relation to the number of nuclei in spores. Multinucleate-spored fungi show greater multiplicity of hybrids varying in degree of sporulation. This was shown to be due to different proportions of nuclei of the two types. The binucleate spores show a much smaller proportion of hybrids, and these are of only one type; uninucleated spores naturally are all homotypes. Conversely, homogenic spores decrease in frequency with an increase in the nucleation of spores. In uninuclear-spored fungi, each spore represents a single nuclear type present in the mycelium. Segregation is ideal here and testing single-spore cultures will indicate the components of the heterocaryon.

The main concept of Hansen and his school has been confirmed and broadened, the principal contributions genetically being those of Baker (1944), Pontecorvo and Gemmell (1944), and Lindegren and Andrews (1945) for *Penicillium notatum;* and Dodge (1942), Lindegren (1942), and Beadle and Coonradt (1944) for species of Neurospora, the former dealing with morphological tracers of heterocaryosis. Some data on physiological and biochemical factors under heterocaryotic control are now available, further demonstrating the multifarious opportunities for origin of different physiological strains (i.e., strain specificity) which situation is indeed the one seemingly observable at all times. Lindegren and Andrews studied heterocaryosis with reference to penicillin-producing powers in *P. notatum* and showed that definite effects are obtainable (Table 2).

TABLE 2

PENICILLIN PRODUCTION BY P. NOTATUM INDIVIDUAL STRAINS AND THEIR HETEROCARYONS[1]

Expt. I		Expt. II	
Strain	Penicillin, units/ml.	Strain	Penicillin, units/ml.
No. 49	20	49	18
No. 72	47	72	90
No. 75	25	75	22
Nos. 49 and 72	12	49 and 72 and 75	2
Nos. 49 and 75	7		
Nos. 72 and 75	47		

[1] From Lindegren and Andrews (1945).

The data indicate that No. 49 definitely reduces the penicillin-producing powers of Nos. 72 and 75 when in heterocaryotic combination with them. Cultures 72 and 75 are, however, clearly compatible for penicillin production in heterocaryotic combination. The significance of these results is obvious in relation to the potential penicillin-producing powers of a given strain. It makes clear that the main reason conidial progeny from a colony show great individual differences in penicillin-producing powers, or any biochemical function for that matter, is that the mycelium producing those conidia is heterocaryotic with nuclei of wide genetic range in relation to the biochemical function. Mass transfers of conidia from this type apparently permit the low-penicillin nuclei to gain ascendancy in proportion to the others, the culture thus being said to have undergone physiological degeneration. The genetic range of nuclei in relation to penicillin can best be obtained by a study of penicillin powers of numbers of single conidia derived from one parent.

Beadle and Coonradt (1943) have furnished the most detailed study of heterocaryosis from the standpoint of biochemical activities. Of particular emphasis for this discussion is the fact that dominance and recessiveness are just as much at play and presumably have the same physiological basis in heterocaryons as in ordinary diploid organisms (i.e., where nuclear fusion occurs). Thus, if two biochemically deficient mutants of *Neurospora crassa*, one p-aminobenzoicless* and the other nicotinicless,* are crossed by hyphal fusion, the heterocaryon grows independent of vitamins, that is, the resulting organism is now in the wild type condition. This means that both deficient genes are recessive to their normal alleles carried in the complementary nucleus. The nucleus from the p-aminobenzoicless mutant carries the normal gene for synthesis of nicotinic acid, and vice versa. The heterocaryon may then be pictured as having p.a.b.−, n+, and p.a.b.+, n− genes. As the new organism now synthesizes both vitamins, the only conclusion possible is that the wild type, or + genes, in each case are dominant over the recessive one or else both vitamins would still be required for growth. Robbins (1941) apparently was one of the first to attribute hybrid vigor to complementary powers in relation to vitamin synthesis, though he worked with tomato roots. A striking demonstration of the true significance of heterocaryotic vigor in the competitive struggle for survival in nature is provided by Dodge for *Neurospora tetrasperma* (1942). Hyphal fusion between a dwarf strain (No. 16) and a normal wild type of the same sex produced a heterocaryon which grew at two to three times the rate of either parent. Along the line of Robbins' idea, this increased vigor was interpreted as a complementary synthesis of growth factors, in which both parent strains were partially deficient.

Pontecorvo and Gemmell (1944) came to the same conclusions for the

---

* Mutants unable to synthesize these two vitamins respectively, hence require the particular one to be furnished in order for growth to take place.

spore pigment in *P. notatum;* four x-ray mutants characterized by absence of green conidial pigments formed the normal green pigment when fused in the appropriate pairs. Hence the pigment-normal allele is dominant. A further complexity from the standpoint of variety and multiplicity of strains in nature is evident from the fact that pairing studies in this case showed that the four white mutants were non-allelic, i.e., four independent different gene mutations had occurred with respect to green pigment formation. Incidentally, a non-conidial mutant was found to be dominant to the conidial form, a finding which, if applicable to other genera, provides a logical explanation for the high frequency of non-conidial or mycelial (M) types found in nature by Hansen. The work of Beadle and Coonradt contains many other interesting aspects of the heterocaryon condition, especially with respect to dominance vs. recessiveness, and with respect to the evolutionary significance of this mechanism and its relation to the evaluation of sexual reproduction.

In some cases heterocaryon dominance and recessiveness was shown to be a matter of degree, depending on the proportion existing between the component nuclei. If each component by itself is characterized by a submaximal rate of growth, there will be a selection against hetero-caryotic hyphae with too great a proportion of either slow-growing type, and so in theory, the hybrids selected or surviving in nature are those with greatest vigor endowed by the appropriate ratio of component nuclei. Several experimentally-established nuclear ratios show that the wild-type growth rates may be obtained from submaximal growers over a rather wide range of nuclear ratios, possibly up to 50:1.

It is also possible to determine quantitatively the relative degree of recessiveness vs. dominance existing between two alleles for any one character. Thus in the case of a normal growth rate heterocaryon in which a pantothenicless mutant was crossed with a morphological mutant, pantothenicless nuclei comprised from 31.2 to 94.6 per cent of all the nuclei present, permitting the obvious conclusion that the mutant gene is relatively recessive since its numerical abundance in the cells is not manifested by a reduced rate of growth. Where the latter figure obtained, only one out of seventeen nuclei carried the normal allele, yet this was sufficient to give the normal growth rate.

It is evident that heterocaryons involving three, four, and many more components are possible, and doubtless occur all the time. It is clear that information of this type enables us to understand the basic causes for population shifts of various physiological kinds within cultures carried artificially in the laboratory. The data of Whiffen and Savage discussed on p. 188 must be interpretable on this basis, though enough genetic facts in this case are not available to give the whole story. In the vegetative state the optimum heterocaryotic proportion for penicillin formation is apparently maintained, whereas this situation changes radically when nuclear segregation takes place via sporulation. Individuals are formed, or other nuclear combinations apparently take place, and though inferior in penicillin yields, they have superior growth vigor.

In mycogenetics one must bear in mind that chances for hyphal fusion and heterocaryosis would appear not to be too good among hyphae maintained in a state of continued agitation such as is done in submerged or shake cultures, owing to the fact that the opportunities seem physically remote for two hyphae to be in close enough proximity long enough to effect cytoplasmic and nuclear exchange via an anastomosis.

It is evident that heterocaryosis is an efficient survival mechanism for organisms in nature. Numerous different combinations are possible, resulting in a heterocaryotic vigor and consequently selection and survival. The very number of possible types of nuclear makeup, the abundant occurrence of fusion and anastomosis both from the same and different strains, species, or genera, and the wide range of nuclear ratios sufficient to maintain heterocaryotic vigor, suggest a versatility and flexibility conducive to survival vigor even superior to diploid organisms.

In studies dealing with mutation rates in fungi one must ascertain that a homocaryotic strain is used, else the results will be fallacious due to formation of heterocaryons.

Beadle and Coonradt have an extremely important concept, contributing to our ideas and knowledge of the evolution of sexual reproduction in which the heterocaryotic condition is one stage. This hypothesis is presented schematically in Fig. 4.

They picture the evolution of sexual reproduction as a series of successive steps, each of which would have selective advantage over the preceding condition. The interesting feature is that the hypothesis is built around the idea of loss of ability to synthesize growth factors, though other cellular requirements obviously must be included also. The steps are:

(1) An organism homogeneous and relatively autonomous in growth factor synthesis.
(2) Differentiation of individuals through gene mutation into two groups deficient in abilities to synthesize growth factors. This can be accomplished experimentally.
(3) Intercellular symbiosis that arises from a change in environment and results in the unavailability of externally supplied growth factors, thus making survival of two deficient types depending on the symbiotic relation between them. This can be accomplished experimentally.

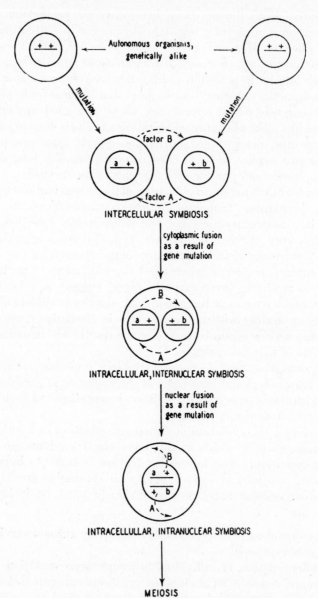

FIG. 4.—Schematic representation of postulated steps in the evolution of sexual
reproduction (from Beadle and Coonradt, 1944).

(4) Vegetative fusion of cells without nuclear fusion, with an increase in the efficiency of the symbiotic relation—heterocaryosis. This can be accomplished experimentally.

(5) Nuclear fusion with a still further increase in the efficiency of the complementary gene action—the sexual stage, followed by meiosis, etc.

Each step in this hypothesis reduces the size of the combining units through the series: cell, nucleus, chromosome, and gene. Each advance would, therefore, increase the evolutionary flexibility of the species.

EVOLUTION OF BIOCHEMICAL SYNTHESES

The reader interested in mechanisms of evolution should be aware of the attractive hypothesis recently advanced by Horowitz (1945) with respect to biochemical syntheses (see Chapter 6). This concept states that the order of attainment of the individual steps in a chain of reactions has been in the reverse direction from that in which the synthesis proceeds, i.e., the last step was the first to be acquired in the course of evolution, the penultimate step was next, and so on. The species originally could not synthesize substance A, and obtained it from the environment, which also contains substances B and C capable of reacting via enzymes to give A. Through continued growth of the organism the supply of A becomes depleted until it limits further growth. Here a spontaneously arising mutant, which is able to carry out the reaction $B + C = A$, will be endowed with marked selective advantage that eventually enables it to displace the parent strain from the population. In the now A-free environment a back mutation to the original stock would be lethal.

Eventually the available supply of B becomes limiting for the species, necessitating its synthesis from other substances in the environment, D and E, which will permit some new mutant to emerge, and the population shift now consists of a species characterized by the genotype $D + E = B$, $B + C = A$. This same process could recur until long reaction chains are built, as we know them today.

Horowitz' stimulating hypothesis is predicated on the assumption that the first living entity was a completely heterotrophic unit, reproducing itself at the expense of prefabricated organic molecules in its environment. A good argument for the latter is made by Oparin (1938). The conditions necessary for the operation of the mechanism ceased to exist with the ultimate destruction of the organic environment. Further evolution was, according to Horowitz, probably based on the chance combination of genes, to a large extent resulting in the development of short reaction chains utilizing substances whose synthesis had been previously acquired.

REFERENCES

Baker, G. E.   1944.   *Bull. Torrey Botan. Club* **71**, 367–373.
Beadle, G. W., and Coonradt, V. L.   1944.   *Genetics* **29**, 291–308.
Buell, C. B., and Weston, W. H.   1947.   *Am. J. Botany* **34**, 555–561.
Craigie, J. H.   1940.   Genetics of Pathogenic Organisms. Publ. Am. Assoc. Adv. Sci. No. 12, 66–72.
DeBary, A.   1884.   Vergleichende Morphologie und Biologie der Pilze, Mycetozoen, und Bakterien. W. Engelmann, Leipzig, 558 pp.
Dodge, B. O.   1942.   *Bull. Torrey Botan. Club* **69**, 75–91.
Foster, J. W., Woodruff, H. B., and McDaniel, L. E.   1943.   *J. Bact.* **46**, 421–433.
Hansen, H. N.   1938.   *Mycologia* **30**, 442–455.
Hansen, H. N.   1942.   *Phytopathology* **32**, 639–640.
Hansen, H. N., and Smith, R. E.   1932.   *Phytopathology* **22**, 953–964.
Hansen, H. N., and Smith, R. E.   1935.   *Zentr. Bakt. Parasitenk. Abt II* **92**, 272–279.
Hansen, H. N., and Snyder, W. C.   1944.   *Science* **99**, 264–265.
Horowitz, N. H.   1945.   *Proc. Natl. Acad. Sci. U. S.* **31**, 153–157.
Ingold, C. T.   1946.   *Nature* **157**, 614–616.
Lindegren, C. C.   1936.   *Am. Naturalist* **120**, 404–405.
Lindegren, C. C.   1942.   *Iowa State Coll. J. Sci.* **16**, 271–280.'
Lindegren, C. C., and Andrews, H. N.   1945.   *Bull. Torrey Botan. Club* **72**, 361–366.
Oparin, A. I.   1938.   The Origin of Life.   Translated by S. Morgulis, Macmillan, New York.
Pasteur, L. 1876.   Études sur la Bière.   Gauthier-Villars, Paris.   (a) p. 125, (b) p. 138.
Pontecorvo, G., and Gemmell, A. R.   1944.   *Nature* **154**, 514–516.
Raper, K. B., and Alexander, D. F.   1945a.   *Mycologia* **37**, 499–525.
Raper, K. B., and Alexander, D. F.   1945b.   *J. Elisha Mitchell Sci. Soc.* **61**, 74–113.
Robbins, W. J.   1941.   *Am. J. Botany* **28**, 216–225.
Rodenhiser, H. A.   1940.   Genetics of Pathogenic Organisms. Publ. Am. Assoc. Adv. Sci. No. 12, 73–76.
Schulz, G.   1937.   *Planta* **27**, 196–218.
Skinner, C. E., Emmons, C. W., and Tsuchiya, H. M.   1945.   Chapter 2 in Henrici's Molds, Yeasts and Actinomycetes. Wiley, New York.
Snyder, W. C., and Hansen, H. N.   1940.   *Am. J. Botany* **27**, 64–67.
Stakman, E. C.   1940.   Genetics of Pathogenic Organisms. Publ. Am. Assoc. Adv. Sci. No. 12, 9–17.
Stakman, E. C.   1947.   *Am. Scientist* **35**, 321–350.
Thom, C., and Raper, K. B.   1945.   Manual of the Aspergilli. Williams & Wilkins, Baltimore.
Thom, C., and Steinberg, R. A.   1939.   *Proc. Natl. Acad. Sci. U. S.* **25**, 329–335.
Westerdijk, J.   1947.   *Antonie van Leeuwenhoek* **12**, 221–231.
Whiffen, A. J., and Savage, G. M.   1947.   *J. Bact.* **53**, 231–240.
Wilhelm, S.   1947.   *Mycologia* **39**, 716–724.
Wolf, F. A., and Wolf, F. T.   1947.   Fungi. Vol. 2, Wiley, New York.

CHAPTER 6

MUTATIONS, PHYSIOLOGICAL GENETICS, AND BIOCHEMICAL SYNTHESES

The idea of mutation connotes a sudden permanent change in some character of an organism. As the change occurs independent of nuclear behavior, i.e., is independent of hybridization and segregation and cannot be shown to be within normal cells of the organism, and because it is permanent and inheritable, the seat of this phenomenon must be the chromosomes and genes. Each individual biochemical reaction, whether it is manifested as a morphological or cultural change or not, is controlled by a single gene. Permanent alteration or destruction of a gene will, therefore, result in a biochemical (or subsequent cultural) change in the organism, and, as the chromosomes containing the genes transmit the gene in question in its altered form to the progeny cells, all future generations will in general be true copies of the mutated cell.

Microorganisms are ideal subjects on which to study mutations and inheritance owing to the enormous populations of individuals one may work with, and also because of the rapid turnover of generations and increase in progeny numbers. Here mutation work can be put on a statistical basis because of the large numbers involved; with higher plants and animals a much longer time is required to obtain the numbers of individuals essential to a mutation study on account of the relatively slow generation time. Furthermore, the large microbial populations can be maintained under rigorously controlled conditions for special treatments; and, of especial importance, these conditions will be truly homogeneous for all cells in the population. Finally, in the fungi in particular, sexual reproduction is so common a feature that it is often possible to put the suspected mutants to the ultimate test, that is, if the change is genetic, it must follow the basic pattern of Mendelian inheritance. The study of mutations and genetics of true fungi has, to a certain extent, an advantage over bacterial genetics because the former have structural differentiation, and hence afford a greater possibility for genetic analysis by mere inspection.

SPONTANEOUS MUTATIONS

All biological species have been found to undergo a small but nevertheless measurable rate of spontaneous mutation wherever a large

209

enough population has been studied. This mutation rate occurs independent of any condition which will create mutants artificially, hence the designation "spontaneous." In general, the frequency rate is about one to a few mutants per million unicellular individuals. Doubtless this occurs continually in nature and, together with the mechanisms described in the preceding chapter, accounts for the diversity of individual species types.

This type of mutation in fungi is easiest, if not most frequently, observed during the development of colonies of single cell (spore or vegetative) origin on the surface of an agar plate. The best conditions are those where a "giant" colony is obtained, i.e., where only one colony, in the center of the plate, is present. The colony develops over a much larger area of the plate when it alone consumes all the available nutrients; the presence of more than one colony reduces the nutrients available to each colony, hence each one is much smaller. Considering the enormous number of cells making up a discrete fungus colony, it is not unexpected that an occasional one will mutate spontaneously, and, in a sense, a colony presents a large enough population for examination for the occasional mutant. Since by definition all the progeny of that mutant cell must breed true, it is evident that all cells in the colony derived from the mutant will be mutants themselves in comparison with the rest of the colony cells. Colonies develop radially on account of the geometric nature of the cell proliferation, and accordingly, the mutant cells will appear as a wedge-shaped sector in the whole colony, with the apex at the point of the original mutated cell, and the base generally at the periphery of the colony. The obvious and most commonly encountered mutations discernible this way are changes in spore or mycelial pigmentation, the intensity of sporulation itself and the rate of growth. This "sectoring" phenomenon is almost as old as the pure culture technique itself, and has been designated as variation, saltation, dissociation, mutation, etc. A transplant from the sector ordinarily gives rise only to the sector (mutant) type, a proof of true mutation. Some colonies may demonstrate many sectors; and, occurring spontaneously as they do, their apices are located at random throughout the colony area. On the other hand, some fungi show this phenomenon only rarely. Thus cultures may be relatively stable or unstable in this respect. Sectors are visible only because cultural changes are produced. It is evident that unapparent sector areas must also develop, the mutants in these cases being biochemical, and detectable only upon physiological testing and analysis. Virulence change, for example, is one of the features commonly encountered in plant pathogenic fungi.

In theory, a sector could arise owing to the formation of a heterocaryotic hybrid at the apex, but in reality this mechanism is extremely unlikely because all the cells would theoretically be heterocaryotic to begin with, and, secondly, anastomoses would occur at such great frequency that, if the hyphae were compatable, the typical sector formation would not develop. Furthermore, this could not explain the sector formation in colonies of single uninucleated spore origin, and hence is doubtless not the causative agent in the case of colonies of multinucleated spored fungi.

The actual geometrical form of the sectoring may vary according to the population dynamics in the colony, and some interesting theoretical considerations are possible which bear upon the circumstances in the colony at the time of mutation, and also upon the metabolic competition between the normal and the mutated cells. In the main, the observed sector shapes are explained by Pontecorvo and Gemmell (1944) on the basis of growth rate differentials and resultants. According to these authors, a spontaneously (or artificially) mutating cell in the mass of hyphal tips at the periphery of the growing colony must be endowed with a higher growth rate than its neighbors, or, by excretion of chemical substances, must suppress the innumerable hyphae in the vicinity else, on a simple numerical basis, it would never have a chance to manifest itself in the competition for nutrients with the neighboring normal hyphae. Statistically then, a much larger number of mutations probably occur than ever develop to mature as sectors; with few exceptions they do not survive the intense competition.

Spontaneous mutation doubtless is universal in fungi, although much more marked in some than in others. As a matter of fact, this very tendency to mutate is in itself genetically controlled, as shown by Stakman (1936) for *Ustilago zeae*. In the smut fungus cross between *Sphacelotheca sorghi* and *S. cruenta*, described in the previous chapter, the mutation tendency appears to be a recessive character. Both haploid parents had never been observed to undergo sectoring, and this was true of five out of the ninety progeny strains. In the remaining eighty-five strains, the mutation tendency apparently segregated out, and four in particular were very unstable, colonies showing ten sectors not being uncommon. *Helminthosporium sativum* is an outstanding example of a mutable fungus; single colonies of this organism may show up to forty viable sectors (Christensen, 1940).

Cultivation of a fungus under abnormal environmental conditions often provokes colonies or cultures abnormal in appearance, though this rarely shows the typical sector picture, being instead characteristic of the entire colony. These instances are the response variations mentioned in Chapter 4 and are not to be regarded as mutations, because transferring these cultures back to normal conditions at once restores the original characteristics, whereas genetically altered forms would, of course, be transmitted regardless of the medium, if they were true mutants.

Christensen (1940) summarizes much information which shows that the spontaneous mutants arising as described actually are different from their parent organism.   Aside from visible differences, mutants differ from the parent in tolerance to dyes and toxic substances, in the production of organic acids and enzymes, and in temperature relations; and these physiological differences may be accompanied by visible cultural and morphological alterations.   In the case of plant pathogens, the virulence of mutants from any one parent may equal, exceed, or be less than the parent.   The factor of sex itself in heterothallic fungi may mutate so that the mutant will not cross with strains which do cross with the parent.

As parent cultures may be unstable and produce mutants, so may mutants be of varying degrees of stability.   Thus, the majority will retain the mutant characters indefinitely, whereas others may, upon transfer, revert to the parent type after varying periods of time.   A detailed study of back-mutation of an x-ray induced nutritional mutant of Neurospora is given by Ryan (1946).

FACTORS INFLUENCING MUTATION FREQUENCIES

Though commonly designated as "spontaneous," the rate of appearance of mutants can be greatly influenced and altered by the environmental conditions, including nature of the growth medium, salt concentrations, pH, temperature, light, inhibitory substances, and radiations of various sorts.   In all but a relatively few it is difficult to place these instances on a rational basis.   The particular treatment is merely observed to evoke a type of response and beyond that little is known on which to construct a hypothesis as to the nature of these actions.   However, in recent years some fundamental information has been accumulating which makes it possible to appraise these events in a more scientific manner, and this is discussed in the next section.   In such cases the effects may be considered as having general applicability to almost all fungi (also bacteria) because the mechanisms are fundamental, thus lending themselves to integration.   On the other hand, many reports are available in which clear cut mutation influences are at play, but they are highly specific for only one or a few organisms, for special media, and in general, the mutation responses are unpredictable.   Conditions bordering on those unfavorable for maximum growth rate appear to be those conducive to spontaneous mutations.   Included here are extremes of temperature, pH, high salt concentrations, especially zinc salts, and poisons, especially the heavy metal type. Ostensibly, these factors exert their influence by altering the genes in some unknown manner. The reader is referred to Christensen (1940) for a survey of these factors.

INDUCED MUTATIONS

Factors known to have a rational basis for their mutating action, and whose mutating action can be predicted to occur with a reasonable chance of success for any fungus (or other microorganism) will be discussed in this section. These factors are in two categories: chemical and irradiation.

1. INDUCTION OF FUNGUS MUTATIONS BY CHEMICALS

a. Nitrous Acid

Probably the first attempt to induce mutation by direct alteration of the gene proteins in the cell was done by Thom and Steinberg in 1939 (see also Steinberg and Thom 1940a, b). Their paper, entitled "Chemical Inductions of Genetic Changes in Fungi," represents the beginnings of a still expanding era of the study of the chemical nature of the gene, especially in relation to the problem of mutations. In the future this discovery may well rank in the same category as Muller's discovery of the production of mutants as a result of x-ray irradiation of the fruit-fly Drosophila, because the work of these two mycologists demonstrates that the gene material itself can be attacked at certain reactive linkages in the living cell, these alterations resulting in mutations. Since then, this line of attack has been repeatedly confirmed and extended to a wide variety of different chemical mutating agents, all employed with the objective of altering the chemical structure or composition of the genes without impairing the viability of the cell.

Thom and Steinberg were attempting to find some explanation which would account for the enormous numbers of strains or varieties of any one type of fungus found in nature, each obviously different from the other, but equally obviously forming a homogeneous group. They reasoned that the varieties must have originated from a single type by mutations of various degrees of severity. A slightly altered mutant could then change further, and so on, until mutants radically different from the parent stock were obtained. A variety of miscellaneous chemicals were tested on *Aspergillus niger*, *A. amstelodami* and *Penicillium caseicolum*, purposely chosen as mutating material because for 20 to 30 years in the laboratory these three strains had never shown any indication of spontaneous mutation. Striking cultural mutations of the two Aspergilli were repeatedly obtained by culturing the organisms in a mineral salts solution containing d-mannitol (5 per cent) and NaNO₂ (0.2 per cent) as the sole carbon and nitrogen sources, respectively. Massive spore inoculations were made into this medium, and the culture allowed to develop for a minimum of 1 month at which time manifestly abnormal portions of the sporulated mycelial mass were isolated. The normal organism ceased growth by that time but the nitrite cultures tended to form secondary growths, transfers of which generally proved to be mutants. Owing to the fact that even in the nitrite medium the massive portion of the fungus matter consisted of normal mycelium growing normally, the appearance of the mutant very likely could not be ascribed to spontaneous mutation and selection.

The changes observed in the mutants included increased vegetative mycelium, increased production of yellow to orange color in the hyphae, reduction in conidia-producing apparatus in the form of diminutive stalks, reduced size of head, elimination or reduction of the primary sterigmata, great reduction in the numbers of spore-producing cells and the production of comparatively few spores. Interestingly enough, these artificially induced variants were comparable in type and range to the sixty-three strains of Aspergilli isolated from nature present in Biourge's collection and described by Mosseray (1934).

The action of the nitrite was ascribed to its reactivity with free primary amino groups, with a consequent stripping of free amino groups from the proteins concerned in the transmission of hereditary characters, i.e., the genes. Actually, nitrous acid is the reactive form, this being generated as the organism generates organic acids from the carbohydrate. This change is apparently sufficient to alter the character of the gene but is not lethal. The concentration of nitrite is of significance: one-tenth of the usual amount of nitrite failed to yield a single mutant. In the regular trials it was stated conservatively that 50 per cent of the trials should yield visible mutants, and mannitol appeared to be superior to sucrose as a carbon source for frequency of mutation.

Other chemical substances known to have an action comparable to nitrous acid in deaminating amino groups of amino acids and proteins, namely, ninhydrin, chloramine T, hexamethylenamine and potassium iodide, all were capable of forming mutants. The types of mutants were quite similar to the nitrite mutants, indicating that the basis of their action is identical with that of nitrite. In this case the mutants were extended to seven different species of Aspergilli.

Testing of the above amino group hypothesis led Steinberg and Thom (1940b) to express the idea (which anticipates a modern theory) of the origin of chemically induced mutations via the mechanism whereby the cell builds up the gene from nutrient building blocks.   If altered building blocks are provided in the medium, these, being chemical analogues of the normal gene components, are indiscriminately synthesized into the gene nucleoprotein, giving in effect a gene analogue or inexact gene replicate which gives rise to the mutants (Stone *et al.*, 1947). According to Steinberg and Thom, if the genes bereft of free amino groups, i.e., mutants, could have their amino groups restored, reversion of the mutant forms to the normal might be expected.   High concentrations of *d*-lysine were employed with the expectation that in some instances the added amino acid would be introduced intact into the modified (nucleo-) proteins during their synthesis.   Free amino groups in proteins are known to be associated with the presence of *d*-lysine. This treatment resulted in reversion to varying degrees in *A. niger* and *A. amstelodami.*

The lysine reversion effect was considered indicative of a function of this amino acid in the processes of differentiation and reproduction in fungi, since the observed mutants were more or less defective in these two features.

More extensive studies later (Steinberg and Thom, 1942) showed that mixtures of amino acids were even better for reversion, a combination of lysine, valine, and nicotinic acid giving best results with *A. niger*. *A. amstelodami* reverted only with a mixture of lysine and threonine. Although the mutants did differ from the parents in efficiency of utilization of amino acids as the sole N source for growth, the differences in assimilability of the amino acids could not account for the reversion effect.

b. Colchicine

In general, this alkaloid agent, whose mutating action depends on its ability to inhibit mitosis, resulting in a form containing multiple numbers of chromosomes (polyploidy), has had only limited success in inducing mutation in fungi.   A common manifestation of polyploidy in plants is the giant size of the mutant, and this has been reported to take place in *Penicillium notatum* (Gordon and McKecknie, 1946).   Steinberg and Thom (1940b) attribute the many unsuccessful attempts to obtain mutants of fungi with colchicine to the fact that this base is hydrolyzed by acid to form colchicein, which is inactive as a mutating agent.   Fungi generally are cultivated in acid media, or the media become acid through organic acid formation during growth and metabolism of the fungus, and this inactivates the alkaloid.   The addition of excess calcium carbonate as a neutralizing agent prevents this inactivation and mutants were readily obtained with a number of different Aspergilli.   Colchicine was also able to induce partial reversion of a mutant of *A. amstelodami.*

c. Mustard Gas

The discovery of Auerback & Robson in 1946 that treatment of the fruit fly Drosophila larvae with mustard gas caused mutations of this insect, has led to extensive application of this principle to microbiology. Fungi also mutate under the influence of this chemical substance. Actually two types of mustards are known and are useful, the nitrogen mustards, methyl-bis(β-chloroethyl) amine, and the sulfur mustards, bis(β-chloroethyl) sulfide. In general the mutation procedure is to add the mustard gas to an aqueous suspension of asexual spores of the fungus to a final concentration of approximately 0.1 to 1.0 per cent. The sulfur mustard is liquid and the nitrogen mustard is solid at room temperature. After different periods of exposure, samples are withdrawn and the spores plated out on a complete medium. Mutants are detected in the usual manner: morphological and cultural mutants by comparative inspection, and biochemical deficiency mutants by testing for growth in basal minimal medium vs. one with various organic supplements. This simple technique is, of course, applicable only to uninucleate spores. Multinucleated spores, as in Neurospora, must be crossed with the normal wild type of opposite sex, by fusion and fruiting, to obtain the sexual spore, in this case, ascospores. In other words, segregation must be achieved to isolate the mutant. The ascospores, one from each perithecium, are then isolated and tested on minimal medium, etc. Details of this technique are given in the next section under Irradiation.

Highly efficient mutation rates are obtainable in fungi by the mustards, to judge from results with *Neurospora crassa* and *Penicillium notatum* (Horowitz et al., 1946; Stahmann and Stauffer, 1946). The frequency is in the same range as that obtainable by ultraviolet irradiation of these same organisms. With Neurospora, about 7.6 per cent of the spores surviving the treatment were mutants, somewhat less than half being biochemical (deficiency) mutants, and the remainder cultural (visible) mutants. Among the former were strains unable to synthesize one of a number of different individual amino acids and vitamins. Methionine deficient mutants preponderated (50 per cent of biochemical mutants), as they do in ultraviolet irradiation mutants.

The older the conidiospores of Neurospora, the smaller the mutation rate, and the evidence is good that treatment of germinated spores and the young mycelium itself offers the highest percentage of mutants (McElroy et al., 1947). The explanation of this possibly lies in easier penetration and access to the nuclei. It appears quite clear that actively dividing nuclei are more susceptible to the mutating influence of mustards. Up to 17 per cent of germinated ascospores obtained from crosses between treated and wild normal cultures were mutants, 7.8 per cent being morphological (cultural) and 9.2 per cent biochemical (deficiencies).   Table 1 shows the trends evident with the biological condition of Neurospora cells (data from McElroy et al., 1947).

TABLE 1

MUTATION SUSCEPTIBILITY OF NEUROSPORA IN DIFFERENT BIOLOGICAL STATES[1]

Biological condition of Neurospora	Asco-spores tested	Germi-nated spores, per cent	Num-ber isolated	Mutants, per cent of germinated spores
Old conidia (7–15 days)........	1137	90	0	0 0
Protoperithecia...............	291	61.5	15	8.4 (8.4 × 2) = 16.8
Young conidia (2–3 days)......	481	72.5	14	4.0 (4.0 × 2) = 8.0
Germinating conidia (4–5 hours)	231	70	16	9.9 (9.9 × 2) = 19.8

[1] One-tenth per cent nitrogen mustard treated for 30 minutes.

No significant difference in types of mutants obtained from the two types of mustard has been revealed so far, and, as a matter of fact, both are quite similar to ultraviolet mutants.   Methionine mutants always are the largest single class of biochemical mutants obtained.   In this particular study the biochemical mutants were distributed as follows: six methionine, four leucine, two adenine-hypoxanthine, three inositol, two thiamine, two p-aminobenzoic acid, two arginine, one proline, one yeast nucleic acid, one threonine, one lysine, fifty-three unidentified (different from above).

As in the case of irradiation, the great majority of the spores in the suspension undergoing mustard treatment are lethal mutants, i.e. are mutated in a fashion inconsistent with growth, and for all practical purposes are killed.   The highest mutation rate of the survivors comes when the latter is a very small fraction of the original spore count.   With ultraviolet irradiation, the maximum mutation rate does not coincide with the highest killing rate, there being a maximum for each organism and set of conditions, which is experimentally ascertainable.   Doubtless further work with mustards will find this true of them also.   Characteristic data of a mutation run on *Penicillium notatum* No. 832 comparing a nitrogen mustard (methyl bis(β-chloroethyl) amine) and ultraviolet irradiation are given in Table 2 (from Stahmann and Stauffer, 1945).

In this work the absolute mutation rate doubtless was appreciably higher than recorded, for only visible morphological and cultural mutants are reported. The plating medium contained peptone, hence the biochemical deficiency mutants were not detected.

TABLE 2

INDUCTION OF MUTANTS IN PENICILLIUM NOTATUM

Treatment (min.)	Survival per cent	Mutants	
		Per cent of survivors	Per cent of original spores
By methyl-bis(β-chloroethyl) amine			
0	100.0	0.1	0.1
1	60.1	0.2	0.1
2	41.3	1.8	0.7
4	31.5	8.7	2.7
8	8.9	19.6	1.7
16	3.6	29.5	1.1
33	2.6	44.4	1.1
By ultraviolet irradiation (2750 A.)			
0	100.0	0.1	0.1
5	81.0	2.2	1.8
10	48.6	8.9	4.3
15	24.5	20.0	4.9
20	3.6	23.3	0.8
25	1.6	15.4	0.2
30	1.2	10.0	0.1

The mechanism of action of the mustards is not known, but the most widely accepted hypothesis is much along the lines of the nitrous acid action described above, namely, the highly reactive mustard chemicals react with various groupings on proteins, presumably including the nucleoproteins making up the genes, thereby altering them in a manner consistent with mutations. The mustards react with sulfhydryl and amino groups of several amino acids including arginine, lysine, histidine, methionine and threonine (Hartwell, 1946; Kinsey and Grant, 1946).

d. Antibodies

The above cited mutation-producing treatments are in a sense indiscriminate, that is, they affect other parts and constituents of the cell in addition to the vital gene material and a high percentage of lethals always ensues. This is a natural result of their non-specific chemical affinities, non-specific at least in relation to the desoxyribonucleoprotein of the genes. The well-known high degree of specificity in antigen-antibody reactions has led Sturtevant (1944) and also Emerson (1945) to postulate that antibodies produced in response to gene proteins injected into experimental animals, should, when made accessible to the organisms from which the gene antigens were extracted, react specifically with the gene antigens *in situ* in the cell, i.e., in this case the very genes themselves. This specific reaction should create some alteration manifesting itself as a mutant. The work of Landsteiner, Marrack, Pauling, and others have demonstrated that the unique specificity of antibody-antigen reactions is due to the surface architecture of the two molecules, these being mutually complementary in shape and in arrangement of reactive groups (i.e., oppositely charged groups, groups capable of forming hydrogen bonds, etc.). The gene would be visualized as a sort of template, on which the gene antibody fits to complete the serological reaction between the two. The synthesis of enzymes, proteins, and duplication of genes also is visualized as fashioned by the primary template, i.e., the gene. For further details the reader is referred to the above mentioned articles.

That alteration of the gene surface by the specific antibody is possible and is recognizable in the form of mutants seems indicated by data advanced by Emerson (1944). Mycelial extracts of *Neurospora crassa*, and also culture filtrates, were injected as immunizing antigens into rabbits, and both the mycelium and conidia were exposed for 1 to 2 days to the antisera. A total of 695 isolates were made from treated material and tested for their ability to utilize sucrose, cellobiose, maltose, starch, and α-amylodextrin, all of which the normal wild type utilizes readily. Twenty-five of these isolates proved to be mutants unable to utilize one of the sugars, including also two morphological mutants. All of the eleven which were tested were shown to be single gene mutants by sexual crossing and segregation with the normal wild type. The control series (untreated) yielded no mutants out of 276 isolates. Further suggesting that mutants are induced by the antigen-antibody reaction, is the higher mutation rate when the fungus conidia are exposed to the antisera at low temperatures (2°C.) known to favor more complete antigen-antibody reactions (e.g., precipitin and complement-fixation tests).

e. Other Possible Mutating Chemicals

It is now well established that extracts or culture filtrates from certain bacteria, when added to other strains of the same species, may cause the latter to undergo an inheritable mutation, which change, when occurring spontaneously, is known as dissociation or variation. This has been demonstrable so far in pneumococci, *Escherichia coli* and *Shigella paradysenteriae*, and doubtless will prove to be a general phenomenon in bacteria. In some cases, for example, the pneumococci and *E. coli*, the mutating agent ("transforming factor") has been isolated and identified as a protein of the desoxyribonucleic acid type, of which genes are composed. The isolated desoxyribonucleic acid is the active material. The active protein is actually believed to be genetic material which, upon assimilation by the susceptible organisms, reproduces itself in true genetic fashion. This information is presented because it points the way to similar types of mutating activity among the fungi, although so far no reports dealing with this subject are available. If this does occur among the fungi (and it is apt to) it would provide one more mechanism whereby variation can be caused. That the products of other organisms can actually cause mutation in fungi already has some supporting evidence; "staling products," (culture filtrates) from fungi and bacteria are known to influence mutations in fungi, inhibiting the mutation rate in some cases, and, in others, stimulating mutations. Certain strains of *Helminthosporium sativum*, for example, give a marked mutation increase, as indicated by sectoring, when cultivated in media containing as little as 1 to 2 per cent of culture filtrates of a strain of *Bacillus mesentericus* (Christensen and Davies, 1940). Obviously the latter produces a substance(s) inducing mutation. The filtrates generally were toxic to *H. sativum*, the growth rate of the latter being reduced 25 to 50 per cent. The effect is not, however, one of spontaneous mutation followed by selection of strains resistant to the toxic action, for some of the mutants thus obtained were less resistant to the toxic principle than the normal culture. Furthermore, the mutation rate was reduced by higher concentrations of the toxic bacterial filtrate, again indicating selection is not the prevailing factor. Also, other strains and species of Helminthosporium, though markedly inhibited by the toxic filtrate, failed to yield mutants. Conclusive proof of the true mutating nature of the effect as independent of selection seemingly is afforded by destruction of the mutating factor in the filtrate by the growth of *Penicillium sp.* and *Cephalosporium sp.* without affecting the toxicity. Furthermore, a coccus bacterial form growing in the filtrate destroyed the sector-promoting principle but did not destroy the factor inhibiting the growth of Helminthosporium. Finally other bacterial filtrates, though retarding growth of *Helminthosporium sativum*, did not induce sector formation. These facts, plus the not unexpected unique specificity of bacterial vs. fungus strains, strongly indicate that *Bacillus mesentericus* produces a mutation-inducing chemical substance. This work has not received the attention it merits in connection with mutation and the nature of the gene. This appears to be the first clear cut indication of a biologically produced substance capable of inducing mutations in another biological entity.

f. Medium Constituents

The nature of the medium is well known to play a marked role in the incidence of spontaneous mutations in fungi (see Christensen, 1940). Certain strains of fungi sector freely on one medium and other strains of the same species do not, and vice versa. Data of this kind indicate that substances in the medium induce mutation, and this observation is not inconsistent with the theory expressed earlier, e.g., gene proteins synthesized by direct assimilation from the medium of one or more imperfect building blocks, may be sufficiently altered to act as a mutant. It would be surprising, indeed, if such substances of biological origin were not much more widely present in non-synthetic microbiological media than hitherto recognized. Media prepared from complex nitrogenous materials of biological origin such as peptones, extracts, autolysates, and infusions would be expected to contain a great variety of cellular components, including intact and degraded desoxynucleoproteins. Theoretically, the chances are good that certain of these building blocks derived from one organism are different, but nevertheless sufficiently chemically related to be assimilated directly by another organism, incorporated into the gene material, yielding mutants.

The medium constituents themselves can be collectively and separately altered by irradiation and chemical treatment so as to produce what presumably are analogues of gene protein building blocks (Stone et al., 1947; Wyss et al., 1947). Up to now this has been demonstrated only for bacteria but there is no reason why this should not also apply to fungi. Indeed, exposure of Neurospora conidia to a previously irradiated organic medium does generate biochemical deficiency mutants, a result significant because, despite the vast amount of work done on untreated Neurospora conidia, spontaneous deficiency mutants have never hitherto been observed (Fuerst, 1948).

The ultraviolet irradiation of the medium generates hydrogen peroxide, and this oxidizing agent is what causes the actual changes, as its addition in the absence of irradiation yields comparable mutation rates. Incidentally, treatment of the medium itself with nitrogen mustard gas also induced mutations. Results like this may provide one more mechanism of variation in nature, for presumably the action of ultraviolet wavelengths of sunlight on the organic matter of soil and of bodies of water would create similar mutating nutrients. Extension of this work to fungi is highly desirable.

2. INDUCTION OF MUTATIONS IN FUNGI BY IRRADIATION

A mass of general biological information dealing with the influence of various radiations on fungi may be found in Smith (1936). Mechanisms, chemical aspects, and mutations are not included in that review, and this discussion will be limited to these aspects.

Numerous different types of radiations are known to exert both lethal and mutating effects on fungi. Probably all high energy radiations have this action. Among those used have been ultraviolet light (UV), x-rays, high and low velocity cathode rays (electrons), radium, and neutrons. Most information in relation to microorganisms deals with the first two, and in particular ultraviolet irradiation. The widespread application of ultraviolet light as a means of sterilization of air is a principal factor responsible in the accumulation of a mass of information dealing with its lethal action.

a. Cathode Rays

This low energy electron radiation differs from the high energy (x-ray and UV) ones in that the killing curves are of the "multiple hit" form, indiacting that the absorption of more than one electron is necessary for death of spores of *Aspergillus niger* (Haskins, 1938). At relatively low cathode ray energies, of the order of 1.5 to 3 kv., a definite stimulation in development of the spores is obtained as compared with an unirradiated control suspension. Noted were earlier signs of swelling, more rapid swelling, a larger average size at any given time, and a higher percentage of production of germ tubes. At any given time, these differences in the treated spores were approximately 20% greater than in the controls (Buchwald and Whelden, 1939). A similar stimulation is characteristic of low doses of UV and of x-rays. The cathode rays, like UV and x-rays, dissipate their energy by ionization, but over such a small range that the ionization must be concentrated in the spore walls and membrane with little or none reaching the nucleus. The changes induced appear to be manifested as increased permeability of the cell wall, which may be a change in the cell wall or in osmotic conditions in the cytoplasm conducive to enhanced inibibition, to the point where spores so treated are sometimes found to have exploded suddenly when placed in moist agar.

Slow and fast (24 Mev, million electron volts) electrons have been used to secure variation in *Penicillium notatum* with marked success, both in cultural character and in penicillin formation (Hanson *et al.*, 1946). Only conidia yielded mutants when exposed; actively growing cultures were not affected.

Stimulation by mild doses of radium radiation has also been reported for specific physiological processes in fungi, such as citric acid formation (two- to threefold increase) by certain strains of *A. niger* (Kresling and Stern, 1936) and also penicillin production (Jahiel *et al.*, 1944), but these reports have not yet been confirmed. In these cases, the question of mutation is not involved; the action is one on the growing cultures. Furthermore, some strains react just the opposite.

At higher cathode ray dosages (12 kv.) the survival rate was somewhat less than 50 per cent, and an appreciable fraction of these proved to be cultural mutants induced by the irradiation, the method of detection being such as to preclude spontaneous mutation and selection (Whelden, 1940).

b. Uranium

Fries (1947) mentions that of spores of *Ophiostoma multiannulatum* with impregnated uranyl nitrate have a biochemical deficiency mutation rate even higher than with conventional methods. Further details are lacking.

c. Ultraviolet Irradiation

A great deal of information has accumulated on this subject in recent years, and for details the papers of Hollaender, one of the most active workers in this field, maybe consulted (1945, for summary). The biologically active wavelengths in UV are between 2000 and 3200 A. Activity of this range is a direct function of absorption of the radiation energy by specific biochemical substances. Proteins in general have a low absorption band in the 2800 A. region and a high absorption at wavelengths shorter than 2300 A. The situation is more or less reversed with nucleic acids, which show an extremely high absorption at 2600–2650 A.

Being the "vital" structure of the cell, and preponderately of nucleoprotein composition, the nucleus would be expected to absorb UV strongly in the 2600–2650 A. range, and the evidence shows this to be true. Maximum killing and mutation rates are obtained with most fungi at this wavelength, others being much less efficient at a comparable energy input. In many fungi, the maximum sensitivity to this range is obscured by the protective absorption of pigments, but wherever this range has been tested with assurance that the radiation could penetrate freely to the nucleus, the maximum killing and mutation rate have been observed. Monochromatic irradiation of fungi at wavelengths longer than 3300 A. results in growth inhibition and a low killing rate at high energy inputs, but no mutations or signs of genetic effects were evident. Detailed studies on these points have been made on the dermatophytic fungus *Trichophyton mentagrophytes*. Monochromatic irradiation of a conidial suspension at 2650 A. to a 90 to 99 per cent kill results in a cultural mutation rate up to 40 per cent of the survivors, and, in some similar cases, mutation rates of 80 per cent have been obtained. These are, however, quite a bit higher than the usual mutation rates.

As in the case of cathode rays, the energy input at any wavelength is of crucial importance in relation to survival and mutation rate. Hollaender and Emmons (1939, 1941) and Hollaender *et al.* (1945a, b) give detailed data on these points for *Neurospora crassa;* Fig. 1 shows a typical relation between mutation and survival rate in *Aspergillus terreus* (the latter being a direct function of energy absorption). It is clear that the mutation rate reaches a peak at a point considerably before the great

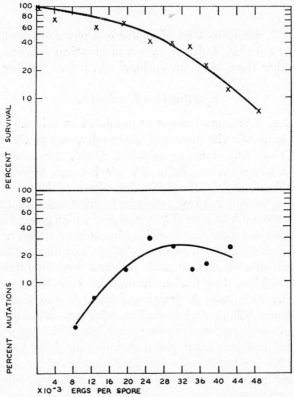

FIG. 1.—Relation between mutation and survival rates of *Aspergillus terreus* spores irradiated with ultraviolet light (from Hollaender *et al.*, 1945).

majority of spores have been killed, then declines more or less slowly depending on the organism. In fact, with *A. terreus*, a significant mutation rate was obtained after only about a 20 per cent kill, whereas data for most other organisms show this to be the case only after about 50 to 70 per cent kill. The main conclusion is that the UV mutation rate rises to a maximum with increased energy, then falls off equally as rapidly as the dosage is increased further. The killing rate naturally continues proportional to dosage. With x-rays the increase in mutation rate with increasing energy is more or less linear.   In this study the interesting point was established by crosses with the wild type that twenty-four of sixty mutants tested were actually multiple mutants.   This possibility arises from the fact that Neurospora conidia are multinucleate, different nuclei in one spore each being subject to mutation.

Westinghouse "sterilamps," which emit more than 90 per cent of the energy at 2536 A., a highly effective mutation range, are widely used in experimental work of this kind.

Ford (1948) describes an interesting type of lethal colony of *Chaetomium globosum* obtained by UV or x-ray irradiation which is made up of microscopic mutants because the colony size is less than 1 mm. in diameter when growth ceases.   In nature or in normal cultures these would of course have little survival chance.   The microscopic size was an inheritable character and was obtainable at the exceptionally high rate of 3,860 microscopic mutants in 7,053 germinated spores (54.7 per cent).

A feature distinctly of theoretical as well as practical importance in radiation mutation work is the observation made with two fungi, *Trichophyton mentagrophytes* and *Aspergillus terreus*, that plate counting survivors immediately after irradiation does not reflect the true state of viability and mutation, because incubation in various solutions for a few days before plating out yields significantly higher total counts and mutation percentages.   The latter increment may be two- to threefold. At present there is no completely satisfactory explanation for this delayed recovery (Hollaender and Emmons, 1941; Hollaender, *et al.*, 1945b).

UV and x-ray irradiation have been widely used in mutation work on a variety of different fungi.   Beadle's group first at Stanford University, then at the California Institute of Technology, has been the center of biochemical mutation work in this country.   This group (Beadle and Tatum, 1945) tested 68,198 single spore strains of Neurospora derived from material treated with x-rays and UV (and a small fraction with neutrons) and obtained more than 380 strains with altered nutritional requirements, mainly lack of ability to synthesize various B vitamins, amino acids, purines and pyrmidines, etc.   In each case, where tested, the mutants differed by a single gene from the parent wild type strains.

Another very extensive survey resulted from a program to secure increased production of penicillin in the form of a mutant of *Penicillium notatum—chrysogenum* (Bonner, 1946a).   Deficiency mutants were detected in the usual way for Neurospora (see above, and also later) but, because this organism is imperfect, crossing and genetic transmission as proof of the single gene mutation is not possible.   However, analogy with Neurospora and other organisms leaves no question of the genetic nature of the changes, which are permanent. A total of 85,595 single spore isolates were tested, yielding 398 strains, each deficient in the ability to synthesize some component of its cell material. Cultural mutants were not accounted for in this work. The frequency distribution of the mutants is depicted in Table 3.

TABLE 3

Biochemical Mutants from 85,595 Strains of P. notatum-chrysogenum[1]

Factor required for growth	No. of strains[2]	Factor required for growth	No. of strains
Biotin	5	Arginine-proline	13
Choline	9	Cystine-methionine	50
Inositol	6	Histidine	16
Nicotinic acid	5	Isoleucine	1
p-Aminobenzoic acid	6	Leucine	12
Pyridoxine	6	Lysine	54
Thiamin	18	Methionine	32
Yeast nucleic acid	19	Phenylalanine	4
Nitrate reducers	31	Proline	14
Unknowns	43	Tryptophane	2
Arginine	52		

[1] From Bonner (1946a).
[2] Total = 398.

Alteration in Carbohydrate Metabolism

Similar to penicillin, the idea of obtaining a mutant with increased fermentation abilities though irradiation had been tested with certain other organisms producing metabolic products of industrial interest. Though few reports have appeared, it is almost a certainty that many large microbiological industries support mutation programs with the object of securing superior strains to carry out a particular microbiological process. This is especially true in the case of penicillin, streptomycin, citric acid, and doubtless others.

This subject had already received attention in 1936 when citric acid formation by radium-and UV-induced mutants of *Aspergillus niger* was studied (Kresling and Stern, 1936). A radon induced mutant from a low yielding stock strain produced more citric acid than the stock, but, in most cases, the mutants produced less citric acid. Particularly instructive are the rather radical shifts in metabolic products of carbohydrate metabolism in different mutants, all of which varied sharply in relative acid yields (Table 4).

Noteworthy is the complete elimination of citric acid in mutant II notwithstanding the preponderance of this acid in the parent. The general trend is toward greatly reduced total acid formation as well as shifts in the ratios of the various acids. It will be understood that changes of this type are true biochemical mutants, although there is an erroneous tendency to consider only nutritional deficiencies as biochemical mutants.

TABLE 4

SHIFT IN ACID YIELDS IN RADIUM MUTATIONS OF A. NIGER[1,2]

	Acid formation			Sugar used	Mycelial dry wt.
	Citric	Gluconic	Oxalic		
Strain 6 (parent)........	11.88 g.	1.16 g.	0.33 g.	18.7 g.	3.55 g.
Mutant I..............	0.68	0.84	0.33	15.0	3.87
II.............	0.00	2.33	0.20	14.0	4.76
III.............	7.52	0.73	1.00	15.4	3.64

[1] Data from Kresling and Stern (1936).
[2] Per 100 ml. culture medium.

Aspergillus terreus has been subjected to a comprehensive mutation program from the standpoint of yields of itaconic acid produced from sugar (Hollaender *et al.*, 1945a; Lockwood *et al.*, 1945) for the purpose of developing an industrial fermentation. The numerous *A. terreus* mutants have been described morphologically in rather exhaustive detail, including also a few biochemical deficiency mutants, and several photographs depicting the mutant types are available (Raper *et al.*, 1945). Illustrative of the influence of physiological and biochemical reactions on the morphology and cultural characteristics of a fungus are the extremely aberrant forms which develop on synthetic media deficient in a growth factor the particular mutant requires. Cultivated on a complete medium, the organism demonstrates the appearance of the normal parent.

Two hundred and seventeen isolates from a UV irradiation were studied with special reference to itaconic acid production from glucose. The distribution of about 140 of these strains based on efficiency of conversion of itaconate from glucose is charted in Fig. 2.

This chart is rather typical of the mutation effect on acid formation by fungi, and the sizable number of strains studied enhances the validity of these distribution frequencies. The non-irradiated parent falls in the 31–35 per cent yield group. It is evident that well over half of all the strains represented in the group had reduced acid yields, about one-third were unchanged and about 6 per cent of the strains gave increased yields the highest being about 45 per cent better than the non-irradiated control. About one-fourth of the strains represented in Fig. 2 gave drastically reduced itaconic acid yields. In the entire study, including more strains than depicted in Fig. 2, about equal numbers of cultures showed no alteration or nearly complete failure to accumulate acid. The loss in acid formation by fungi appears to be a prominent biochemical character in fungus mutations. Chapter 13 contains further information relative to additional differences and shifts in metabolic products in these strains: total acidity, per cent of total acidity comprising itaconic acid, neutral non-reducing materials, presence of nonacidic unsaturated compounds, the identification of a new fermentation product in filtrates of one of the mutants, namely, itatartaric acid, and so forth.

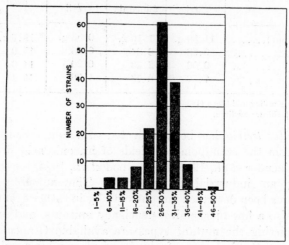

FIG. 2.—Frequency distribution of *Aspergillus terreus* mutants with respect to acid-producing powers (from Lockwood *et al.*, 1945).

The properties of the morphologically unchanged vs. altered strains may be summarized thusly:

Morphologically Unchanged, 76 Strains	Morphologically Altered, 141 Strains
Unaltered biochemically, 59 More itaconic acid than parent, 13 No itaconic acid, 4	Unaltered biochemically, 42 More itaconic acid than parent, 0 Little itaconic acid, 88 Failed to grow on test medium, 11

showing that regardless of appearance, some strains were altered biochemically and others not, a result typical of all mutation work.

TECHNIQUE OF OBTAINING NEUROSPORA MUTANTS

The historical as well as the model exemplary aspects of this most widely employed organism in the field of microbiological genetics make it almost mandatory that the student of fungus metabolism be conversant with the principles and technology used in its study.   In reality, this approach represents the essence of working with any fungus whose sexual phase is of concern.   Only the main features will be discussed here. For further details the many articles of Beadle and coworkers may be consulted (especially Beadle and Tatum, 1945; and Beadle, 1947).

A water suspension of conidia from a Neurospora strain of known mating type or sex is exposed to the mutating agent which may be any form of radiation or chemical, and (after removal of the chemicals) the suspension is applied to an agar culture of the normal wild strain of Neurospora of opposite mating type.   This culture contains proto-perithecia (embryonic fruiting bodies).   The conidia either fertilize the protoperithecia directly, resulting in a fusion nucleus typical of the sexual process, or the hyphae derived from germinating conidia undergo hyphal fusion with hyphae of the wild strain, also resulting in a fusion zygote nucleus typical of the sexual process.   The (diploid) fusion nucleus then undergoes the usual fission, each of the progeny undergoing two further divisions resulting in eight nuclei, one each of which becomes closed off as a spore.   The eight ascospores are the characteristic number for Neurospora (as for most Ascomycetes) and they are arranged linearly in a sac, the ascus, whence the name ascospore.   Numerous asci are contained in each fruiting structure, the perithecium.   The asexual and sexual cycle and the above-mentioned structures are pictured in Fig. 3.

Individual ascospores are then isolated from asci by crushing the perithecia, then teasing out the spores with a lance-tipped needle under a dissecting microscope with a 10 to 48X magnification.   The separated ascospores are treated with 1.5 per cent sodium hypochlorite solution (50 per cent commercial Chlorox or its equivalent) which kills conidia, mycelial fragments, and most contaminants.   Individual spores are then transferred to the surface of an agar medium (complete medium: contains sugar and a complex mixture of nitrogenous materials such as vitamins, amino acids, nucleic acids etc., in the form of yeast extract, peptone, etc.).   This enables the investigator to allow the spores to age for several days; the aging appreciably increases the percentage germination.   The agar slant tubes containing individual isolated ascospores are heat activated for 30 minutes in a 50- to 60°-water bath before incubation for growth.   Without this heat activation the percentage germination of Neurospora ascospores is almost insignificant (Goddard, 1939).   (See also Chapter 9.)

In practice, only a single spore per perithecium is taken for mutation testing to insure that only a single descendant of a particular mutant gene produced by the treatment is involved.   Two or more chosen from the same ascus are merely sisters derived from the original mutant gene.

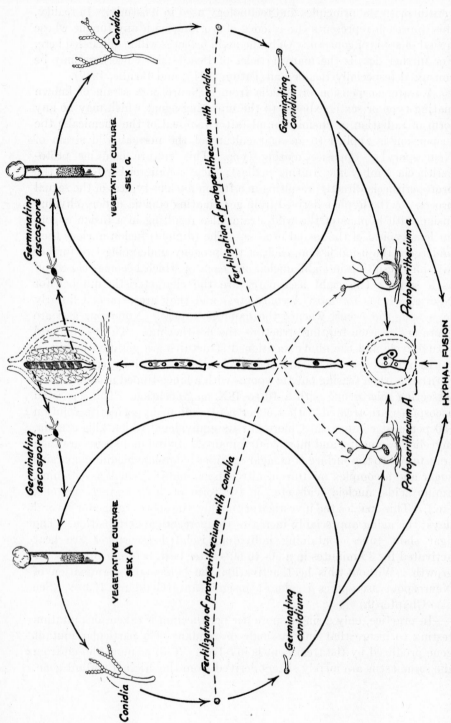

FIG. 3.—Diagram of the life cycle of *Neurospora crassa*. In addition to the asexual cycle shown, the mold is able to multiply asexually by microconidia and by means of fragments of mycelium (from Beadle, 1947)

However, two mutants controlling the same biochemical reaction, but derived from different perithecia indicate two independent mutations in different conidia, the importance being that they may be concerned with different steps in one biochemical process, i.e., are non-allelic. In general practice, it is best to obtain perithecia in numerous small tubes, to be certain of independent mutation. As will be seen later, in cases where proof of the Mendelian nature of the inheritance of the altered gene is desired, all eight ascospores from a single ascus must be isolated and tested. However, for ordinary mutation work, this is unnecessary.

The isolated ascospores carrying mutant alleles of genes controlling the synthesis of individual biological compounds, i.e., which are unable to synthesize any one of these substances, do, however, germinate and develop to full mycelial and conidial prime because the particular deficiency is furnished in the complete medium, presumably containing all such substances possible. The mature cultures are now tested for the presence of mutant alleles (deficient genes) by subculture into liquid minimal medium.* The normal wild strain can grow abundantly on this medium. (Neurospora has a biotin requirement, hence this vitamin must naturally be present in all media cultivating this fungus.) Good growth of the subculture means that the organism has no mutant allele of the gene controlling synthesis of any biochemical essential, and it grows well because it is able to synthesize all its cellular constituents from the simple nutrients in minimal medium. Such cultures are of no further interest. If, however, no growth or feeble growth is made on minimal medium, the mutant allele is presumed to be present and synthesis of some vital cellular constituent which it controls is blocked.

The nature of the deficiency is next determined by subculturing into each of four media: complete, minimal, minimal containing mixture of all known amino acids, and minimal containing mixture of all known vitamins. If the mutant is so with respect to synthesis of a vitamin, it will not grow where the vitamin is absent, namely in the minimal and in the minimal plus amino acids. On the other hand, it will grow readily in the other two media, namely, complete and minimal plus vitamins. Once ascertained to be deficient in ability to synthesize some vitamin, the culture is now tested in minimal medium in several tubes, each containing a single pure vitamin. Naturally, growth is possible only with the tube containing that vitamin the mutant has lost the power to synthesize. The system for testing biochemical deficiencies is demonstrated in Figs. 4 and 5.

* Minimal medium, grams per liter: NH_4 tartrate 5, NH_4NO_3 1, KH_2NO_4 1, $MgSO_4 \cdot 7H_2O$ 0.5, NaCl 0.1, $CaCl_2$ 0.1, Sucrose 15, biotin 5×10^{-6} g. Also as salts, mg.; B 0.01, Cu 0.1, Fe 0.2, Mn 0.02, Mo 0.02, Zn 2.0.

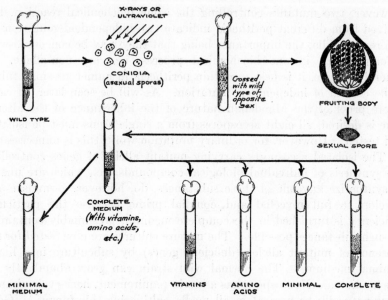

FIG. 4.—Method of producing Neurospora mutants and locating the biochemical group in which a deficient mutant belongs, e.g., vitamins, amino acids, or unknown substances in (complete) yeast extract. Note that growth occurs only in tubes that contain a vitamin mixture and are complete (from Beadle, 1947).

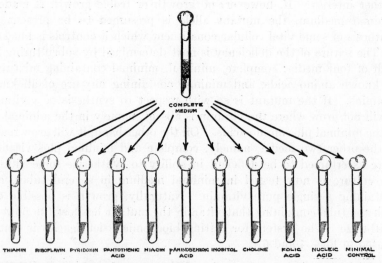

FIG. 5.—Method of identifying the specific mutation deficiency within a given biochemical group determined in Fig. 4. Note growth only in pantothenic acid (from Beadle, 1947).

The only absolute proof that the deficiency is actually genetically controlled, and that the mutant differs from the parent wild type only in a single gene, is to show that the particular character (deficiency) obeys the Mendelian laws of inheritance. Figure 6 demonstrates schemetically how this is done. The mutant is crossed with a normal wild strain of opposite mating type, resulting in typical perithecia, asci, and ascospores. A single ascus is separated and each individual spore in it is isolated in order, cultivated on complete medium as described

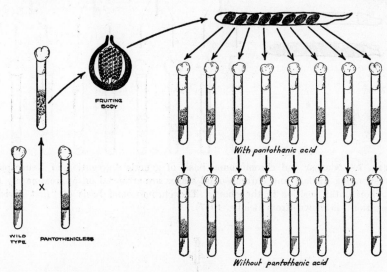

FRUITING BODY

With pantothenic acid

WILD TYPE   PANTOTHENICLESS

Without pantothenic acid

FIG. 6.—Scheme by which the inheritance of a mutant type is determined.   Transfers from medium supplemented with pantothenic acid to minimal medium are made by using conidia (from Beadle, 1947).

above, and then subcultured into minimal medium and minimal medium plus the particular vitamin as shown in Fig. 6. Naturally, no deficiency exists in the medium containing the vitamin, whereas growth occurs in the vitamin-less medium only in the tubes testing the first 4 spores (in order) but not in the last four. This is the typical pattern of single gene inheritance, showing that the mutant allele and the normal allele of the gene controlling the vitamin synthesis segregated meiotically (reduction division) to the haploid state in the first two divisions of the fusion (zygote) nucleus, each then subsequently undergoing one further mitotic division (Fig. 7). Each nucleus then becomes an ascospore. Thus, each genotype produced in meiosis is represented by duplicate spores in the ascus. Thus, the mutant character is transmitted through the sexual stage, and to one-half the progeny, conforming fully to the Mendelian pattern of inheritance. The mutant differs, therefore, from

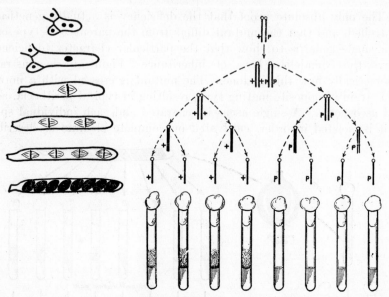

Fig. 7.—Nuclear and chromosomal basis of genetic segregation in Neurospora. Corresponding nuclear and chromosomal stages are arranged on approximately the same horizontal position in the chart. The chromosomal basis of "first division segregation" is shown (from Beadle, 1947).

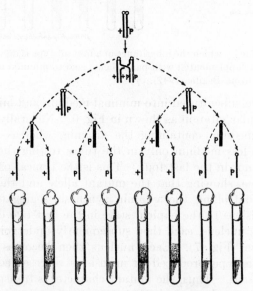

Fig. 8.—Chromosomal basis of "second division segregation" of pantothenicless mutant type (from Beadle, 1947).

the parent wild strain by a single gene difference.   The half and half arrangement of the progeny is proof that reduction division occurred in the first division of the zygote.   Sometimes the alternate pairs are observed in the progeny, as depicted in Fig. 8.   This means that reduction division or segregation must have occurred in the second nuclear division, this condition resulting from "crossing over" of chromosomes during the first division.   Again this latter is a well known Mendelian pattern.   Incidentally, Neurospora has seven chromosomes.

Chromosome maps showing the relative locations of particular genes on the chromosomes have been made for Neurospora similar to chromosome maps for insects and plants (Beadle, 1947).

Fries (1947) has developed a technique for increasing the efficiency of isolation of mutants in fungi.   The conidia surviving after irradiation or other mutagenic treatment are allowed to stand in distilled water for several hours.   Normal conidia tend to germinate and form germ tubes and rudimentary mycelia in the normal fashion, using reserve foodstuffs in the spores.   Deficiency mutants do not behave like this or are much retarded.   It is possible to filter out the normal germinated spores thus enriching the filtrate in ungerminated mutant spores.   In this way Fries obtained a mutation rate in *Ophiostoma multiannulatum* of 12–15% of the survivors in the filtrate, as compared to 1.83 per cent in the suspension before the pregermination process.   However, in essence this method also selects for slow-growing normal strains.

BIOCHEMICAL SYNTHESES

The importance of biochemical mutations is that gene mutant blocks may occur at varying steps in the synthesis of any essential cellular compound.   Thus, compound D may be required because the mutants may have gene blocks at various stages in the synthesis of the compound D. This synthesis may be pictured as passing successively through steps such as A, B, and C.

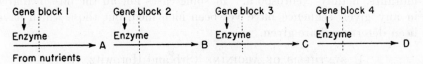

A mutant with a gene block before A lacks the gene-controlled enzyme that enables it to convert further nutrients into A, which is a precursor of D in the biochemical synthesis.   As only this enzyme is lacking, all steps prior to A take place normally, but the immediate predecessor of A cannot be converted to A owing to enzyme lack, and hence the predecessor compound accumulates in the cells or is excreted into the medium. Similarly a gene block between A and B, allows A to accumulate, and so forth. Obviously, if the mutant is furnished any compound occurring in the series after the block, the organism can further convert it to D and grow normally, as it will if D itself is furnished.

It is evident, then, that the nature of the course of biosynthesis of any compound can be ascertained by determining the compounds that pile up in mutants with gene blocks at different stages in the synthesis of the cellular constituent, and much information has been obtained from the study of Neurospora mutants in this way. Obviously no growth will be made if the mutant is not furnished some of the particular essential. Usually enough is furnished to allow about 50 per cent of maximum growth, and this cell material synthesizes the intermediate compound which, owing to the fact that the gene block does not permit it to be further converted, accumulates and can be isolated and identified. By testing the products of gene block in the various mutants concerned with the synthesis of any one substance, such as a vitamin, the relative positions of the mutant in the synthetic sequence can be established. Thus, the accumulated precursors of any mutant will permit growth of all mutants preceding it in the synthetic sequence. The mutant with gene block 4 (see above) accumulates a precursor that permits growth of mutants with blocks 1, 2, and 3, because, in essence, it bypasses the need for those synthetic steps once the product of those steps is furnished preformed. On the other hand, accumulated precursors in mutant 1, 2, or 3 will not serve for mutant 4 because it performs these syntheses itself and is deficient only in conversion of the last step, i.e., $C \rightarrow D$. When D, the final product, is furnished, all mutant blocks in its synthesis are circumnavigated.

With this approach, a number of steps in the synthesis of various amino acids and vitamins have been elucidated, largely through the school of Beadle, Tatum, Horowitz and Mitchell. The following summarizes a major portion of the chemical information obtained from biochemical mutants, mainly Neurospora. In some cases not all the intermediates in any given sequence have yet been identified, but those which have been determined are given.

1. SYNTHESIS OF ARGININE (Srb and Horowitz, 1944)

This *Neurospora* sequence is known as the ornithine cycle and is identical with the Krebs' cyclic synthesis and breakdown of arginine in mammalian liver, a fine example of the universality of comparative biochemistry, and indicating that intermediary metabolism elucidated in fungi may clarify the corresponding mammalian metabolism. New information from Penicillium mutants (Bonner, 1946c) reveals that

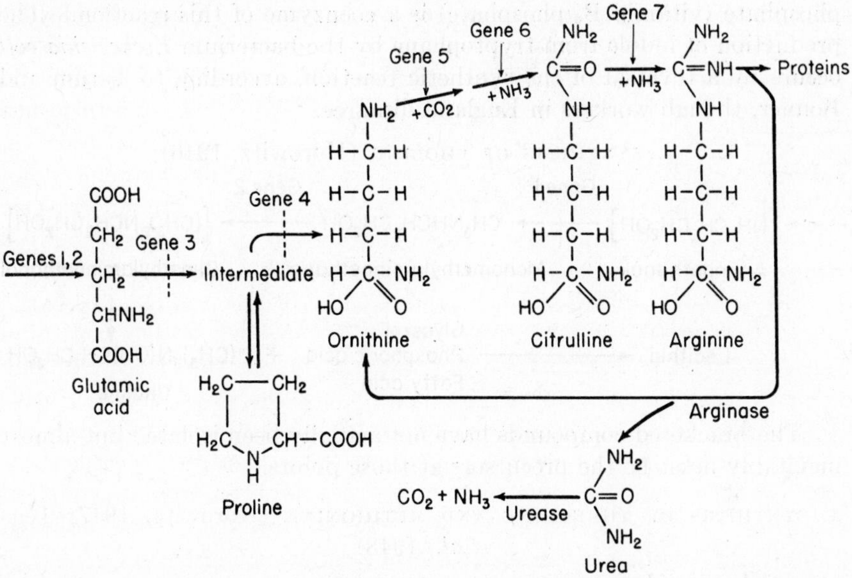

Gene 7

Gene 6

Gene 5

Gene 4

Gene 3

Genes 1,2

Glutamic acid

Proline

Ornithine

Citrulline

Arginine

Arginase

Urease

Urea

Intermediate

Proteins

$CO_2 + NH_3$

glutamic acid functions as a precursor of ornithine and also of the amino acid proline. The latter also can serve as a precursor of ornithine.

2. SYNTHESIS OF TRYPTOPHANE (Tatum and Bonner, 1944; Tatum and Beadle, 1944)

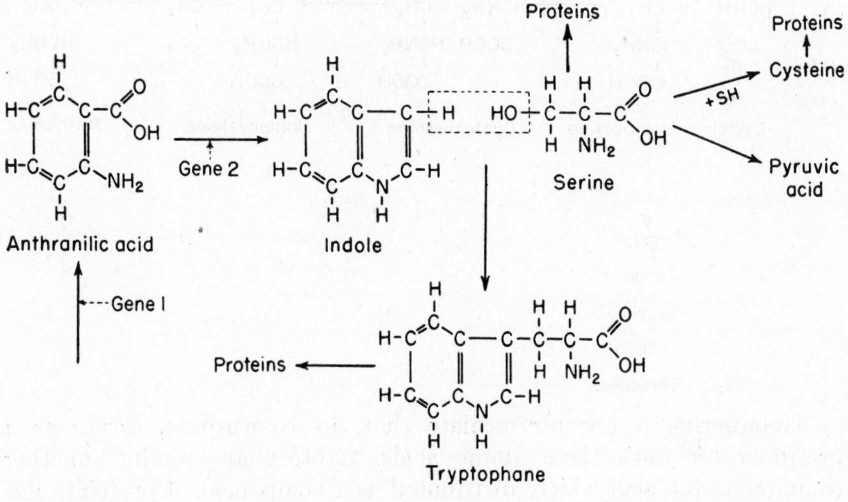

Proteins

Proteins

Cysteine

Pyruvic acid

Serine

Anthranilic acid

Indole

Gene 2

Gene 1

Proteins

Tryptophane

Condensation of serine with indole to form tryptophane is accomplished by the enzyme tryptophanase, which is extractable from Neurospora mycelia in cell free condition (Umbreit *et al.*, 1947). Pyridoxal phosphate (vitamin B_6 phosphate) is a coenzyme of this reaction. The production of indole from tryptophane by the bacterium *Escherichia coli* occurs by a reversal of the synthetic reaction, according to Tatum and Bonner, though workers in England disagree.

3. SYNTHESIS OF CHOLINE (Horowitz, 1946)

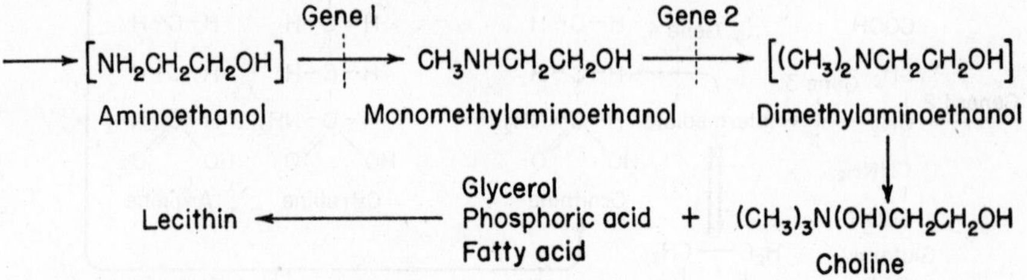

Gene I   Gene 2

$$\longrightarrow [NH_2CH_2CH_2OH] \xrightarrow{\quad} CH_3NHCH_2CH_2OH \xrightarrow{\quad} [(CH_3)_2NCH_2CH_2OH]$$

Aminoethanol   Monomethylaminoethanol   Dimethylaminoethanol

$$Lecithin \longleftarrow \begin{array}{c} Glycerol \\ Phosphoric\ acid \\ Fatty\ acid \end{array} + (CH_3)_3N(OH)CH_2CH_2OH$$

Choline

The bracketed compounds have not actually been isolated but almost inevitably must be the precursors at those points.

4. SYNTHESIS OF THREONINE AND METHIONINE (Horowitz, 1947; Teas *et al.*, 1948)

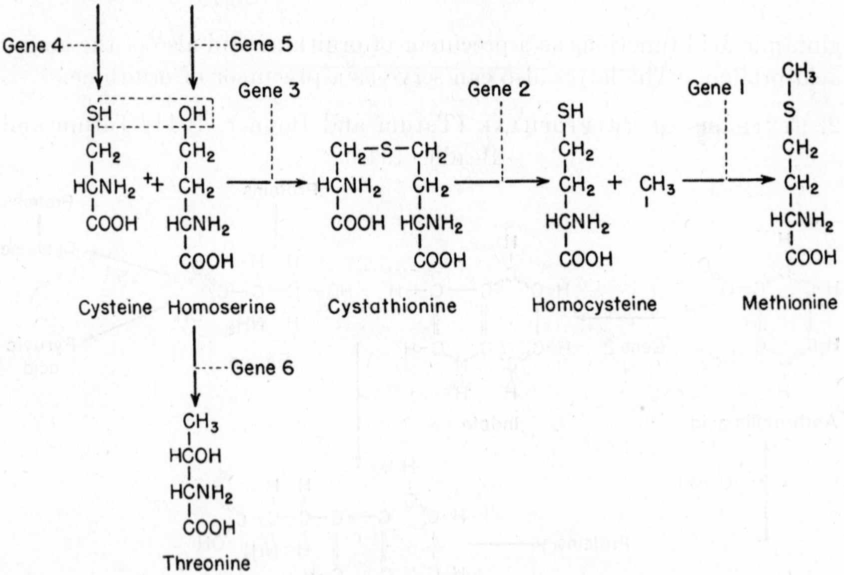

Cysteine   Homoserine   Cystathionine   Homocysteine   Methionine

Threonine

Homoserine is an intermediate that, in Neurospora, serves as a precursor for both these amino acids. Note that cysteine, another common amino acid widely distributed as a component of proteins, also participates in the synthesis of the amino acid methionine.
(Analogy with synthesis of the amino acid tryptophane from another amino acid—serine.)

5. SYNTHESIS OF NICOTINIC ACID (Beadle, *et al.*, 1947; Mitchell and Nyc, 1948)

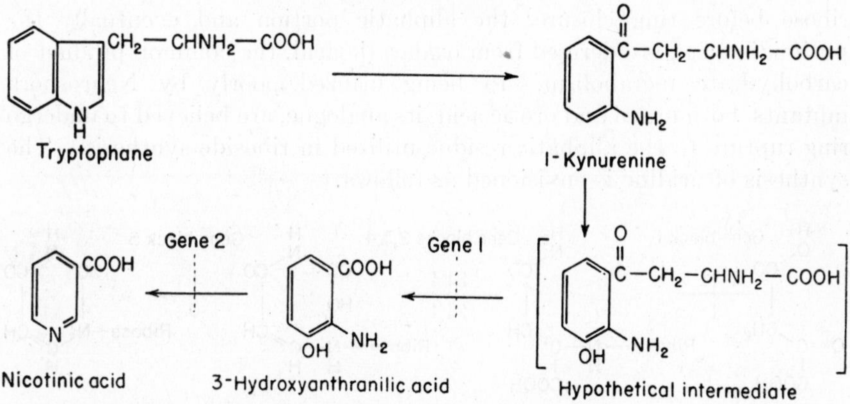

Tryptophane

l-Kynurenine

Gene 2   Gene I

Nicotinic acid   3-Hydroxyanthranilic acid   Hypothetical intermediate

Outstanding in significance here is the fact that an amino acid functions as a precursor in the synthesis of a vitamin and also that this system of biochemical genetics has identified *l*-kynurenine with a biological significance hitherto not known. This conversion clarifies the well-known observation in animal and human nutrition that nicotinic acid and tryptophane are interchangeable in counteracting pellagra symptoms, caused by nicotinic acid deficiency. In the above series, two substances have been isolated after accumulating at gene block 1, between kynurenine and nicotinic acid (Bonner and Beadle, 1946). These substances have been only partially characterized but have properties suggesting they are both oxypyridine carboxylic acids, probably the immediate precursors of nicotinic acid. One of these has been isolated and identified as 3-hydroxyanthranilic acid (Mitchell and Nyc, 1948). The presence of amino and hydroxyl groups on adjacent carbon atoms in the benzene ring, *o-* and *m-* to a carboxyl, probably renders the ring unstable, permitting entrance of the N to form the pyridine ring after preliminary rupture between the amino and hydroxy groups.

6. SYNTHESIS OF NUCLEIC ACIDS (Loring and Pierce, 1944; Mitchell and Houlahan, 1947; Mitchell, *et al.*, 1948)

Until the work with Neurospora mutants, it was a generally accepted belief that nucleic acids were synthesized via the component bases, cytosine, uracil, thymin, adenine, and guanine. When Neurospora mutants were found to utilize uracil and cytosine very poorly compared to the ribosides of these bases, it was suspected that the free bases are not the normal intermediates in nucleic acid biosynthesis, although they may actually be utilized for that purpose.   Furthermore, the synthesis of the riboside uridine does not occur via condensation of ribose and uracil, but rather through intermediate aliphatic derivatives of ribose before ring closure: the aliphatic portion and eventually the pyrimidine ring are derived from oxalacetic acid, the common product of carbohydrate metabolism.   In being utilized poorly by Neurospora mutants, both uracil and orotic acid, its analogue, are believed to undergo ring rupture to the aliphatic residue utilized in riboside synthesis.   The synthesis of uridine is envisioned as follows:

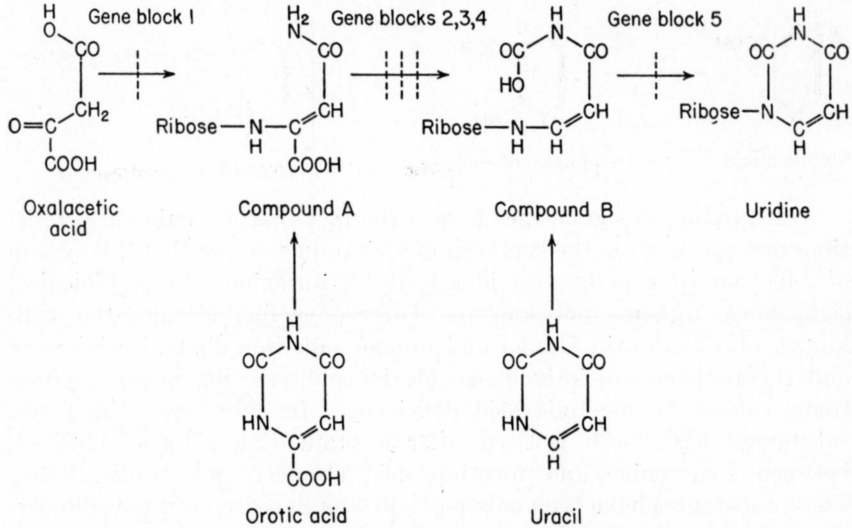

Oxalacetic acid   Compound A   Compound B   Uridine

Orotic acid   Uracil

Orotic acid is a byproduct and not a normal intermediate.   One mutant strain (gene block 5) accumulates orotic acid in the medium from which it is readily crystallized by simple concentration.   Since it is not utilized by the mutant with gene block 4, it is not a normal intermediate and its formation by gene block 5 obviously represents conversion of the normal intermediate B to orotic acid via shunt metabolism.   This section is best summarized by the following scheme:

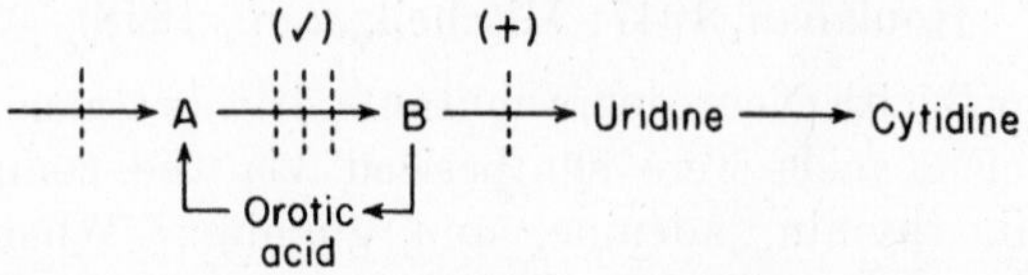

Orotic acid is not utilized by strain ($\checkmark$) though it is accumulated by strain ($+$).

The aliphatic portion of the ribose precursor is suggested to be amino-fumaric acid,

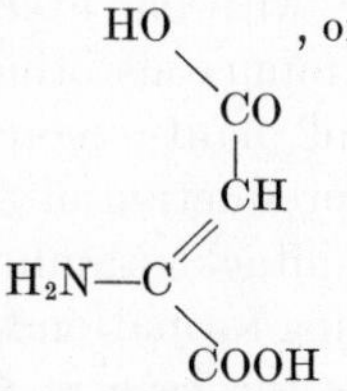

$$\begin{array}{ccc} & \text{HO} & \text{, or aminofumaric acid diamide, } H_2N \\ & \diagdown & \\ & \text{CO} & \\ & | & \\ & \text{CH} & \\ & \diagup\!\!\diagup & \\ H_2N\!-\!C & \\ & \diagdown & \\ & \text{COOH} & \end{array} \qquad \begin{array}{c} \\ \diagdown \\ \text{CO} \\ | \\ \text{CH} \\ \diagup\!\!\diagup \\ H_2N\!-\!C \\ \diagdown \\ \text{CONH}_2 \end{array}$$

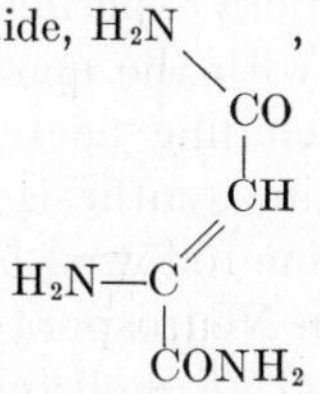

or some similar compound as all these were as effective as oxalacetic acid in the synthesis of uridine in the special test mutants.

The biosynthetic sequence in a series of mutants (seven genotypes) of Neurospora concerned with the purine adenosine has been established as follows (Mitchell and Houlahan, 1946a):

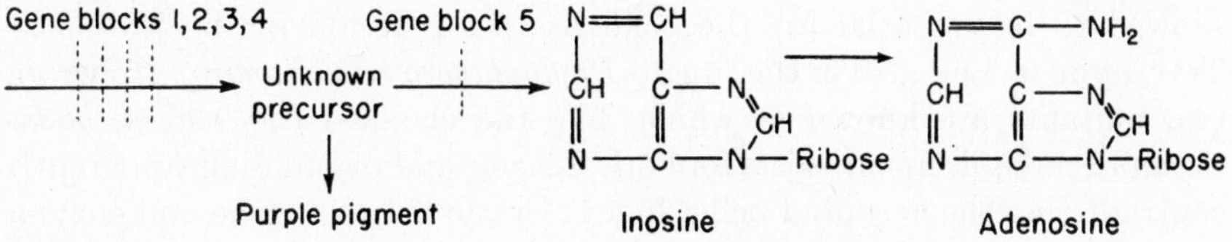

Again the evidence contraindicates synthesis of this ribosidic component of nucleic acid via the free base adenine, but via the ribosidic homologue by amination. As a matter of fact, a good piece of evidence indicating that adenine itself is not biologically active *per se* is the fact that Neurospora mycelium contains an enzyme, adenosine deaminase, which converts adenosine to inosine, but no enzyme which deaminates adenine. A similar situation is believed to apply in the case of the remaining purine constituents of nucleic acid, namely, that the riboside guanosine is the biologically active form of guanine.

7. SYNTHESIS OF BIOTIN (Tatum, 1945)

As the normal wild strain of Neurospora requires biotin for growth, this organism cannot be utilized to study the biosynthesis of biotin. Work with biotinless mutants of Penicillium reveals that one mutant can use desthiobiotin equally as well as biotin, and another cannot substitute the analogue for biotin itself. As a matter of fact, the gene block in the latter prevents the insertion of sulfur into desthiobiotin to make biotin, the desthiobiotin accumulating in the medium where it can be demonstrated by its growth promoting ability for the first mutant strain. Desthiobiotin is known to be the precursor of biotin in a number of bacterial systems as well as yeast.

8. SYNTHESIS OF THIAMINE (Tatum and Bell, 1946)

Neurospora experiments on this subject are, with one exception, fully consistent with the mass of information from numerous other biological sources, including bacterial, fungus, yeast, and plant systems, namely, that thiamine synthesis proceeds through the production of thiazole and of pyrimidine followed by coupling to give the intact vitamin. Thiazole synthesis in Neurospora does not proceed via ring formation from chloro-acetylpropyl alcohol and thioformamide, as is the case in isolated pea roots (Bonner and Buchman, 1938).

One mutant requires only the thiazole portion of thiamine, and synthesizes and accumulates excess pyrimidine. Another, requiring intact thiamine, synthesizes and accumulates both thiazole and pyrimidine moieties, but is unable to condense them to thiamine. This particular deficiency does not require the factor S, which Kidder and Dewey (1942) showed to be essential for the condensation reaction in the protozoan Tetrahymena and also in the fungus *Phytophthora cinnamomi*. However, two mutants are known in which, like the classical *Phycomyces blakesleeanus*, a requirement exists for both thiazole and pyrimidine, apparently contradicting the accepted belief in a 1:1 ratio between gene and enzyme reaction, for it would appear that more than one enzyme is involved here. However, information on this point is still meagre, and there is no reason to question the one to one hypothesis. Possibilities are discussed by Tatum and Bell (1946).

9. SYNTHESIS OF ISOLEUCINE AND VALINE (Bonner, 1946b, c)

Several Neurospora strains have a growth requirement for both these amino acids, but the evidence does not support the idea that the mutants have gene blocks for a precursor common to both. This rather complex situation appears to be on the way to resolution, the following summarizing presently available information:

In the strain with gene block 3, α-ketovaleric acid is the precursor of valine in the presence of adequate isoleucine.   In strains with gene block 2, α-keto-β-methyl-n-valeric acid is the precursor of isoleucine in the presence of adequate valine.   Now, because gene block 2 prevents the conversion of isoleucine precursor to isoleucine, the precursor accumulates, and, in a sense, overflows and inhibits the conversion of valine precursor to valine.   Being homologous compounds, a kind of competitive inhibition of the particular enzyme is easy to visualize.

10. LYSINE

Mitchell and Houlahan (1948) have shown by means of Neurospeora mutants that a precursor of this amino acid is α-aminoadipic acid.

$$\underset{\underset{\text{α-Aminoadipic acid}}{\text{NH}_2}}{\text{COOH}\cdot\text{CH}_2\text{CH}_2\text{CH}_2\text{CH}\cdot\text{COOH}} \qquad \underset{\underset{\text{Lysine}}{\text{NH}_2}}{\text{H}_2\text{N}\cdot\text{CH}_2\text{CH}_2\text{CH}_2\text{CH}_2\text{CH}\cdot\text{COOH}}$$

The transformation of the precursor depends upon conversion of the carboxyl group into a $\text{H}_2\text{N}\cdot\text{CH}_2$— group.   Details are unknown.   A point of revealing interest is that α-ketoadipic acid, $\text{COOH}\cdot\text{CH}_2\text{CH}_2\text{CH}_2\text{CO}\cdot\text{COOH}$, is not used by this organism, rather at variance with the general belief that α-keto acids are the immediate precursors of α-amino acids.   Conventionally, one would predict α-ketoadipic acid to be the precursor of α-aminoadipic acid.

11. OTHER NEUROSPORA MUTANTS

A large number of additional mutants, each deficient in a single enzyme, are known, but their biosynthetic sequences have not yet been worked out as in the above described cases.   Mutants deficient in the ability to synthesize many other vitamins and amino acids are known. Also known are mutants deficient in the gene-controlled enzymes which permit them to attack various carbon sources and such nitrogen sources as nitrate.   Mutant strains of *Aspergillus nidulans* have been obtained which can utilize cystine sulfur for growth but not sulfate sulfur (Hockenhull, 1947).

Lewis (1948) described a Neurospora mutant with the genetic block occurring in the carbohydrate metabolism of the organism, the first instance of this type, though reminiscent of the events in alteration in organic acid producing abilities described earlier.   The block occurs in the Krebs tricarboxylic acid respiratory cycle (Chapter 12), the evidence indicating the block to be between isocitric acid and its decarboxylation product, α-ketoglutaric acid.   Only α-ketoglutarate and products subsequent to it in the cycle (C_4-dicarboxylic acids, etc.) would permit growth, whereas isocitrate and its immediate predecessors would not permit growth.

Several mutants are unique in that the deficiencies are manifest only under special environmental conditions, the organism behaving like the normal wild type under other conditions. Two outstanding examples are pyridoxineless and riboflavinless mutants. The former grows normally in the absence of added pyridoxine, synthesizing its own pyridoxine so long as the reaction of the medium is pH 5.8 or above (Stokes *et al.*, 1943). At these pH values, the mutant requires ammonia nitrogen, other forms being unsuitable. Below pH 5.8, the organism requires exogenous pyridoxine and behaves like a typical mutant. A relation between pyridoxine and thiamine metabolism in this organism is evident from the fact that at any given level of pyridoxine nutrition, the mutant shows a growth response proportional to the amount of thiamine added, though some growth is made in the absence of thiamine. The effect is appreciably greater at low levels of pyridoxine nutrition. This evidence suggests that, apart from its own coenzyme functions, pyridoxine participates in the synthesis of thiamine. In reality, therefore, a pyridoxine deficiency actually causes a pyridoxine and a thiamine deficiency.

The riboflavinless Neurospora mutant requires an exogenous supply of this vitamin only when cultivated above a temperature of 28°C (Mitchell and Houlahan, 1946b). Below this (25°C.) it requires no riboflavin and is similar to the normal wild strain in that it synthesizes its own. Actually, if supplied with submaximal "primer" doses of riboflavin, the mutant does synthesize riboflavin very slowly, and eventually reaches maximal growth. Lumichrome (6,7-dimethylisoalloxazine, riboflavin minus the ribityl side chain) competitively inhibits the utilization of riboflavin by the mutant at the elevated temperatures. A molecular ratio of lumichrome to riboflavin of about 2.5 gives 50 per cent growth inhibition, and a ratio of 6 to 8 produces complete inhibition. Lumiflavin (6,7,9-trimethylisoalloxazine) is only $\frac{1}{20}$ as active as lumichrome.

A curious Neurospora mutant is that which requires sulfonamides for growth, especially at somewhat elevated temperatures (30–35°C.) (Emerson, 1947). *p*-Aminobenzoic acid competitively inhibits the growth, a 50 per cent inhibition being caused by a 1:100 molecular ratio of *p*-aminobenzoic acid to sulfanilamide. Zalokar (1948) has shown that this strain is exceptionally sensitive to inhibition by *p*-aminobenzoic acid, being poisoned completely by 10^{-7} M concentration; smaller concentrations permit and are necessary for growth though folic acid may substitute. The poisoning effect of the higher concentration is nullified by sulfonamide. These results make it probable that sulfonamide requiring strains of Neurospora require sulfonamide because they produce more p-aminobenzoic acid than they can tolerate—a sort of autoinhibition that the sulfonamide protects against. In fact, under normal conditions, this situation could be considered only as a lethal mutant, for it never would develop except under artificial conditions where it is supplied with the antagonist of the toxic material. A similar explanation may account for "streptomycin-requiring" strains of bacteria discovered in the past year or two.

A Theory Interpreting "Acquired" Mutant Characters

Mutants characterized by loss of some property can be logically interpreted on the basis of loss of a specific enzyme determinative in the property concerned. Not so transparent, however, are the cases where to all appearances a property or character in the mutant has been *acquired*. One might assume that the specific gene involved is present all the time in the normal wild strain but is inactive because it is an imperfect replica of the gene which creates the acquired change in the mutant. Any condition which brings about this change would therefore result in a mutant characterized by the acquired property. It seems that this situation is rather unlikely although in certain instances there is some evidence indicating it is not impossible. For example, certain mutants characterized by synthetic deficiencies back mutate to the normal wild type now able to synthesize the particular nutritional essential. The best studied example of this is a leucineless Neurospora mutant (Ryan, 1946) although several other examples could be given, especially among the bacteria. This phenomenon is called reversion, and is a genetic change, not an enzymatic adaptation, which is a non-inherited mechanism. In such instances it is not difficult to visualize that the mutant gene is chemically altered so that the transition back to the normal would not necessitate a radical change. At least, one may surmise that the basic parental gene structure or pattern is already existent in the mutant.

In cases of no known relation to a parent normal gene, the sudden acquisition of a new character is not explicable on a hypothesis as attractive as the one above. There are several examples available of a so-called acquired character. First may be mentioned the formation of pigments not previously produced by an organism. The two most notable examples are those of Neurospora mutants deficient respectively in the ability to synthesize adenine and nicotinic acid. Furnished suboptimal amounts of these compounds so the organisms can synthesize a certain amount of cell material, these mutants produce pigments not formed by the normal wild strain, or at least not apparent. The gene block in the adenineless mutant prevents the conversion of adenine precursor (actually inosine precursor, as the biosynthesis goes precursor → inosine → adenosine) into adenine (inosine), it accumulates and is converted into a brilliant purple-red pigment, both in the medium and in the mycelium (Mitchell and Houlahan, 1946a). Pigment formation always segregates with the adenine requirement in sexual crosses. In older cultures, the pigment appears as insoluble red-brown or black granules in the mycelial vacuoles and amounts to as much as 15 per cent of the dry mycelial weight.

The pigment in the nicotinicless Neurospora mutant is reddish-brown and appears in the medium. Its production is associated with a loss in nicotinic acid precursor activity of the filtrates and evidently represents a product of further metabolism of the precursor, or a spontaneous chemical change resulting in the colored compound.

A mutant from a strain of *Aspergillus terreus* producing itaconic acid forms a compound not found in the parent culture, namely itatartaric acid (Stodola *et al.*, 1945) (Chapter 13). Here, then, is a new product of carbohydrate metabolism, to all appearances a character acquired as a result of the mutation.

Finally, one may cite the well-known cases where the appearance of a *new* substance in the mutant is not involved, but rather increased intensity of production of substances produced normally by the parent. Outstanding as an example here are the *Penicillium notatum-chrysogem* mutations yielding amounts of penicillin greatly superior to the parent cultures (Chapter 18). Other instances of enhanced productive activity of mutants are known.

What is the interpretation of these "acquired" characteristics? Is it to be assumed that new genes have actually been established in the organisms, presumably by conversion of a gene precursor to the active form? This idea seems rather remote, especially when one considers that in some cases (penicillin, etc.) there is no new character but only a more intense one. A logical and attractive hypothesis is to consider this type of acquired character mutations in exactly the same category as all the other mutations considered in this chapter, i.e., loss of function. The fact that some mutants appear to have acquired certain characteristics would then be an inevitable corollary of the principles of shunt metabolism discussed in Chapter 4. As detailed above, loss of function in a mutant signifies a metabolic block at some point in the metabolism so that some intermediate precursor cannot be further converted, owing to a deficiency of the enzyme specifically under single gene control. Inasmuch as all other enzymes in the organism are intact, and presumably function normally, the cells will continue, to a greater or lesser degree, to carry on metabolism up to the point of gene-controlled enzyme deficiency.

These metabolic products (intermediate precursors) accumulate at the block and may be excreted as such, or may be acted upon by other enzyme systems in the cell, also capable of utilizing the precursor in question. In other words, several enzymes in the cell compete for the precursor. Thus pigments or itatartaric acid may represent an unchanged precursor, or more likely, may represent the precursor after further conversion by other enzymes. That is to say, intermediary products in metabolism may well have several outlets so that when any one is blocked, the metabolic sequence becomes diverted through other enzyme channels. In the normal organism these may be latent, or operative only to a minor extent, so that the particular function is not apparent. When the normal outlet is blocked the intermediary products are shunted to these other enzymes, which now carry out their particular functions with intensified activity owing to the new availability of substrate. A function like improved penicillin production could, on the basis of shunt metabolism, be viewed as caused by increased availability to the penicillin synthesizing enzymes of some intermediary precursor, which in the parent type is being disposed of via other enzyme channels. A mutation that blocks one of these other outlets now permits a greater proportion of the intermediary precursor to be available to the penicillin synthesizing sequence, and if the amount of that particular precursor has been the limiting factor in the activity of the synthetic enzymes in the normal strain, the mutant strain will therefore demonstrate this enzyme activity with augmented vigor, resulting in increased penicillin yields. Since the block can occur at many different points, each of which may divert a different amount of precursor to the penicillin enzymes, penicillin synthesis to varying degrees will characterize the different mutants.

Illustrating the probability of further conversion of intermediary precursors in metabolism are experiences dealing with mutants of *Penicillium chrysogenum* and of *Streptomyces griseus* characterized by complete loss of synthesis of penicillin and streptomycin. Assuming the loss of synthesis to be due to a gene block, one might expect accumulation of precursor at the gene block. This should be detectable by the stimulating power on penicillin or streptomycin synthesis (as the case may be) of culture filtrates of the mutants on each other or on the normal strain. So far this has not been observed, and one may conclude that the precursors do not accumulate as such, but are further metabolized.

As intimated above, the accumulating precursor need not necessarily be further metabolized via other enzyme systems. All or a part of it may accumulate as such, or, if the compound has reactive groupings, it may spontaneously condense intermolecularly or polymerize to a higher

molecular weight compound.   The adenine and nicotinic pigments mentioned above may represent actions like this.   It is evident that enzyme
imbalance can arise from more causes than mutation alone, and, as discussed in Chapter 4, it may be that many of the multitudinous fungus
pigments known, especially those that accumulate to appreciable percentages of the total cell weight, arise from this imbalance.

If the shunt metabolism idea provides a workable hypothesis to
explain acquired mutant characteristics, also implicit in it is the idea
that all mutants must therefore exhibit some acquired characteristic,
for loss of enzyme function inevitably must influence some other enzymatic, physiological, morphological, or cultural aspect of the organism.
The chemical instances cited above are those sought for, or easily detectable.   The numerous morphological and cultural mutations also must
be considered as end results of single enzyme alterations, in essence,
manifestations of shunt metabolism.   Finally, in some, if not all, fungi
known to be mutants solely by virtue of their inability to synthesize a
given nutritional factor, some subtle and not so conspicuous evidence for
concomitant acquired characteristics might also exist.   In other words,
theoretically, loss of function is always accompanied by an acquired
characteristic.

MUTANTS AS ASSAY ORGANISMS

An organism known to require a given chemical substance for growth
can be utilized to assay any non-toxic material for the content of the
particular substance.   Mutants are well suited for this purpose since,
in many cases tested, the growth response is proportional, within limits,
to the amount of factor present.   The specificity is also good, meaning
that under the conditions of the assay only the single substance analyzed
for is capable of influencing the growth response.   The growth response
may be measured by dry mycelial weight or by rate of advance of the
mycelium along the surface of agar in tubes (Tatum and Beadle, 1942).
Certain other requisites for any biological assay must be satisfied, but
numerous Neurospora deficiency mutants have found useful application
in assaying natural materials.   Certain vitamins and amino acids can
be determined successfully, including p-aminobenzoic acid, pyridoxine,
choline, leucine, etc.   In reality, mutation techniques now make it
possible to produce an assay organism theoretically for any constituent
known to be a normal component of protoplasm.

REFERENCES

Auerbach, C., and Robson, J. M.   1946.   *Nature* **157**, 302.
Beadle, G. W.   1947.   Science in Progress. 5th Series, Yale Univ. Press, New
   Haven, pp. 166–196.

Beadle, G. W., Mitchell, H. K., and Nyc, J. F. 1947. *Proc. Natl. Acad. Sci. U. S.* **33**, 155–158.

Beadle, G. W., and Tatum, E. L. 1945. *Am. J. Botany* **32**, 678–686.

Bonner, D. 1946a. *Am. J. Botany* **33**, 788–791.

Bonner, D. 1946b. *J. Biol. Chem.* **166**, 545–554.

Bonner, D. 1946c. *Cold Spring Harbor Symposia Quant. Biol.* **11**, 14–24.

Bonner, D., and Beadle, G. W. 1946. *Arch. Biochem.* **11**, 319–328.

Bonner, J., and Buchman, E. R. 1938. *Proc. Natl. Acad. Sci. U. S.* **24**, 431–438.

Buchwald, C. E., and Whelden, R. M. 1937. *Am. J. Botany* **26**, 778–784.

Christensen, J. J. 1940. Genetics of Pathogenic Organisms. Publ. Am. Assoc. Adv. Sci. No. 12, 77–82.

Christensen, J. J., and Davies, F. R. 1940. *Phytopathology* **30**, 1017–1033.

Emerson, S. 1944. *Proc. Natl. Acad. Sci. U. S.* **30**, 179–183.

Emerson, S. 1945. *Ann. Missouri Botan. Garden* **32**, 243–249.

Emerson, S. 1947. *J. Bact.* **54**, 195–207.

Ford, J. M. 1948. *Australian J. Exptl. Biol. Med. Sci.* **26**, 245–251.

Fries, N. 1947. *Nature* **159**, 199.

Fuerst, R. 1948. Master's Dissertation, University of Texas.

Goddard, D. R. 1939. *Cold Spring Harbor Symposia Quant. Biol.* **7**, 362–376.

Gordon, W. W., and McKechnie, J. A. 1946. *Anal. farm. bioquim.* **17**, 12–17.

Hanson, H. J., Myers, W. G., Stahly, G. L., and Birkeland, J. M. 1946. *J. Bact.* **51**, 9–18.

Hartwell, J. L. 1946. *J. Natl. Cancer Inst.* **6**, 319–324.

Haskins, C. P. 1938. *J. Applied Phys.* **9**, 553–561.

Hockenhull, D. 1947. *Nature* **161**, 100.

Hollaender, A. 1945. *Ann. Missouri Botan. Garden* **32**, 165–178.

Hollaender, A., and Emmons, C. W. 1939. *J. Cellular Comp. Physiol.* **13**, 391–402.

Hollaender, A., and Emmons, C. W. 1941. *Cold Spring Harbor Symposia Quant. Biol.* **9**, 179–186.

Hollaender, A., Raper, K. B., and Coghill, R. D. 1945a. *Am. J. Botany* **32**, 160–176.

Hollaender, A., Sansone, E. R., Zimmer, E., and Demerec, M. 1945b. *Am. J. Botany* **32**, 226–235.

Horowitz, N. H. 1946. *J. Biol. Chem.* **162**, 413–419.

Horowitz, N. H. 1947. *J. Biol. Chem.* **171**, 255–264.

Horowitz, N. H., Houlahan, M. B., Hungate, M. G., and Wright, B. 1946. *Science* **104**, 233–234.

Jahiel, R., Guberman, E., and Kazdan, R. 1944. *Science* **100**, 298.

Kidder, G. W., and Dewey, V. C. 1942. *Growth* **6**, 405–418.

Kinsey, V. E., and Grant, W. M. 1946. *Arch. Biochem.* **10**, 311–320.

Kresling, E., and Stern, E. 1936. *Zentr. Bakt. Parasitenk. Abt II* **95**, 327–340.

Lewis, R. W. 1948. *Am. J. Botany* **35**, 292–295.

Lockwood, L. B., Raper, K. B., Moyer, A. J., and Coghill, R. D. 1945. *Am. J. Botany* **32**, 214–217.

Loring, H. S., and Pierce, J. G. 1944. *J. Biol. Chem.* **153**, 61–69.

McElroy, W. D., Cushing, J. E., and Miller, H. 1947. *J. Cellular Comp. Physiol.* **30**, 331–346.

Mitchell, H. K., and Houlahan, M. B. 1946a. *Federation Proc.* **5**, 370–375.

Mitchell, H. K., and Houlahan, M. B. 1946b. *Am. J. Botany* **33**, 31–35.

Mitchell, H. K., and Houlahan, M. B. 1947. *Federation Proc.* **6**, 506–509.

Mitchell, H. K., and Houlahan, M. B. 1948. *J. Biol. Chem.* **174**, 883–887.

Mitchell, H. K., Houlahan, M. B., and Nyc, J. F.   1948.   *J. Biol. Chem.* **172**, 525–531.

Mitchell, H. K., and Nyc, J. F.   1948.   *Proc. Natl. Acad. Sci. U. S.* **34**, 1–5.

Mosseray, R.   1934.   *La Cellule* **43**, 203–286.

Pontecorvo, G., and Gemmell, A. R.   1944.   *Nature* **154**, 532–540.

Raper, K. B., Coghill, R. D., and Hollaender, A.   1945.   *Am. J. Botany* **32**, 165–176.

Ryan, F. J.   1946.   *Cold Spring Harbor Symposia Quant. Biol.* **11**, 215–227.

Smith, E. C.   1936.   Biological Effects of Radiation.   McGraw-Hill, New York, pp. 889–918.

Srb, A. M., and Horowitz, N. H.   1944.   *J. Biol. Chem.* **154**, 129–139.

Stahmann, M. A., and Stauffer, J. F.   1946.   *Science* **106**, 35–36.

Stakman, E. C.   1936.   *Genetica* **18**, 372–389.

Steinberg, R. A., and Thom, C.   1940a.   *J. Heredity* **31**, 61–63.

Steinberg, R. A., and Thom, C.   1940b.   *Proc. Natl. Acad. Sci. U. S.* **26**, 363–366.

Steinberg, R. A., and Thom, C.   1942.   *J. Agr. Research* **64**, 645–652.

Stodola, F. H., Friedkin, M., Moyer, A. J., and Coghill, R. D.   1945.   *J. Biol. Chem.* **161**, 739–742.

Stokes, J. L., Foster, J. W., and Woodward, C. R.   1943.   *Arch. Biochem.* **2**, 235–245.

Stone, W. S., Wyss, O., and Haas, F.   1947.   *Proc. Natl. Acad. Sci. U. S.* **33**, 59–66.

Sturtevant, A. H.   1944.   *Proc. Natl. Acad. Sci. U. S.* **30**, 176–178.

Tatum, E. L., 1945.   *J. Biol. Chem.* **160**, 455–459.

Tatum, E. L., and Beadle, G. W.   1942.   *Proc. Natl. Acad. Sci. U. S.* **28**, 234–243.

Tatum, E. L., and Beadle, G. W.   1944.   *Arch. Biochem.* **3**, 477–478.

Tatum, E. L., and Bell, T. T.   1946.   *Am. J. Botany* **33**, 15–20.

Tatum, E. L., and Bonner, D.   1944.   *Proc. Natl. Acad. Sci. U. S.* **30**, 30–37.

Teas, H. J., Horowitz, N. H., and Fling, M.   1948.   *J. Biol. Chem.* **172**, 652–658.

Thom, C., and Steinberg, R. A.   1939.   *Proc. Natl. Acad. Sci. U. S.* **25**, 329–335.

Umbreit, W. W., Wood, W. A., and Gunsalus, I. C.   1947.   *J. Biol. Chem.* **165**, 731–732.

Whelden, R. M.   1940.   *Mycologia* **32**, 630–643.

Wyss, O., Stone, W. S., and Clark, J. B.   1947.   *J. Bact.* **54**, 767–772.

Zalokar, M.   1948.   *Proc. Natl. Acad. Sci. U. S.* **34**, 32–36.

CHAPTER 7

TRACE ELEMENT NUTRITION OF FUNGI

Certain metallic substances are just as important nutrients for fungi as the carbon source, nitrogen source, and the traditional minerals like magnesium, potassium, phosphorus, sulfur, etc. In general, however, the amounts required are so small relative to the others that the designation "trace elements" is applied. Sometimes the term "microelements" or micronutrients is used.

The association of certain trace elements with the development of fungi goes back to the very first studies dealing with the growth of filamentous fungi in synthetic media. Pasteur's student, Raulin, in a classical research into the nutrition of *Ascophora nigrans* (*Aspergillus niger*) in 1869, supplied the ash of *A. niger* mycelium as a complete mineral supplement. Both zinc and iron were recognized to be present by chemical analysis of the ash, and, moreover, they had to be furnished in adequate amounts in order to obtain maximum dry weight yields of fungus, all other factors being constant.

Subsequent work has not only confirmed Raulin's observations on the response of fungi to small amounts of added zinc and iron, but his work has been extended to include manganese, copper, molybdenum and gallium, and possibly a few more. Furthermore, they are required for more than to obtain maximum growth; they must be present, in smaller quantities, to get any growth at all, although in some cases this may be difficult to establish experimentally. All are specific and cannot be replaced by any other element.

Generally, where fungus growth is required for stock culture collections, or for routine testing purposes, the requirements for trace elements are ignored. On the other hand, any physiological or biochemical interest in a fungus almost inevitably leads to control, if not systematic study, of the trace element nutrition of the organism.

It goes without saying that in those instances where the trace elements are not purposely added, they are present anyway in sufficiently large amounts as impurities in the nutrients, water, glassware, and inoculum to permit the organism to make abundant growth. Where simply routine growth is desired, as mentioned above, these conditions are most favorable, because complex organic materials are supplied as nitrogen sources and/or agar, both of which are rich reservoirs of trace elements. It is safe to predict that conspicuous trace element deficiencies show up readily only in synthetic liquid media using an inorganic N source, and where reagent grade chemicals are employed.

Before these ideas became rather common knowledge to the microbiologist and the mycologist, an interesting historical concept had developed, mainly at the instigation of the famous plant physiologist, W. Pfeffer, in 1895.   Impressed by the minute amounts of trace elements that could evoke relatively huge increases in fungus growth as compared to the standard nutrients employed by plant physiologists in the latter part of the last century, Pfeffer concluded that these substances were active through what he called chemical stimulation.   It is evident that Pfeffer was unaware of the fact that the reason he got any growth at all was that his media were contaminated with these substances, and this doubtless led him to view, then, these trace elements as things foreign to the normal metabolism or requirements of the cells.   In fact, Pfeffer considered the simple salt mixture widely used in plant physiology as adequate for the growth of fungi, and this mixture, known as Pfeffer's solution, has since been widely adopted for cultivation of fungi.*

Pfeffer's idea that the greatly accelerated growth in fungi caused by trace elements was a response to the toxicity of the substance apparently was similar to the old Arndt-Schulz Law pertaining to the stimulatory effect of organic poison on animal cells (Niethammer, 1927) and particularly to the well known "oligodynamic effect" first promulgated by Nageli before the turn of the century.   The oligodynamic effect states that strong poisons actually may be stimulatory if furnished in subinhibitory doses.   Pfeffer designated this supposed response to toxicity of these stimulants ("Reizstoffe") as "Gegenreaktionen."   This concept was adopted as a working hypothesis by many investigators in the subject for a period of over twenty years (see Foster, 1939).   It must be remembered that this concept originated from the observation that good growth could be obtained in media to which no trace elements had been added and hence could be presumed to be free of them.   Thus, when the deliberate addition of trace amounts of certain metals resulted in growth exceeding that of the control, the metals could be interpreted only as "stimulants."

The American plant physiologist, Steinberg, is credited with demonstrating the truth of the situation and revealing the fallacy of the Pfeffer concept of chemical stimulation, although the French investigators Bertrand and Javallier had already rejected this idea some years previ-

* Sucrose, 50 g.; NH_4NO_3, 10 g.; KH_2PO_4, 5 g.; $MgSO_4 \cdot 7H_2O$, 2.5 g.; distilled water, 1 liter.

ously.   Beginning in 1919, and continuing for a period of some twenty years, Steinberg introduced and applied the required fastidious techniques indispensable for work of this nature.   By developing an efficient purification method, he was able to remove almost completely the small amounts of trace elements present in media containing the standard nutrients, and was able to show that this purified medium, though adequate in the then considered essential nutrients, supported such scant growth of *Aspergillus niger* that it could be considered negligible, but such large growth increments when traces of zinc and iron were added that the theory of chemical stimulation at once became untenable. Instead, zinc and iron, (and others) must be considered as absolutely indispensable for fungus growth as nitrogen, carbon, potassium, phosphorus, sulfur, and others.

Thus, the very basis, or premise, on which the chemical stimulation concept was created, namely, that the basal medium allowed growth in the absence of some trace elements, was rendered false, thereby undermining the concept.   Actually, though these were not purposely added, the basal medium must have had trace elements as impurities, else no growth would have occurred.   Steinberg points out (1934) that, in the highly purified medium, as little as 0.5 mg. dry weight of *A. niger* is obtained per 50 ml., but upon addition of small amounts of zinc a 230,900 per cent growth increase results, an effect which hardly could be construed as stimulative.

On the basis of the above, and much subsequent work, trace elements can be considered only as nutrients.   However, it is evident that the exceedingly minute amounts of these substances that suffice to evoke disproportionate growth and metabolic responses in fungi must be due to some special attribute of these elements.   Modern biochemical, and especially enzyme, knowledge reveals that the trace elements indeed are endowed with a special property—they are either vital components of enzyme systems or, as coenzymes, they are essential for the action of enzymes.   Thus, in the main, they owe their remarkable effects to the fact that they function as catalysts, indirectly through enzymes.   Though the latter actually perform the changes, their activity is conditioned on the presence of the trace elements.   This will be discussed in detail later. It is interesting to note that Bertrand and Javallier, long before our current concepts of enzymes and coenzymes, ascribed a role of biocatalysis to the trace elements.

ESTABLISHMENT OF TRACE ELEMENT REQUIREMENTS

The principle is to furnish all the nutrients required, except the one under test, and in separate flasks include the test element.   If the particular element is essential there should be a significant difference between the deficient and the supplemented medium. In general, a basal carbohydrate-mineral medium consisting of reagent-grade sucrose or glucose, K_2HPO_4, $MgSO_4$, and $(NH_4)_2SO_4$ or NH_4NO_3 is subjected to special purification. This purified basal medium is distributed into specially cleaned flasks, each of which may be supplemented with one or more of the known essential trace elements (Fe, Zn, Cu, Mn, Mo, etc.) as salts. Care must be taken that of all the nutrients in the particular treatment, only the particular element under consideration is limiting. The pH should be on the acid side to prevent precipitation of various salts. Following sterilization and uniform inoculation with the test fungus using special precautions, the amount and the nature of the growth is followed during the incubation period. Relative rates of development are observed as well as features like pigmentation, surface vs. submerged or subsurface mycelia, sporulation, and other characters distinctive to the organism.

For physiological studies the respiratory CO_2 may be measured by aeration into standard alkali. Sometimes the different treatments may be set up in numerous replicates, enabling removal of duplicates or triplicates at different periods during the incubation, thus permitting measurements of pH, acid formation, sugar consumption, nitrogen consumption, specific acids, etc., and dry weights. Where the interest is in growth response, the surface fungus growths are removed, together with any submerged mycelium which may also have developed, washed to free from adhering nutrients, dried at 80°C., and weighed.

The basal medium containing no added trace elements should yield, per 50 ml. medium, no more than 10–15 mg. dry fungus weight if the proper precautions have been carried out successfully. The treatments to which the trace elements had been added individually will show from twenty to one-hundred or more times as much as the basal medium, especially with zinc or iron, the differences between the individual elements being a reflection of how much each is the one limiting growth. This is also a rough measure of the extent of the deficiency in relation to the amount of the element present as impurity. Combinations of trace elements always give growth yields in excess of those individually, another indication that no one element alone suffices, and it seems reasonable that a growth response to any element added to a mixture of the others is a fair indication of the requirement by the organism for that element even though the addition of that element alone to the basal medium does not produce a striking response.

In general, zinc and iron are the trace elements required in largest amounts for fungi, and consequently it is easiest to demonstrate these deficiencies, or, conversely, these give the largest responses when added singly to basal media.

1. TRACE ELEMENT CONTAMINATIONS

The 10–15 mg. yield mentioned above is merely a reflection of the near impossibility of absolutely ridding the medium of trace elements, although on rare occasions complete suppression of growth by a deficiency has been reported (Bortels, 1927; Roberg, 1928). The diversity and amounts of trace elements always contained in even the highest grade chemicals, as well as those in distilled water, those dissolving from the glass of the culture vessels, the transfer pipettes, dust, plugging cotton, and those introduced in the cells of the inoculum do not provide difficulties in ordinary chemical work, but do provide serious obstacles to biological work of this nature. As a matter of fact, the situation is quite comparable to that in growth factor work with various biological systems where the absolute removal of all traces of these catalytic substances is no mean task. Lack of appreciation of this situation has in the past led to some classical controversies as to whether or not a particular element was essential.

Despite the fact that these elements are of a magnitude which is beyond the range of sensitivity of most chemical analytical procedures, they occur in amounts sufficient to cause profound modification in the yields and nature of fungus growths, and in biochemical activity also. For example, while the exceptionally sensitive analysis for iron can determine concentrations as little as 0.1 mg. Fe per liter, the optimum concentrations of the essential trace elements for *A. niger* are, as determined by Steinberg (1935b, 1936a), per liter: Fe, 0.20; Zn, 0.18; Cu, 0.04; Mn, 0.02; Mo, 0.02 and Ga, 0.02 mg. The astonishing sensitivity of this organism to infinitesimal quantities of certain of the trace elements in a rigorously purified basal medium is evidenced by a twofold dry weight increase caused by 1 part per billion of zinc (Steinberg, 1935a) and by a large increase in growth with 1 part of manganese per 10 billion in the nutrient medium (Bertrand, 1912a).

(a) The chief source of trace element impurities lies in the sugar and nutrient salts comprising the culture solution. The excellent growth secured by using ordinary reagent grade chemicals is testimony of the quantities of metals they contain. The best demonstration of this is the following summary denoting some of the ions detected as impurities in the chemically-pure reagent chemicals that go into the basal medium used in trace element nutritional work, as established by spectroscopic analysis (Steinberg, 1937).

Ingredient	Contaminants Identified Spectroscopically
NH_4NO_3	Na, Mg, Ca, K (?)
K_2HPO_4	Al, Pb, Na, Ca, Mg, Ag
$MgSO_4 \cdot 7H_2O$	Na, Cu
$ZnSO_4 \cdot 7H_2O$	Fe, B (?), As, Mg, Sn (?), Cu, Si, Na, Mn
$CuSO_4 \cdot 5H_2O$	Fe, Mn, Sn, Mg, Cu, Pb
$MnSO_4 \cdot 2H_2O$	Na, Fe, Cu, Al, V, Cr, Si, Mg, Ca
Na_2MoO_4	Cu, Mn, Fe, Al, Ni, Mg, K, Na, Mn, Si, Li, V (?) Ca
Dextrose	Li, Na, Sr, Ca, Rb, K, Mn, Al, Fe, Rh, Ni, Ag, Cu, Mg, Sn, B, Si

The ash prepared from the mycelium of *A. niger* contained the following mineral elements according to spectroscopic tests: K, Mg, Fe, Cu, Mn, Na, Cu, Sr, Bi, Al, Pb, Ag, Ti (?), and V (?) (see also Mann, 1932). It is curious that zinc was not listed as being present in any of the materials tested, including the mold mycelia ash, for it is well known that this is one of the most commonly occurring element contaminants, and, almost by definition according to the discussion above, must have been present in the mold ash. Though chemicals are "chemically pure," it is obvious that they may be far from being "biologically pure." One will note that this philosophy is identical in relation to vitamin work especially when other substances of natural origin are supplied in the medium or diet. For example, chemically-pure asparagine, isolated from plant materials, is notoriously contaminated with biotin, if not other vitamins.

Two factors contribute to the nature and amounts of trace impurities in chemicals. Chemicals isolated from natural sources are apt to contain more impurities than those prepared synthetically because the natural materials exist in nature in a mixture with virtually every mineral impurity known. Second, the purification procedures, particularly the universal practice of recrystallization, falls short of rendering these natural substances biologically pure owing to the fact that the impurities actually form stable chemical complexes with the substance being isolated, and furthermore, elements closely related in the periodic table exhibit a marked tendency to coprecipitate so that it is extremely difficult to get rid of the last traces of the coprecipitant.

Stable soluble non-ionic complexes between nutrients in question and cationic impurities are especially characteristic of organic compounds, in particular hydroxy and polyhydroxy compounds, and also certain amino acids, notably aspartic and glutamic acids; in general, of any organic compound forming chelate type substances. As sugars almost always furnish the carbon and energy source in trace element nutrition work it is evident that complications arise. The severity of this problem in relation to sugar is manifest from the above chart. The same holds for other sugars and carbon sources frequently employed in nutritional studies, citric acid, lactic acid, etc. Synthetic media containing amino acids present special problems in trace-element purification by the conventional $CaCO_3$ technique owing to the fact that the amino acids bind trace elements tenaciously (Steinberg 1942a).

Coprecipitation is a well-known property of inorganic salts, and recognizing the natural origin of these substances, at once indicates the likelihood of interference from this source. At least twenty elements tend to be coprecipitated with calcium, for example (Hutner, 1946).

It is a rather general observation that growth rates and amounts of growth obtainable with amino acids and protein hydrolysates are difficult to reproduce in synthetic media, and this has been ascribed (Hutner, 1946) to the presence of certain unidentified essential trace elements of extraordinarily high biological potency in combination with these nitrogenous materials. While this may be true to a certain extent, it must be borne in mind that trace elements are not at the root of all the problems of biology. One must not forget that the direct assimilation itself of preformed organic compounds renders it possible for the organism to utilize its energy source more efficiently and thus grow more rapidly and abundantly, especially when the complex mixture contains substances whose synthesis by the organism is the limiting factor in growth. For example, most lactic acid bacteria can develop in the absence of purine bases (adenine, uracil, etc.) but they are greatly accelerated by the availability of these substances preformed.

Perhaps a more striking example of the direct incorporation and utilization of medium constituents into the metabolism of a fungus without preliminary breakdown of the substances is the conversion of various precursors to penicillin when the former are furnished to appropriate strains of *Penicillium chrysogenum*. Here, the addition of small amounts (0.1 to 0.5 per cent) of phenyl acetic acid or simple derivatives enable them to be utilized directly and incorporated into the penicillin molecule. Thus, the type of penicillin formed is altered to a preponderance of G-penicillin (benzylpenicillin) in which the distinctive substituent side chain is the phenyl-acetyl radical. Experiments with deuterium-labeled phenylacetic acid have confirmed that phenylacetic acid is utilized intact (see Chapter 18).

Although organic compounds that form stable complexes with metallic cations complicate the study of trace element nutrition of organisms, this binding capacity can serve a desirable role by preventing the precipitation of essential trace elements as insoluble phosphates, hydroxides, and carbonates through interaction with the other nutrients during heat sterilization. The element is not available to the organism in such insoluble combinations. Only when the organic substance involved is of known satisfactory purity can it be added for this purpose (see below). It is obvious that the bound elements will be liberated in free (ionic) form as the organism consumes the organic compound for carbon and energy. On the other hand, if the dissociation of the element from the stable complex is nil or negligible, that particular element could become limiting in rate of growth and may even prevent growth (Macleod and Snell, 1947). The inhibition is cleared by adding metal in excess of the binding capacity of the organic compound. It is worthy of mention that this type of organic substance serves a useful and protective function by binding and immobilizing certain elements which may be toxic to the organism. For example substances containing sulfhydryl groups (—SH) will revive organisms apparently killed by mercury salts, by combining with the cation through the sulfhydryl.

The complexity of the situation is further exemplified by the fact that, during growth, many fungi produce metabolic products that accumulate and that themselves are the types binding metal cations. Among the most common of these are hydroxy organic acids, and especially neutral polyhydroxy substances such as mannitol and other polysaccharides of diverse sorts, both within and without the cells. Among the acids may be included gluconic, lactic, malic, citric, and kojic acids. Also included are many miscellaneous substances characterized by phenolic hydroxyl groups and many ring-type pigments that form chelates readily. The absolute trace element requirements of an organism must of course be integrated against a background of the changing status of the culture fluid, and with these factors in mind it is quite likely that Steinberg's optimum amounts given above merely represent the resultant of all these factors. Steinberg's culture apparently was producing considerable organic acidity, to judge from the pH values. It would be well that such work be done with a system which characteristically metabolizes the sugar to CO_2. Furthermore, the slimy outer layer on fungus hyphae in contact with the culture solution, which consists of polysaccharide, must in itself represent a rather concentrated reservoir of bound trace elements. For this reason the outer cell layer of all microorganisms may, in essence, be a concentrate of minerals, and is probably a mechanism facilitating growth in exceedingly dilute mineral solutions.

The formation of citric acid, or other metal binding acids is, however, less of a trace element interference if the culture is unbuffered and the pH drops, for the stability of this type complex is greatly retarded as the pH is lowered (Bobtelsky and Jordan, 1945). Indeed, Steinberg (1936a) has observed that acidity decreases the optima, i.e., increases the availability, of trace elements for *A. niger*. However, in the presence of buffered media, or insoluble neutralizing agents, this binding difficulty may be a real factor.

(*b*) Unless special precautions are taken, the distilled water entering into nutrient-deficient media may be a troublesome source of trace element contaminations. Perquin (1938) traced abnormal reduction in citric acid formation by *A. niger* to iron in the distilled water. Repeatedly-distilled water from pyrex glass, and preferably from quartz, should be used though eventually dissolution from the glass limits this technique. Double-distilled water has been found to contain as much as 5 mg. of solids per liter, including lead, copper, and boron (Cliquet *et al.*, 1913). Developments in the field of ion absorption synthetic resins (amberlites, etc.) now make it possible to secure a quality of water which, in respect to minimal amounts of mineral salts, is considerably superior to ordinary distilled water.

(*c*) Glassware involved in work of this type has long been recognized as an important contributor to the impurity of the culture solution through dissolution of trace elements from the glass. Besides the trace elements, the major bases like Na, Ca, Mg, and also Si are contributed. Naturally, the type of glass, its quality, and its source make a big difference in the influence it exerts on the growth of fungi, some permitting excellent growth, others not (see Foster, 1939). Quartz glassware has generally proved to be the best for this purpose, but, of course, is too expensive and not ordinarily available to the laboratory. Pyrex glass is quite satisfactory and is almost universally employed. Care in the handling of the glassware is essential for best and for reproducible results. As an example of the rather unexpected influences at work in this type of experimentation, one may cite the fact that use of dry-heat sterilized glassware may give twice as much growth as unheated flasks (Yoshimura, 1934), presumably owing to the fact that the heating causes minute flaking of the glass surface, thus presenting a larger, as well as fresh surface for leaching. Steinberg (1919a) has demonstrated beyond question the leaching out of zinc from the glassware, and by repeated use of the same vessels has been able to secure gradually reduced yields in zinc-deficient media, the glass becoming depleted, at least with regard to the inner surface in contact with the liquid.

(*d*) Carrying over of element contaminations in the inoculum itself may invalidate the most rigorously purified system. It is evident that under no circumstance should adhering medium be introduced to the deficient test vessels; wherever possible, dry spores should be used. Owing to the fact that fungus spores not only contain trace elements, but may actually store them, it behooves the careful worker to cultivate the inoculum on submaximum or even suboptimum levels of the element in question, in order to deplete the spores.   Aso (1900) found that *Aspergillus oryzae* spores contain iron, which, as Fe_2O_3, amounted to 5 per cent of the ash.   The dependence on copper for pigment deposition within spores (Bortels, 1927; Gollmick, 1936) indicates that this element, as well as others, is probably stored in the spores.   The physiological activities of the fungus may, to a large extent, be a function of the trace element carry-over in spores.   For example, manganese is stored in the spores of a citric acid-producing strain of *A. niger*, already indicated by the stimulation of spore formation by addition of this element (Shu and Johnson, 1947), and clearly proved by the fact that the spores contain more manganese than the mycelium (Rennerfelt, 1934).   Inoculum spores from a sporulation medium containing 9.3 mg. Mn per liter lowered the citric acid yield to one-half that of controls, and 1.9 mg. per liter was decidedly harmful.   The relative content of Mn in spores as a function of the content in the medium is shown in the following tabulation from Shu and Johnson.

Mn Added to Sporulation Medium, Mg./Liter	Mn in Spores, μg./Aliquot
0.0	<0.02
0.93	0.4
9.3	3
93.0	16

A further means of reduction in mineral content of spores after growth on minimal media is to extract them with weak alkalies such as $KHCO_3$ or NH_4OH (Steinberg, 1935a).   The situation of inoculum carry-over of trace elements is exactly comparable to the carry-over of growth factors in the study of bacterial vitamin nutrition.

2. PURIFICATION TECHNIQUES

The most practical approach is to purify the final basal medium rather than the individual components before combination.   In certain cases it is feasible to purify the carbon source separately, provided a distillable substance, thereby easily purified, is used, e.g., fatty acids, alcohols. Generally, sugar is the preferred carbon source.   The calcium carbonate method of Steinberg first successfully applied in 1919(b) still remains one of the most useful from the standpoint of simplicity and efficacy. The basal nutrient solution is heated in an autoclave 15 minutes at 15 lbs. pressure in the presence of excess precipitated $CaCO_3$ (15 g./liter) and filtered through paper while hot.   Removal of the trace element impurities is caused by the increased alkalinity, which causes a precipitation of the alkaline-earth metal (Ca) simultaneously with the other undesired trace cationic elements as phosphates, hydroxides, carbonates, or basic carbonates. The calcium precipitate itself serves as a gatherer or adsorbent.

Recrystallization of individual nutrient salts is wholly unsatisfactory as a method of purification in this type of work (Roberg, 1928). The successful use of adsorbing agents has been reported. Bortels (1927) used activated carbon in alkaline solution with a small amount of $(NH_4)_2S$ as a precipitant. The quality of the carbon doubtless would be of importance here. Roberg (1928, 1931) tested several purification methods and selected Bortels' as the best; further refinement was achieved by subjecting the carbon to a preliminary acid wash in order to remove ash constituents, especially iron, which otherwise might be imparted to the medium (see also Steinberg, 1935a). Washed $Ca_3(PO_4)_2$ has been employed with success as an absorbent type purifier in media on the acid side (pH 5.5) (Sakamura, 1936). Aluminum hydroxide precipitate, generated by adding $Al_2(SO_4)_3$ (alum) to the medium and adjusting to pH 9 with ammonium hydroxide, also can be used successfully (Shu and Johnson, 1948).

In the case of particular elements, special methods designed for the removal of these alone may be utilized. Last traces of manganese can be removed by oxidizing this ion to MnO_2 followed by adsorption of the latter on insoluble $MgNH_4PO_4$ (Bertrand, 1912b). Vestiges of copper have been successfully removed by an electrolytic method (Wolff and Emmerie, 1930).

An interesting method of purification dating back to the early days of trace element nutrition is that first used by the famous plant physiologist H. Molisch in 1892, and since by other workers (Roberg, 1928; Molliard, 1929; Waring and Werkman, 1942) to rid the culture solutions of residual iron: the impure solution was inoculated with *A. niger*, which continued to grow until it had exhausted all the iron whereupon the mycelium was removed, and the solution then used as the basal medium for deficiency studies. In the final analysis, the biological test is the most critical criterion of purity.

Recent developments in the field of organic chemistry have opened a new, simple and rapid technique for elimination of traces of metal cations from culture solutions. Certain substances are now available which form colored stable inner chelate complexes with metals, the complex being insoluble in water, but readily soluble in certain organic solvents immiscible with water. Actually, such substances, on account of their characteristic color with traces of specific metals, form the basis of colorimetric methods of quantitative analysis for these metals (Prodinger, 1940; Sandell, 1944). The metal is recovered in the form of the stable complex by shaking with the solvent, which then is removed, carrying the metals.

8-Hydroxyquinoline (oxine) has been used successfully to provide media deficient in iron for fungi (Zentmeyer, 1944) and even for bacteria, (Waring and Werkman, 1942), the latter test more rigorous than that for fungi owing to the much smaller amount of cell synthesis performed. The ferrous and ferric hydroxyquinolates were extracted from the medium with chloroform, yielding an Fe-deficient medium in only 1 hour. Final iron content was 0.7 to 3.0 μg./liter.   Butylnitroso (p-$tert$-butyl-o-nitrosophenol) is another such reagent forming metallic complexes soluble in ligroin or petroleum ether (Baudisch and Heggan, 1942). As these reagents remove all the metal ions present in trace amounts, it is essential to add back to the medium all those except the one(s) under investigation.   A check on the success in removing the trace metals may be made with dithizone reagent (diphenylthiocarbazone), which forms colored complexes with the various metal cations and is regarded as one of the most sensitive tests known (Stout and Arnon, 1939).

Inhibition of fungus growth can be obtained by leaving the reagents right in the medium, the inhibition being due to immobilization of the essential ions as demonstrated by the fact that addition of excess metals restores growth (Albert, et al., 1947).   These authors point out that not all chelating substances are antimicrobial, hence the specific molecular architecture is also critical, presumably due to steric factors since the chelate is supposed to combine with the metal while it, the metal, is attached to the enzyme protein.   Zentmeyer (1943, 1944) proved by three criteria that oxine inhibition was due specifically to trace element (zinc) immobilization in the case of several different fungi including Fusarium, Ceratostomella and Penicillium:

(1) Oxine did not inhibit below pH 3, for the compound does not chelate in strong acidity.

(2) Inhibition of the fungus could be overcome merely by adding excess zinc.

(3) Increasing amounts of oxine were required for inhibition in the presence of increasing concentrations of zinc.

3. TESTING EFFECT OF ADDED SUBSTANCES ON GROWTH AND METABOLISM

A routine physiological study of a fungus culture generally involves finding the optimum concentrations of energy source, phosphates, N sources, etc., and frequently certain organic compounds such as amino acids, growth factors, special buffers, poisons, etc.   From the foregoing, it is evident that these substances are very likely to be seriously contaminated with trace elements.   If the basal medium happens unintentionally to be deficient in one or more trace elements, the effect of the added material will be confused with the effect caused by the trace elements unwittingly introduced at the same time. In work of this type it is mandatory that trace elements not be deficient. The literature is strewn with work in which this uncertainty prevails. This type of error is especially apt to be connected with substances added in appreciable quantities, such as testing different sugars or other carbon sources, phosphates, sulfates, etc., rather than substances being tested in vitamin-like amounts. Incidentally, the apparent toxic effects of certain heavy metals, especially barium, is due, not to a toxicity *per se*, but to the precipitation of sulfate in the medium, resulting in sulfur deficiency of the organism (Steinberg, 1936b).

General Observations on the Biological Function of Trace Elements

The effects of the individual elements on the overall aspects of growth and metabolism of fungi will be given in detail below, but before going into these effects it would be well to consider briefly the nature of the actions which result in the observed effects. In other words, what is known of the specific function of the trace elements as a class?

As indicated above, it is obvious that the minute amounts effective in generating such large amounts of cell material must indicate a role for these trace elements quite apart from the structural use to which the major nutrients are put, carbon, nitrogen, oxygen, sulfur, phosphorus, and possibly others. To a certain extent this view had been anticipated in the early part of this century by the French school of Bertrand and his student Javillier, who considered these elements as biocatalysts. The tremendous advances in the field of enzymology in recent years support this view by making it clear that the trace elements are largely functional or dynamic in metabolism because they are in tight or loose combination with the catalysts of the cell, the enzymes. The majority of enzymes, especially non-hydrolytic ones, are dependent on certain trace elements (including magnesium) for their activity, and the significance of this for growth and biochemical reactions in the cell is manifest—without the trace elements the enzymes of the cell become inoperative, and no growth results. Or individual enzymes may become retarded through selective trace element deficiencies, thereby greatly altering the pathways of metabolism.

Some trace elements are inseparably associated with the enzyme proteins and the enzyme is therefore considered as a metal-protein compound; the protein cannot be obtained free from the metal. In these cases the metals are indispensably a part of the enzyme, and are therefore specific, no other metal fulfilling its function. On the other hand, there are enzymes in which the trace metal is in such loose combination with the enzyme protein that it may easily be separated from this labile combination, dialysis generally being successful; though not always. In this type of enzyme, the metallic ion is not actually a structural component of the enzyme as in the first case, and the enzyme protein can be prepared free of the particular metal. But the presence of the metal is indispensable for the functioning of that enzyme protein, so that in the end, the metal is actually a part of the enzyme system, represented as protein-metallic ion in labile combination. In this type of enzyme system the metal ion is known as a coenzyme because it is a small-molecular-weight, stable, diffusible substance essential for the activity of the enzyme. It will be recalled that another type of coenzyme is now well-known—these are organic in nature and generally are phosphorylated vitamins.

For those enzymes that require metal coenzymes, the requirement is rather nonspecific, other metals of equivalent valency often being interchangeable in activating the enzyme, though with different degrees of efficiency. Almost all our information relative to the specific functions of trace elements comes from isolated enzyme systems of animal tissues and yeast and to some small extent from bacteria. Virtually nothing along these lines has been done on the fungi. Though the precepts of comparative biochemistry allow us to predict almost with certainty that these same enzymes function in fungi also, with rare exceptions they have not been demonstrated in or isolated from fungi, nor their relative amounts and importance established as determinative factors in the metabolism characteristic of particular fungi. In this connection it may be noted that because of the massive amount of fungus cell material obtainable under the controlled conditions of synthetic media, it is easy to secure marked deficiencies with respect to individual trace elements, and such systems should afford ideal material for the study of the mechanisms of action of the individual trace elements.

The following tabulation derived mainly from Sumner and Somers (1947) is intended solely to demonstrate the types of actions and the enzymes in which trace elements are known to participate. As intimated above, this does not mean that these enzymes are known to occur in fungi, but rather that because these enzymes have been demonstrated in other biological systems, on the grounds of comparative biochemistry they may occur in some if not all fungi. It may be taken for granted that if the enzyme is identified in fungi, the same metal coenzyme will be essential for its action, and this will explain at least one reason for the requirement by the fungus of the particular trace element. The important conclusion is that we are approaching the point where the trace element requirements of fungi need not be regarded as something empirical, as has largely been the case in the past, but where the need for them can be put on a rational biochemical basis. They are required for the activation of definite enzyme systems, and the probability is that, at most, a small number of enzymes are activated by particular metals. Mechanisms of action of heavy elements are discussed comprehensively and authoritatively in a monograph by Otto Warburg (1946). Understanding these mechanisms as we do now, at once reveals why Pfeffer's theory of chemical stimulation is invalid. On the contrary, when one adds a few milligrams of, for example, $FeCl_3$ to a liter of fungus medium, it is with the express rational purpose of ensuring the full activity of the cytochrome respiratory enzyme system, as well as catalase and doubtless others.

1. IRON-CONTAINING PROTEIN ENZYMES (HEMATINS)

Catalase, peroxidase, verdo-peroxidase, cytochromes, cytochrome oxidase (indophenol oxidase), cytochrome peroxidase.

2. COPPER-CONTAINING PROTEIN ENZYMES (HEMOCYANINS)

Tyrosinase (polyphenol oxidase), laccase, ascorbic acid oxidase.

3. ZINC-CONTAINING PROTEIN ENZYMES

Carbonic anhydrase.

4. ENZYMES ACTIVATED BY BIVALENT METAL IONS, ORDINARILY Mg^{++}, Mn^{++}, Zn^{++}, Co^{++}, Fe^{++}, or Ca^{++}

Arginase, phosphoglucomutase, alkaline and acid phophatase, adenosine triphosphatase, β-glycerophosphatase, pyrophosphatase, hexosediphosphatase, phosphoenol transphosphorylase, phosphoguanidine-transphosphorylase, hexokinase, phosphoglyceromutase, nucleotidases, prolidase, dipeptidase, leucyl peptidase, isocitric dehydrogenase, vitamin B_c (folic acid) conjugase, zymohexase (aldolase), carboxylase, pyruvic dehydrogenase, oxalacetic carboxylase, enolase, dehydropeptidase, α-keto glutaric carboxylase.

GROSS INFLUENCE OF TRACE ELEMENTS ON METABOLISM OF FUNGI

For the most part only generalities can be covered owing to the huge literature on this subject. For details the comprehensive review of Foster (1939) is recommended.

1. MORPHOLOGICAL AND CULTURAL CHARACTERISTICS

Naturally the effect will vary according to the organism but it is safe to say that the growth appearance in a complete medium versus that in media deficient in zinc, iron, manganese, and copper, either singly or in combination, is strikingly different with respect to amount of cell material (dry weight), physical aspects of the growth, sporulation, and pigmentation, the latter in the spores, in the mycelium, and in the medium.

Regarding the reaction of a particular fungus species to metals, (zinc), it should not be said that uniformity exists, for different strains of the same species show different optimum zinc concentrations and maximum cell yields.   This is one more example of the universality of strain specificity (Mosseray, 1932).

The marked influence of zinc in altering chemical composition of the mycelium of *A. niger* has already been described (Chapter 3).   The actual physical nature of the (surface) mycelium also is altered, the consistency of zinc and of manganese cultures being dry and brittle as compared to the loose and elastic nature of corresponding deficient cultures (Buromsky, 1913; Steinberg, 1935b).   The deficiencies lead to a thin, whitish, rubbery, smooth pellicle of *A. niger*, which, in media of a high degree of purity, is slimy and submerged with no surface pellicle formation; when zinc is added, however, the mycelial mat is much thickened and takes on a heavily wrinkled and corrugated appearance typical of abundant growth within a confined space (Porges, 1932a).   Iron-, manganese- and copper-deficient cultures behave similarly.   A similar zinc behavior is noted with penicillin-producing strains of *Penicillium notatum* (Foster *et al.*, 1943).

Certain cytological and morphological features of fungi are subject to modification by trace metals, and illustrate how profound are the effects of these elements on metabolism.   They have been observed to increase vacuolization within the hyphae and promote more branching in the mycelium (Iwanoff, 1904), cause appearance of starch granules in the cells (Molliard, 1929), cause formation of peculiar aberrant spherical-shaped cells (Yoshimura, 1934), and induce extra long conidiophores in *Aspergillus giganteus* (Mosseray, 1932).   Even sterigmata and conidia are transformed into these abnormal cells.   Manganese induced distinct morphological alterations in *A. niger* (Yoshimura, 1936).   Thus two or three conidia on a sterigma, and vesicles without sterigmata, or with mycelium instead, have been found.   Multiple head formation and even double heads on a single stalk were also observed.   Here then, is structural differentiation as a function of trace element nutrition.

2. SPORULATION

Sporulation effects are among the most conspicuous actions of trace elements on fungi.   As conidiospores in fungi almost universally contain a pigment(s) of one kind or another, one might expect pigment effects to go hand in hand with structural aspects of the sporulation process, and this actually is the case. In general, a fairly common pattern of response is observed, and where response is contradictory to this pattern, one might suspect that the degree of deficiency, or amount of trace element added, would explain the discrepancy. To secure any given amount of vegetative development a certain minimal amount of trace element is essential. The most common observations indicate that if this threshhold is not exceeded sporulation may be markedly if not entirely inhibited. No record has been seen by the author where a mycological study of this situation has been made to establish if the spore bearing apparatus is formed at all in such cases, and if spore suppression can actually be made complete, and not merely a reduction unapparent to the naked eye.

Next there appears to be a threshhold limit within which spores are formed but without (or with diminished intensity) the characteristic spore pigments. The appearance of the latter is conditioned by the amount of trace element available and may run the entire range from virtual absence to presence in sufficient abundance to give the full deep distinctive spore colorations characteristic of the majority of filamentous fungi. In certain cases rather striking effects are obtained if the trace element is added in amounts beyond those just adequate for the complete response mentioned (see below). This does not, however, invalidate the idea that the availability of trace elements increases the rate and total amount of growth, causing a more rapid completion of the vegetative phase of the life cycle, and consequently hastening the reproductive or fructification phase.

The common laboratory subject, *A. niger*, exhibits, with excess zinc ion, a characteristic inhibition of sporulation; the surface felt is white and practically sterile in contrast to the profuse brown to black sporulation commonly associated with this classical organism (Porges, 1932a; Roberg, 1928). Sometimes it is observed that the formation of conidia is decreased in direct proportion to the vegetative growth promotion, to the stage of complete absence of the spores, and this reversal was observed also with pigmentation; as the concentration of zinc approaches the critical concentration for spore inhibition, the color of the *A. niger* spores changes from the typical jet-black to a yellow-brown to yellow color (Roberg).

Obviously, alterations in metabolic behavior induced by trace element imbalances account for such responses in fungi, and in some cases establishment of a certain balance with other ions abolishes the distinctive action. For example, the spore inhibiting power of zinc was overcome by addition of one one-hundredth that amount of iron (Gollmick, 1936). The idea of "ion antagonism" is frequently brought up in cases like this, where the activity of one element is altered by another; but, until demonstrated otherwise, use of this term may be considered simply as evidence of our ignorance of the true mechanism of the counteracting phenomenon.

More information is available concerning the dependence of spore pigmentation on iron, manganese, and copper than there is for zinc, and it would appear that not only spore formation but also spore pigmentation is closely bound up with these particular elements.   It is to be emphasized that deficiencies of these elements severely prevent the vegetative growth of the numerous different species and genera of fungi which have been tested.   The manganese and iron content in spores has been described earlier.   It is curious that adequate amounts of all of these elements are essential for the typical black pigmentation of *A. niger*, for deficiencies of any one of these result in completely sterile mycelia or sporulation with varying degrees of pigmentation up to the real black color.   The black pigment apparently is not a single chemical substance, and may differ in the various cases (see later under this heading).

The spore and spore pigmentation of *A. niger* is so quantitatively and reproducibly a function of the supply of copper in the medium that a method has been devised for copper assay in soils (and presumably other materials) based on spore and pigment sensitivity to minute amounts of copper (Mulder, 1938).   One gram of air-dry soil is added to portions of purified copper-deficient solution, and after inoculation is incubated stationary for several days whereupon the intensity of spore color on the surface pad is compared with a series of standards prepared in the same way with graduated amounts of copper.   Maximum pigmentation was secured with 2.5 μg. copper per 40 ml.   For manganese, Bertrand (1912b) reports spores were blackest with the rather high figure of 5 μg./ml., eighty times the copper figure.   For further details on manganese and fungi the reader is referred to the numerous works of Bertrand in the French literature.

In 1891 Linossier extracted the black spore pigment of *A. niger* by means of alkali; in dilute solution it is brown.   He named it aspergillin, and found that it contains iron and behaves similar to hemoglobin.   The pure pigment contains 0.26 per cent iron (Quilico and Di Capua, 1933). Linossier regarded the inability of the fungus to synthesize aspergillin as the cause of lack of spore formation in iron-deficient cultures (1911). Sauton (1910, 1911, 1913; Javallier and Sauton, 1911) has made the most penetrating study of the relation of iron to sporulation.   He observed that sporulation was best when access of air was greatest; lack of oxygen had the same restrictive effect as lack of iron.   Accordingly, he concluded that sporulation is accompanied by a fixation of oxygen through the intermediary of iron which therefore was considered as a respiratory catalyst. Sauton argued that if iron were essential only for the formation of aspergillin pigment, as Linossier claimed, then leucospores (colorless) should be formed in the absence of iron. As this was not the case in his experiments, he considered this support for his idea that the inability to fix oxygen due to iron deficiency is responsible for spore failure. Modern knowledge of the vital role of iron in various oxidases (energy liberating systems) make it not unlikely that the iron actually is essential for both the process of spore formation and for aspergillin formation, independently.

The period immediately preceding sporulation is one of intense physiological activity and the need of oxygen would be acute, and would be expected to be mediated by iron-containing enzyme systems. Bortels (1927) claimed that aspergillin is not a pure substance but is a mixture of humic substances, and that the iron is bound physically rather than chemically. The humic substances are formed during the course of protein-breakdown, and the ultimate nature of the pigment is governed by heavy metal catalysts such as copper and iron. Iron was supposed to give rise to humin via a yellow ether-soluble pigment (cf. Quilico and Di Capua who reduced aspergillin to a yellow pigment). These ideas are not inconsistent with modern comprehension of humuslike substances and their chemical behavior (Waksman, 1936), and are compatible with the observation that deficiencies of the different trace metals (Fe, Cu, Mn) each results in pigment curtailment, and ultimate suppression; as implicit in Bortel's work, possibly a different black pigment complex is formed in each case, or the same type of pigment complex formed by different oxidation catalysts, which iron, copper, and manganese are. According to Quilico (1933) the pigment is a particularly pure true humic acid similar if not identical with that in peat, and is believed to be derived from carbohydrates.

The trace element requirements of *A. niger* are independent of the nitrogen source, for Steinberg (1942a) has shown that the same requirements exist when the fungus is utilizing amino acids as N source instead of inorganic N. This apparently is the only report on this aspect due probably to the difficulty in purifying amino acid media of trace elements as compared to inorganic N media.

3. VEGETATIVE PIGMENTATION

In fungi these pigments are multifarious and naturally one would not expect to find a predictable response pattern with respect to trace elements. Nevertheless ample evidence is available from which one can only deduce that the formation of these pigments appears to be intimately associated with the heavy metal nutrition of the organisms. The chemistry of a number of these pigments has been elucidated by H. Raistrick and his collaborators.   In addition to the spore pigments just discussed there are two other dispositions: (1) mycelial and (2) dissolving into substrate.   This delineation is merely a function of permeability and/or solubility.   Also noteworthy is the fact that rarely is only a single pigment in a fungus; a multiplicity is more the rule. These observations are particularly applicable to organisms belonging to the Fungi Imperfecti, and particularly, though not exclusively, to Aspergilli and Penicillia.   These simply have been the most popular experimental material.   The most detailed and extensive study on this subject is by Metz (1930).   He considered that pigmentation was related to the development of the mycelium, which in turn was dependent primarily on zinc and to a lesser degree on iron and copper.   All three must be present, each alone or pairs being insufficient to evoke the colors usually associated with a particular organism.   A deficiency of zinc was especially inhibitive to mycelial pigmentation of *Macrosporium sP.*, and all zinc-deficient cultures varied markedly from the normal.   Metz' broad conclusions were based on experiments with the following varied organisms: *Aspergillus niger, A. flavus, Penicillium sulfureum, P. luteum Penicillium sp., Fusarium, Macrosporium, Phoma betae, Ovularia, and Botrytis cinerea.*   The organisms tested could be classified into groups according to pigment sensitivity to heavy metals, the highly pigmented forms being most sensitive.

Pigment changes in the medium as a function of trace element nutrition is a common laboratory observation, particularly when the fungus is cultivated in synthetic glucose-mineral medium.   Probably the most widespread single instance of this kind is the formation of the yellow-orange pigment complex (chrysogenin) by the well-known high-penicillin-yielding strains of *Penicillin chrysogenum* and *notatum*, both in surface and submerged culture.   Yellow coloration in glucose-mineral medium is invariably associated with the presence of zinc in the medium, zinc-deficient cultures showing very little pigment formation; the amount formed is roughly proportional to the zinc content even up to 25 p.p.m., which already is inhibitory to growth (Foster, *et al.*, 1943).   (See also Buromsky, 1913; Niethammer, 1938.)   Another yellow-green pigment, riboflavin, is formed by certain strains of *A. niger* deficient in magnesium (Lavollay and Laboray, 1939).

Without a doubt it is possible to alter the pigment excretion of any fungus seriously by trace element nutrition.   Generally one finds that organisms with adequate trace elements tend to form dark reddish-brown coloration of the culture medium after autolysis sets in (Roberg, 1928). This may well be a universal point, possibly accounted for, according to Bortels, as humin-, or melanin-type substances, both greatly influenced by catalytic elements.

Always to be kept in mind is the possibility that the trace element effect may be only apparent instead of real. Certain fungus pigments, like bacterial and actinomycetal pigments, act as pH indicators, changing color according to the pH of the environment. As trace elements are highly influential in the degree of acid formation, change in pigment color may be due to pH and not the appearance of a new pigment.

Two other points about pigmentation: as mentioned in Chapter 14, metabolic products, colorless *per se*, may be formed and excreted by the fungus into the medium where they react with certain constituents of the medium to yield a colored compound. The red coloration of kojic acid with iron is an outstanding example.

Finally, an instance apparently clear cut with respect to complete independence of pigment formation from trace element nutrition: a mutant of *Neurospora crassa* genetically deficient in the ability to convert adenine precursor into adenine, instead shunts the precursor through reactions (polymerization?) which convert it to a purple pigment that accumulates in the medium and mycelium to the extent of 15 per cent of the mold dry weight (Mitchell and Houlahan, 1946). Other examples of this type action are given in Chapter 6. Ostensibly trace elements are not determinative here, as the parent culture, with identical trace element nutrition, does not form this pigment.

It is clear however that in these cases pigment formation depends on an adequate supply of the appropriate pigment precursors. It is quite possible that the distinctive action of the trace elements on pigmentation can be ascribed to the same type of action. By regulating certain enzyme reactions, the metals generate an adequate supply of precursors which eventuate as pigments. As discussed in Chapter 6 the first named case arises via shunt metabolism when normal outlets of the precursors are blocked genetically. The latter case may also be looked upon as shunt metabolism through formation by metal enzymes of excessive amounts of the precursors which become pigments (see also Chapter 4).

It is probable that the effect of zinc on formation of other metabolically synthesized molecules may be interpreted on this line of reasoning. Texera (1948) finds that zinc governs the nature of antibiotics produced by *Fusarium hyperoxysporum*. In the absence of zinc the culture filtrates inhibited both gram-positive and gram-negative bacteria; with zinc present, only gram-positives were inhibited.

4. PHYSIOLOGICAL AND BIOCHEMICAL ACTIVITIES (CARBOHYDRATE METABOLISM)

It is impossible to treat here all the individual metabolic activities that trace elements are known to influence or alter in the great numbers of different fungi worked with. For the most part, the major effects of individual processes are discussed in connection with those processes in various parts of the book. This treatment will be limited to gross effects. Interpretation of the main trace element effects have been covered adequately in Chapter 4 and will be mentioned here only briefly.

Probably the outstanding effect of trace elements is that, when added to a deficient medium a remarkably large weight gain is made by the organism. In certain respects this is no different from the response one gets by furnishing nitrogen to a medium deficient in this nutrient element, or phosphate, or sulfate. However, the typical trace element effect (for Zn, Fe, Cu, Mn) is revealed when one compares the growth increment in relation to the amount of substrate carbon consumed. Invariably this ratio is much greater in the element-deficient cultures than in the corresponding element-containing controls. This ratio is expressed as the "economic coefficient" of the organism under the particular conditions, $\dfrac{\text{g. sugar consumed}}{\text{g. dry weight of fungus growth}}$, and, where the element is deficient, the economic coefficient is increased. That is to say, it takes more sugar to produce a gram of fungus material under deficiency conditions than under sufficiency conditions. As an example of the magnitude of this effect, the actual efficiency increase in carbon and energy utilization induced by a trace of zinc may be as much as 300 per cent (Foster and Waksman, 1939). In a perfectly balanced mineral medium, the carbon assimilation is unusually high, dry weight of mold being 1.175 g. out of 2.5 g. sucrose supplied, an economic coefficient of 47 per cent (Steinberg, 1936a); values from 50 to 55 per cent have also been obtained (Steinberg, 1942a, 1948).

It must be emphasized that although occasional mention is made of this type of effect with iron, manganese, and copper, concrete information is available only for zinc, and a wealth of information has amassed describing this most characteristic effect of zinc (Foster, 1939). Though specific experimental evidence is lacking, it seems probable that in cases where a large growth response is elicited by manganese, iron, or copper, the action is apt to be similar to the zinc effect.

The respiratory coefficient, $\dfrac{\text{g. }CO_2\text{ evolved}}{\text{g. dry weight of fungus}}$, is another physiological index always decidedly increased by traces of zinc (Buromsky,

1913; Wassiljew, 1935a, b).   In other words, more CO_2 is produced per unit of cell material synthesized, i.e., the greater the intensity of respiration.   This will be discussed below.

The universality of the zinc effect is best demonstrated by the fact that besides innumerable different strains of the traditional *Aspergillus niger* series, numerous and diverse species are affected in like manner: *Penicillium glaucum, P. notatum, Trichothecium roseum, Rhizopus nigricans,* and many others.

According to the above two indices of metabolism, the presence of zinc means that despite the fact that less sugar is utilized per gram of cell material synthesized, more CO_2 is produced.   This can be interpreted not only as more efficient utilization of carbohydrate for cell synthesis, but also as a more thorough or complete oxidation of whatever carbohydrate was utilized by the organism.   The increased yield of CO_2 is indicative of this.   Expressed conversely, in the absence of zinc the organism is considerably less efficient in its utilization of the carbon and energy in the carbohydrate.   The most telling proof of this is the characteristic accumulation of metabolic by-products in the medium under conditions of zinc deficiency.   From the standpoint of the economy of the organism it means the carbohydrate is utilized inefficiently.   It means that the portion of the carbon and the energy in the sugar that has been attacked has not been utilized for cell synthesis and respiration, but instead is excreted and accumulates in the form of these by-products, which in the final analysis represent incompletely oxidized sugar.   These incompletely oxidized carbohydrate by-products are known to be simple organic acids which accrue in the medium in amounts approaching 50 per cent or more of the sugar decomposed, depending on the organism and the acid.   The fundamental nature of this metabolic principle is best demonstrated by the fact that it holds true regardless of the acid involved, for the adverse effect of zinc on the accumulation of organic acids holds true for oxalic acid formation by *Aspergillus niger,* gluconic acid by *A. niger* and *P. chrysogenum,* citric acid by *A. niger* and by Citromyces, lactic and fumaric acid by Rhizopus.   In some of these cases acid formation is suppressed entirely.   The significance of acid formation in relation to the theory of shunt metabolism is described in Chapter 4, and the above feature may be known as the "zinc shunt."

In the cases where the particular organism is not distinguished by its ability to form extracellular organic acids it is quite likely that other soluble metabolic products would represent the residue of partially utilized sugar molecule, but there is no specific study of this available. Similarly, insoluble shunt products also might function in this capacity, but again these have never been studied directly with this point in mind.

One is reminded of the significant alteration in the composition of cell material caused by zinc and discussed in Chapter 3 (see Porges, 1932a; Schulz, 1937; Kauffman-Cosla and Brüll, 1935).

Returning now to the economic and respiratory coefficients, we see why they are' changed as they are by zinc. If the sugar is not wasted in the forms of organic acids, obviously more cell material may be synthesized per unit of sugar. Similarly, carbon which otherwise would be left in the form or organic acids instead eventuates as CO_2, the extra energy liberate thereby being to the advantage of the organism (see also Wassiljew, 1935a, b; Watterson, 1904).

Mechanism of Action of Zinc

What is the mechanism by which the above described overall effects are achieved? The effect seems to center about the conversion, i.e., assimilation, of initially formed carbohydrate split products into the components of cell material. According to the idea of shunt metabolism, if this conversion proceeds smoothly, cell material results and no excess split products ensue. On the other hand if this conversion is restricted, the split products are shunted through other metabolic channels which are separate from the primary assimilation reactions, and which generate the organic acids. There is no direct evidence to prove this point, but the information available is readily and uniformly explainable by the assumption that zinc ion is either a part of an enzyme, i.e., zinc-protein, or is a coenzyme of an enzyme concerned with the primary reactions undergone by the sugar split products in the series that leads to their incorporation into cell material. In zinc deficiency this reaction is greatly retarded, resulting in shunt metabolism to organic acids. In view of the recognized central role of the C_4 and C_5 dicarboxylic acids and corresponding amino acids in assimilation, one is tempted to speculate that the zinc effect may center about these. A second possibility lies in the generation of split products from carbohydrate. If this rate is higher than the assimilation rate, shunt metabolism will ensue. It is of interest that zymohexase, the enzyme generating triose from hexose diphosphate, is activated by zinc.

This association of the zinc effect specifically with carbohydrate metabolism is substantiated by the fact that this element exerts its characteristic effect on *Aspergillus niger* only when the latter is grown on sugar and has but little influence when tartaric, succinic, and gluconic or quinic acids are used as a source of energy. Also, no effect is obtained on ammonia and oxalic acid formation from peptone. (Wassiljew, 1930; Butkewitsch, 1922.) In experiments of this kind one must always entertain the possibility that failure to evoke a response to added zinc may be due, unless proved otherwise, to the presence of sufficient zinc as an impurity in the medium.

Zinc and the other trace elements are required when amino acids are supplied as the source of nitrogen, just as in the case of inorganic nitrogen (Steinberg, 1942a). Carbohydrate is the energy source, the metals probably playing similar roles in both cases in relation to carbohydrate metabolism. Worthy of mention also is that zinc-grown mycelium of *A. niger* and of *Rhizopus nigricans*, acting on carbohydrate in replacement cultures in the absence of nitrogen and minerals, formed little acid, combusting the sugar entirely to CO_2 with oxidative assimilation taking place concomitantly (Bernhauer, 1928; Foster and Waksman, 1939). Thus, in some cases at least, the idea of assimilation is not restricted to synthesis of protein and other cellular constituents, but may be merely resynthesis of cellular polysaccharides. More information on this point is highly desirable.

Certain other manifestations of the zinc action are known. The composition of the cell material has already been noted. Biochemically different strains of *A. niger* react differently to the presence of zinc (Wassiljew, 1935b). Some citric acid strains gave increased citrate yields whereas gluconic acid strains gave decreased yields under the same conditions. The citric acid enhancement in certain strains of *A. niger* has been observed repeatedly (Perquin, 1938; Porges, 1932b; Wassiljew, 1935a, b). Any attempt to rationalize the contrasting effects of zinc on citric acid production by different strains of *A. niger* would be pure speculation, as there is no sound basis on which to make conclusions. It is evident that different strains respond differently to this and other trace elements. One possibility, however, is that in the strains whose citric powers are favored by zinc some other factor is limiting in assimilation. Also, in many cases the complete picture of the zinc effect is lacking owing to the failure to study the effects of different concentrations of this element.

As described in Chapter 4, the intensity of the zinc effect stands in direct relation to the carbon-nitrogen ratio of the medium, i.e., the carbohydrate concentration. Thus an amount of zinc sufficient to suppress acid formation from one carbohydrate concentration is insufficient to suppress acid formation from higher carbohydrate concentrations, and in the latter case, addition of extra zinc suppresses acid formation (Foster and Waksman, 1939). Other metabolic alterations have been accounted for by the presence of zinc, leading to the appearance of certain products not formed in the absence of this element. Oxalic acid may be found in zinc cultures, and none in zinc-deficient cultures (Wassiljew, 1935b). In the cases of *Rhizopus nigricans* and *Aspergillus niger*, the total acidity formed in the presence of zinc was not accountable as fumaric, citric, and oxalic acids respectively, as it was normally (Foster and Waksman, 1939; Porges, 1932b).

Zinc, and manganese also, appreciably increase the assimilation of minerals from the media so that the ash content of the mycelium is distinctly higher than in controls (Bertrand, 1911; McHargue and Calfee, 1931; Porges, 1932a). The zinc added in trace amounts is actually taken up by the organism and becomes fixed as a part of the cell substance (Javillier, 1908). Above a certain level, a progressively decreasing percentage of the available zinc is fixed. The total nitrogen content of fungus cell material is always decreased by adequate amounts of zinc.

IRON

As mentioned previously, there are very few reports dealing with energy utilization by fungi as modified by iron or other trace elements other than zinc; and so no general conclusion may be drawn, although the limited data which are available do indicate a behavior similar to that of zinc (see Foster, 1939). Strain specificities resulting in conflicting yields by citric acid-producing organisms are encountered, as in the case of zinc. A few other distinctive effects of iron have been reported. Proximate analysis of A. niger cell material shows that iron restricts the formation of ligninlike materials, at the same time favoring the formation of polysaccharides and fat (Schulz, 1937; Kauffman-Cosla 1937). Sakamura (1934) and Currie (1917) reported that iron and copper particularly were active in determining the selective absorption of NH_4^+ or NO_3^- from NH_4NO_3 by Aspergilli. Normally, the fungus assimilated the ammonium ion chiefly, i.e., it was ammoniophilic. When, however, iron was supplied, the organism became nitratophilic, and growth and metabolism were accelerated; no effect was obtained by iron with NH_4^+ or asparagin as the N source. The likelihood that this effect is strain specific or that the effect is an indirect one comes from the negative results of Gollmick (1936) and Steinberg (1937).

OTHER TRACE ELEMENTS

Virtually everything of fundamental significance pertaining to manganese and copper in fungi has already been stated or intimated in the foregoing. While the literature dealing with trace elements other than those discussed above in fungus nutrition is scanty and inconclusive, a few notable exceptions may be mentioned. Molybdenum and gallium appear to be essential elements at least for A. niger (Steinberg, 1937, 1938, 1939a). Molybdenum has for some years been known to play a vital role as a biocatalyst in biological nitrogen-fixing systems of all kinds, including bacteria and blue green algae (Jensen and Spencer, 1947) and its requirement by a non-fixing organism, *A. niger*, indicates perhaps a more general biological significance for this element than hitherto suspected. The requirement is unique in this case because molybdenum is essential only when the nitrogen source is an oxidized form of nitrogen, viz., nitrate, nitrite, or nitrohydroxylaminic acid. Omission of Mo is without effect when ammonium or organic nitrogen is used. Steinberg concluded that molybdenum is essential for activation of an enzyme, nitrate reductase, in the process whereby nitrate is reduced to ammonia for synthesis of amino acids and protein by the fungus. This important work has not yet been confirmed, and information on the essentiality of Mo for other nitrate utilizing fungi, and on the nature of the Mo activation of nitrate reductase will be worthy contributions.

Omission of gallium from an otherwise adequate purified medium resulted in growth yield of only 38 per cent that obtainable with 0.01 mg. of this element per liter of medium (10 p.p.b.), leading to the inevitable conclusion of the indispensability of this element for growth, and also sporulation. Its effect was specific, none of seventy-seven other elements tested replacing it.

The association of certain trace elements with special nutritional conditions may be more widespread than is commonly appreciated. A situation similar to the molybdenum effect with nitrate also exists for scandium with respect to carbon nutrition of *A. niger* according to Steinberg (1939b). In media with highly purified ingredients, no trace elements had any effect on growth when sugars were used as the carbon source. But when glycerol was the carbon source the yield of cell material could be doubled by addition of traces of scandium to a medium containing the other known essential trace elements, viz., Zn, Fe, Cu, Mn, Mo, and Ga. No other element tried could reproduce the scandium effect, and one is led to conclude that scandium is beneficial in the utilization of glycerol only.

It is worth reminding the student of trace element nutrition that such specialized functions for trace elements as already described mean that although an element may not be essential for maximum growth of a fungus, it may still exert marked influences on the metabolic processes. With his fine purification techniques, Steinberg has found that of seventy-six tested, only the six trace elements discussed above are essential for maximum growth of *A. niger*, and though this situation may change for other fungi, it is nevertheless a fact that profound effects are obtained by other trace metals in physiological processes apart from growth. As an example may be cited the favorable effect of only the following five metals of a large number tested on fat formation by *Penicillium javanicum:*

colombium, molybdenum, tungsten, iron, and chromium (Lockwood, et al., 1934.). Obviously there is a marked specificity involved here. Quite possibly the explanation of these and similar effects with other so-called unessential elements may be due to the point discussed at the beginning of this chapter, that many enzymes of intermediary metabolism are activated by a variety of different metals, so long as they are of equivalent valency. On the other hand, they may block certain reactions, shunting metabolism to fat synthesis.

It appears that zinc, iron, manganese, and copper are required by all fungi. This may not be the case for other trace elements. In other words, some may require an element for maximum growth and others may not, an exhibition of strain specificity. For example, A. niger, the traditional experimental fungus, allows maximum growth in a medium containing only faint spectroscopic traces of calcium (Steinberg, 1937, 1945), yet Steinberg (1948) shows that growth of other fungi is decreased to varying degrees in calcium-deficient media, indicating Ca requirements for some fungi, and not for others. The yield of growth obtained for various fungi in a Ca-free medium as compared to a Ca-containing medium was as follows: *Aspergillus niger*, 100 per cent; *Fusarium oxysporum* var. *nicotianae*, 100 per cent; *Cercospora nicotianae*, 90.1 per cent; *Thielaviopsis basicola*, 82.0 per cent; *Pythium irregulare*, 60.1 per cent; *Sclerotium rolfsii*, 49.5 per cent; *Rhizoctonia solani*, 14.3 per cent. For maximum yields 2 to 6 p.p.m. Ca were required.

In instances where Ca is not required by the fungus, this element will nevertheless be assimilated and will accumulate in the mycelium (Rippel and Stoess, 1932). A similar situation has been reported for silver which, by spectroscopic analysis, may amount to 0.001 to 0.01 per cent of the dry fungus (Trischler, 1931).

Now that vitamin B_{12}, which is essential for the synthesis of the thymidine portion of desoxyribonucleic acid (Shive *et al.*, 1948), is known to contain cobalt and appears to be a cobalt coordination complex (Rickes *et al.*, 1948), it is likely that refined purification techniques will reveal a cobalt requirement in fungi.

TRACE ELEMENTS AND CO_2 UTILIZATION

Steinberg (1942b) claims that trace elements play a specific role in the utilization of CO_2 by *A. niger*, just as they do in green plants. This conclusion is based on experiments in which the cell material synthesized was reduced appreciably more by deficiencies of iron, zinc, copper, or gallium under conditions of CO_2 removal from the atmosphere than by those same deficiencies when the CO_2 atmosphere was normal. Such results are not surprising considering the fact that trace elements are coenzymes for various reactions directly or indirectly associated with CO_2 fixation. Thus zinc and possibly some other divalent metals are coenzymes in carbohydrate dissimilation generating pyruvic acid, one of the precursors of the fixation reaction via oxalacetic acid. As a matter of fact, manganese is itself a specific coenzyme for the principal CO_2-fixing reaction in heterotrophic cells, namely, oxalacetic carboxylase and oxalosuccinic carboxylase. Unfortunately, the effect of CO_2 removal on manganese-deficient cells was not tested, for theoretically, one would expect perhaps the greatest effect with this element. Not to be overlooked are other CO_2 fixation mechanisms, as yet unknown or imperfectly known, which may require metal coenzymes.

REFERENCES

Albert, A., Rubbo, S. D., Goldacre, R. J., and Balfour, B. G. 1947. *Brit. J. Exptl. Path.* **28**, 69–87.
Aso, K. 1900. *Bull. Coll. Agr. Tokyo Imp. Univ.* **4**, 81–96.
Baudisch, O., and Heggen, G. F. 1942. *Arch. Biochem.* **1**, 239–245.
Bernhauer, K. 1928. *Biochem. Z.* **197**, 287–308.
Bertrand, G. 1911. *Compt. rend.* **153**, 1337–1340.
Bertrand, G. 1912a. *Bull. soc. chim. France IV* **11**, 494–498.
Bertrand, G. 1912b. *Ann. inst. Pasteur* **26**, 241–246.
Bobtelsky, M., and Jordan, J. 1945. *J. Am. Chem. Soc.* **67**, 1824–1831.
Bortels, H. 1927. *Biochem. Z.* **182**, 301–358.
Buromsky, I. 1913. *Zentr. Bakt. Parasitensk. Abt II* **36**, 54–66.
Butkewitsch, W. 1922. *Biochem. Z.* **129**, 445–454.
Cliquet, R., Guilbert, J., and Penan, H. 1913. *J. pharm. chim.* **18**, 321–324.
Currie, J. N. 1917. *J. Biol. Chem.* **31**, 15–37.
Foster, J. W. 1939. *Botan. Rev.* **5**, 207–239.
Foster, J. W., and Waksman, S. A. 1939. *J. Bact.* **37**, 599–617.
Foster, J. W., Woodruff, H. B., and McDaniel, L. E. 1943. *J. Bact.* **46**, 421–433.
Gollmick, F. 1936. *Zentr. Bakt. Parasitenk. Abt II* **93**, 421–442.
Hutner, S. H. 1946. *J. Bact.* **52**, 213–221.
Iwanoff, K. S. 1904. *Zentr. Bakt. Parasitenk. Abt II* **36**, 54–66.
Javallier, M. 1908. *Compt. rend.* **146**, 365–367.
Javallier, M., and Sauton, B. *Compt. rend.* **153**, 1177–1180.
Jensen, H. L., and Spencer, D. 1947. *Proc. Linnean Soc. N. S. Wales* **72**, Pts. 1–2, 73–86.
Kauffmann-Cosla, D. 1937. *Arch. intern. pharmacodynamie* **57**, 188–194 (*C. A.* **32**, 1736).
Kauffmann-Cosla, D., and Brüll, M. 1935. *Bull. soc. chim. biol.* **17**, 1828–1835.
Lavollay, J., and Laborey, F. 1939. *Compt. rend.* **206**, 1055–1056.
Linossier, G. 1891. *Compt. rend.* **112**, 489–492.
Linossier, G. 1911. *Compt. rend.* **151**, 1075–1076.
Lockwood, L. B., Ward, G. E., May, O. E., Herrick, H. T., and O'Niell, H. T. 1934. *Zentr. Bakt. Parasitensk. Abt II* **90**, 411–425.
Macleod, R. A., and Snell, E. E. 1947. *J. Biol. Chem.* **170**, 351–365.
McHargue, J. S., and Calfee, R. K. 1931. *Botan. Gaz.* **91**, 183–193.
Mann, M. L. 1932. *Bull. Torrey Botan. Club* **59**, 443–490.

Metz, O. 1930. *Arch. Mikrobiol.* **1**, 197–251.

Mitchell, H. K., and Houlahan, M. B. 1946. *Federation Proc.* **5**, 370–375.

Molisch, H. 1892. Die Pflanze in ihren Beziehungen zum Eisen. Gustav Fischer, Jena. Pp. 97–117.

Molliard, M. 1929. *Compt. rend.* **189**, 417–420.

Mosseray, R. 1932. *La Cellule* **41**, 113–128.

Mulder, E. G. 1939. *Arch. Mikrobiol.* **10**, 72–86.

Niethammer, A. 1927. *Biochem. Z.* **184**, 370–382.

Niethammer, A. 1938. *Arch. Mikrobiol.* **9**, 23–30.

Perquin, L. H. C. 1938. Bijdrage tot de kennis der oxidativen dissimilatie von *Aspergillus niger*. Dissertation, Delft.

Pfeffer, W. 1895. *Jahrb. wiss. Botan.* **28**, 205–268.

Porges, N. 1932a. *Botan. Gaz.* **94**, 197–207.

Porges, N. 1932b. *Am. J. Botany* **19**, 559–567.

Prodinger, W. 1940. Organic Reagents Used in Quantitative Inorganic Analysis. Elsevier, New York.

Quilico, A. 1933. *Gazz. chim. ital.* **63**, 400–410.

Quilico, A., and DiCapua, A. 1933. *Atti accad. Lincei* **17**, 177–182.

Raulin, J. 1869. *Ann. sci. nat. Botan. et biol. vegetale* **11**, 93–299.

Rennerfelt, E. 1934. *Planta* **22**, 221–239.

Rickes, E. L., Brink, N. G., Koniuszy, F. R., Wood, T. R., and Folkers, K. 1948. *Science* **108**, 134.

Rippel, A., and Stoess, V. 1932. *Arch. Mikrobiol.* **3**, 492–506.

Roberg, M. 1928. *Zentr. Bakt. Parasitenk. Abt II* **74**, 333–371.

Roberg, M. 1931. *Zentr. Bakt. Parasitenk. Abt II* **84**, 196–230.

Sakamura, T. 1934. *J. Faculty Sci. Hokkaido Imp. Univ. Ser. V* **3**, 121–138.

Sakamura, T. 1936. *J. Faculty Sci. Hokkaido Imp. Univ. Ser. V* **4**, 98–117.

Sandell, E. B. 1944. Colorimetric Determination of Traces of Metals. Interscience, New York, Vol. 3, 487 pp.

Sauton, B. 1910. *Compt. rend.* **112**, 489–492.

Sauton, B. 1911. *Ann. inst. Pasteur* **25**, 922–928.

Sauton, B. 1913. *Compt. rend. soc. biol.* **74**, 38–39.

Schulz, G. 1937. *Planta* **27**, 196–218.

Shive, W., Ravel, J. M., and Eakin, R. E. 1948. *J. Am. Chem. Soc.* **70**, 2614–2615.

Shu, P., and Johnson, M. J. 1947. *J. Bact.* **54**, 161–167.

Shu, P., and Johnson, M. J. 1948. *J. Bact.* **56**, 577–585.

Steinberg, R. A. 1919a. *Bull. Torrey Botan. Club* **46**, 1–21.

Steinberg, R. A. 1919b. *Am. J. Botany* **6**, 330–372.

Steinberg, R. A. 1934. *Bull. Torrey Botan. Club* **61**, 241–248.

Steinberg, R. A. 1935a. *J. Agr. Research* **51**, 413–424.

Steinberg, R. A. 1935b. *Bull. Torrey Botan. Club* **62**, 81–90.

Steinberg, R. A. 1936a. *J. Agr. Research* **52**, 439–448.

Steinberg, R. A. 1936b. *Botan. Gaz.* **97**, 666–671.

Steinberg, R. A. 1937. *J. Agr. Research* **55**, 891–902.

Steinberg, R. A. 1938. *J. Agr. Research* **57**, 569–574.

Steinberg, R. A. 1939a. *J. Agr. Research* **59**, 731–748.

Steinberg, R. A. 1939b. *J. Agr. Research* **59**, 749–763.

Steinberg, R. A. 1942a. *J. Agr. Research* **64**, 455–475.

Steinberg, R. A. 1942b. *Plant Physiol.* **17**, 129–132.

Steinberg, R. A. 1945. *Plant Physiol.* **20**, 600–608.

Steinberg, R. A.   1948.   *Science* **107**, 423.

Stout, P. R., and Arnon, D. I.   1939.   *Am. J. Botany* **26**, 144–149.

Sumner, J. B., and Somers, G. F.   1947.   Chemistry and Methods of Enzymes. Academic Press, New York.

Texera, D. A.   1948.   *Phytopathology* **38**, 70–81.

Trischler, J.   1931.   *Wiss. Arch. Landw. Abt. A, Arch. Pflanzenbau* **7**, 39–78.

Waksman, S. A.   1936.   Humus.   Williams and Wilkins, Baltimore.

Warburg, O.   1946.   Schwermetalle als Wirkungsgruppen von Fermenten.   Saenger, Berlin, 195 pp.

Waring, W. S., and Werkman, C. H.   1942.   *Arch. Biochem.* **1**, 303–310.

Wassiljew, G.   1930.   *J. Exptl. Biol. Med. USSR Ser. A* **14**, (37), 17–21, cited in Wassiljew (1935).

Wassiljew, G.   1935a.   *Arch. Mikrobiol.* **6**, 250–275.

Wassiljew, G.   1935b.   *Biochem. Z.* **278**, 226–234.

Watterson, A.   1904.   *Bull. Torrey Botan. Club* **31**, 291–307.

Wolff, L. K., and Emmerie, A.   1930.   *Biochem. Z.* **228**, 441–450.

Yoshimura, F.   1934.   *J. Faculty Sci. Hokkaido Imp. Univ. Ser. V* **3**, 89–99.

Yoshimura, F.   1936.   *J. Faculty Sci. Hokkaido Imp. Univ. Ser. V* **4**, 117–139.

Zentmeyer, G.   1943.   *Phytopathology* **33**, 1121.

Zentmeyer, G.   1944.   *Science* **100**, 294.

CHAPTER 8

LACTIC ACID FORMATION BY FUNGI

The ability to form lactic acid from hexose sugars is so common a property of biological systems, including animal and microbial cells, that it is surprising to learn it is a relative rarity in fungi. Among the microorganisms, the formation of this acid is commonly believed to be a property peculiar to bacteria though protozoa and algae also may be included. It is understandable how widespread this conception may be when even a prominent investigator of the chemistry of molds stated not long ago, "It is a striking fact that lactic acid has never been reported as a mold metabolic product, although it is produced in larger or smaller quantities by many bacteria."

As a matter of fact, lactic acid had been reported several times prior to that as occurring in mold culture filtrates, and considerable work has been done since that time. With few exceptions, all fungi concerned with lactic acid production belong to the family Mucoraceae, of the Phycomycetes, and chiefly to the genus Rhizopus. Another phycomycete, *Blastocladia pringsheimii* has this property (Emerson and Cantino, 1948) as has a new species of Monilia, *M. tamari* (Miyaji, 1930).

The amount of study devoted to this process in molds has been greatly exceeded by other mold processes involving organic acid formation, even though its history in mold biochemistry dates back almost to the very beginnings of this subject, when citric acid and oxalic acid were still new discoveries in the field. As in so many mold processes, study and development of lactic acid formation apparently was greatly retarded due to lack of practical or industrial application, especially when one considers that the industrial potentialities of oxalic and citric acids, particularly the latter, was very much a subject of major interest in the eighteen-nineties. In substantiation of this statement, only after practical utilization of the mold process appeared to have some possibilities, as it has in the last decade, was considerable work done on the process and much detail and fundamental characteristics revealed.

Why a simple product of glycolytic metabolism like lactic acid should not be encountered more frequently among molds, which as a group are active sugar decomposers, has no satisfactory explanation at this time. As shown in Chapters 4, 9 and 10, the main metabolic pathway of

282

metabolism centers about C_2 compounds, and presumably pyruvate appears only transitorily during aerobic conditions, being rapidly decarboxylated to C_2. Aerobically the presence of oxygen might be considered to suppress the tendency of pyruvate to act as H acceptor and become reduced to lactate. However, available evidence on such organisms under anaerobic conditions indicate an alcoholic glycolysis and not a lactic. This situation is a parallel of yeast fermentation and also apparently in most higher plants where alcoholic fermentation is the main anaerobic characteristic.

Eijkmann in 1894 suggested, without positive proof, that the acid formed in small quantities by *Mucor rouxii* was probably lactic acid, although Calmette (1892) claimed that the acid formed by this organism was oxalic acid. Doubtless the then unrecognized fact of strain specificity was involved here, for different strains of Mucor are known to produce both acids. Even though Eijkmann's original assertion was later confirmed by Chrzaszcz (1901), the great Wehmer (1910) was inclined to doubt the validity of these two reports on the grounds that lactic acid hitherto had never been reported to be a metabolic product of the filamentous fungi. Wehmer was also skeptical as to the validity of a British patent already issued in 1899 (Boulanger) and in Germany in 1901 for the production of lactic acid by a mold called "Lactomyces." This organism probably was a number of the Mucorales, most likely Rhizopus or Mucor.

In 1911 Saito, and in 1919 Ehrlich reported small amounts of lactic acid in cultures of Rhizopus. An interesting example of specificity with regard to optical isomers of mold lactic acid is revealed by these two works. The former showed that *Rhizopus chinensis* produced levo (l) lactic acid and the latter that *R. nigricans* and *R. tritici* produced dextro (d) lactic acid. Ehrlich's organisms chiefly produced fumaric acid, and besides lactic acid, succinic and l-malic acids were present in small amounts. Similar kinds of physiological specificity of optical activity are known in the case of lactic acid formation by the rod-shaped lactic acid bacteria, and more recently the 2:3-butylene glycol formed by different bacterial species has been shown to be d-, l- or *meso*-, respectively.

Because of the importance of various members of the Mucorales group in domestic fermentations and food preparations, the physiology of this group of fungi has for years been studied intensively by the Japanese. Takahashi and Sakaguchi (1925) first demonstrated the high yields of lactic acid which might be expected in mold cultures. On the basis of sugar consumed, a 38 per cent yield of l-lactic acid was obtained in Rhizopus cultures. Lactic acid accumulation in molds is never the sole metabolic product, as it is, for example, in the homofermentative

lactic acid bacteria.   It more nearly corresponds to the heterofermenta-
tive lactic acid bacteria, for generally numerous other metabolic products
accompany the lactic acid in mold cultures, although under certain conditions their formation can be repressed and their presence amounts to
but a small percentage of the lactic acid formed.   The Japanese workers
found varying small amounts of fumaric, succinic, malic, formic, and
acetic acids, and ethyl alcohol in good lactic acid culture.   A few species
of Mucor, close relatives to the genus Rhizopus, were found to produce
traces of lactic acid in a fermentation which was principally alcoholic and
in which acetaldehyde, pyruvic acid, and succinic acid were also present
(Takahashi and Asai, 1933).

The first real physiological studies of the mold lactic process were
made by the Russian Kanel (1934, 1935).   He obtained 40 per cent
conversion of invert sugar into *d*-lactic acid with *Rhizopus japonicus*.
Almost all fungi of the Mucoraceae, especially the genus Rhizopus,
are not capable of forming invertase, and cannot utilize sucrose, hence
the emphasis on invert sugar.   As noted previously, fumaric acid
accompanies the lactic acid and tended in particular to accumulate in the
older cultures together with small quantities of other unidentified acids.
The association of fumaric and lactic acids in Mucorales cultures is an
almost invariable phenomenon.   This is discussed below.   Kanel
claimed that lactic and fumaric acids were in a kind of equilibrium.
Conditions of a low oxidation-reduction potential of the medium favored
the formation of lactic acid by Rhizopus, whereas a high potential shifted
the equilibrium to a preponderance of fumaric acid.   This may be true
within limits, but as most recent work on these organisms demonstrates,
it is not a general phenomenon and probably is more a strain characteristic.   Kanel's method of raising the oxidation potential was to have the
mycelium in contact with the atmosphere as contrasted to having it
submersed in the medium.   Later work has demonstrated that Kanel's
reasoning is only partly correct: first because of the factor of strain specificity, and, secondly, because while low redox potentials (as induced by
anaerobic conditions) appear to favor the glycolytic mechanism giving
rise to lactic acid, this can be true only up to 50 per cent weight conversion
of sugar, the maximum obtainable under anaerobic conditions (see later).
However, lactic acid formation is not a typical glycolytic mechanism,
for the presence of oxygen is indispensable for maximum yields, which
under ideal aerobic conditions may reach as high as 75 per cent of the
sugar consumed.   Expressed differently, under anaerobic conditions
1.0 mole of lactic acid is formed per mole of glucose consumed; aerobically 1.5 mole is formed per mole of glucose.   (Waksman and Foster,
1939; Ward *et al.*, 1938; see also Waksman and Hutchings, 1937; Ward
et al., 1936.)

The attainment of such high yields of lactic acid reopened the possibilities for industrial scale production, and stimulated interest in and study of the organisms concerned by the above two groups of workers at the New Jersey Agricultural Experiment Station and at the United States Department of Agriculture laboratories in Washington. The former emphasized the physiological aspects of the process and the latter the development of an industrial process.

On a commercial basis, lactic acid manufactured by Rhizopus could not compete with the ordinary technical lactic acid from the fermentation (anaerobic) of molasses or starch by thermophilic lactic acid bacteria. The larger capital investment in a plant for an aerobic process, as well as the lower yields (75 vs. 95 per cent) and costlier ingredients of the medium, make lactic acid produced by the mold process appreciably more costly than the bacterial product. However, mold lactic acid has certain superior properties which indicate a potential use when such properties are at a premium, such as, for example, in the food and beverage industry. Because mold lactic acid can be obtained by direct isolation as the calcium salt from a mineral-glucose medium, the resulting product is one of extremely high and reproducible purity; the free acid is liberated by the addition of the required amount of H_2SO_4, the insoluble $CaSO_4$ being filtered off. Bacterial lactic acid is obtained from carbohydrate media rich in protein and other nitrogenous materials and their breakdown products, and these contaminate the finished lactic acid so that unless special purification of the initially obtained lactic acid (salt) is made, the small amounts of impurities impart color, off-flavors, and odors, which are objectionable in food and beverage products. Highly purified lactic acid is a costly and difficult thing to make, starting with the bacterial product; mold lactic acid, pure by direct isolation, might then find special usage. The initial high grade of the mold product should facilitate the preparation of pure crystalline lactic acid. Commercial scale mold lactic acid production is not believed to be in operation currently.

General Aspects

The ability to form lactic acid from glucose seems to be a general characteristic of the genus Rhizopus. Where lactic acid is not detected, it is possible that the latent ability might be brought forth by providing the right conditions. In addition to the species mentioned above the following organisms are known to form lactic acid: *Rhizopus nodosus, R. arrhizus, R. chinensis, R. pseudochinensis, R. elegans, R. oryzae, R. salebrosus, R. shanghaiensis, R. stolonifer* and *R. tritici.*

Certain strains of *R. nodosus* and *R. oryzae* were most vigorous and were selected for detailed study. These organisms develop actively in a synthetic medium containing glucose, starch, or inulin as the sole energy source, and form an abundance of lactic acid. Almost any simple nitrogen source is available to these organisms with the exception of nitrate, which is not used by most Mucorales. The accumulation of acid rapidly diminishes the growth rate of the organism due to a lowering of the pH to about 4.0. Acid formation virtually stops at this stage although growth may precede very slowly until a somewhat lower pH value is reached. Addition of neutralizing agents, soluble, or insoluble such as $CaCO_3$, maintains the pH in a favorable range for active growth and acid formation and accumulation. In surface cultures, an interesting difference in mycelial development occurs between neutralized and unneutralized cultures. In the former a thick wrinkled continuous pad is formed whose reverse side has a leathery appearance. The upper surface has, of course, the typical phycomycetous appearance of a high fluffy aerial mycelium, white at first, and darkening as sporiangium formation sets in. Unneutralized cultures have no tendency to form the dense leathery surface pellicle, the mycelial development being almost entirely aerial with the appearance of having a minimum contact with the unfavorable medium. Very little vegetative mycelium is formed and the organism rapidly goes over into the spore state. In neutralized media the thick vegetative pad, as contrasted with aerial mycelium, accounts for the bulk of the dry weight, which always greatly exceeds that on unneutralized media.

Calcium carbonate is generally used as a neutralizing agent, an excess being present, which is gradually dissolved by the acid as it is formed, neutralizing the acid and forming soluble calcium lactate. This permits a considerable accumulation of this salt, and since the organism can act efficiently on media containing 10 to 15 per cent carbohydrate, fairly high concentrations of calcium lactate are obtainable. The implications for a practical process are obvious.

In the higher sugar concentrations, with adequate neutralizing agent present the calcium lactate may build up to a supersaturated solution leading to its sudden precipitation to a degree which actually "sets" or solidifies the medium, presumably due to the hydrophilic nature of calcium lactate. This is particularly true of stationary cultures where supersaturated solutions can be built up due to the undisturbed state. In submerged experiments with aeration and agitation, the salt begins to crystallize out as very fine, snow-white particles as soon as saturation concentration is reached, the agitated state preventing the building-up of large crystals or aggregates.

The stage of crystallization of calcium lactate, or any mold product for that matter, usually signifies the decline of efficiency of the organism in converting carbohydrate to product. As saturation approaches, crystals build up first on the under side of the mycelial pad, or throughout the mycelial mass in submerged cultures. This presents a physical barrier to the diffusion of carbohydrate to the cells, and the whole process is slowed down. In the submerged process aeration is impeded and the efficiency of agitation is greatly diminished by the mass of crystals and mycelium. In surface cultures this phenomenon is observed best by using preformed pellicles acting on 10–15 per cent glucose solution containing calcium carbonate. A shallow layer of liquid is desirable for better neutralization efficiency with the carbonate, which settles to the bottom. Periodic shaking with a rotary motion aids neutralization and accelerates carbohydrate turnover, by facilitating diffusion. In submerged cultures 13 per cent sugar is the critical concentration for crystallization of calcium lactate.

Preformed pellicles convert the sugar to lactic acid at maximum efficiency. Growing cultures consume a fair portion of the sugar for cell synthesis and the reduced acid yield delays precipitation, although with sufficient initial carbohydrate concentration the saturation point will eventually be reached. The solidification of the culture fluid is preceded by crystal deposition hanging from the underside of the surface pad and also gradually increasing deposits on the bottom of the vessel.

A variety of simple and complex nitrogen sources are suitable for these lactic acid-producing molds. The only exception is nitrate nitrogen, which cannot be used as a source of nitrogen by most, if not all Mucorales. Urea or $(NH_4)_2SO_4$ are entirely suitable. A temperature of 28–30°C. is generally optimum. Small amounts of fumaric acid and other dicarboxy acids tend to accumulate in older cultures, probably due to further conversion of initially formed ethyl alcohol as the carbohydrate supply becomes depleted.

FATE OF CARBOHYDRATE AND THE ZINC EFFECT

The effect of zinc is very marked on the metabolism of these fungi. In the first place total removal of zinc by special purification methods results in only a trace of growth. Other essential heavy elements for growth are iron, manganese, and copper. The ordinary laboratory media, to which no zinc is added, always contains traces of this element as an impurity, which is sufficient to allow fair growth. Addition of a few p.p.m. zinc to this medium generally evokes the typical striking response in growth and metabolism.

In a medium without added zinc, and in which the lactic acid had been periodically neutralized by KOH as it was formed during growth, the following carbon balance was obtained with *Rhizopus MX* (Waksman and Foster, 1939):

	Grams	*Per cent*
Glucose C consumed.................	7.54	
Lactic acid C......................	5.34	72.1
CO₂-C.............................	1.52	20.1
Mycelium-C........................	0.49	6.5

In this case the cell material comprised a very small portion of the total sugar consumed. Three and eleven times as much carbon went to CO_2 and lactic acid respectively, as went into cell material. Ward *et al.* (1938) found only 7.2 per cent of the glucose went to CO_2 with an accumulation of 8.0 per cent of the sugar as ethanol. If this ethanol had been oxidized the CO_2 figure would be in line with that of the surface culture carbon balance.

In another surface culture experiment in which $CaCO_3$ was the neutralizing agent the following summary typifies the zinc effect (in a 6-day-old culture):

Sugar consumed, g.		Mycelial wt. g.		Lactic acid, g.		Conversion, per cent	
No Zn	Zn	No Zn	Zn	No Zn	Zn	No Zn	Zn
26.05	38.47	97	336	15.45	7.43	59.3	19.3

It is evident that zinc enables the organism to grow much more luxuriantly, at the expense of lactic acid accumulation. Without added zinc the reverse was true. Not only does the presence of zinc in the lactic acid-mold cultures reduce the total conversion yields of lactic acid, but its presence also accelerates the decomposition of the initially-formed lactic acid, so that it is oxidized rather rapidly, especially after the carbohydrate supply is depleted.

The economic coefficients and the conversion efficiencies computed from data on a large zinc experiment are correlated in Table 1. Two to three times as much glucose was required to produce 1 g. of cell substance when zinc was absent. It is clear that in the zinc cultures more glucose must have been completely oxidized (or utilized for cell synthesis) than in the no-zinc cultures, for, in the latter more lactic acid, each molecule of which represents 50 per cent of the glucose molecules, had accumulated. Important here, however, is that the same two to three ratio prevailed for acid production (conversion efficiency) in inverse proportion to that just mentioned for growth. Where two to three times as much glucose was required to produce one unit of cell substance, there was also just two to three times as much lactic acid produced. Thus, irrespective of the total amount of cell substance synthesized, a unit of cell substance in both zinc-free and zinc-containing cultures produced the same amount of lactic acid per unit of glucose consumed. From these facts, it may be deduced that zinc catalyzed the oxidation of that portion of the glucose molecule (or of its breakdown products) other than that which gives rise to lactic acid. There is reason to believe that growth is at the expense of the accumulation of ethyl alcohol which is also formed in these cultures, although in much smaller amounts where zinc is present. (See also Chapter 11.) It is this ethyl alcohol which gives rise to the small amounts of C_4-dicarboxylic acids usually accompanying lactic acid in Rhizopus cultures.

TABLE 1

CORRELATION OF ECONOMIC COEFFICIENTS AND CONVERSION EFFICIENCIES

Age of culture, days	Economic coefficient[1]			Conversion efficiency[2]		
	No Zn	Zn	$\dfrac{\text{No Zn}}{\text{Zn}}$	No Zn	Zn	$\dfrac{\text{No Zn}}{\text{Zn}}$
				per cent	per cent	
6	18.8	5.8	3.2	59.3	19.3	3.1
11	11.0	5.1	2.2	51.9	18.5	2.8
16	9.1	4.5	2.0	52.4	21.3	2.5
29	9.5	4.6	2.1	49.0	19.8	2.5

[1] $\dfrac{\text{Glucose consumed}}{\text{Wt. growth}}$.

[2] $\dfrac{\text{Lactic acid produced}}{\text{Glucose consumed}}$.

The only published data on this process done under ideal submerged conditions with aeration and agitation are those of Ward et al. (1938) using Rhizopus. Results of a 35-hour old culture in an aerated rotating drum experiment are as follows:

	G./100 Ml.
Glucose consumed	12.8
Ethyl alcohol produced	0.62
Lactic acid equivalent to dissolved calcium	10.12
Lactic acid found by analysis	9.66
Acidity due to lactic acid, per cent	95.4
Conversion yield of d-lactic acid, per cent	75.5

During maximum rate the hourly consumption of glucose per 100 ml. culture was 0.6 g.

CARBOHYDRATE DISSIMILATION BY LACTIC ACID RHIZOPUS

If preformed cell material (pellicles) of a good lactic acid-producing strain of Rhizopus (MX) is allowed to act on glucose solution under aerobic and anaerobic conditions, and the main products of the dissimilation are measured after a suitable incubation period, results comparable to those in Table 2 may be expected.

Under anaerobic conditions, as the last column shows, there is, within experimental error, equimolar relations between glucose consumed and lactic acid and ethyl alcohol formed. These figures would be in agreement with the following equation expressing the anaerobic dissimilation of sugar by this organism.

$$C_6H_{12}O_6 \rightarrow C_3H_6O_3 + C_2H_5OH + CO_2$$

Aerobically the situation is quite different. Here much more than one mole of lactic acid is formed and much less ethyl alcohol. Interestingly enough, if one recalculates the data from the above-cited experiment of Ward et al. (1938) done under quite different conditions, namely in submerged culture under 5 lbs. air pressure and with flowing air for 35 hours, one obtains a remarkably good agreement with the aerobic treatment reported for the 15-day surface culture in Table 2. The figures actually are 1.0: 1.48: 0.19 for the submerged culture.

TABLE 2[1]

AEROBIC AND ANAEROBIC DISSIMILATION OF GLUCOSE BY RHIZOPUS *MX*

Days	Oxygen supply	Glucose consumed		Lactic acid produced		Ethyl alcohol produced		Glucose: lactic acid: ethyl alcohol
		g.	mM.	g.	mM.	g.	mM.	
15	Anaerobic	53.9	300	28.5	316	13.1	286	1.0:1.05:0.95
20	Anaerobic	57.3	318	29.4	327	15.8	344	1.0:0.98:0.93
15	Aerobic	82.8	460	61.5	684	4.3	94	1.0:1.49:0.20

[1] From Waksman and Foster (1939).

The fact that aerobic conditions lead to a marked reduction in ethyl alcohol formation, a product of fermentative reactions, is in accord with well-known concepts embracing the idea that the presence of oxygen always suppresses the fermentative reactions in normal cells. This is one aspect of the Pasteur effect.

However, the formation of lactic acid from sugar has always been considered a glycolytic (i.e., fermentative) reaction whose formation in normal cells (especially animal tissues) invariably is suppressed in the presence of oxygen. One specifies *normal cells*, for the failure of oxygen to suppress lactic acid formation by malignant tissue is the outstanding metabolic characteristic of these cells. They are said to possess, consequently, a high aerobic glycolysis.

In the case of Rhizopus not only is lactic acid formation unsuppressed by oxygen, but it is markedly enhanced by good aeration conditions. Can, then, lactic acid formation in Rhizopus be considered a glycolytic process? It would seem that at least two-thirds of the lactate formed aerobically, i.e. one mole per mole of sugar consumed, could well be considered as originating through a typical glycolytic mechanism, for we have seen that one mole does arise under conditions where only glycolysis can take place, namely anaerobically. Thus, one of the two triose intermediates formed per mole of hexose dissimilated is accounted for.

It is to the second triose intermediate that we must look to interpret the aerobic happenings. The presence of the small amount (0.2 mole) of ethanol in the aerobic cultures is probably without quantitative significance and probably indicates the failure of oxygen to penetrate to the interior of all the cells at a rate sufficient to block this anaerobic conversion (see Chapter 9). There is no need at this time to assume that the extra one-half mole lactate originates through any other mechanism than the well-known reduction of pyruvate, although it has been represented without experimental evidence, as being formed through decarboxylation of malic acid (Bernhauer and Knoblock, 1941; Rotini *et al.*, 1936). This idea was postulated to explain the presence of lactic acid in cultures accumulating C_4-dicarboxylic acids mainly, but this interpretation requires substantiation in the fungi. The fact does remain, however that this reaction has been established in other systems.

The fact of the presence of the alcohol which could have been derived only from pyruvate, and of the extra one-half mole lactate, also derivable only from pyruvate, indicates that the second triose molecule also must have been transformed mainly, if not entirely, to pyruvate. A small portion of this pyruvate (one-fifth) becomes decarboxylated to acetaldehyde and is then reduced to ethanol. One-half of the pyruvate is reduced to lactic acid. Both these reduction processes may be expected to be coupled with the oxidation of more triose leading to the generation of more pyruvate. On the basis of modern schemes for carbohydrate dissimilation 3-glyceraldehyde phosphate is oxidized to 3-phosphoglyceric acid, meanwhile reducing the above hydrogen acceptors through the agency of aldehyde reductase and coenzyme II.

$$
\begin{array}{cccc}
& \text{COOH} & & \text{COOH} \\
\text{Pyruvate} & |\;\text{CO} & & |\;\text{CHOH} \quad \text{Lactic acid} \\
& |\;\text{CH}_3 & \text{CHO} & |\;\text{CH}_3 \\
& \text{or} & +\;|\;\text{CHOH} \longleftarrow \text{or} & +\;|\;\text{CHOH} \\
& & |\;\text{CH}_2\text{OPO(OH)}_2 & |\;\text{CH}_2\text{OP(OH)}_2
\end{array}
$$

Pyruvate

COOH
| CO
| CH₃   CHO
or   + CHOH ⟶ or
    CH₂OPO(OH)₂

COOH
| CHOH   Lactic acid
| CH₃
       COOH
      + CHOH
       CH₂OP(OH)₂

Acetaldehyde
CH₃
| CHO

CH₃   Ethanol
| CH₂OH

3-Glyceraldehyde
phosphate

3-Phospho-
glyceric acid

According to the data presented above, and this scheme, 0.3 moles of triose are unaccounted for. Two possible explanations might account for it: (1) complete oxidation to CO_2 and H_2O, or (2) oxidative assimilation whereby one, two, or three of the carbon atoms of the missing triose are converted into intracellular carbohydrate. Analytical data on CO_2 evolution by "resting cells" of Rhizopus acting aerobically on glucose would clearly differentiate between these two possibilities, and unpublished manometric data of Foster and Denison show that both do take place. There is reason for believing that oxidative assimilation accounts for well over half of the low concentration of glucose supplied under the usual manometric conditions. The assimilation can be suppressed by suitable poisons, in particular, 2:4-dinitrophenol.

The fact that the lactic acid and ethanol are formed in essentially simple fractional values may not be without significance. Characteristic of oxidative assimilation is that the assimilated portion is a simple fraction representing one, two, three, or more carbon atoms of any particular molecule. In this case the missing triose, amounting to 0.3 out of a theoretical 2.0 moles possible from sugar, or 15 per cent, corresponds closely with 17 per cent, the theoretical if one carbon of the six in the glucose chain were assimilated. Actually, probably the single carbon is not assimilated as such, but rather sufficient normal intermediary split-products equivalent to an average of 15.47 per cent of the glucose. In this case either 0.3 mole triose or the equivalent acetaldehyde derived from

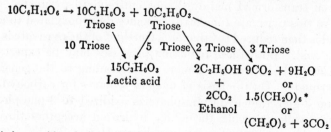

$$10C_6H_{12}O_6 \rightarrow 10C_3H_6O_3 + 10C_3H_6O_3$$

Triose   Triose

10 Triose   5 Triose   2 Triose   3 Triose

$15C_3H_6O_3$ $2C_2H_5OH$ $9CO_2 + 9H_2O$
Lactic acid   +   or
           $2CO_2$ $1.5(CH_2O)_6$ *
         Ethanol   or
               $(CH_2O)_6 + 3CO_2$

* Empirical composition of cell material as represented by the primary assimilation product.

it, would be the primary assimilatory unit. As indicated a final interpretation will depend on the amount of CO_2 liberated. The aerobic
dissimilation of sugar by this organism can then be represented as
shown in the preceding formula.

Pyruvate Dissimilation by Rhizopus MX

Some preliminary experiments (Foster, unpublished) have been made
with resting washed cell suspensions, obtained in shake culture, acting
on pyruvate, both aerobically and anaerobically. The anaerobic conversion is simple: from 1.69 mM. pyruvate consumed 1.45 mM. lactate
was formed, or 0.858 mole lactic acid per mole of pyruvate, or almost
exactly 5 moles of every 6 moles pyruvate decomposed. To reduce such
a large portion of the pyruvate to lactate, the remaining one-sixth of the
consumed pyruvate must have served as a reducing agent by virtue of
dehydrogenation and oxidation. The complete oxidation of pyruvate
under anerobic conditions may be represented as follows: $CH_3COCOOH$
$+ 3H_2O \rightarrow 3CO_2 + 10H$. Full dehydrogenation liberates ten available
hydrogens per mole of pyruvate. This is just the required amount for
the reduction of five moles of pyruvate to lactic acid, as observed.

$$5CH_3COCOOH + 10H \rightarrow 5CH_3CHOHCOOH$$

Thus, the reduction of 5 moles of pyruvate is accomplished by the
simultaneous complete dehydrogenation (oxidation) of 1 mole of pyruvate.

Aerobically the metabolism is still largely lactic. From 2.48 mM.
pyruvate consumed 1.61 mM. lactate was formed, a ratio of 0.65 mole per
mole of pyruvate. These figures agree very nearly with the conclusion
that two of every three moles of pyruvate consumed are reduced to
lactate, the reduction being possible only through the oxidation (dehydrogenation) of the remaining third of the pyruvate which disappeared.
However only two-fifths of this fraction would be necessary for the
reduction (4H). The fate of the remaining three-fifths of the missing
pyruvate, and the smaller amount of pyruvate reduced aerobically than
anaerobically, very likely can be ascribed to the fact that in the former
pyruvate is not the exclusive H acceptor, molecular oxygen also functioning in this manner and competing for available hydrogen. This will
naturally result in lower yields of the reduced product, namely, lactic
acid. Doubtless some of the missing pyruvate was also decarboxylated,
ending up as ethanol, but this was not determined.

Rhizopus MX and the Pasteur Reaction

It is evident from the above data that not only can lactic acid formation from sugar by this mold proceed in the presence of oxygen, i.e.,
pyruvate can compete effectively with oxygen for available hydrogen,
but it is, moreover, even enhanced by the presence of oxygen. Lactic

acid formation in this case is then an exception to the general behavior of normal cells in which, according to the Pasteur reaction, this glycolytic process is suppressed concomitantly with the admission of oxygen. Burk (1939) considers this system an abnormal Pasteur reaction. The quantitative increase in lactate formation is unique in its natural occurrence, although Burk cites several instances where aerobic glycolysis can be accelerated artificially. Glucolysis in the lactic acid water mold *Blastocladia pringsheimii* (Cantino, 1949) should also be mentioned as an example of oxygen failing to suppress lactate formation.

A second property contradictory to the classic Pasteur reaction concept relates to substrate consumption as affected by O_2, especially, in its strictest application, that oxygen reduces the consumption of sugar which goes to form the measurable cleavage (glycolytic) product. In this case not only does oxygen induce a larger total sugar consumption, but also a larger proportion of the consumed sugar is converted to the cleavage product.

The fact that this organism really performs double fermentation (lactic-alcohol) doubtless accounts for its anomalous behavior. The unexpected finding is that only one of the fermentations is suppressed by oxygen, instead of both, as expected from considerations of the Pasteur reaction.

BLASTOCLADIA PRINGSHEIMII (Emerson and Cantino, 1948; Cantino, 1949)

This organism converts up to 54 per cent of the glucose used to lactic acid. Up to 7 per cent accumulates as succinic acid, the remainder as unidentified products, but not CO_2. This curious fact warrants emphasis. Cultivated aerobically in a stream of CO_2-free air, this organism produced no detectable CO_2 despite the turnover of an appreciable amount of carbohydrate, and the amounts of acids produced aerobically and anaerobically by preformed mycelium were the same, a rather unusual occurrence.

No volatile neutral or acidic fraction was formed indicating alcohol and acetic acid were absent. Thus this organism has, at best, a weak pyruvate decarboxylation mechanism. Any small amount of decarboxylation which may take place obviously must be obscured by intracellular reassimilation of the CO_2, which participates in the synthesis of the found succinate (Cantino, 1949). The C_2 librated by the hypothetical decarboxylation either was assimilated or was condensed to succinate. More details and discussion of this point are provided by Cantino. For a detailed discussion of analogous events see Chapter 11.

The lack of an active C_2-forming mechanism at once places this organism apart from the great majority of fungi known and discussed throughout this book. One wonders if the possession of the C_2-forming mechanism does not represent a more highly evolved stage of metabolic efficiency. *B. pringsheimii* would therefore be considered as possessing a more primitive metabolism. The significance of this idea becomes more evident when one considers that the C_2-mechanism is an added means of energy liberation via subsequent reactions (see Chapter 4) lending survival value to such organisms. On the other hand, despite the disadvantage of inefficient energy utilization, *B. pringsheimii* and other water molds with high lactic metabolism, have survival advantage by virtue of their ability to thrive in extremely low oxygen tensions, such as exist in natural water accumulations.

Two other noteworthy points: (1) *Blastocladia pringsheimii* can thrive in remarkably small oxygen tensions, appreciably less than that required for other fungi, namely a partial pressure of oxygen of about 0.7 mm. of Hg. Nevertheless, this oxygen is required, for no growth is made in its absence (see Chapter 4). (2) Contrary to the inhibition obtained with most fungi (Chapters 11 and 12) *B. pringsheimii* thrives in the presence of 99.5 per cent CO_2 under which condition an abundance of fully developed, heavy walled, resistant sporangia was formed. The contrast to cultures in normal atmosphere was striking.

REFERENCES

Bernhauer, K., and Knobloch, H. 1941. Die Methoden der Fermentforschung. Part 7, G. Thieme, Leipzig, pp. 2456–2457.

Boulanger, E. 1899. Brit. Patent 13,439; 1901. German Patent 118,063.

Burk, D. 1939. *Cold Spring Harbor Symposia Quant. Biol.* **7**, 420–459.

Calmette, A. 1892. *Ann. inst. Pasteur* **6**, 605–620.

Cantino, E. 1949. *Am J. Botany* **36**, 95–115.

Chrzaszcz, F. 1901. *Zentr. Bakt. Parasitenk. Abt II* **7**, 326–338.

Ehrlich, F. 1919. *Ber.* **52**, 63–64.

Eijkmann, C. 1894. *Zentr. Bakt. Parasitenk. Abt II* **16**, 97–102.

Emerson, R., and Cantino, E. C. 1948. *Am. J. Botany* **35**, 157–171.

Kanel, E. 1934. *Microbiology, USSR* **3**, 259–265.

Kanel, E. 1935. *Microbiology, USSR* **4**, 636–654.

Miyaji, K. 1930. *Kagami Kenkyu Hokoko. Research Bull. Gifu Imp. Coll. Agr.* **10**, 1–5.

Rotini, O. T., Damann, E., and Nord, F. F. 1936. *Biochem. Z.* **288**, 414–420.

Saito, K. 1911. *Zentr. Bakt. Parasitenk. Abt II* **29**, 289–290.

Takahashi, T., and Asai, T. 1933. *Zentr. Bakt. Parasitenk. Abt II* **89**, 81–84.

Takahashi, T., and Sakaguchi, K. 1925. *J. Agr. Chem. Soc. Japan* **1**, 46.

Waksman, S. A., and Foster, J. W. 1939. *J. Agr. Research* **57**, 873–899.

Waksman, S. A., and Hutchings, I. J. 1937. *J. Am. Chem. Soc.* **59**, 545–547.

Ward, G. E., Lockwood, L. B., May, O. E., and Herrick, H. T. 1936. *J. Am. Chem. Soc.* **58**, 1286–1288.

Ward, G. E., Lockwood, L. B., Tabenkin, B., and Wells, P. A. 1938. *Ind. Eng. Chem.* **30**, 1233–1235.

Wehmer, G. 1910. In Technical Mycology. F. Lafar, II, Charles Griffith & Co., Ltd., London. Translated from the German by C. T. C. Salter.

CHAPTER 9

ALCOHOLIC FERMENTATION BY MOLDS

This subject receives, unfortunately, scant mention nowadays in treatises on general metabolism of fungi, but, nevertheless, it has an extremely interesting history in relation to the concepts of aerobic respiration versus anaerobic fermentation which make up such an important chapter in the development of general physiology and biochemistry. It is little known, and seemingly little mentioned or referred to, that Pasteur himself studied certain fungi extensively from the standpoint of corroborating and generalizing his concept of fermentation already conceived with ordinary brewers yeast.

Pasteur's Contributions

Examination of Pasteur's works leaves one with the unmistakable impression that it was the results from molds which convinced Pasteur of the universality of the phenomenon he discovered in yeast. He even says,

" . . . the study of varieties of the genus *mucor*, grown in natural or artificial saccharine liquids, is of great importance to the establishment of the physiological theory of fermentation . . . ."

He used molds in experiments that furnished the death blow to the then flourishing doctrine of transmutation of species. These classical researches, related in detail in the famous "Études sur la Bière," published in 1872, stand as the first controlled studies on mold metabolism.

As is well known, the idea of alcoholic fermentation as conceived by Pasteur is, to use his words "C'est la vie sans air . . . ." Yeast, molds, and other living tissues proliferate in the presence of air, producing, if the oxygenation is complete, no alcohol; but, deprived now of air, these cells do not immediately perish; if sugar is present, they secure energy for the maintenance of life and vital activity by fermentation. As yet, there is no convincing evidence to dispute the contention of Pasteur that, in order to achieve alcoholic fermentation with molds and yeasts, cells of the organism must first develop utilizing oxygen; and that significant growth of the organism starting with inoculum cannot take place exclusively by fermentation, i.e., in the absolute absence of molecular oxygen. The importance of this idea becomes manifest in the consideration of the origin of alcohol under the ordinary so-called aerobic conditions of cultivation. Actually, in keeping with Pasteur's findings, the alcohol (i.e., fermentation) is produced not by the cells enjoying oxygen nutrition, but instead by cells *after* they have developed with the utilization of oxygen; because of the physical circumstances developing in a rapidly growing mold culture, the cells soon find themselves deprived of this vital gas. The factors involved in the oxygen deprivation are mainly physical, and are described in Chapter 2. The cells being deprived now of oxygen, but still having access to sugar, fermentation proceeds, and alcohol results. This obviously is what takes place with cells in the interior of the mold pad, and especially with those cells in the lower levels of the mold growth and immersed below the surface of the culture liquid. Pasteur fully distinguished this fact. It is evident, as pointed out in Chapter 2, that the amount of alcohol formed in any given culture, is, apart from the specific organism and the nutrient medium, the resultant of the metabolism of cells in many different stages of oxygenation, ranging between the extremes of excellent access to and complete deprivation of oxygen.

It is a monument to the genius of Pasteur that his exceedingly conclusive and painstaking experiments, and the acute observations and deductions made from them and described so logically and lucidly, still stand today as the most complete and most effective recitation available of the events attendant to alcohol fermentation by molds. The seventy-odd years which have elapsed since his work on this subject have in no way vitiated or altered the applicability and validity of his penetrating conclusions. Because of the special historical significance of molds in connection with the theory of alcoholic fermentation, and to cover the facts pertinent to alcoholic fermentation by molds accurately and adequately, it is appropriate to review here Pasteur's experiments; scientifically, there is no more effective presentation than in Pasteur's own words.* It must be pointed out that Pasteur was not the first to observe anaerobic alcohol formation by filamentous fungi in saccharine liquids. Bail, 15 years earlier, in 1857, had already made this observation.

Pasteur's first concern with molds was to prove that such organisms, if pure to begin with, could not give rise to "ferment" (i.e., yeast), as numerous of Pasteur's opponents maintained. He worked mainly with *Penicillium glaucum*, *Aspergillus glaucus*, and *Mucor mucedo*, proving that the only circumstance under which other organisms arose "spontaneously" in media inoculated with any one of these three fungi, was that

* Studies on Fermentation: The diseases of beer, their causes and the means of preventing them. 1872. A translation of Pasteur's Études sur la Bière. F. Faulkner and D. C. Robb, MacMillan & Co., London, 1879.

where the other organisms were introduced as contaminants with the fungus spore inoculum.

Pasteur was deeply impressed with the observations he made that *P. glaucum* sometimes formed no alcohol from sugar and at other times formed it abundantly, and that the amounts were irregular and bore no relation to the dry weight of the mold growth.

The numerous experiments we have made seem to demonstrate positively that the amounts of alcohol are dependent upon variations in the amount of air or oxygen that is supplied to the fungoid growths, whether, that is, the vegetating mycelium alone be submerged, or the whole plant with its organs of fructification. When the plant has at its disposal an excess of oxygen, as much as its vitality can dispose of, there is no alcohol, or very little, formed. If, on the other hand, the plant vegetates with difficulty, in the presence of an insufficiency of oxygen, the proportion of alcohol increases; in other words, the plant shows a certain tendency to behave after the manner of ferments. . . .

These results apply to all the fungoid growths that we have studied, but they vary considerably with nature of the organisms. *Aspergillus glaucus* is, in this respect, one of the most curious. . . .

These results show that the *aspergillus* when in full growth, with plenty of air at its disposal, does not yield alcohol, and that if we submerge it, so as to prevent the oxygen of the air from readily coming into contact with its various parts, it decomposes sugar, after the manner of yeast, forming carbonic acid gas and alcohol.

Studying the microscopic appearance of the mold developing under different conditions of alcohol formation, Pasteur goes on:*

Amongst the ordinary filaments of mycelium belonging to the plant . . . and which were not more than $\frac{1}{300}$ of a millimetre (nearly $\frac{1}{7500}$ in.) in diameter, we perceived much larger ones, swollen and contorted in the most singular manner, and measuring as much as $\frac{1}{50}$ of a millimetre across their broadest parts. There was also a multitude of the ordinary spores of *aspergillus* mixed with others of larger size, and big, inflated cells, with irregular or spherical protuberances, full of granular matter. As there are all the stages between the normal spores of the plant and the big cells, and between these latter and the filaments, it must be admitted that the whole of this strange vegetation results from spores which change their structure under the influence of special conditions to which they are exposed. Beyond doubt these cells and irregularly shaped segments, in vegetating with difficulty, gave rise to the fermentation, which, although insignificant, was sufficiently marked to produce more than a gramme (15 grains) of alcohol. The oxygen of the air failing, or existing in insufficient quantity for the regular development of the filaments of mycelium belonging to the plant, and for the germination of its submerged spores, filaments and spores vegetated as the yeast of beer might have done if deprived of oxygen.

If we study the vegetation of *aspergillus glaucus* with this preconceived idea, we shall soon recognize the fact that these spherical forms of mycelium are the result of a

---

* Here also Pasteur's studies were anticipated by the mycological investigations of Bail (1857) who published several plates depicting structures quite similar to Pasteur's. In his "Études sur la Bière" Pasteur makes no reference to the prior works of Bail, and, indeed, may have been unaware of it.

greater or less deprivation of air. The filaments of this mycelium which develop freely in the aerated liquid are young and transparent, small in diameter, and exhibit the ordinary ramifications. Those which are situated about the center, in the denser or more complicated parts, to which oxygen cannot penetrate in consequence of its absorption by the surrounding parts, are more granular in appearance as well as larger, and inclined to develop swellings. We can observe no *conidia* on these filaments, but we may say that they are on the point of appearing, for the spherical segments often tend to assume an appearance of close jointing, as when they take the form of those rows of swelling, or cells, ... This is represented in the accompanying sketches (Fig. 1), which we have purposely contrasted with two similar ones which relate to the *mucor*, of which we shall soon speak. The *conidia** of these latter are very remarkable, and their fermentative character becomes apparent as soon as their growths are deprived of air.

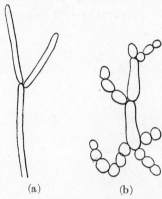 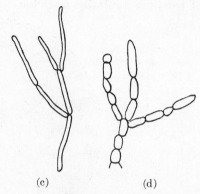

(a)	(b)	(c)	(d)

Aspergillus glaucus	*Mucor racemosus*

(a) Growth with abundant air-supply at the edge of the mycelium crust.

(b) Growth with reduced air-supply in the central and deeper parts of the mycelium.

(c) Growth with abundant air-supply at the edge of the mycelium tuft.

(d) Growth with reduced air-supply in the central and deeper parts.

FIG. 1.—From Pasteur, 1876.

Pasteur also appears to have been the first to aerate a mold culture artificially, thus anticipating the *modus operandi* of large industrial mold fermentations in years to come. He observed the striking stimulation in growth as a result of aeration, from the following data on *Aspergillus glaucus:* mold growth in the aerated flask, 0.92 g.; in the closed flask, 0.16 g.

The preceding facts, taken altogether, seem to us to demonstrate once more, in the most conclusive manner:—

Firstly, that neither *penicillium* nor *aspergillus glaucus* can change into yeast, even under conditions that are most favorable to the life of that ferment.

Secondly, that a fungoid growth which vegetates by using the oxygen of the air,

* It would appear that the use of the term here is a loose one. It is evident that Pasteur means conidialike vegetative cells. (J. W. F.)

and which derives from the oxidating action of that gas, the heat that it requires to
enable it to perform the acts necessary to its nutrition, may continue to live, although
with difficulty, in the absence of oxygen; that, in such a case, the forms of its mycelian
or sporic vegetation undergo a change, the plant, at the same time, evincing a great
tendency to act as alcoholic ferment, that is to say, decomposing sugar and forming
carbonic acid gas, alcohol, and other substances which we have not determined, and
which probably vary with the different growths.

One of the outstanding characters of the alcoholic fermentation is
the large amount of sugar fermented, and alcohol formed, in relation to
the weight of the fermenting agent.   Going into detail with the study of
the common Mucor, in one fermentation 0.25 g. dry Mucor weight
produced 4.1 g. alcohol, i.e., 16.4 times its own weight.   Now Pasteur
relates in a typically fastidious study his observations on Mucor—a

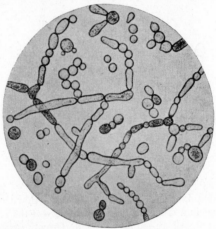

FIG. 2.—Mucor vegetating submerged in deficit of air (from Pasteur, 1876).

classical description of an indefinite physiological situation, which, on
account of this lucid presentation, can today be demonstrated and
identified easily.

The structure of the plant differs considerably when it lives surrounded by air,
and when it is more or less completely deprived of that fluid.   If it has an abundance
of air at its disposal, if it vegetates on the surface of a moist substance or in a liquid in
which the air held in solution may be renewed without being incessantly displaced
by carbonic acid gas, we shall see it develop as an ordinary fungoid growth, with a
mycelium consisting of filaments more or less slender, branching, and entangled,
sending up from the surface of the liquid aerial organs of fructification.   This is the
well-known form of vegetation of the common *mucor*.   On the other hand, if we
compel the *mucor* to live in a saccharine liquid with insufficiency of air, at least for
some of its parts, the mode of vegetation will change completely, as we have seen in
the case of *penicillium*, *aspergillus* and *mycoderma vini* when submerged, but with this
difference, that in the case of the *mucor* the changes in question, and the activity of
nutrition under these new conditions, are much more marked than in the case of those
other organisms.   The spores grow larger and the filaments of mycelium which do

develop are much stronger than those in the normal plant. These filaments put forth, here and there, other filaments which detach themselves and vegetate at the side of the others, being terminated or interrupted by chains of large cells, species of spores which can live by budding and reproducing cells similar to themselves or by elongating into filaments.

By taking portions of Mucor growth submerged at a little depth and at a greater depth, i.e., under progressively greater oxygen insufficiency, Pasteur showed that the filamentous tendency of the fungus is proportionally reduced, being smaller and rudimentary at the greatest depths, in favor of oval or spherical sporelike vegetative cells, originating as buds from the few short filaments present, and themselves capable of

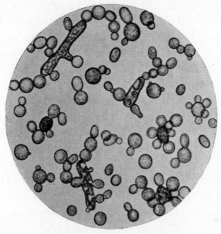

FIG. 3.—Ferment of Mucor (from Pasteur, 1876).

budding in yeastlike fashion. Figures 2 and 3 demonstrating these points are those accompanying Pasteur's original description of this phenomenon.

Pasteur pointed out that the tendency to form these enlarged spherical cells under conditions of oxygen deprivation was much stronger in Mucor than in Aspergillus and Penicillium; and it is still true that this tendency is very marked in the Phycomycetes at large, to which Mucor belongs, in comparison with other major groups of fungi.

It is not to be overlooked, however, that various fungi have often been reported (by, among others, Wehmer, 1913; Molliard, 1924; Frey, 1927; Sakamura, 1930) to form aberrant-shaped cells similar to those described above. Bail (1857) called them gemmae, but since then they have been called giant cells or vesicle cells ("Blasenzelle"), and in the case of *Aspergillus oryzae*, the photographs of Sakamura show the identical features portrayed in Pasteur's plates (Figs. 2 and 3). The cytology of these structures has been studied in detail by Frey (1927). The formation of these abnormal cells can be obtained experimentally under many conditions unfavorable for growth, as for example, low pH, starvation for certain nutrients (potassium), osmotic pressure, and addition of poisons. One wonders whether all these effects may be indirect, all suppressing normal growth through interfering with normal oxidation processes and forcing the organism into fermentative metabolism even in the presence of air, giving rise to these swollen cells typical of fermentation conditions. Unfortunately, alcohol content and fermentation were not investigated in these studies, nor were Pasteur's findings even alluded to.

ALCOHOL PRODUCTION BY DIFFERENT FUNGI

As Pasteur pointed out, the tendency to carry out alcoholic fermentation is not equal for all fungi, at any given degree of oxygen tension. Two main groups of fungi, namely, the Mucorales and the Fusaria, are generally associated with strong alcoholic fermentation tendencies under the usual aerobic surface culture conditions, and will carry out vigorous alcohol formation where most other organisms would form little or none. The fallacy of generalization on this point is evident from the fact that although the genus Aspergillus ordinarily is evaluated as strongly oxidative (carboxy acids), the outstanding metabolic feature of certain species is the extremely high alcoholic fermentation powers. This is especially true of *A. clavatus*.

In the years immediately following Pasteur's work on this subject, several investigators* examined the fermentation balances in Mucorales cultures and confirmed the virtual identity with yeast fermentation from the standpoint of alcohol to CO_2 ratios, and also in the isolation of small amounts of succinic acid and glycerol.

Kostytschew (1904) was among the first to follow up Pasteur's work on alcoholic fermentation, extending it to higher plants, but also verifying the latter's observation that different Mucors behaved differently regarding fermentation tendencies. Using respiratory quotients (CO_2/O_2) under aerobic conditions, and CO_2 evolution in absence of oxygen, he characterized *M. stolonifer* as the most aerobic of the three tested, it however being able to adapt to temporary anaerobiosis (fermentation); *M. racemosus* was highly fermentative even in the presence of air, and *M. mucedo* was intermediate. Letcher and Willaman (1926) found great variation in alcohol fermention among nine different strains of *Fusarium lini*, the flaxwilt organism. In one experiment, 20-day-old cultures gave filtrates ranging from 2.50 to 0.59 per cent in alcohol content. Interestingly, the two lowest fermenting strains were the least virulent for flax. From the fact that *Aspergillus oryzae* produced no alcohol,

---

* The contributions of Fitz, Gayon, Brefeld, and Hansen, all made before 1890 are reviewed adequately in Lafar's Handbuch der Technische Mycologie. 2nd edition. Gustav Fischer, Jena.

whereas under the same condition *A. flavus* converted 15–25 per cent of the carbohydrate consumed into alcohol, amounting to 2 to 3 per cent of the filtrate, Yuill (1928) concludes that the physical nature of the thick surface pad of the latter accounts for its fermentation activity. He affirmed Pasteur's deduction that much of the cell material in the lower regions of the growth existed under anaerobic conditions, and that the alcohol was formed by that portion. Some citric acid accompanied the alcohol, good evidence that aerobic and anaerobic conditions could exist simultaneously in a fungus culture.

Alcohol Formation under Aerobic Conditions

Despite the clear-cut nature of Pasteur's experiments regarding the suppressive influence of oxygen on fermentation, it is a well established fact that in certain instances even extremely high oxygenation conditions fail to suppress alcohol formation entirely; it would appear that fermentative activity was being effected by cells under aerobic conditions. Three instances in point are: (1) the production of 0.2 mole ethanol per mole of glucose consumed by *Rhizopus oryzae* under what appears to be nearly the theoretical maximum aeration conditions, essential for maximum yields of lactic acid simultaneously formed by this organism (Ward *et al.*, 1938). A high flow of air finely dispersed through the culture fluid, and further distributed by mechanical agitation of the liquid in a rotating drum, and finally, under 2 atmospheres air pressure, still allowed this very significant rate of alcohol formation. (2) Ethanol formation by *Fusarium oxysporum* growing under submerged aerated conditions in an aeration bottle containing 200 ml. of 15 per cent glucose and having a sintered-glass false bottom through which the air passed and became finely divided at the rate of 50 ml./minute (Lockwood *et al.*, 1938). Here 4.7 g. ethanol were formed from the decomposition of 17.3 g. sugar, 53 per cent yield assuming a perfect alcoholic fermentation of the sugar, or one mole per mole of sugar fermented. (3) Formation of 48.5 per cent of theoretical alcohol yield by a kojic acid-producing strain of *Aspergillus flavus* under aeration conditions (Kluyver and Perquin, 1933).

Tamiya (1928) shows that the balance in *A. oryzae* surface mycelium fermentation under aerobic vs. anaerobic conditions is a function of the age of the mycelium:

Age of culture, days	1	2	4
Alcohol production anaerobically	5.2	7.9	16.6
Alcohol production aerobically	1	1	1

Alcohol formation aerobically is markedly suppressed, being, in the youngest culture, only one-fifth that anaerobically. It progressively decreases with age, until the ratio is $\frac{1}{16}$. As Fig. 4 shows, the fermentation capacity decreases with age, so in this case the oxidative capacity of the mycelium must become markedly higher during the four days.

The property of fermenting sugar to alcohol must in these cases be of an order of resistance to oxygen that transcends any possibility Pasteur envisaged. It could be argued that despite physical aeration of the culture liquids, the amount of oxygen penetrating to the interior regions of the individual cells is insufficient to saturate the oxidation potentialities

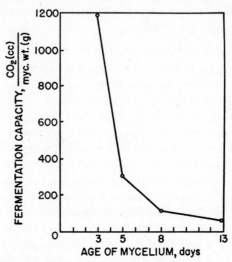

Fig. 4.—Age and fermentation capacity of *Aspergillus oryzae* (from Tamiya, 1928)

of the cell in regard to the excess of carbohydrate available to those regions (see Chapter 2). Consequently, aerobic respiratory metabolism is carried to the limit permitted by the penetration of oxygen, the fermentative activity meanwhile proceeding on the excess sugar available. In other words, the physical size of the fungus cells and possibly spatial arrangement of the enzymes in the cell conceivably could account for these results, and bring them in line with Pasteur's concepts; however, this is pure speculation. One is tempted to speculate further what the outcome of Pasteur's thinking would have been had he used a Fusarium in his experiments instead of the Mucor he did, apparently by chance. Another factor driving metabolism toward fermentation would be a relative deficiency of the cytochome complex or any step in the aerobic enzyme sequence, thereby restricting aerobic metabolism even in the presence of air.

COMPARATIVE FERMENTATION STUDIES AND CELL-FREE FERMENTATION

The best comparative data on fermentation capacity of various fungi are those of the Japanese physiologist H. Tamiya (1928) and his coworker

Miwa (Tamiya and Miwa, 1928) and of the Raistrick group (Birkinshaw *et al.*, 1931). Tamiya cultivated the various organisms listed in Table 1 in special calibrated tubes; he withdrew the growth medium and replaced it with sugar solution so that the mycelium was entirely immersed in the liquid, in effect achieving anaerobic conditions. The magnitude of activity was expressed by the fermentative capacity equal to ml. CO_2 evolved per mg. dry weight of fungus. *Aspergillus clavatus* far exceeds all other Aspergilli in fermentation capacity (Tables 1 and 2). The younger the cell material, the more CO_2 was evolved per unit cell material. Thus, 10-day-old *A. clavatus* cell material displayed only one-quarter the activity of the 4-day-old mycelium.

TABLE 1

ALCOHOLIC FERMENTATION CAPACITY OF VARIOUS ASPERGILLI[1]

Aspergillus Species	Fermentative Capacity[2]
clavatus	4,161
gymnosardae, soya, candidus	Approx. 500
japonicus, oryzae	300–400
awamori, luchuensis, aureus, niger	200–300
oniki, ostianus	50–100
ochraceus, melleus, mannitus, wentii	10– 50
giganteus, fumigatus, nidulans, minimum, glaucus	0– 10

[1] From Tamiya and Miwa (1928).
[2] Ml. CO_2/mg. dry wt.

This effect in *A oryzae* is represented graphically in Fig. 4. The exceptionally high fermentative capacity registered for *A. clavatus* in Table 1 may be further indicated by the fact that a pellicle weighing 0.107 g. evolved fermentation CO_2 at the rate of 2 ml./hour for 10 days, and at a slower rate for some weeks after. Worthy of note is the disparity in fermentative capacity between *A. clavatus* and *A. giganteus*, the only two organisms considered sufficiently closely related on morphological grounds by Thom and Raper (1945) to be included in their *A. clavatus* group. Tamiya and later Tomlinson (1937) also dispelled a notion put forth by the famous Kostytschew and his coworker Afanassjewa

(1921) to the effect that in order for an organism (*A. niger*) to develop the sugar fermenting zymase, the organism must be grown in the presence of sugar. The Japanese workers were able to show that several different species of *Aspergillus*, all grown in sugar-free peptone solutions, possessed strong zymase systems as evidenced by abundant CO_2 evolution when transferred to sugar solutions and in the absence of oxygen. The zymase content of such cultures was roughly proportional to the fermentative capacities of the organisms when grown on sugar solutions, but all only about one-fifth to one-sixth of this value, although one, *A. gymnosardae*, had the same fermentative capacity regardless of growth history. Similar results were obtained by Tomlinson whose data shows that peptone-grown mycelium anaerobically produced 0.14–0.27 mg. CO_2—C per gram dry weight per hr. from sugar, as compared to 1.05 mg. for glucose-grown mycelium. The peptone-mycelium aerobically produced CO_2 from sugar at a rate sixty times its anaerobic formation. Kostytschew's experiments were of such short duration that the very small amounts of CO_2 (and alcohol) could have escaped detection. Incidentally, although these experiments have not before been cited in this connection, they represent one of the first clear-cut examples of constitutive vs. adaptive enzymes, in the sense of Karstrom (1938).

The Japanese workers were also able to secure, in cell-free condition, active zymase extracts of several fungi by macerating them in 50 per cent glycerin solution for 5 hours. Other Japanese workers have obtained active zymase and carboxylase preparations from Rhizopus; acetone-dried Rhizopus preparations also contained these enzymes complexes in active form (Takahashi and Asai, 1928; Sakaguchi and Asai, 1927).

Active press juices similar to those obtained from yeast by Buchner in his classical cell-free fermentation, have been obtained from several fungi ordinarily not considered as alcohol fermenters (*Allescheria gayonii*, Mazé, 1902.) The following data from Junitzky (1907) for *A. niger* press juice exemplify how nearly the ratio of alcohol to CO_2 formed agree with that of typical yeast fermentation, where it is approximately a 1:1 ratio:

Press juice preparation	CO_2, mg.	Alcohol, mg.
A = no sugar	....	0
B = + sugar	68.8	54.4
C = + sugar	90.4	83.4
D = + sugar	70	63.1

In addition to a complete sugar fermenting zymase system in acetone preparations of *Penicillium glaucum*, a lactic dehydrogenase is present so that the addition of lactate results in oxidation to pyruvate, which generates CO_2 owing to decarboxylation by the carboxylase system (Herzog and Meier, 1908). As discussed later, cell-free juice obtained by grinding Fusarium mycelium possesses vigorous zymase activity (Wirth and Nord, 1940).

The extremely comprehensive carbon balance studies made on scores of different fungi by the Raistrick group at the London School of Hygiene and Tropical Medicine and reported in detailed tabulation in their celebrated Philosophical Transactions article (Raistrick *et al.*, 1931) offer some interesting deductions. While the data were not constructed purposely to ascertain fermentative capacities, calculations and retabulation of some of the data in that treatise provide an interesting confirmation of theoretical expectations and is a first class example of how important deductions may be made from a set of data originally not designed to reveal these points. These experiments were performed uniformly in surface culture conditions in Czapek's medium, for rather prolonged incubation periods. On the basis of the accepted mechanism of alcohol formation, one mole of CO_2 is formed per mole of alcohol, both arising from pyruvic acid. It is expected, therefore, that organisms with high fermentative capacities, acting under ostensibly aerobic conditions, and which, by analysis, show a high alcohol content of the medium, would also reflect this tendency in its CO_2 output, and also that there should be correspondence between these two criteria. A compilation of these comparative data is given in Table 2, where numerous species of Aspergilli, Penicillia and Fusaria are examined. The column heading "carbon in neutral volatile compounds" is, of course, except for minor amounts of acetaldehyde, virtually entirely ethanol. The carbon dioxide output is expressed as "respiratory quotient" because the experiment was done under aerobic conditions and the true representation of fermentation CO_2 is that over and above the usual respiration CO_2 during consumption of oxygen. It is evident that, the higher the R.Q., the greater the CO_2 excess due to fermentation CO_2.

Table 2 shows a remarkably fine agreement between these two characteristics, and emphasizes again the very wide spread found between the species in any one genus, and also the overlapping between genera. It may also be noted that where the R.Q. is in the neighborhood of 1.0–1.3, the alcohol accumulation is almost negligible. The genus Fusarium, with the highest R.Q.'s and alcohol production, nevertheless has certain species which are exceeded by the more active organisms in both the genera Aspergillus and Penicillium. Note also that the *A. clavatus* strains stand clearly higher than the other Aspergilli (cf. Tamiya and Miwa, 1928), and that there is a rough agreement in the relative positions of the particular species tested in both Raistrick's and Tamiya's work (Tables 1 and 2). The apparent discrepancy in the case of alcohol formation by *A. terreus* may be an indication that the C_2 fractions (acetaldehyde) were not reduced to ethyl alcohol but were instead further utilized, perhaps for itaconic acid, which this organism is known to form abundantly.

TABLE 2

SUMMARY OF FERMENTATION CAPACITY DATA CALCULATED FROM CARBON BALANCES OF BIRKINSHAW, ET AL.[1]

Group	Respiratory quotient	Carbon in neutral volatile compounds, g.	No. of strains
Aspergilli			
clavatus....................	1.91	1.247	6
flavus-oryzae................	1.79	0.796	7
ochraceus...................	1.78	.676	10
nidulans type A.............	1.63	.843	3
terreus.....................	1.62	.330	2
niger.......................	1.58	.792	15
white.......................	1.25	.123	14
fumigatus...................	1.12	.015	5
versicolor..................	1.29	.015	8
sydowi......................	1.25	.028	6
nidulans type B.............	1.31	.017	4
glaucus.....................	1.01	.006	10
minimus.....................	1.17	.004	2
wentii......................	1.12	.009	3
ustus.......................	1.12	.003	1
Penicillia			
I...........................	>1.60	1.48	20
II..........................	1.60–1.41	.95	11
III.........................	1.40–1.21	.32	18
IV..........................	1.20–1.01	.036	32
Fusaria			
I...........................	6.0–4.01	2.30	7
II..........................	4.0–2.01	1.93	9
III.........................	2.0–1.01	0.88	7

[1] From Birkinshaw, J. H., Charles, J. H. V., Raistrick, H., and Stoyle, J. A. R. 1931. *Trans. Roy. Soc. London* **B220**, 93–98.

A survey of alcohol-fermentation propensities of the genus Mucor, well known in this regard, has been reported by another group of Japanese investigators (Takahashi and Asai, 1933a). Twenty-four species were examined, with two, *M. rouxii* and *M. corymbifer*, yielding over 4 per cent alcohol in the culture solutions, and twelve other species falling between 3 and 4 per cent. These organisms behave like yeast with regard to glycerol formation from sugar. Normally, glycerol yields ranged from 3.8 to 9.0 per cent of the sugar decomposed. In the presence of sodium bisulfite or sodium carbonate (Neuberg's "second and third forms of fermentation") 6.0 and 4.0 per cent respectively glycerol yields increased markedly up to 23.5 per cent of the glucose consumed (Takahashi and Asai, 1933b).

Significance of Alcoholic Fermentation in Production of Carboxylic Acids Aerobically

Alcohol fermentation in fungi has a special significance which transcends its importance as a physiological process *per se*, owing to the fact that the most acceptable and modern ideas as to the origin of the highly oxidized products characteristic of carbohydrate metabolism in fungi, e.g., di-, and tricarboxy acids, interpret their formation as proceeding through two stages. The first is a preliminary phase, fermentative or glycolytic in character according to Neuberg's scheme, which gives rise to C_3- and C_2-split-products of carbohydrate (ethanol, acetaldehyde). The second stage consists now of a further conversion of these initially-formed glycolytic products with the involvement of molecular oxygen. Thus, the fermentative activity of the so-called highly oxidative mold is an essential prerequisite of the aerobic stages, which may consist of further combustion of the C_2-fragments to CO_2 and H_2O via the Krebs' cycle, or of condensation and oxidation culminating in C_4- and C_6-di- and tribasic acids.

This concept of a resynthesis of carboxylic acids from smaller primary break-down products has been considered by many workers, of which perhaps the main exponents have been the Polish investigators on mold metabolism, Chrzazscz and Tiukow (1930). Principal evidence on behalf of this theory is that acetates (formed from acetaldehyde or ethanol in the presence of oxygen) give rise to substantial yields of C_4-dicarboxylic acids and also citric acid, depending on the organism. Thus, metabolically speaking, various fungi differ largely as to the qualitative and quantitative extent to which they can dispose of initially-formed products of fermentation. The anaerobic or (alcoholic) fermentative processes would assume a rather universal importance in the filamentous fungi. These ideas are discussed further in Chapters 4 and 12.

Furthermore, if the products of fermentation metabolism are intercepted by trapping agents such as sodium bisulfite, not only do they accumulate in high yields, but even more important, the organic acids accumulating abundantly in normal cultures are formed only in greatly reduced yields and may even be virtually suppressed (Bernhauer and Thelen, 1932).

In chapters 4 and 12 is discussed the idea that acetaldehyde is the key C_2 intermediate of mold carbohydrate metabolism (in view of the fact that it is probably formed actively in most fungi), there being two subsequent fates, or reactions, competing for the aldehyde. When the oxygen supply is inadequate it is reduced, and this accounts for the ubiquity of alcohol in mold cultures. With abundant oxygen supply it is believed that some or all of the aldehyde is oxidized to acetate, which then further undergoes varying degrees of oxidation, through the Krebs' organic acid cycle. The different degrees of oxidation may be represented as passage through the stages of C_4 dicarboxylic acids, then C_6 (citric acid), then breakdown with formation of CO_2 and water.

Though there is no direct evidence to support it, it is probable that aerobic acetate formation does not take place via acetaldehyde as an intermediate product. More likely aldehyde formation itself is suppressed, i.e., anaerobic decarboxylation of pyruvate is checked, and the pyruvate generates acetate directly via oxidative decarboxylation, a reaction discovered by F. Lipmann in *Lactobacillus delbrückii* and now known to occur in other systems (Lipmann, 1941). Carbon dioxide is also formed. The oxidation is coupled with the phosphorylation of adenylic acid, and acetylphosphate is formed as an intermediate. The reactions:

$$CH_3COCOOH + H_3PO_4 \xrightarrow[-2H]{+O} CH_3 \cdot CO \cdot O \cdot PO_3H_2 + CO_2$$

Pyruvic acid   Acetylphosphoric acid

$$2CH_3 \cdot CO \cdot O \cdot PO_3H_2 + \text{Adenylic acid} \rightarrow 2CH_3COOH + \text{Adenosine triphosphate}$$

Acetic acid

It seems improbable that alcohol or acetaldehyde themselves are essential intermediates. They probably represent under oxygen deficiency incidental excursion pathways of glucose metabolism which yield active acetate upon further oxidation, the degree of oxygenation governing the extent to which the "alcohol excursion" supersedes the competing aerobic decarboxylation of pyruvate.

The acetaldehyde trapping experiments discussed above on this page do not prove this compound is an intermediate in the synthesis of carboxylic acids. In the first place this conclusion would be valid only when acid formation occurs via the alcohol excursion, a situation prevailing only under limited aeration conditions and probably not otherwise. Secondly, the removal of aldehyde in the form of sulfite addition complex drives the equilibrium in the direction of aldehyde formation, thus channeling more pyruvate away from the normal pathway of aerobic decarboxylation and resulting in reduced yields of carboxy acids.

FERMENTATION OF PENTOSES

The outstanding alcoholic fermentation tendencies of the Fusaria naturally has made organisms of this group the best ones for the study of detailed characteristics and mechanism of the fermentation process. Birkinshaw (1937) called the Fusaria " . . . the alcohol former *par excellence*" of the lower fungi. Another distinctive property of the Fusaria, namely, that they represent the only organisms known to carry out what essentially is a true alcoholic fermentation of pentoses, has frequently led to consideration and testing of practical methods for production of ethanol from cheap pentose-containing materials such as waste sulfite liquors from the pulp industry, and also from acid-hydrolysates of wood, wheat, stillage and other materials high in pentosans. Most natural materials of plant origin have appreciable amounts of pentoses, mainly in the polymerized state as pentosans. Presumably, a successful large-scale operation of this process does not appear feasible, except under critical supply conditions, due to the dilute concentration of sugars in sulfite liquor, making alcohol recovery costly, and also due to the fact that substances toxic to Fusaria occur in such materials and would have to be removed. Lignosulfonic acids, tannins, resins, etc. are among the poisonous substances found.

In the laboratory of F. F. Nord, where these practical possibilities have been investigated, these growth-inhibiting materials could be removed by pretreatment with 1–2 per cent activated charcoal (Loughran, *et al.*, 1944). When a *Fusarium lini* fermentation was carried out in suitably prepared wood hydrolysate medium which had previously been subjected to yeast fermentation to ferment out hexoses, the alcohol yield from Fusarium action (surface culture) amounted to only 1 per cent of that formed by the yeast, a useless process. This small fraction was, moreover, equivalent to only 2.2–4.7 per cent of the alcohol theoretically expected from the residual carbohydrate content calculated as pentose.

In this same laboratory Sciarini and Wirth (1945) made extensive investigation of the amount of alcohol obtainable from the pentoses of wheat after the hexoses had been fermented out by ordinary yeast fermentation. In H_2SO_4-hydrolyzed wheat mashes, fermentations conducted in this way gave extra alcohol yields 6–12 per cent over that obtained in yeast fermentation alone. HCl-hydrolyzed mashes were unsatisfactory.

MECHANISM OF PENTOSE SPLIT BY FUSARIUM

To interpret a pentose fermentation in which all the carbohydrate is accountable as ethyl alcohol and carbon dioxide in the observed 1:2 molar ratio, calls for a scheme different from that for hexose where two trioses represent the initial sugar split. It is obvious that the shift in alcohol to CO_2 ratio of $1:1$ in hexose to $1:2$ in pentose is a direct consequence of the difference in number of carbons in the sugar molecule. Virtually no satisfactory evidence exists to support it, but a C_3—C_2 split is assumed to take place, the C_3 fraction proceeding via pyruvate to alcohol and CO_2 (Dietrich and Klammerth, 1939).

$$C_5H_{10}O_5 \rightarrow \qquad C_3 \qquad + \quad C_2H_4O_2$$
$$\text{Triose intermediate} \quad C_2 \text{ Fraction}$$
$$\downarrow$$
$$C_3H_6O_3$$
$$\text{Pyruvic acid}$$
$$\downarrow$$
$$C_2H_5OH + CO_2$$

$$3C_2H_4O_2 \rightarrow C_6H_{12}O_6 \rightarrow 2C_2H_5OH + 2CO_2$$
$$C_2 \text{ Fraction} \quad \text{Hexose}$$

The easily detectable pyruvate in Fusarium cultures is offered in support of this idea (Nord and Mull, 1945), not an unreasonable speculation. The C_2 fraction is assumed by Nord and Mull (1945) to be glycolaldehyde although none could be detected and no other evidence is offered. The fact that Fusarium can oxidize added ethylene glycol to glycolaldehyde (Goepfert and Nord, 1942) in no way incriminates the latter compound in pentose fermentations, and indeed this oxidation probably can be effected by a great many different fungi. The nonspecificity of this dehydrogenation is evident from the fact that the same organism produced the corresponding simple dehydrogenation products of six other alcohols: formaldehyde from methanol, acetaldehyde from ethanol, acetylmethylcarbinol from $2:3$ butylene glycol, triose from glycerol, erythrulose from erythritol and a hexose mixture from sorbitol. According to Dietrich and Klammerth's (1939) scheme, the C_2 moiety is condensed (three moles) to yield a hexose intermediate sugar which then is fermented to alcohol and CO_2 in the conventional manner. The overall reaction is given then as:

$$C_5H_{10}O_5 \rightarrow \tfrac{5}{3} C_2H_5OH + \tfrac{5}{3} CO_2$$
$$51.12 \text{ per cent } 48.88 \text{ per cent yield}$$

While this mechanism accounts for all the sugar, it is at variance with the observed weight yields as well as molar ratios of the products obtained in actual practice. Fusarium fermentation of pentoses corresponds to the equation:

$$C_5H_{10}O_5 \rightarrow C_2H_5OH + 2CO_2$$

(Anderson, 1924; Reynolds, 1926; White and Willaman, 1928a; Letcher and Willaman, 1926). Yields of the two products accounted for only about 80 per cent of the fermented pentose and it was believed that another reduced 1-carbon compound must accompany the fermentation. The missing fraction could not be detected although, because an arithmetical balance of the equation shows that 1C and 4H atoms are missing, methane (CH_4) was suggested as a fourth component of the system, but this has never been confirmed and is exceedingly unlikely. It is not necessary to hypothesize the formation of CH_4 at all. Water might be involved in the oxido-reduction processes concerned with the transformation of pentose; and secondly, what is more likely, the missing carbon might well be converted into cell material either through oxidative or fermentative assimilation, a process now well established for yeasts and other microorganisms (Clifton, 1946; also see Chapters 2 and 4). Small amounts of other metabolic products always accompany mold fermentations, just as they do yeast fermentation, and these would originate ultimately from fermented carbohydrate. A precise understanding of the pentose fermentation awaits further study.

BIOCHEMISTRY OF ALCOHOLIC FERMENTATION IN FUNGI

In relation to yeast, the intermediate biochemistry and enzymology of sugar fermentation by fungi has scarcely been touched, and what has been done is limited largely to the Fusaria. The accumulated evidence clearly reveals a similarity between the two groups of organisms in this respect, although in general fungi differ from yeast in their ability to transform further, into other products (carboxylic acids), the initially formed and accumulated alcohol.

The fermentation of hexoses corresponds to the equation of yeast fermentation, $C_6H_{12}O_6 \rightarrow 2CH_3CH_2OH + 2CO_2$, in which the molar ratio of ethanol to CO_2 is 1:1. Also similar to yeast is the fact that *Fusarium sp. H.* grown on glucose ferments only glucose, mannose and fructose; but galactose is fermented when the cells are previously cultivated on that sugar (Gould and Tytell, 1941), presumably an example of constitutive vs. adaptive enzymes (Karstrom, 1938). The glucose fermentation mechanism is present irrespective of growth substrate.

An extensive survey of the metabolic products of twenty-nine strains of Fusaria, including twenty-two species, under highly aerated submerged culture conditions showed that succinic acid, acetic acid, acetaldehyde, and alcohol were the main products, produced in varying degrees by different strains (Lockwood *et al.*, 1938). The highly aerobic conditions led to the formation of so much acetaldehyde in aerated cultures that the concentration of this substance, volatilized by the air stream, was high enough in the atmosphere of the incubation room to irritate the throats of persons entering the room. Doubtless the explanation for this is that oxygen competes with acetaldehyde for active hydrogen which normally would be available to reduce the aldehyde to ethyl alcohol. A typical aerated-culture carbon balance for *F. oxysporum* is shown in the following tabulation from Lockwood *et al.*

Carbon as

Glucose consumed..	17.30 g.
Ethyl alcohol..	4.70 g.
Unidentified compounds..............................	1.23 g.
CO$_2$..	6.05 g.
Volatile organic compounds (acetaldehyde)...............	2.23 g.
Mycelium..	0.88 g.
Total carbon accounted for..........................	15.09 g.
C not accounted for.................................	2.21 g.

The origin of the acetic and succinic acids invariably associated with Fusarium cultures, and, indeed, most mold fermentations where ethanol is formed with access of oxygen, can be explained by dehydrogenation of the initially formed alcohol (see Chapter 11).

Succinic acid tends to accumulate in old cultures of Fusaria, generally when the alcohol content begins to diminish due to further conversion by the organism. The Fusaria are greatly inferior to yeasts in relation to accumulation of alcohol, a maximum of 3 to 4 per cent already being toxic (White and Willaman, 1928a). These workers also made the observation previously emphasized in Chapter 4 in connection with organic acids, that an inverse proportion existed between growth of Fusaria and the ethyl alcohol formed.

The pathway between carbohydrate and alcohol in these organisms still needs much work before the picture is complete. There is no reason to believe that the mechanism fundamentally is any different from that in yeast fermentation of hexoses, although F. F. Nord has for years maintained a view that is contrary to the ideas which are almost universally accepted as the sequence of steps in alcoholic fermentation; he employs the *Fusarium* fermentation in support of his contentions. This will be discussed later.

Gould and Tytell (1941) studied the endogenous and exogenous glucose metabolism of resting cells of Fusarium manometrically under the influence of poisons, and concluded that the CO$_2$-producing mechanisms in Fusaria, respiratory and fermentative, bear a striking similarity to the events in resting suspensions of yeast. Semeniuk (1944) came to the same conclusion using macerated preparations of *Chaetomium funicola*.

PYRUVATE DECARBOXYLATION

Before 1933, Neuberg's methyl glyoxal theory was the favored mechanism of sugar fermentation. Methyl glyoxal, $CH_3 \cdot CO \cdot CHO$, could be isolated from fermentations and further converted to pyruvic acid and alcohol.   Since 1933, the key triose intermediate is known to be phosphoglyceraldehyde, according to the well-known Embden-Meyerhof-Parnas scheme.   The methyl glyoxal is formed as a side reaction. Though phosphoglyceraldehyde, or its oxidation product phosphoglyceric acid, has not yet been demonstrated in fungi in support of the Embden-Meyerhof-Parnas scheme, the side product methyl glyoxal has, and this provides presumptive evidence that events in the fungi are comparable to those in yeast (but see p. 320).   Methyl glyoxal was produced from hexose diphosphate by washed living *Aspergillus niger* mycelium under toluene (Suthers and Walker, 1932) and by alcohol-ether dried cells of *Torula coeliculosa* in 77 per cent yield (Yamasaki, 1930).   Again antedating the newer theory, Chrzaszcz and Tiukow (1930) and Chrzaszcz *et al.* (1932) picture the events in alcoholic fermentation by fungi according to this sequence:

Hexose → Hexose diphosphate → Methylglyoxal → Pyruvate → Acetaldehyde
→ Alcohol

This theory provides the basis for their concept of the origin of carboxylic acids by further oxidation of the alcohol.

As in yeast fermentation, pyruvic acid can be readily isolated as an intermediate in alcohol fermentation from Fusarium cultures with hexoses and pentoses as carbohydrate source.   In contrast to yeast, which accumulates pyruvate only when poisoned, or by special trapping methods, no special precautions are necessary.   This is probably due to a deficiency in the carboxylase enzyme system which further acts on the pyruvate, breaking it down to acetaldehyde and CO_2.   In support of this idea is the experiment in which added thiamine, the precursor of cocarboxylase, the coenzyme for carboxylase, reduced the accumulation of pyruvate quite appreciably.   A control culture without added thiamine produced 171 mg. pyruvate per 100 ml. culture whereas the one containing added thiamine accumulated only 24 mg. (Wirth and Nord, 1942).

Later the interesting point was revealed that pyruvate accumulated only when nitrate was used as a source of nitrogen in the medium (Wirth and Nord, 1943; Sciarini and Nord, 1944), only traces being formed with ammonia- or organic-N.   Nitrite and hydroxylamine were formed by reduction of the nitrate, the nitrite exerting a specific inhibitory effect on pyruvic carboxylase so that decarboxylation is prevented.   The inhibition presumably has to do with inactivation of cocarboxylase as it can be reversed by the addition of thiamine.   Reduced Coenzyme I is suggested as the means of nitrate reduction.

Hida (1935) found that high concentrations of sulfite (5 per cent) in replacement cultures of *Aspergillus niger* on 5 per cent sugar, caused formation and accumulation of pyruvic acid, and a derivative, dimethyl pyruvic acid, $(CH_3)_2CHCOCOOH$, both of which were isolated. The presence of NH_4^+ favored production of the latter, and suppressed formation of pyruvic acid.

There is no question that pyruvate is a precursor in alcohol formation by these organisms, and that it can be utilized for growth in the absence of carbohydrate, as can dihydroxyacetone. In such cases alcohol does not accumulate, as it is consumed by the organism faster than it is formed (White and Willaman, 1928b). On the other hand, alcohol does accumulate when the mold is furnished acetaldehyde. Just as in yeast fermentation, acetaldehyde is the immediate precursor of alcohol in sugar fermentation by Fusaria. It can almost always be detected in traces in fungus cultures containing carbohydrates, and can be caused to accumulate under special conditions, such as the presence of aldehyde-binding substances (bisulfite or dimedon; see Chapter 2) (Letcher and Willaman, 1926) or intense aeration of the culture (Lockwood et al., 1938). Many molds were shown by Nagayama (1921) to produce acetaldehyde from calcium pyruvate; it accumulated free in the medium and when trapped with bisulfite reached 34 per cent of theoretical yield. Organisms tested included *Monilia candida, Oidium lactis, Aspergillus niger mutante, Mucor plumbeus, M. rouxii* and *M. racemosus*. Carboxylase activity in dry preparations of *Torula coeliculosa* gave an 87 per cent yield of aldehyde under bisulfite conditions (Yamasaki, 1930).

Rippel and Wiangke (1941) give some attention to the devious results obtainable at times using the sulfite trapping method in fungi, particularly *Aspergillus niger*. In their experiments only 0.23 per cent acetaldehyde was trapped, yet the alcohol yield under anaerobic conditions was 30.0 per cent. The failure of the sulfite to block alcohol formation was attributed to permeability properties of the mold cell walls, preventing the intracellular acetaldehyde from penetrating out of the cells. Hence it cannot react with the bisulfite and is not trapped nor detected. The effectiveness of bisulfite is believed to vary for different organisms. It works well for yeast, and in strains of fungi on which it does work (*A. niger*, Bernhauer and Thelen, 1932) it is less effective anaerobically than aerobically. According to Rippel and Wiangke, the sulfite itself probably is the cause of the lowered permeability where the latter is encountered.

THIAMINE INHIBITION

The Swiss botanist Schopfer in 1935 discovered the interesting phenomenon of inhibition of the growth of several fungi belonging to the genus Rhizopus by small amounts of thiamine in a glucose-salts-asparagine medium, and this has been confirmed (Robbins and Kavanagh,

1938). Species inhibited were *R. sinuis, R. nigricans, R. maydis, R. oryzae, R. chinensis, R. bovinus, R. tritici, R. tonkinensis, R. nodosus,* and *R. japonicus.* The inhibitory effect on *R. sinuis* has been studied in great detail by Schopfer and Guilloud (1945). About 0.5 μg. thiamine per 25 ml. medium resulted in 30 to 40 per cent less dry weight mycelium than thiamine-free controls. The thiamine effect is a function of time, maximum inhibition occurring between the 44–49th hours of growth. In the early stages the thiamine stimulates growth up to 50 per cent more than the controls. This rapidly passes through the inhibitory stage, and then later the thiamine-containing cultures catch up to the controls. The pyrimidine portion of the thiamine molecule at high levels reproduces the thiamine effect; thiazole has no effect. Addition of *meso*-inositol reduces the inhibitory effect of thiamine.

The inhibited cultures contain considerably more alcohol than the controls, the difference tending to diminish with age due to further consumption by the fungus upon exhaustion of the sugar. In some experiments nine times more alcohol was present in the thiamine cultures. Since alcohol added to the cultures retards growth of the fungus to a certain extent, Schopfer and Guilloud conclude that the thiamine inhibition in reality is due to the extra alcohol formation its presence induces, though some other was also suspected.

Foster and Goldman (1948) proved that weight for weight the thiamine-grown mycelium of *R. nigricans* harvested at the time of maximum inhibition has substantially higher carboxylase activity than the non-thiamine mycelium. This doubtless accounts for the increased alcohol formation observed. These authors believe that alcohol itself may not be the *cause* of the inhibition, as Schopfer believed, but rather the *result.* The inhibition is looked upon as a forced fermentation, obliging the fungus to utilize its carbohydrate by the inefficient anaerobic breakdown rather than by the more efficient aerobic oxidation. Aerobically a gram-mole of glucose yields 674 kcals.; fermentation to alcohol yields only 22 kcals. Hence, $\dfrac{674 - 22}{674} \times 100$, or 97 per cent of the energy level of the glucose fermented remains potential in the form of alcohol. Upon exhaustion of the sugar, the alcohol is further attacked and oxidized; the secondary utilization of the extra alcohol in the thiamine cultures, yielding energy and carbon, now enables the thiamine cultures to catch up with the non-thiamine controls in respect to dry weight. In a sense, the thiamine has imposed an excursion in the complete utilization of glucose, via temporary accumulation of alcohol. Eventually the oxidation is as complete as in the controls.

Goddard (1939) has studied the carboxylase reaction in ascospores of *Neurospora tetrasperma*. These spores are unique in that they are dormant when placed in nutrient media, but may be induced to germinate by a short period of heat treatment, for example, 20 minutes heating at 52–60°C., which gives a 96 per cent germination rate. The curious feature of this phenomenon is that the activation is reversible. If activated spores are maintained for an appreciable time after activation under anaerobic conditions, or in cyanide, they deactivate. The deactivation is virtually complete after 4 hours. The activation process consists of activation of both aerobic respiration of the spores and fermentation, the latter judged by CO_2 evolution in an N_2 atmosphere. Goddard furnishes some evidence and has provisionally accepted the view that it is the enzyme system carboxylase which undergoes reversible activation in heat treatment. The likelihood was presented that the cocarboxylase constituent of the enzyme is the reversibly activatable step, for this coenzyme functions both in anaerobic decarboxylation of pyruvate and aerobic decarboxylation of pyruvate, thereby explaining the heat activation observed in both fermentation and respiration.

Coenzymes in Alcohol Fermentation of Fungi

The carboxylase-cocarboxylase system of Fusaria has been studied quite thoroughly by Tytell and Gould (1941). It had been observed previously (Dammann, *et al.*, 1938) that addition of vitamin B_1 to Fusarium cultures fermenting sugars increased yields of alcohol. The suggestion was made that the B_1 was converted to cocarboxylase resulting in more vigorous decarboxylation of pyruvate and alcohol formation. Tytell and Gould's results indicate this explanation is not the whole story. In their experiments added B_1 increased the cocarboxylase of the mycelium up to threefold during early stages of growth, but no appreciable increase in alcohol production was apparent although there was a small alcohol difference in older cultures. Thus, low carboxylase activity was not the limiting factor in alcohol production. It is possible that the different strains (*F. tricothecoides* vs. *F. graminearum*) behave differently in this respect and that in the organisms of Wirth and Nord (1941) and Dammann, *et al.* (1938), the cocarboxylase content was the determinative factor in pyruvate accumulation and alcohol formation. Tytell and Gould established the presence of good carboxylase activity in powdered, air-dried mycelium of *F. tricothecoides*. The enzyme was present regardless of the carbohydrate on which the organism was grown. Properties such as pH optimum and divalent ion activation corresponded to those for the well-known yeast pyruvic carboxylase, and there is no reason for doubting their identity. The coenzyme could be washed out by 0.10 M Na_2HPO_4, giving inactive apoenzyme (protein) whose activity could then be restored by addition of crystalline cocarboxylase. The mycelium contained 2.8–4.2 μg. coenzyme per gram dry tissue. However, synthesis of cocarboxylase from vitamin B_1 could not be demonstrated in resting cell suspensions or dried cell preparations using inorganic or organic phosphate donors.

It is possible to obtain, by means of the Booth-Green wet crushing mill, cell-free juices of Fusaria which exhibit strong zymase activity, producing CO_2 from sugar and carrying out phosphate transformations similar to zymase preparations obtainable from yeast. The activity of the Fusarium zymase appears to be of the order of the activity of the living system (Wirth and Nord, 1940).

A second coenzyme, of general occurrence in yeast fermentation and in virtually all biological systems, is known to play an active part in alcoholic fermentation by Fusarium. This is cozymase or diphosphopyridine nucleotide (DPN), known as coenzyme I. One striking dissimilarity between yeast and Fusarium fermentation is the very slow rate of the latter. The addition of nicotinamide results in appreciable stimulation of the (pentose) fermentation in rate and total accumulation of alcohol (Dietrich and Klammerth, 1939). This suggests that the nicotinamide might be utilized for the synthesis of DPN by the fungus, otherwise deficient in this vital H-transport, and that the enrichment in DPN accounts for the accelerated fermentation. This hypothesis was confirmed by some neat experiments of Gould, et al. (1942). DPN was shown to be a normal constituent of F. tricothecoides mycelium grown on synthetic medium and hence synthesized in entirety by the organism. The content is relatively low and the addition to the medium of minute amounts of DPN gave a sevenfold stimulation in fermentation without influencing growth. Nicotinic acid was less effective, indicating its conversion to the more active form as DPN. Alcohol production by this organism was in direct relation to the DPN content of the mycelium, and the mycelium enriched in DPN (167 μg./g. dry weight) had a fermentation rate 20 to 25 times greater than the controls. Thus, the limiting factor in alcohol fermentation by these organisms is DPN, the well-known mediator of biochemical oxidation. According to these workers, the available evidence points to the origin of ethyl alcohol by living Fusaria as follows:

$$\text{Pyruvate} \xrightarrow{\text{Carboxylase}} \text{Acetaldehyde} + CO_2$$

$$\text{DPN·}H_2 + \text{Acetaldehyde} \xrightarrow{\text{Alcohol dehydrogenase}} \text{DPN} + \text{Ethyl alcohol}$$

These reactions are identical with those of yeast.

Nord's Theory of Fermentation

For the past decade F. F. Nord and his school, first in Germany and then in this country at Fordham University, has maintained that the yeast fermentation in the living intact cell does not necessarily follow the universally believed dismutation mechanism whereby phosphorylated intermediates are formed. According to Nord, events obtained with zymase preparations, yeast autolysates (cell-free juice containing all the enzymes of alcoholic fermentation) or enzyme preparations from yeast, all indicating the vital participation of the phosphorylation process in the breakdown of sugar to alcohol, represent a pathological imbalance or disorganization totally different from what goes on in a normal cell. Therefore, he maintains that such results cannot be used to interpret the happenings in the intact cell.   The same line of reasoning is applied∙to the Fusarium fermentation, in which Nord and coworkers have concluded phosphorylation plays little or no part. He interprets his results with living Fusarium as supporting the claim that phosphorylation need not take place during yeast fermentation.   Apparently he is in agreement with the prevailing knowledge pertaining to the identity of the organic intermediates between sugar and alcohol, viz., dihydroxyacetone, glyceraldehyde, glyceric acid, pyruvic acid, and acetaldehyde. He does not disagree with the occurrence of phosphorylated derivatives appearing in the course of the dissimilation of hexoses to alcohol in yeast.   However, from studies on Fusarium described in the following in which attempts to demonstrate phosphorylation in Fusarium fermentations have been unsuccessful, Nord concludes that the phosphorylation mechanism does not necessarily signify the *sole* way by which yeast ferments sugars (personal communication, 1948).   This idea is contrary to that accepted by the majority of biochemists.   He also concurs that cocarboxylase and diphosphopyridine nucleotide are active in Fusarium metabolism.

No attempt is made here to resolve this long-standing issue, and details of Nord's contentions may be found in his reviews (1939, 1940; Nord and Mull, 1945).   A principal point in Nord's claim is that once the cell is ruptured the total balance between enzymes is upset, resulting in an accumulation of intermediary products that is contrary to events in living cells.   Thus, the accumulation of hexose diphosphate in yeast zymase first noted by Harden and Young in 1906 is cited by Nord as a prime example of a compound which is never detected in the living cell. Accordingly, instead of carrying out the fermentation of sugar to conform with the classical Gay-Lussac equation

$$C_6H_{12}O_6 \rightarrow 2C_2H_5OH + 2CO_2$$

zymase fermentations carry out alcoholic fermentation as described by the

Harden-Young equation whereby one mole of sugar is oxidized to alcohol and water while a second molecule of sugar ends up as a diphosphate:

$$2C_6H_{12}O_6 + 2Na_2HPO_4 \rightarrow 2CO_2 + 2C_2H_5OH + 2H_2O + C_6H_{10}O_4(PO_4Na_2)_2$$

Recently, however, an explanation has been offered for the Harden-Young equation by Meyerhof (1945). The hexosediphosphate (fructose 1:6 diphosphate; Harden-Young ester) is a normal intermediate, but normally does not accumulate owing to further transformation. It accumulates here simply because an enzyme normally present in living cells does not go into solution readily with the rest of the zymase complex but is retained by the solid portion of the yeast cells which are discarded. If these solids containing the enzyme, adenylpyrophosphatase, are added to the zymase, or if adenylpyrophosphatase from potato is added, the hexosediphosphate disappears and the rate of fermentation is restored to the maximum. From adenosine triphosphate (ATP) the enzyme regenerates adenosine mono- or diphosphate as phosphate acceptor, thus removing the phosphate block that prevents the forward reactions causing decomposition of the hexose. The block develops because all the phosphate carrier piles up at ATP owing to the absence of the enzyme splitting off the pyrophosphate group. Thus it would seem in this case that events believed to occur in the living cell can actually be duplicated independent of the living cell. The mechanisms presumably are, therefore, identical.

The fact that cell-free preparations do not carry out precisely the transformations which the living cells do, need not invalidate the data obtained with the former. Any distortion observed may merely mean that one or more enzymes has been destroyed or lost. If this is replaced the aberration may be restored to normal (e.g., Meyerhof, 1945). It also need not mean that the remaining uninjured enzymes whose action can be demonstrated, do not carry out these same reactions in the living cell. One must admit the balance of products may be different, but the nature of the reactions turns out to be the same *in vitro* and *in vivo*.

Nord and Mull (1945) raise the point that the failure to detect glycolaldehyde as a C_2 intermediate in Fusarium fermentation of pentose (p. 312) may be due to the fact that it is acted on enzymatically at a higher rate than the possible rate of diffusion out of the cell. This contention is strengthened by the fact that from 20 g. ethylene glycol furnished only 0.15 g. of aldehyde was obtained (Goepfert and Nord, 1942), presumed to be due to rapid utilization of the aldehyde by the organism. One could invoke this same line of reasoning to explain the inability to isolate significant amounts of phosphorylated sugar split-product intermediates and phosphate carriers from Fusaria mycelium.

The *amounts* are not so significant as the *rate of turnover* of what is present. The fact remains that adenosine triphosphate, a key substance in yeast fermentation, is present in Fusarium cells (0.4 mg./100 g.) (Nord, 1939) and its only known function in metabolism is that of phosphate carrier. So far experiments conclusively eliminating as possibilities in Fusaria the functions ATP plays in yeast and muscle have not been provided.

Two other arguments advanced by Nord as evidence contraindicating the participation of phosphorylated intermediates in Fusarium fermentation are: (1) an attempt to isolate phosphoglyceric acid from fluoride-containing cultures acting on carbohydrate failed (Nord *et al.*, 1937). With yeast this intermediate accumulates in isolatable quantities. (2) Phosphoglyceric acid is not utilized by Fusarium when supplied as a source of carbon (Wirth, 1943).

Regarding the first point, negative results may merely mean that the correct experimental conditions did not prevail. It could be that the cells of the fungus were not permeable to the fluoride, or that phosphatase action prevents accumulation of the phosphorylated compound, or some similar situation. With reference to the second point, phosphorylated compounds are notoriously inferior in regard to permeability into living cells. Furthermore, phosphatases might hydrolyze the added compound rapidly (Mann, 1944).

Phosphate Transformations in Fungi

Fungi do actively convert inorganic orthophosphate (PO_4) into organic phosphates which can be detected in the culture medium and in the mycelium; the significance of this fact for theories of alcohol fermentation is obvious. The amounts of such complexes are far in excess of that ascribable to the content in P-containing coenzymes. Some thorough investigations have been made on this point with various fungi, the studies of Semeniuk (1944) and Mann (1944) being particularly instructive (see also Michel-Durand, 1938). Each of a variety of different fungi, including the cellulose decomposer *Chaetomium funicola*, *Aspergillus niger*, several Fusaria and Penicillia, all convert inorganic P into organic form. In the mycelium the bulk of the P is in organic-bound form although considerable ordinary orthophosphate occurs free in the mycelium. The bound phosphate exists in the conventional different analytical fractions: an appreciable portion consisted of a trichloracetic acid-soluble fraction; 7- and 30-minute hydrolyzable P ("easily- and difficultly-" hydrolyzable P) fractions were also present. In most cases only a small portion was in the "difficultly-hydrolyzable" form.

Autolytic processes mineralize the bound phosphate, liberating it as orthophosphate which accumulates in the medium. This also results when the mycelium is macerated. Appreciable quantities of organic P (coenzymes) are also excreted by the actively developing fungus and may be found in the medium. Generally the mineralization is associated with exhaustion of utilizable carbon source, whether the originally supplied source or initially accumulated products such as organic acids, alcohol, etc. Mann observed that hexose phosphates, in particular Cori ester (glucose-1-phosphate) and Embden ester (fructose-6-phosphate) could be utilized by living *Aspergillus niger* mycelium, the P being liberated as inorganic phosphate. The conversion of inorganic P to organic P in the mycelium of this organism was strictly dependent on the presence of oxygen and accompanied oxygen uptake, a feature different from the phosphorylation processes of yeasts and animal tissues.

It seems not unreasonable to assume that the not insignificant amounts of organic phosphates which these organisms synthesize may be, in part at least, the same as those occurring in yeast, bacteria, etc. during carbohydrate dissimilation, i.e., phosphorylated intermediates. However, it remains that available data afford no proof of this, and for this reason conclusions to this effect have been rightly criticized (Nord, 1945). Doubtless bound phosphate as phospholipides and nucleoproteins partially account for the transformations reported. The fact also remains that although methylglyoxal, pyruvic acid and acetaldehyde were isolated during glucose fermentation by *Chaetomium funicola*, the key intermediate in the scheme of phosphorylated sugar fermentation, namely, phosphoglyceric acid, could not be detected (Semeniuk, 1944). This confirms the main facts obtained in Fusaria by Nord and coworkers, and discussed above, and supports his contention.

Another point that Nord makes is that added phosphate donors were assimilated by Fusarium but their presence failed to alter the course of the fermentation. One would expect alteration only if phosphate donors were the limiting factors in the metabolism of the organism, a feature not necessarily existing in any particular strain or in any given conditions. It will be recalled that this approach was useful in relation to cocarboxylase deficiency.

Another point worth mentioning is the observation by Mann (1944) that experiments designed to test the effect of added phosphate donors on the physiological activity of the mold mycelium, may be suspect owing to the possible formation by the organism and presence in the medium of active phosphatases which promptly liberate the P as inorganic P, in which form it then is assimilated. This was shown for *Aspergillus niger* only, but it may invalidate conclusions made in this type of experiment with other organisms unless the enzyme is proved to be absent.

The attitude of workers in the field towards Nord's hypothesis may perhaps be summarized in the words of the enzyme authorities, Sumner and Somers (1947), that, "He presents evidence, largely indirect, which leads him to the conclusion that phosphorylation represents only one path in the course of alcoholic fermentation by living yeast." While this possibility has not been disproved, it must be said that an over-whelming array of incontrovertible evidence exists in favor of phosphorylation. On the other hand, the proof advanced for the non-phosphorylation fermentation cannot as yet be considered unequivocal. Confirmation of Nord's experiments and additional intermediate enzyme chemistry would be valuable support of his views. (See Chapter 15 for non-phosphorylation oxidation of sugars to sugar acids, even in Fusarium.)

REFERENCES

Anderson, A. K. 1924. *Res. Publ. Univ. Minn. Biol. Sci.* **5**, 237–280.

Bail, T. 1857. *Flora* **40**, 417–430, 433–444.

Bernhauer, K., and Thelen, H. 1932. *Biochem. Z.* **253**, 30–36.

Birkinshaw, J. H. 1937. *Biol. Revs. Cambridge Phil. Soc.* **12**, 357–392.

Birkinshaw, J. H., Charles, J. H. V., Raistrick, H., and Stoyle, J. A. R. 1931. *Trans. Roy. Soc. London* **B220**, 93–98.

Chrzaszcz, T., and Tiukow, D. 1930. *Biochem. Z.* **229**, 343–357.

Chrzaszcz, T., Tiukow, D., and Zakamorny, M. 1932. *Biochem. Z.* **250**, 254–269.

Clifton, C. E. 1946. *Advances in Enzymol.* **6**, 269–308.

Dammann, E., Rotini, O. T., and Nord, F. F. 1938. *Biochem. Z.* **297**, 185–202.

Dietrich, K. R., and Klammerth, O. O. L. 1939. *Chem. Ztg.* **63**, 763–766.

Foster, J. W., and Goldman, A. 1948. Unpublished.

Frey, A. 1927. *Rév. gen. botan.* **39**, 277–305.

Goddard, D. R. 1939. *Cold Spring Harbor Symposia Quant. Biol.* **7**, 362–376.

Goepfert, G. J., and Nord, F. F. 1942. *Arch. Biochem.* **1**, 289–301.

Gould, B. S., and Tytell, A. A. 1941. *J. Gen. Physiol.* **24**, 655–667.

Gould, B. S., Tytell, A. A., and Jaffe, H. 1942. *J. Biol. Chem.* **146**, 219–224.

Herzog, R., and Meier, A. 1908. *Z. physiol. Chem.* **57**, 35–42.

Hida, T. 1935. *J. Shanghai Sci. Inst. Ser. IV* **1**, 201–214.

Junitzky, N. 1907. *Ber. deut. botan. ges.* **25**, 210–213.

Karstrom, H. 1938. *Ergeb. Enzymforsch.* **7**, 350–376.

Kluyver, A. J., and Perquin, L. H. C. 1933. *Biochem. Z.* **266**, 68–81.

Kostytschew, S. 1904. *Zentr. Bakt. Parasitenk. Abt II* **13**, 490–503; 577–589.

Kostytschew, S., and Afanassjewa, M. 1921. *Jahrb. wiss. Botan.* **60**, 628–650.

Letcher, H., and Willaman, J. J. 1926. *Phytopathology* **16**, 941–949.

Lipmann, F. 1941. *Advances in Enzymol.* **1**, 99–162.

Lockwood, L. B., Stubbs, J. J., and Senseman, C. E. 1938. *Zentr. Bakt. Parasitenk. Abt II* **98**, 167–171.

Loughran, G. A., Soodak, M., and Nord, F. F. 1944. *Arch. Biochem.* **6**, 163–164.

Mann, T. 1944. *Biochem. J.* **38**, 339–345.

Mazé, P. 1902. *Compt. rend.* **135**, 113–116.

Meyerhof, O. 1945. *J. Biol. Chem.* **157**, 105–119.

Michel-Durand, E. 1938. *Bull. soc. chim. biol.* **20**, 399–412.

Molliard, M. 1924. *Compt. rend.* **178**, 1865–1867.

Nagayama, T. 1921. *Biochem. Z.* **116**, 203–206.

Nord, F. F. 1939. *Ergeb. Enzymforsch.* **8**, 149–185.

Nord, F. F. 1940. *Chem. Revs.* **26**, 423–472.

Nord, F. F. 1945. *Iowa State Coll. J. Sci.* **19**, 225–226.

Nord, F. F., Hofstetter, H., and Dammann, E. 1937. *Biochem. Z.* **293**, 231–255.

Nord, F. F., and Mull, R. P. 1945. *Advances in Enzymol.* **5**, 165–203.

Pasteur, L. 1876. Études sur la Bière. Gauthier-Villars, Paris.

Raistrick, H., Birkinshaw, J. H., Charles, J. H. V., Clutterbuck, P. W., Coyne, F. P., Hetherington, A. C., Lilly, C. H., Rintoul, M. L., Rintoul, W., Robinson, R., Stoyle, J. A. R., Thom, C., and Young, W. 1931. *Trans. Roy. Soc. London* **B220**, 1–367.

Reynolds, E. S. 1926. *Plant Physiol.* **1**, 151–164.

Rippel, A., and Wiangke, H. 1941. *Arch. Mikrobiol.* **12**, 124–127.

Robbins, W. J., and Kavanagh, F. 1938. *Am. J. Botany* **25**, 229–236.

Sakaguchi, T., and Asai, T. 1927. *Bull. Agr. Chem. Soc. Japan* **3**, 87–92.

Sakamura, T. 1930. *J. Faculty Sci. Hokkaido Imp. Univ. Ser. V* **1**, No. 1, pp. 1–27.

Schopfer, W. H. 1935. *Z. Vitaminforsch.* **4**, 187–206.

Schopfer, W. H., and Guilloud, M. 1945. *Z. Vitaminforsch.* **16**, 181–296.

Sciarini, L. J., and Nord, F. F. 1944. *Arch. Biochem.* **5**, 435–443.

Sciarini, L. J., and Wirth, J. C. 1945. *Cereal Chem.* **22**, 11–21.

Semeniuk, G. 1944. *Iowa State Coll. J. Sci.* **18**, 325–358.

Sumner, J. B., and Somers, G. F. 1947. Chemistry and Methods of Enzymes. Academic Press, New York, p. 353.

Suthers, A. J., and Walker, T. K. 1932. *Biochem. J.* **26**, 317–322.

Takahashi, T., and Asai, T. 1928. *Bull. Agr. Chem. Soc. Japan* **4**, 15–18.

Takahashi, T., and Asai, T. 1933a. *Zentr. Bakt. Parasitenk. Abt II* **88**, 276–284.

Takahashi, T., and Asai, T. 1933b. *Bull. Agr. Chem. Soc. Japan* **9**, 443–448.

Tamiya, H. 1928. *Acta Phytochim. Japan* **4**, 77–218.

Tamiya, H., and Miwa, Y. 1928. *Z. Botan.* **21**, 417–432.

Thom, C., and Raper, K. 1945. Manual of the Aspergilli. Williams and Wilkins, Baltimore, 373 pp.

Tomlinson, T. G. 1937. New Phytologist **36**, 418–434.

Tytell, A. A., and Gould, B. S. 1941. *J. Bact.* **42**, 513–526.

Ward, G. E., Lockwood, L. B., Tabenkin, B., and Wells, P. A. 1938. *Ind. Eng. Chem.* **30**, 1233–1235.

Wehmer, C. 1913. *Ber. deut. Botan. Ges.* **31**, 257–268.

White, M. G., and Willaman, J. J. 1928a. *Biochem. J.* **22**, 583–591.

White, M. G., and Willaman, J. J. 1928b. *Biochem. J.* **22**, 592–595.

Wirth, J. C. 1943. Dissertation, Fordham Univ. Cited in Sciarini, L. J., and Nord, F. F. 1943. *Arch. Biochem.* **3**, 261–267.

Wirth, J. C., and Nord, F. F. 1940. *Science* **92**, 15–16.

Wirth, J. C., and Nord, F. F. 1941. *J. Am. Chem. Soc.* **63**, 2855–2856.

Wirth, J. C., and Nord, F. F. 1943. *Arch. Biochem.* **1**, 143–163.

Yamasaki, I. 1930. *Biochem. Z.* **218**, 468–471.

Yuill, J. L. 1928. *Biochem. J.* **22**, 1504–1507.

CHAPTER 10

OXALIC ACID METABOLISM

Oxalic acid occupies a unique situation in the history of mold metabolism since it was the first oxidation product resulting from the aerobic breakdown of carbohydrate found to accumulate in fungus cultures. It was the forerunner of a great variety of oxidation products since discovered to be formed by this group of organisms and to accrue in the medium in amounts representing a very appreciable bulk of the sugar consumed. Stemming from this discovery is the tremendous interest in microbiological products of industrial import, and as well, inquiry into the mechanisms of formation of the various biochemical entities.

Botanists have known for a long time that oxalic acid occurs in various plants and that it is present in higher or fleshy fungus forms. Zellner (1907) gives an account sufficient to indicate that oxalate is of rather widespread occurrence in these organisms. Free oxalic acid occurs in *Boletus sulfureus* and probably *Calvaria flora*. Calcium oxalate is deposited as granules or minute crystals in the membranes of many common fleshy fungi: Agaricus, Lactarius, Russula, Cantharellus, Boletus, Polyporus, Fistularia, Lycerperdon, Lectia and Peziza. Considerable variation in oxalate content was observed with respect to species, strains and age of the organism. De Bary (1887) points out that crystallized oxalate salts in the walls of mycelial strands of *Psalliota campestris* and several other forms is sufficient to give the mycelium a chalky appearance. Sometimes oxalate deposits occur in specialized spherical cells in the stalk and capitum, these cells being entirely filled with crystalline oxalate deposits. De Bary (1886) found potassium oxalate deposits in the sclerotia as well as mycelium of *Peziza sclerotinia*. The press juice of these higher fungi invariably contained oxalate in solution. According to Simo (1939) two types of crystals of sodium oxalate deposit in the mycelium of *Aspergillus niger*, $Na_2C_2O_4$ and $Na_2C_2O_4 \cdot H_2O$. Zopf (1889) reported for the first time the formation of oxalate by a yeast, *Saccharomyces hansenii* n. sp.

It is a rather widespread concept that the German botanist Carl Wehmer discovered oxalic acid formation by filamentous fungi. This is erroneous, for several investigators had observed this before Wehmer, but to Wehmer goes the credit for examining this feature as a physiological process and systematically studying it from every aspect. This research, embodied in a series of papers classical in the field of mold metabolism, and numbering twenty-three separate communications, was published in 1891, and stands today as a pattern for any physiological examination of a fungus. However, Wehmer himself points out that several investigators before him, notably De Bary (1886), had observed the formation of oxalic acid salts by filamentous fungi and even identified this as a consequence of incomplete combustion of the carbohydrate in the medium, a concept with which Wehmer later concurred.

WEHMER'S CONTRIBUTIONS

From the standpoint of general mold biochemistry and physiology, Wehmer's basic contribution through his researches on oxalate formation by fungi was this: according to the cultural conditions imposed on an organism, its physiological response may vary enormously (Wehmer, 1892). Thus the need for systematic study of factors influencing any particular biochemical feature with the object of being able to exercise rigorous control over it, and, as well, to aid in elucidating other aspects, such as mechanisms. Wehmer revealed that it is not so much the amount of growth a fungus makes, but the physiological potentialities, or, as we known it today, the enzyme makeup of the cell material which is responsible for the effects, and that the same organism has the potentialities for exhibiting radical extremes in metabolism.

Wehmer's interest in oxalate formation by fungi stemmed from his studies on the excretion of this substance by certain higher plants. Although working mainly with *Aspergillus niger* and *Penicillium glaucum*, he extended his findings to several other fungi, viz.: *Peziza sclerotiorum*, *Peziza fuckeliana* (*Botrytis cinerea*), *Mucor stolonifer* (*Rhizopus nigricans*), *Aspergillus glaucus*, *Phycomyces nitens*, *Pilobilus crystallinus*, and *Mucor mucedo*. The results obtained in these extensive studies are too numerous to cover in detail here, but the main conclusions will be summarized.

1. The amount of oxalate formed depends upon the amount of substrate decomposed and continues to accumulate as long as the organism is alive and has available carbohydrate. The increase may continue for as long as 200 or more days.

2. Light decomposes oxalate spontaneously, especially in the presence of certain metals such as iron, but neither light nor iron affects the formation or further destruction of oxalate by the fungus itself. (See also Wehmer, 1891c.)

3. Oxalate may be formed in high yields from diverse substrates like carbohydrates, acetate, tartrate, malate, citrate, glycerol and peptone, the amounts being proportional to the amount of substrate consumed. Rather high sugar concentrations are optimal, i.e., about 10 per cent.

4. The most critical single factor in oxalate formation is the presence

of free base (cations) to form oxalate salts, which then accumulate in the medium. Thus the presence of alkaline neutralizing agents such as $CaCO_3$, $Ca_3(PO_4)_2$ and Na_2HPO_4 are conducive to maximum yields of oxalate. Prevalence of acid conditions, such as by initial acidification of the medium with mineral acids, and absence of neutralizing agents, never allows accumulation of oxalate, even in traces. It should be recorded that De Bary (1886) had previously observed that the presence of calcium leads to more oxalate formation, but the full significance of this observation apparently was not grasped by him.

5. Consequently, the source of nitrogen is a critical factor in this process: inorganic nitrogen salts giving rise to physiological acidity as a result of cation consumption, i.e., NH_4Cl and $(NH_4)_2SO_4$ never allow formation of oxalic acid. Insofar as one can exclude the existence or formation of free base in the medium, one can exclude oxalic acid formation. Nitrogen sources conducive to physiological alkalinity allow accumulation of oxalate as salts of corresponding cations. Included here are $Ca(NO_3)_2$, KNO_3, $NaNO_3$, NH_4NO_3, $(NH_4)_2HPO_4$, and peptone. The effectiveness of peptone is ascribed to liberation of NH_4^+. These salts vary in the degree to which they accumulate oxalate, presumably on account of different degrees of residual basicity.

6. Oxalate accumulation is considered to be the result of a fixation as a salt of the free oxalic acid occurring always in the normal metabolism of the fungi, but, which in the absence of base, is quickly decomposed further by the organism so that it can never be detected in more than traces. As a salt, oxalate is immune to mold attack, and thereby accrues in the medium.

7. Titration studies show that some free oxalic acid may exist in small amounts i͟n cultures containing oxalate salts. Thus, in NH_4NO_3 cultures all the oxalate is as free acid and is all eventually destroyed by the mold upon prolonged incubation, because it is free acid, with KNO_3 or $NaNO_3$ part is free acid, part salt. With $Ca(NO_3)_2$, $(NH_4)_2HPO_4$ or alkaline salts the oxalate exists only as salt. Thus, in one experiment in KNO_3 medium containing 7.5 per cent dextrose, 1.961 g. free oxalic acid and 0.791 oxalate salt were present. There was further decomposition only of the free oxalic acid in this experiment. Modern knowledge makes it quite likely that the important factor here is the pH of the medium. Oxalate molecules can be attacked only when in the undissociated state, i.e., free acid, doubtless because only in this state is the cell membrane permeable to it.

8. Different fungi behave differently regarding the accumulation of free oxalic acid, but all behave alike with respect to oxalate salts.

9. Free oxalic acid added to a culture fluid is rapidly destroyed by the fungi, whereas added salts are not. Soluble oxalates added to the

medium up to 7 per cent concentration are without effect on the formation and accumulation of extra oxalate from sugar in presence of base. However, it has been observed that only 1.3 per cent free oxalic acid suppresses further production from glucose (Allsopp, 1937).

10. Optimum growth temperature for *Penicillium glaucum* was 37°C., which was least favorable for oxalate formation, owing to the high rate of oxalate consumption by the organism at that temperature. Highest yields of oxalate were obtained at temperatures just above the minimum for growth, i.e., 8–10°C. (Wehmer, 1891b). The temperature effect pertains only to free oxalic acid, no differences being observed when the acid is rendered unavailable to the fungus as rapidly as it is formed from sugar, as for example, by fixation with soluble or insoluble alkalies such as NH_4^+ or $CaCO_3$.

11. Particularly high yields of oxalate may be obtained from tartrate and from peptone. Thus from 20 g. ammonium tartrate (in NH_4NO_3 medium) were formed in 107 days 15.46 g. oxalate and 0.53 g. mycelium (dry weight). From 3 g. peptone as sole source of carbon .712 g. oxalate was formed, and from 5 g., was formed 2.02 g. oxalate (NH_4NO_3 medium). The oxalate was considered to arise from the tartrate by simple split into two C_2 fragments and oxidation to oxalate. Excess NH_4^+ must be present. No mechanism is offered for the exceptionally high yields of oxalate from the heterogeneous substance peptone. It may, incidentally, be observed that all Wehmer's experiments lasted for extremely long periods as judged by current mold research, from 20 to 244 days. Doubtless autolysis is a factor that, to some extent, must be taken into account relative to mycelial weights.

12. Oxalate formation may be considered as an intermediate in the metabolism of sugar by fungi and is therefore a product of incomplete sugar oxidation (Verbrennung). From the standpoint of energetics and cell synthesis it means little to the organism, as oxalic acid is so nearly the endpoint of complete oxidation that its further utilization by the organism entails little advantage. For example, the fact that a fungus accumulates large amounts of oxalate, or none at all, from a given amount of sugar has no significant effect on the amount of cell material the organism synthesizes concomitantly, owing to the fact that the calorific content of the oxalate is a small per cent of the sugar consumed (see below). Thus, *A. niger* was cultivated in the absence and in presence of excess base to secure extremes in oxalate accumulation, which are evident in the following tabulation. Yet, despite these great deviations the mycelial synthesis was, if anything, less where none or little carbohydrate was diverted to oxalate.

In considering the high weight yields of oxalate (as salt) from carbohydrate it is well to keep in mind that the compound is a highly oxygenated one and that ample consumption of molecular oxygen is involved in the production of such high weight yields of oxalate. As high as 70 per cent weight conversion on basis of anhydrous free acid was obtained in some experiments. Calculated on the basis of molar equivalents of carbon from the consumed sugar, the yields are quite reasonable.

FROM 1.5 G. GLUCOSE

No neutralizing agent			Ca phosphate (5–15 per cent)		
Mold wt., g.	Oxalate, g.	Age, days	Mold wt., g.	Oxalate, g.	Age, days
0.120	0.070	16	.250	0.950	9
.252	.072	17	.220	1.520	23
.185	.170	23	.268	2.033	39
.225	.278	37	.358	1.310	78
.298	.267	66	.287	1.050	82
.250	0	86	.272	1.140	89
.282	0	97	.341	1.160	92
.238	.014	175	.380	0.829	97

13. Analyzing further the energy implications for the organism relative to oxalic acid formation, Wehmer concluded that the caloric content of oxalate is small with respect to the carbohydrate consumed in the genesis of that oxalate, and, therefore, further consumption of that intermediate or not was without significant influence on cell synthesis. By this line of reasoning, from substrates whose caloric content is smaller than carbohydrate, and such that the oxalate caloric content may amount to a significant percentage of these substrates consumed in the genesis of the oxalate, it would be expected that the accumulation or lack of accumulation of oxalate would not be without significant effect on the energetics of the system, manifesting itself in the efficiency of cell synthesis.

In a fine example of one of the early real physiological studies on mold metabolism Wehmer was able to prove this point. Following is the caloric content of several commonly used organic substrates for fungi, as given by Wehmer.

	Cal./g. Mol.
Oxalic acid	60
Formic acid	70
Acetic acid	199.4
Tartaric acid	211
Citric acid	486
Glycerol	392.5
Glucose	705

It is evident that oxalic acid is quite small compared to glucose. It becomes significant in relation to tartrate and citrate, and, according to the above hypothesis, any accumulation of oxalate during consumption of these acids as substrates ought to deprive the organism of significant amounts of energy (and carbon).   In other words, oxalate formation in such cases would be at the expense of cell synthesis, where with sugar it would not.   The following data offer striking confirmation of this idea. Oxalate was induced to accumulate by furnishing a base in the form of the ammonium salt of the acid.   Consumption of the free tartaric and citric acid resulted in no oxalate formation.   Clear cut disparities in mycelial weight were obtained, in every case greatly in favor of those cultures producing no oxalate.   (See also Jaquot, 1938b.)

50 ml. culture solution					
1.5 g. tartaric acid			1.5 g. K(NH$_4$) tartrate		
Mold wt.	Oxalate	Age	Mold wt.	Oxalate	Age
(g.)	(g.)	(days)	(g.)	(g.)	(days)
.110	0	27	0.030	0.767	34
.075	0	41	.040	.525	70
.155	0	42	.048	.760	116
.165	0	72	.032	.550	46
.105	0	72	.767		
1.5 g. citric acid			1.5 g. (NH$_4$)$_3$ citrate		
.240	0	101	.056	.390	86

TRAPPING EFFECT OF FREE BASE

With few exceptions Wehmer's conclusions on the oxalic acid process have stood the test of time.   In certain respects his results have been extended.   For example, Wehmer believed that *Aspergillus niger* was the only organism capable of carrying out a true oxalic acid "fermentation" for, despite formation of some oxalate by the other organisms mentioned above, only *A. niger* accumulated it in large amounts, and under certain conditions, as the free acid.   Sometime later it was shown (Currie and Thom, 1915) that the ability to produce oxalate was widespread among the Penicillia, since all twenty-three strains tested formed some oxalate.   Several produced free oxalic acid in the absence of neutralizing agent and hence come under Wehmer's "fermentation" category.   One species, the now well-known *P. oxalicum*, was outstanding and produced up to 0.8 per cent solution of free oxalic acid out of total of more than 1 per cent oxalate.   The ubiquity of oxalic acid in Penicillium cultures led these authors to consider it as common or typical a Penicillium metabolic product as lactic acid is among the bacteria. Since that time oxalate formation has been shown to be a property of many and diverse species of fungi.

Beyond a doubt discrepancies between later workers and Wehmer may be ascribed to strain specificity, a feature which the latter author failed to detect because he worked with only one strain of *A. niger*. While others (Currie, 1917) have shown that other strains of *A. niger* did, contrary to Wehmer's strain, give substantial amounts of free oxalic acid from glucose solutions acidified with mineral acid, the main implications of Wehmer's observation that alkaline cations fix or trap oxalate, thus enabling it to accumulate, have never been disputed. Much larger amounts of oxalate accumulate in the presence of an alkaline trap than in its absence. Similar conflicting metabolic results presumably due to strain specificity have been reported relative to the ability to form oxalate from salts of various organic acids such as formate, lactate, tartrate, glycolate, glyoxylate, etc. *Sclerotium delphinii* accumulates sufficient free oxalic acid to lower the pH of the medium to 1.5; production of oxalate was enhanced in the presence of $CaCO_3$ as a neutralizing agent (Perlman, 1948).

Raistrick and Clark (1919) disputed Wehmer's emphasis of significance of the inorganic nitrogen source based on their own results in which they allowed *A. niger* to act on sodium acetate with four different sources of inorganic nitrogen [NH_4Cl, $(NH_4)H_2PO_4$, NH_4Cl, $(NH_4)_2SO_4$] and obtained about 40 per cent weight yield of oxalate irrespective of the nature of the nitrogen source. However, their experiment was radically different from Wehmer's: the latter got differences because physiological alkalinity resulting from nitrate consumption was sufficient to trap considerable oxalic acid formed from the neutral carbohydrate. On the other hand, with ammonium nitrogen salts, the acidic anion accumulated during cation consumption resulting in appreciable lowering of pH sufficient to prevent accumulation of oxalate. (See also Jaquot, 1938a.) The experiments of Raistrick and Clark could hardly be considered comparable, for in each case sodium acetate was the sole source of carbon. Consumption of the acid would lead to physiological alkalinity far in excess of the acidity that could result from ammonia consumption, hence oxalate would be trapped uniformly regardless of source of nitrogen.

Furthermore Raistrick and Clark's assertion that the ammonium ion consumption by an organism is so small that it could hardly cause appreciable pH lowering by accumulation of anion acidity, seems at variance with experiences generally encountered in mold metabolism where, in the absence of buffering agent, very slight growth of many organisms already leads to enough acidity to inhibit further growth, and in cases where organic acids are absent. A very small amount of free HCl or H_2SO_4 generated from the corresponding ammonium salts causes a sharp lowering of the pH in unbuffered solutions owing to the fact that these are strong acids.

PRACTICAL ASPECTS

It was early recognized that, notwithstanding the attractively high yields of oxalate obtainable from a concentrated carbohydrate solution under controlled conditions, such a biological process could not compete with modern chemical methods for manufacture of this valuable industrial chemical. It is possible to obtain 70–90 per cent weight conversion yields from carbohydrate, but the time factor, overhead, and, particularly, contamination problems incident to the conduct of this process at neutral or slightly alkaline reactions rule out commercial feasibility. Nevertheless, Wehmer apparently had hopes for this process, for patents covering it were issued to him. Oxalic acid may be manufactured commercially by two methods: by alkali fusion of cheap cellulose materials such as sawdust or substances containing the grouping —CHOHCHOH—, or by heating sodium formate in the presence of NaOH or Na_2CO_3 yielding sodium oxalate (Fieser and Fieser, 1946):

$$\left.\begin{array}{l} \text{H}\,\text{COONa} \\ \text{H}\,\text{COONa} \end{array}\right. \xrightarrow{\;360°\;} \left.\begin{array}{l} \text{COONa} \\ \\ \text{COONa} \end{array}\right| + H_2$$

This reaction may be recognized as a chemical dehydrogenation of two moles of formate yielding oxalate, and is of particular interest because, as will be shown later, evidence has been provided for the origin of oxalate from formate by *A. niger*, presumably by the same dehydrogenation reaction only carried out enzymatically. Current market price of oxalic acid is $13\frac{1}{2}$ cents per lb., a figure probably 50 per cent lower than that indicated for the biological production, based on cost estimates typical of modern industrial fermentations.

In any consideration of potential industrial aspects of microbiological oxalate it would be remiss to overlook the fact that the strictly academic finding made by Wehmer apropos the suppressive effect of high acidity (low pH*) on oxalate accumulation is one of the main foundations for the success of the mold citric acid industry. The direct favorable effects of the low pH on the formation and technology of citric acid production are discussed in Chapter 12, but it is appropriate to bring out that if oxalate were formed at the expense of citrate, as it generally is at higher

---

* Soerenson's concept of pH had not yet been formulated.

pH's, the yields of citrate might be sufficiently lowered to raise the cost of mold citric acid to a point where citric acid from the citrus fruit industry easily compete on a cost basis, and might even be cheaper than mold citric acid. This development arose particularly from the work of Currie (1917), who showed that Aspergilli producing a mixture of oxalic and citric acids could be made to produce citric acid exclusively if the cultivation is done at pH 2 to 3.

MECHANISM OF OXALIC ACID PRODUCTION BY FUNGI

SPLITTING OF HEXOSE CARBON CHAIN

Because *Aspergillus niger* strains are generally the most potent oxalic acid producers, studies on mechanisms and intermediary oxalate precursors have been confined almost exclusively to this organism. Available information falls logically into two sections: formation from carbohydrate or allied substances and formation from peptone and nitrogenous substances. The latter aspect has been almost entirely neglected.

It is well established that, for this process, like almost all other similar biochemical activities of fungi, many different carbohydrates and allied substances can give rise to oxalate after attack by *A. niger* and *Penicillium oxalicum* in the presence of alkali. This is in keeping with the generally recognized omnivorous nature of these organisms. Among such substances reported to yield oxalate are polysaccharides, hexoses, pentoses and trioses: starch, lactose, glucose, galactose, fructose, arabinose, xylose and glycerol. Such diverse substrates can only mean that intermediary products common to all, and ultimately yielding oxalate, originate from each substrate. Except for this generalization, however, data of this kind furnish no information as to mechanisms.

The next class of compounds, namely, organic acids, has given valuable information pertaining to possible mechanisms and precursors, but unfortunately, instead of incriminating any single mechanism or set of precursors, a number of contradictory possibilities, none of which is certain yet, have been provided. In general, the technique here has been either to allow the organism to grow on the particular compounds, or more generally, to furnish the substance to washed preformed mycelium.

Ever since the first experiments on mechanism of oxalate formation done in 1919 by Raistrick and Clark, acetic acid has been implicated as a precursor by many authors. Actually Currie, in 1917, observing that initially formed citric acid in *A. niger* cultures tended to disappear with concomitant formation of oxalate, hypothesized citrate as an intermediate between glucose and oxalate, but this was largely a speculation, with no supporting evidence. This will be discussed later. Raistrick and Clark tested the ammonium salts of nineteen different organic acids in growth experiments lasting 25–38 days, and found significant oxalate formation, amounting to 40 to 50 per cent weight yield on basis of substrate furnished, in only four cases: succinate, malate, fumarate, and acetate. Only small amounts of traces were observed in tartaric, maleic, pyruvic, glyceric, and glycolic acid media, whereas none occurred in the others, despite good growth in some cases. Failure to obtain oxalate from the C_3-acids led these authors to preclude the usual glucose split to triose, and instead they proposed a hydrolytic $C_4 + C_2$ split of the labilized hexose molecule yielding acetic acid directly; the C_4 would become oxalacetic acid which was believed to yield oxalate by direct hydrolytic fission. The acetic acid in these reactions was considered to be oxidized to oxalate, the mechanism being unspecified. The reactions were visualized as follows on the basis of analogy with organic chemical reactions, an unnecessary argument inasmuch as enzymes eliminate the need for such reasoning. Considerable importance is attached to the fissionability of polyketide compounds (containing —$CH_2.CO$—) in keto-enol equilibrium.

$$
\begin{array}{lllll}
CH_2OH & CH_2OH & COOH & COOH & COOH \\
HOCH & C(OH) & C(OH) & C(OH)\ \ O & COOH \\
HOCH & CH & CH & CH\ \ \ H_2 & CH_3 \quad COOH \\
HCOH & C(OH) & C(OH)\ \ O & COOH & COOH \quad COOH \\
HOCH & CH & CH\ \ H_2 & CH_3 & COOH \\
CHO & CHO & COOH & COOH & COOH \\
 & COOH & & & \\
 & CO & & & \\
 & CH_2 & & & \\
 & CO & & & \\
 & CH_2 & & & \\
 & COOH & & &
\end{array}
$$

As a corollary to this hypothesis the high yields obtained from the C_4-dicarboxylic acids were explained on the basis of conversion of each to the key intermediate oxalacetic acid:

$$
\begin{array}{ll}
\text{Succinic acid} \searrow & COOH \quad COOH \quad COOH \\
\text{Fumaric acid} \rightarrow & CH_2 \quad\ \ CH_3 \quad\ \ COOH \\
\text{Malic acid} \rightarrow & CO \quad\ \ \ COOH \\
\text{Tartaric acid} \nearrow & COOH \quad COOH
\end{array}
$$

Oxalacetic acid

Thus two key intermediates were proposed: (a) oxalacetic acid (enol form) and (b) acetic acid. Curiously enough, oxalacetic acid itself was not tested nor was any interpretation for the conversion of acetate to oxalate provided. Acetate could not be detected in carbohydrate cultures and this was considered understandable on the strength of the fact that Pfeffer (1895) had shown that acetate is utilized preferentially to glucose in a mixture, hence none would accumulate.

Aside from forming a basis for future workers, the evidence furnished for the above schemes is non-critical, and actually there is no evidence whatsoever for the C_4—C_2 sugar split. Recently, interest in a possible C_4—C_2 split of the hexose molecule was revived by Allsopp (1937) after a rather extensive series of tests in which preformed $A.$ $niger$ pellicles were allowed to act on a variety of substances, with special reference to the C_4-dicarboxylic acids that figured so prominently in Raistrick and Clark's work. Oxalacetic acid in particular was studied as free acid and as sodium salt, with insignificant yields of oxalic acid in both cases, and in addition, previous studies whereby oxalate was formed abundantly from succinate and malate could not be confirmed. Inasmuch as the strain of $A.$ $niger$ employed formed free oxalic acid from glucose under acid conditions, the possible precursors in the form of free acid were expected to be converted to oxalic acid, but neither the free nor the salt forms of these acids yielded oxalate. Of all the acids tested, only gluconic acid yielded oxalic acid when present as the free acid; in addition, glucose, fructose, galactose, arabinose, and xylose also yielded oxalic acid. The gluconic acid is of special interest because in different experiments about 0.4 mole of oxalic acid was formed per mole of gluconic acid metabolized. This, plus the fact that oxalate formation was directly proportional to the utilization of gluconate, which itself under the conditions of these experiments was the only substance aside from sugars yielding significant oxalic acid, led to the designation of gluconic acid as a likely intermediate in oxalate formation from glucose. After rejecting all other possibilities on the basis of his own negative experiments with them, Allsopp concluded that oxalic acid probably is formed by oxidation of the two end carbon atoms of molecules with at least five carbon atoms in the chain. Thus the acid would be expected to arise from compounds of the types

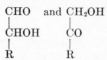

where R contains at least three carbon atoms. These compounds would be oxidized to the keto acid followed by hydrolysis yielding oxalic acid and a compound RH:

$$
\begin{array}{ccc}
\text{COOH} & & \text{COOH} \\
| & & | \\
\text{CO} & + \text{OH} \rightarrow & \text{COOH} \\
| & | & + \\
\text{R} & \text{H} & \text{RH}
\end{array}
$$

or, in the case of glucose

$$
\begin{array}{cccc}
\text{CHO} & \text{COOH} & \text{COOH} & \text{COOH} \\
| & | & | & | \\
\text{CHOH} & \text{CHOH} & \text{CO} & \text{COOH} \\
| & | & |\text{------} \text{OH} + & | \\
\text{CHOH} & \text{CHOH} & \text{CHOH} & \text{CH}_2\text{OH} \\
| & | & + \text{H} & | \\
\text{CHOH} \rightarrow & \text{CHOH} \rightarrow & \text{CHOH} \longrightarrow & \text{CHOH} \\
| & | & | & | \\
\text{CHOH} & \text{CHOH} & \text{CHOH} & \text{CHOH} \\
| & | & | & | \\
\text{CH}_2\text{OH} & \text{CH}_2\text{OH} & \text{CH}_2\text{OH} & \text{CH}_2\text{OH} \\
\text{Glucose} & \text{Gluconic} & \text{Fructuronic acid} & \text{Erythritol} \\
 & \text{acid} & \text{(2-ketogluconic acid)} &
\end{array}
$$

The erythritol was not detected, and indeed, a valuable support for this novel theory is lacking owing to failure to test 2-ketogluconic acid as the supposed precursor undergoing hydrolysis. In fact, the only evidence for this mechanism is by analogy: *A. niger* strains (not this one) are known to oxidize glucose to gluconic acid and a parallel for the conversion of gluconic acid into 2-ketogluconic acid is afforded by the formation of glucosone from glucose by another *A. niger* strain (Walker, 1932).

Even if this is the origin of oxalate from gluconate, it obviously does not necessarily follow that gluconic acid is the intermediate from sugar, nor from the host of other substances of smaller molecular weight from which oxalic acid undeniably may be produced. In fact, the variety is so great, and many of them are such small molecular weight compounds, that the most likely precursor prospect appears to be some simple compound formed in common from the many different sources. It would appear that the abundant formation of oxalate from acetate, C_4-dicarboxylic acids, and other substances should not be overlooked by an author in formulating his hypothesis. It would seem that any hypothesis would have to accommodate and fit *all* the facts bearing on the process, not just selected ones. As brought out in Chapter 4 a great deal of the inconsistencies in this type of work may well be due to strain specificity in relation to the manner of disposal of the provided organic acids by the processes of oxidative assimilation and respiration, particularly in the absence of a carbohydrate. Failure to have one main physiological situation thoroughly defined in all these systems, namely, the simultaneous processes of assimilation and respiration, allows the different fungus strains to manifest the wide extremes of their physiological strain specificity.

The possible importance of competitive reactions influencing the production of oxalic acid is to be had from other experiments of Allsopp. The presence of certain organic acids, in themselves inocuous to growth, inhibited the formation of oxalic acid from glucose. Lactic acid was most striking in this respect, and pyruvic acid less so; other acids e.g., malic, citric, and glycolic, had little effect. A glucose and lactic acid solution in 4:1 ratio yielded only $\frac{1}{5}$ the quantity of oxalate as glucose solution alone; with pyruvate the figure was about two-thirds. The lactic acid was quite actively consumed and hence it is logical to assume that it or its intermediary oxidation products compete successfully for the enzyme systems metabolizing oxalic acid precursors originating from carbohydrate. After the inhibitor acid is consumed, the rate of oxalate formation tends to be restored. It would be interesting to ascertain if the lactic acid was inhibiting glucose utilization, and if not that, the fate of the carbohydrate portion ordinarily going to oxalate. In any case, this is an interesting example of the thesis mentioned above, and described in Chapter 4, to the effect that balances exist between acid-forming enzyme mechanisms in the cell.

Allsopp always obtained small amounts of oxalic acid from mycelium incubated on distilled water, the interpretation being that the oxalate originated from intracellular glycogen, even in mycelium starved for several days. In view of the fact that a fairly constant maximum concentration of oxalic acid was reached followed by slow decline in various experiments, and that this was not exceeded even though excess sugar was available, an equilibrium was considered to exist between the formation and breakdown of oxalic acid pictured as follows:

$$\text{Glycogen} \rightleftarrows \text{Glucose} \rightleftarrows \text{Oxalic acid} \rightarrow CO_2$$

Again, direct evidence for this equilibrium is lacking; it is entirely conceivable that accumulated free oxalic acid manifests a direct cellular toxicity, similar to many acids in the undissociated state, thus retarding the forward rate of the reaction from glucose, and accounting for the limiting maximum obtained. Strong evidence for this is provided by Jaquot's (1938a) experiments in which $0.04\ N$ free oxalic acid strongly inhibited the respiration of A. niger mycelium, sodium oxalate being inactive. In view of the remarkable tolerance of A. niger to high hydrogen ion concentrations, this explanation is inadequate to account for the observed inhibition.

That the undissociated form of the acid, namely, free oxalic acid, is the physiologically active form of the compound as contrasted to oxalate ion, is supported by the experiment of Nord and Vitucci (1947) in which the wood destroying fungus Merulius niveus could utilize the oxalate ion in the form of the free acid but not in the form of sodium oxalate.

It is of interest to note that the only other serious proposal for a C_4—C_2 split of the hexose molecule, namely, to account for the formation of succinic acid and alcohol and acetic acid by coliform bacteria (Virtanen, 1934) was at once rendered untenable by the Wood-Werkman discovery of CO_2 fixation with pyruvic acid to yield C_4-dicarboxylic acids, and that generally succinic acid in microbial metabolism originates in this way.

ACETIC ACID

The bulk of evidence available today places this acid in a key position in the formation of oxalic acid from sugars, owing to the fact that, added to fungus cultures, this substance generally results in rather high conversion yields of oxalic acid in the presence of alkali trap, in several instances making from 40 to 70 per cent weight conversion yield. In certain cases 93 to 100 per cent yields of oxalate on the basis of acetate consumed have been reported (Butkewitsch and Federoff, 1930a, b; Bernhauer and Slanina, 1934b). Although the argument has been advanced that acetic acid is not encountered as a product of fungus metabolism, it must be remembered that traces or small amounts of volatile acidity can almost always be recovered from such cultures, and that the extremely high rate of assimilability of this compound by fungi in general would preclude its accumulation in more than minor amounts. As a matter of fact, appreciable quantities of acetate are present intracellularly in *A. niger* metabolizing glucose, even though none is present in the medium (Chughtai *et al.*, 1947). The numerous physiological fates possible for this compound, and the central role ascribed to it in mold metabolism (Bennet-Clark, 1933) make this fact easily understandable.

The central role of acetate in the di- and tricarboxylic acid metabolism of fungi was first proposed by the Polish workers Chrzaszcz and Tiukow in 1930, and, with various modifications, has since then gained general credence. Perhaps the most decisive evidence implicating the C_2-acid, or rather acetaldehyde, its precursor, in the formation of oxalic acid from sugar is that of Bernhauer and Thelen (1932) showing that acetaldehyde can be trapped by bisulfite during carbohydrate utilization, resulting in greatly reduced yields of oxalic acid as compared to control cultures of *A. niger*. However, any discussion on this point must keep in mind the evidence to the contrary, and also alternative evidence such as that presented in the preceding section. Notwithstanding the fact that acetate may not be the precursor of oxalate from *sugars*, it is an established fact that this acid is formed in appreciable yields from acetate and this mechanism must be examined. Several different proposals exist for this relatively simple conversion.

1. GLYCOLIC-GLYOXYLIC ACID THEORY

The direct conversion of acetate to oxalate would be by oxidation via these two acids:

$$\begin{array}{cccc}
\text{CH}_3 & \text{CH}_2\text{OH} & \text{CHO} & \text{COOH} \\
| & | & | & | \\
\text{COOH} & \text{COOH} & \text{COOH} & \text{COOH} \\
 & \text{Glycolic} & \text{Glyoxylic} & \\
 & \text{acid} & \text{acid} &
\end{array}$$

Both of these intermediate acids have been detected in *A. niger* cultures utilizing acetate (Bernhauer and Scheuer, 1932); in one case 5.7 g. glycolic acid was isolated from a culture furnished with 60 g. calcium acetate (Challenger *et al.*, 1927; Walker *et al.*, 1927). Glycolate could also be converted in small yield to glyoxylic acid (Walker *et al.*, 1927). Thus, there is no question that acetate can be oxidized to these substances. The important question is whether the formation of these acids is the main pathway in sugar or acetate metabolism, or whether they are incidental oxidation reactions through which only a small portion of the acetate is metabolized, the bulk going to oxalate via another route. It is well established that glycolate yields oxalic acid, but on the other hand glycolate has failed to yield oxalate under conditions where the latter is formed abundantly from sugar and other substances, indicating, though not proving, that glycolate is not necessarily the immediate precursor of oxalate formed in these cases (Bernhauer and Slanina, 1934b; Raistrick and Clark, 1919; Bennett-Clark and La Touche, 1935; Allsopp, 1937; Bernhauer and Scheuer, 1932).

Formation of a product in small yields is, in general, weak evidence for identity of any substance as a precursor. Particularly is this true of oxalate, which can originate in small amounts from intracellular materials provided an alkaline trap is present, as it would be when the salt of an organic acid is being tested. As will be shown below, a mold pad may form oxalate in the complete absence of added organic compounds provided the aqueous replacement solution is alkaline.

Failure to obtain oxalic acid from any suspected precursor, including glycolic and glyoxylic acids, might be ascribed to a faster rate of consumption of the oxalic acid than its formation, but in the presence of trapping agents, used in most experiments, this argument is not valid; further consumption of the acid could not occur, hence absence of oxalate means it was not formed at all. One could, however, hypothesize that the free acid might be consumed *in situ* before it is bound by a neutralizing agent, but control experiments could determine this.

With their strain of *A. niger*, Bennet-Clark and La Touche (1935) have ruled out the possibility of glycolic acid as a precursor from hexose because, although it is rapidly consumed by the mycelium, it does not form any oxalate. Nor is it presumably broken down past oxalate via oxidation as no CO_2 is formed in excess of the endogenous rate. These experiments were done in the absence of neutralizing agents and the titratable acidity of the culture fluid decreased, eliminating the possibility of the formation of C_4-dicarboxylic acids or citric acids. Thus, by all available criteria, the glycolate was not oxidized at all; as shown elsewhere (Chapter 12), a reduction to glycolaldehyde is considered to occur, followed by polymerization to intracellular carbohydrate.

This behavior is so anomalous that one wonders if the endogenous CO_2 evolved was actually derived from the breakdown of the added organic acids. The smaller than theoretical amounts of CO_2 liberated might have been due to oxidative assimilation of a good portion of the substrate. That oxidative assimilation can be quantitatively a significant factor in this type of experiment was demonstrated by Bernhauer and Slanina (1934a) who poisoned the assimilation of various organic acids in replacement cultures by means of iodoacetate. Thus, from assimilation, washed mold pads showed 100–115 per cent increase in dry weight, whereas in parallel cultures with 0.001 *M* iodoacetate the increase was cut to 5 to 10 per cent. Unfortunately it is not clear whether the rates of utilization of substrate were identical in both cases. Incidentally, the formation of oxalic acid was the same, irrespective of the presence or absence of the poisons. The accumulation of unidentified reducing substances in the poisoned cultures might have been due to pyruvic acid. Possible fallacies in this concept are discussed in detail in Chapter 12.

Bernhauer (1939) and coworkers have studied this C_2 system in greatest detail, and their work emphasizes the tremendous variation among different strains of one species (*A. niger*) and at the same time makes evident the cause of the divergent results of different workers who concentrated on a single strain. It also is a typical instance of how all the available evidence is irreconcilable to any one theory. Out of twenty-six strains tested on sodium acetate solutions, twelve gave from 23–53 per cent weight conversion to oxalic acid, eight gave lower yields, and six formed no oxalic acid at all. Forty per cent of these cultures gave varying degrees of positive qualitative tests for the presence of glycolic acid, while the remainder gave no test. Similarly, glyoxylic acid could be detected in eighteen, and not in the remaining eight. However, the three strains giving the highest oxalate yields from acetate produced only small amounts from glycolate as the sole carbon source. One strain yielded more oxalate from succinate than from acetate.

Evidence of this kind prejudiced Bernhauer and Scheuer against the glycolic-glyoxylic mechanism. However, in a later paper (Bernhauer and Slanina, 1934b) both the C_2 and C_4 systems are incorporated into one theory in which it is deemed probable that the C_4 acids are broken down via glyoxylic acid. Principal evidence in favor of this statement is that certain *A. niger* strains in replacement cultures gave from 60 to 77.6 per cent weight yields of oxalate from each of succinic, fumaric, glycolic, and acetic acids. Added support for this idea may be had from the finding that glycolic acid is formed in cultures producing oxalate from fumarate (Chrzaszcz and Zakomorny, 1933, see below). In view of its close chemical relation to acetate one might expect that ethyl alcohol, too, would be converted to oxalate, and this has been shown to be the case with several different *A. niger* strains (Bernhauer and Böckl, 1932) and with *Mucor stolonifer* (Butkewitsch and Federoff 1930b).

To summarize views on the glycolate theory, the presence of this and glyoxylate in acetate cultures would be a remarkable coincidence if they did not originate from acetate. The high yields of oxalate obtainable in some cases from glycolate makes it very likely a direct efficient conversion is possible. Yet the totally negative comparative results of other workers, low conversion yields in other cases, rate considerations, and strain specificity differences make it unlikely that the general pathway of oxalate formation from sugars proceeds via this route. Glycolate has never been detected in sugar cultures.

2. ACETATE CONDENSATION

The frequent association of high oxalate yields from C_4-dicarboxylic acids by organisms capable of high oxalate yields from acetate has brought into serious consideration the view first based on Raistrick and Clark's idea that oxalic acid is formed by a hydrolytic split of oxalacetic acid, the latter resulting from a C_4—C_2 split of carbohydrate. Today the oxalacetate is considered to arise from acetate undergoing a Thunberg-Wieland condensation yielding succinate, which, in turn, passes through the C_4-dicarboxylic acid system, eventually ending as the oxalacetate that undergoes hydrolysis to oxalate and acetate.

```
 COOH       COOH        COOH        COOH        COOH      COOH
  |          |           |           |           |         |
 CH3   -2H  CH2   -2H   CH   +HOH   CHOH   -2H   CO    OH  COOH
       →     |    →     ||    →      |      →    --|--------|---  +
 CH3        CH2         CH          CH2         CH2    O   CH3
  |          |           |           |           |         |
 COOH       COOH        COOH        COOH        COOH      COOH
           Succinic    Fumaric      Malic      Oxalacetic
             acid        acid        acid         acid
```

Failure of various workers to obtain oxalate from glycolic and glyoxylic acid, as well as C_3-acids, under conditions where about 40 per cent oxalate yields from acetate, succinate, malate, and fumarate were obtained, led almost by a process of elimination to the conclusion that in fungi a direct relation exists between the acetate and the C_4-acids. This fact is not inconsistent with general biochemical precepts. Considering the fact that a portion of the consumed acetate (or C_4-acid) must be oxidized to CO_2 and possibly glycolate, and doubtless a portion assimilated, the remainder must be converted to oxalate by a rather direct process as the above equation indicates. Nevertheless, up to now this condensation is by inference, for the synthesis has not been actually demonstrated in oxalic acid-forming fungus systems. One may, however, cite the ease of this action by various fumaric acid-forming fungi belonging to the Mucorales group, where clear cut evidence for the synthesis of C_4-dicarboxylic acids from acetate is available, and also the general association in numerous different organisms of C_2 and C_4 compounds (see Chapter 11). The fact that succinate and fumarate are always formed along with oxalate from acetate has also been observed, and this particular strain of *A. niger* gave a 76 per cent conversion yield of oxalate from succinate (Butkewitsch and Federoff, 1930a). One may even go so far as to observe that present indications are that in normal metabolism acetate (or C_2 fragments) is disposed of via oxidative synthesis of succinic acid.

While acetate may appear to be oxidized via the C_4-dicarboxylic acid system, the crucial experiment in this oxalate hypothesis, namely, hydrolysis of oxalacetic acid to yield oxalate, is lacking. As described above, Allsopp's experiments designed to test the crux of this theory all we e negative, leading that author to formulate the 2-ketogluconic acid hydrolysis theory for which, incidentally, the crucial experiment also was lacking. However, an interpretation for oxalate formation in high yields from acetate is needed, and the C_4-acid pathway is seemingly the one feasible and consistent with most experimental evidence. One wonders if the negative results of Allsopp, the only ones really having a direct bearing on the problem, may not have been due to the very rapid spontaneous decomposition of oxalacetic acid into pyruvic acid and CO_2, so that during the experiment oxalacetate was present for a very small portion of the total experimental time, and in rapidly decreasing amounts. The half-life of sodium oxalacetate at 25°C. is only about 1 hour. An important experiment to eliminate alternative metabolic pathways would be the addition of oxalacetate to a culture actively metabolizing carbohydrate, nearly comparable to the normal formation of oxalate from sugar through oxalacetate, if that be the particular com-

pound. Addition of oxalacetate alone might lead to its dissimilation
via other channels, which are saturated when sugar is present (shunt
metabolism, Chapter 4). Also, demonstration of an enzyme in these
organisms capable of hydrolyzing oxalacetate to oxalic and acetic acids
would be convincing evidence for acceptance of this scheme.

It has already been noted that the highest yields of oxalate may
generally be expected from the C_4-dicarboxylic acids and they compare
favorably with carbohydrate in this respect. It also appears that strains
giving high yields from acetate, also do so from C_4-dicarboxylic acids.
The most critically needed evidence is that relating to the mechanism of
the breakdown of C_4-acids, yielding oxalate. As pointed out above,
glycolic acid has been postulated as a product of C_4 breakdown.

Some definitive experiments implicating the C_4-dicarboxylic acids
as intermediates in oxalate formation from carbohydrates have been
provided lately by Butkewitsch and Mel'nikova (1943). Previous
experiments by these authors (Mel'nikova and Butkewitsch, 1939)
had indicated that the oxalate conversion yield from carbohydrate
increased progressively, reaching maximum near the end of the sugar
supply. This suggested that intermediates had accumulated during the
early stage, later being transformed to oxalic acid. At the time, when
almost all the sugar had been utilized, but yet with low oxalic acid yield,
the culture fluid was analyzed and a mixture of the following C_4-dicar-
boxylic acids isolated: fumaric, malic, tartaric. These acids presumably
would be converted to oxalate under normal conditions.

The seemingly contradictory evidence relative to the glycolic vs. C_4
mechanisms may best be reconciled by the conclusion that both mechanisms operate, the fungus strain and the conditions determining which is
active and the relative degrees of activity. Nord and Vitucci (1947,
1948) made this decision for four wood-destroying fungi that produce
oxalic acid, *Merulius niveus*, *M. tremellosus*, *M. confluens*, and *Fomes
annosus*. Experiments with various possible precursors indicate that
acetate is converted to oxalate by two schemes in this organism, both
not necessarily operating at any one time:

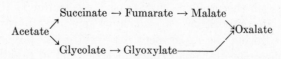

Under conditions when the C_4 mechanism ostensibly was inhibited
namely, succinic dehydrogenase inhibition by quinone, oxalate formation
from acetate was unimpaired, evidence used to support the alternative
C_2 mechanism. However, in these experiments it was not proved that
the succinic dehydrogenase enzyme was actually inhibited.

Formic Acid

In the field of microbiology, metabolism centering around formic acid is generally believed to be limited to bacteria. As will be seen below, this idea is not valid because formic acid can be formed and transformed by filamentous fungi. Oxalic and formic acid metabolism appear to be closely linked in fungi. The ability to utilize formate as the sole carbon source is widespread among fungi, and in 1933 Chrzaszcz and Zakomorny discovered that in the majority of such cases, including Aspergilli, Penicillia and *Rhizopus nigricans*, appreciable oxalic acid is formed. On the other hand, when fungi were furnished oxalate, eight of eleven species tested produced formic acid (Chrzaszcz and Zakomorny, 1934).

One mole of oxalate was considered to arise from the condensation of two moles of formic acid through dehydrogenation. In other words, oxalic acid may be considered the next highest oxidation stage of formic acid. The relations are as follows:

$$\begin{array}{ccc} \text{HCOOH} & & \text{COOH} \\ + & \xrightarrow{-2\text{H}} & | \\ \text{HCOOH} & & \text{COOH} \end{array} \rightarrow CO_2 + \text{HCOOH}$$

Bernhauer and Slanina (1934a, b) have confirmed and amplified these findings, and the formate condensation to oxalate was considered to be a reaction of general significance in fungi. Lower concentrations of formate favored higher conversion yields to oxalate. The enzyme catalyzing the reaction was named *formicodehydrase* (not be confused with formic dehydrogenase, the enzyme in bacteria which dehydrogenates formate completely to CO_2; $HCOOH + A \rightarrow CO_2 + H_2A$, A representing the oxidized form of a hydrogen acceptor).

The enzyme is similar to an oxidase in its action, as methylene blue will not serve as hydrogen acceptor, molecular oxygen being essential. One may note that the condensation of formate to oxalate via dehydrogenation is analogous to the condensation of acetate to succinate.

While these transformations take place with added formate, and while formate has not been detected as an intermediate in the production of oxalate from carbohydrate, it is of interest that formic acid was detected in oxalate-producing cultures utilizing fumarate. Since glycolic acid also was detected the formate was considered to arise via glycolate, as represented by this scheme: Fumaric acid $\rightarrow$ 2 Glycolic acid $\rightarrow$ 2 Formic acid $\rightarrow$ Oxalic acid $\rightarrow CO_2 + H_2O$ (Chrzaszcz and Zakomorny, 1933). The formation of glycolate from fumarate was viewed as involving a hydration and direct splitting of the hydrated C_4-acid. This theory obviously may be an alternative to the as yet unproved hydrolytic split of oxalacetic acid, although there really is no reason why this fumarate decomposition could not proceed via oxalacetate, the formate arising from the further decomposition of the oxalate.

Some objections have been raised (Butkewitsch, 1934) to the idea of oxalate formation from formate by molds. Previous results were explained as being due to oxalate formation from substances in the mycelium even though formate is present, and it was actually shown that considerable amounts are generated from the mycelium in the absence of formate, and furthermore that the amount is in proportion to the amount of acid-binding bases present in the medium. Formate might be destroyed leaving Na^+, which then would lead to oxalate accumulation. In support of this idea are experiments (Butkewitsch and Osnitzkaya, 1936) pointing out that a solution of $NaHCO_3$ also yields oxalate and that oxalate formation is not a function of formate concentration. Under conditions where growth and oxalate formation from either formate or bicarbonate was eliminated (6 per cent Na_2HPO_4) oxalate was formed from acetate. The latter must then be the ultimate origin of oxalate, according to these investigators.

On the other hand, Baba (1941) reports 35 and 10 per cent yields respectively from formate and methyl alcohol by *Aspergillus niger*. Butkewitsch's explanation of alkali generation inducing oxalate formation evidently could not apply to methyl alcohol, and the indications are that with this fungus strain at least, the origin of the oxalate actually was a 1-carbon compound.

As mentioned above, there is a close relation between formate and oxalate metabolism in fungi. Not only is oxalate synthesized from formate by fungi, but the latter is produced during the breakdown of oxalate by fungi (Chrzaszcz and Zakomorny, 1933, 1934). The breakdown was visualized as a hydrolysis as follows, but the stoichiometric balance was not established:

$$\begin{matrix} COOH \\ | \\ COOH \end{matrix} + \begin{matrix} H \\ | \\ OH \end{matrix} \rightarrow HCOOH + CO_2 + H_2O$$

Oxalate is oxidized by certain mosses according to the equation $(COOH)_2 + O_2 \rightarrow H_2O_2 + 2CO_2$ (Niekerk, Blom, 1946).

OXALIC ACID FROM PEPTONE

Unexpectedly high yields of oxalic acid can be produced from peptone solutions functioning as the sole carbon source for fungi. This was first observed by Wehmer, and although little has been done since to clarify the mechanism, the observation has been amply confirmed and extended to other fungi, including *Penicillium glaucum* and *Mucor stolonifer* (Butkewitsch, 1903, 1922). Highest yields obtained have been those of

Wehmer, but this may have been due to the exceptionally long incubation times typical of his experiments. Thus, in one case, with *A. niger* in a solution with NH_4NO_3 as nitrogen source, 0.712 and 2.02 g. oxalic acid respectively were obtained from 3 and 5 g. peptone. Oxalate accumulation from peptone also depends on an alkaline trap, in this case ammonia liberated by deamination of amino acids, for if peptone cultures are acidified with mineral acid, the oxalate accumulation does not ensue. In one case (Butkewitsch, 1922) partial balances were made, from which the following data are typical:

10-day-old culture: *A. niger;* N content of peptone = 12.82 per cent

Peptone furnished	Dry wt. of mycelium	NH_3—N	Oxalic acid
2.50 g.	0.2260 g.	149.4 mg.	.5051 g.

Based on the peptone originally present this represents a 20.2 per cent conversion. If one deducts that amount of peptone diverted to the synthesis of cell material, and that portion of the weight of the peptone appearing as free ammonia, and considers that a certain portion of this heterogeneous substrate was not even attacked, the conversion yield of oxalate is indeed surprisingly high. Indication that a substantial portion of the original peptone was unattacked may be had from the fact that all of the peptone nitrogen cannot be accounted for as free ammonia or as mycelial nitrogen. Thus, out of 320 mg. peptone N, a total of only 172 mg. is accounted for, assuming a 10 per cent N content of the mycelium in this nitrogen-rich medium; however, some NH_3—N may have been lost through volatilization from the alkaline medium. Thus only somewhat more than half of the peptone constituents may have undergone change by the fungus, as deamination generally accompanies the aerobic decomposition of amino acids. Substantial amounts of tyrosine and leucine have actually been isolated unchanged from peptone cultures in which fungi have grown and produced oxalic acid (Butkewitsch, 1903).

Various proteins and individual amino acids have been tested for oxalate formation by *A. niger* with results indicating that this acid can arise from many different nitrogenous compounds (Emmerling, 1903). Glycine, serine, alanine, aspartic acid, asparagine, glutamic acid, and phenylalanine all gave less than 10 per cent oxalate; hippuric acid and glucosamine yielded none as did a mixture of arginine, histidine, and lysine. Gelatine, casein, and egg albumin yielded 1.5, 2.4, and 5.2 per cent respectively, while Witte peptone gave a 15.6 per cent yield. The clear-cut superiority of the peptone over various amino acid components remains unclarified; virtually nothing can be said of the mechanism of oxalate formation from these nitrogenous compounds. Of particular value would be information identifying the final stages of this process with those of sugar and non-nitrogenous acids.

OTHER OBSERVATIONS

Several curious observations in the literature relating to oxalate formation indicate a need for clarification of the mechanisms of formation of this ubiquitous substance. Some of these have been covered in the foregoing. Certain theoretical aspects of the process involving carbohydrate are discussed by Butkewitsch (1934). Experiments by Ritter are cited in which surprisingly high yields of oxalate were produced by *A. niger* washed mycelium in the absence of any added carbon source. A pad 8 days old on 3 per cent sugar-nutrient solution was furnished with 0.2 per cent Na_2CO_3 solution and this solution changed daily for 5 days, the original growth fluid having been withdrawn, and the pad washed. At the end of 5 days a total of 0.503 g. oxalic acid had been formed, the mold pad itself weighing only 0.800 g. Comparable experiments with NaCl, KCl, and $MgSO_4$ gave none or small amounts. That such weight yields could have been derived exclusively from the mycelium seems unlikely, and unfortunately the weight of the pad at the beginning of the experiment was not given. The argument might be presented that intracellular carbohydrate and proteins could account for this in the presence of alkaline solution, but even at high conversion efficiency such high oxalate formation under these conditions seems strange. Could it be possible that some of the oxalate results from reduction of CO_2 by hydrogen donors in the mycelium? Abundant CO_2 would have been present from Na_2CO_3 and endogenous respiration, and the alkaline conditions would trap all oxalate formed.

A similar conclusion appears inevitable from data of Tschesnokov (1932) and by Mel'nikova and Butkewitsch (1939). On a phosphate solution at pH 9.5 the oxalate and CO_2 produced from a sugar solution were in the ratio of $3:1$. If it is assumed that oxalate arises from a C_2 fragment derived ultimately from decarboxylation of a triose via cleavage of the hexose chain, the maximum molar yield would be two moles oxalic acid per mole of hexose.

$$C_6 \rightarrow 2C_3 \rightarrow 2C_2 + 2CO_2$$
$$\downarrow$$
$$2 \text{ Oxalic acid}$$

or,

$$C_6H_{12}O_6 + 5O_2 \rightarrow 2(COOH)_2 + 2CO_2 + 4H_2O$$

The maximum weight yield of oxalate is then, according to theory, 2.05. In view of the obvious discrepancy between theory and observed results,

Butkewitsch (1934) proposed a $C_4 + C_2$ or a $3C_2$ split of hexose. However, an equally plausible theory to account for the CO_2 deficit would be reutilization of some of the CO_2, presumably by reduction directly to oxalic acid, or via oxalacetic acid and the Wood-Werkman reaction, with hydrogen obtained from added organic donors.

Worthy of mention is the fact that *A. niger* mycelium macerated with $CaCO_3$ in a mortar, and then placed in sugar solution, not only formed oxalic acid, but gave 35 per cent conversion yield on the basis of carbohydrate consumed (Bernhauer and Wolf, 1928). No claim is made that the action is due to cell-free juice, as doubtless living cells were present.

REFERENCES

Allsopp, A. 1937. *New Phytologist* **36**, 327–356.

Baba, S. 1941. *J. Agr. Chem. Soc. Japan* **17**, 992–994.

Bennet-Clark, T. A. 1933. *New Phytologist* **32**, 197–230.

Bennet-Clark, T. A., and La Touche, C. J. 1935. *New Phytologist* **34**, 211–231.

Bernhauer, K. 1939. Garungschemie Praktikum. 2nd ed., Springer, Berlin.

Bernhauer, K., and Böckl, N. 1932. *Biochem. Z.* **253**, 16–24.

Bernhauer, K., and Scheuer, Z. 1932. *Biochem. Z.* **253**, 11–15.

Bernhauer, K., and Slanina, F. 1934a. *Biochem. Z.* **274**, 97–111.

Bernhauer, K., and Slanina, F. 1934b. *Biochem. Z.* **264**, 109–112.

Bernhauer, K., and Thelen, H. 1932. *Biochem. Z.* **253**, 30–36.

Bernhauer, K., and Wolf, H. 1928. *Z. physiol. Chem.* **177**, 270–279.

Butkewitsch, W. 1903. *Jahrb. wiss. Botan.* **38**, 147–240.

Butkewitsch, W. 1922. *Biochem. Z.* **129**, 445–454.

Butkewitsch, W. 1934. *Biochem. Z.* **272**, 371–375.

Butkewitsch, W., and Federoff, M. W. 1930a. *Biochem. Z.* **219**, 87–102.

Butkewitsch, W., and Federoff, M. W. 1930b. *Biochem. Z.* **219**, 103–121.

Butkewitsch, W., and Mel'nikova, A. A. 1943. *Compt. rend. acad. sci. USSR* **39**, 148–150. (cf. *Chem. Abstracts* **38**, 1835, 1944.)

Butkewitsch, W., and Osnitzkaya, L. K. 1936. *Compt. rend. acad. sci. USSR (N. S.)* **1**, 361–364.

Challenger, F., Subramaniam, V., and Walker, T. K. **1927**, *J. Chem. Soc.* 200–208.

Chrzaszcz, T., and Tiukow, D. 1930. *Biochem. Z.* **229**, 343–357.

Chrzaszcz, T., and Zakomorny, M. 1933. *Biochem. Z.* **259**, 156–167.

Chrzaszcz, T., and Zakomorny, M. 1934. *Biochem. Z.* **263**, 105–118.

Chughtai, I. D., Pearce, A. A., and Walker, T. K. 1947. *Nature* **160**, 572.

Currie, J. N. 1917. *J. Biol. Chem.* **31**, 15–37.

Currie, J. N., and Thom, C. 1915. *J. Biol. Chem.* **22**, 287–293.

De Bary, A. 1886. *Botan. Ztg.* **44**, 393–404.

De Bary, A. 1887. Comparative Morphology and Biology of Fungi, Mycetozoa and Bacteria. Clarendon Press, Oxford.

Emmerling, O. 1903. *Zentr. Bakt. Parasitenk. Abt II* **10**, 273–275.

Fieser, L. F., and Fieser, M. 1946. Organic Chemistry. Heath, Boston, p. 307.

Foster, J. W., and Davis, J. B. Unpublished.

Jaquot, R. 1938a. *Compt. rend. soc. biol.* **127**, 1431–1432.

Jaquot, R. 1938b. *Compt. rend. soc. biol.* **128**, 69–70.

Mel'nikova, A. A., and Butkewitsch, W. 1939. *Microbiology USSR* **8**, 818–826 (Eng. Summary). (cf. *Chem. Abstracts* **38**, 1835, 1944.)

Niekerk-Blom, C. J. 1946. *Proc. Koninkl. Nederland. Akad. Wetenschap.* **49**, 1096–1100. (*Chem. Abstracts* **41**, 2778, 1947.)

Nord, F. F., and Vitucci, J. C. 1947. *Arch. Biochem.* **14**, 228–241.

Nord, F. F., and Vitucci, J. C. 1948. *Advances in Enzymol.* **8**, 253–298.

Perlman, D. 1948. *Am. J. Botany* **35**, 360–363.

Pfeffer, W. 1895. *Jahrb. wiss. Botan.* **28**, 214.

Raistrick, H., and Clark, A. B. 1919. *Biochem. J.* **13**, 329–344.

Simo, M. 1939. *J. Agr. Chem. Soc. Japan* **15**, 751–752.

Tschesnokov, W. 1932. *Microbiology USSR* **1**, 390. (Cited in Butkewitsch, 1934.)

Virtanen, A. I. 1934. *J. Bact.* **28**, 447–460.

Walker, T. K. 1932. *Nature* **130**, 582.

Walker, T. K., Subramaniam, V., and Challenger, F. **1927**. *J. Chem. Soc.* 3044–3054.

Wehmer, C. 1891a. *Botan. Z.* **49**, 233–246, 249–258, 271–280, 289–298, 305–313, 321–332, 337–346, 353–363, 369–374, 385–396, 401–409, 417–428, 433–439, 449–456, 465–478, 511–518, 531–539, 547–554, 563–569, 579–584, 596–602, 611–620, 630–638.

Wehmer, C. 1891b. *Ber. deut. botan. Ges.* **9**, 163–183.

Wehmer, C. 1891c. *Ber. deut. botan. Ges.* **9**, 218–229.

Wehmer, C. 1892a. *Liebigs Ann.* **269**, 383–389.

Wehmer, C. 1892b. Beiträge zur Kenntnis einheimischer Pilze. Gustav Fischer, Jena.

Zellner, J. 1907. Chemie der höheren Pilze. Leipzig Verlag Wilhelm Engelmann.

Zopf, W. 1889. *Ber. deut. botan. Ges.* **7**, 94–97.

CHAPTER 11

FUMARIC AND OTHER C₄-DICARBOXYLIC ACIDS

It is impossible to treat the individual acids of this group separately because, as in all other biological systems, the interrelationships are so close that the acids must be considered together. Furthermore, the treatment here is not from the point of view of the role of these acids functioning as hydrogen transport systems in respiratory metabolism according to Szent-Gyorgi, but rather mainly from the standpoint of their formation and accumulation in appreciable amounts as end products of carbohydrate metabolism. Beyond a doubt the presence and function of these acids as respiratory catalysts is universal among the fungi, just as it is in other biological systems. As a matter of fact this function has already been specifically identified in the mold *Neurospora crassa* (Ryan *et al.*, 1944). On the other hand, the formation and accumulation of these substances can be recognized as a distinct biochemical feature of only a limited number of organisms.

Rarely does any one acid accumulate to the complete exclusion of the others owing to enzymatic equilibria existing among them, but by rigorous control of environmental conditions it is possible for one to preponderate. Fumaric acid is outstanding in this connection. Because of the attractively high conversion yields of fumarate from carbohydrate and the adaptation of this process to the submerged culture method, fumaric acid manufacture recently became practicable on a cost basis. As a result of the availability of cheap fumaric acid for the first time, several industrial applications of this chemical have been developed, and sufficient demand created to manufacture the chemical on an industrial scale.

Although certain exceptions are known now and more doubtless will be revealed in time, only two C₄-acids, namely, fumaric and succinic acids, are known to preponderate singly in fungus cultures and each instance is with a specific group of organisms. Fumaric acid accumulation is largely confined to organisms of the order Mucorales, and in particular to the genus Rhizopus. Succinic acid accumulation appears to be characteristic of the genus Fusarium. One case only is known which probably is an accumulation of malic acid as the principal metabolic product.

351

Fumaric Acid

1. GENERAL ASPECTS OF GROWTH CULTURES

Only one other unsaturated acid, namely itaconic, is a bulk product of carbohydrate metabolism in fungi. Fumaric acid isolation in 1911 was the first instance in which an unsaturated compound was shown to be a product of carbohydrate metabolism of a microorganism. With only few exceptions fungi active in the substantial accumulation of fumarate belong to the order Mucorales. Notable among these exceptions was an Aspergillus isolated by Wehmer (1918) which was so outstanding in its ability to convert sugar to fumaric acid that he named it *A. fumaricus*. Yields amounting to 70 per cent of the carbohydrate consumed were reported for this organism. However, this organism is only of historical interest today, for upon cultivation for 10 years in the laboratory via stock cultures, it lost its ability to produce fumaric acid and instead produced copious quantities of citric and gluconic acids, like the majority of Aspergilli (Wehmer, 1928). Attempts to restore the fumaric acid powers of the organism by cultivation under a variety of different conditions failed for the most part except for minor amounts under special nutrient conditions (Schreyer, 1928), although by bubbling oxygen into the substrate and obtaining a submerged type of growth, it was later found capable of producing small amounts of fumaric acid (Thies, 1930). Passage of air through a culture with a preformed pellicle had no such effect (Schreyer).

This is an excellent example of the "degeneration" or physiological variation which frequently occurs in microorganisms after prolonged cultivation in the laboratory. It is noteworthy that no other species of Aspergillus has since been described which is at all comparable to Wehmer's original isolation, in respect to fumaric acid yields. A few other instances of fumaric acid isolation from fungi outside the Mucorales group is that in small amounts from *Penicillium griseo-fulvum* (Raistrick and Simonart, 1933), from *A. glaucus* (Sumiki, 1929) from *A. flavus*, *A. oniki*, and *A. wentii* (Sumiki, 1931), and from *Caldariomyces fumago* (Clutterbuck et al., 1940). There is little doubt that fumarate could be detected or isolated from the vast majority of fungi metabolizing carbohydrate where it doubtless is associated with related acids (cf. Sumiki, 1929, 1931, from several Aspergilli). Lack of more extensive occurrence of this acid in fungus cultures merely reflects the lack of study, rather than negative results.

The genus Rhizopus has been identified with fumarate formation repeatedly since the discovery of Ehrlich in 1911 using *R. nigricans* (syn. *Mucor stolonifer*). Actually the property is common to related genera, including Mucor, Cunninghamella and Circinella, although not all species in these genera have it (Foster and Waksman, 1939b). Thus six out of ten Rhizopus strains tested yielded fumarate, one out of eleven Mucor, one out of six Cunninghamella, one out of four Circinella, and none out of six Absidia, two Phycomyces, one Syncephalastrum, and one Mortierella.

Takahashi and Sakaguchi (1925) found that acid-forming members of the genus Rhizopus fell into three groups: (a) those forming mostly fumaric acid with none or a trace of lactic; (b) those forming mostly lactic acid with none or a trace of fumarate; (c) those forming fumarate and lactic acid in varying proportions.

Fungi belonging to the Mucorales are not like Aspergilli in their pH tolerance, and it is a common experience that neutralizing agents are required in the medium to permit good growth and, particularly, high yields of fumarate. Acidity manifests a suppressive effect on the activities of these organisms at approximately pH 5 and lower. The low yields observed by Ehrlich may be attributed to absence of neutralizing agent. The presence of CaCO$_3$ induces a remarkable augmentation in fumarate yields. With high-yielding strains under favorable conditions, the accumulation of calcium fumarate in the culture fluid attains sufficient concentration (about 8 per cent) to reach supersaturation and crystallizes out gradually, filling the body of the liquid. Later, the hydrophilic nature of this salt causes the liquid to "set" to a stiff gel.

Cultivation conditions for growth and fumarate formation by these organisms are virtually identical with those of the lactic acid-producing strains of Rhizopus as discussed in Chapter 8. Any one of a number of carbohydrates, including the polysaccharides starch and inulin, can be used as carbon source. Like most Mucorales, invertase is not formed, hence sucrose cannot be utilized. Similarly, almost any common source of nitrogen, organic or inorganic, may be used with the exception of nitrates. Detailed aspects of cultivation are covered by Foster and Waksman (1939a, b).

As in the case of organic acid production of almost all fungi, the concentration of carbohydrate, and especially the C/N ratio of the medium, is of crucial importance in fumarate formation. Virtually all experimental information available in the literature has dealt with surface cultures. Generally carbohydrate concentrations from 8 to 12 per cent yield most rapid and efficient conversion to fumarate during the growth stage, the efficiency becoming limiting only after crystallization of the fumarate salt reaches sufficient intensity that diffusion processes in the medium become greatly slowed down.

Spore germination of organisms of this group is retarded in the presence of alkali or even at neutrality and germination is best allowed to proceed at a slightly acid pH before the addition of neutralizing agents, generally calcium carbonate. Maximum surface pad development takes place in 5 to 8 days depending on the depth of medium, and particularly on the efficiency of neutralization. Calcium carbonate tends to settle out rapidly and its neutralization efficiency is so reduced that development of free acidity immediately under the fungus growth actually retards growth and efficiency of acid formation. Frequent shaking is necessary to neutralize the acidity, without disturbing or wetting the surface growth. The whole growth process is also speeded up thereby, for carbohydrate diffusion limitations are relieved. A neutralizing agent is essential for rapid development and high conversion yields of fumarate in growth cultures (Foster and Waksman, 1939b; Butkewitsch and Federoff, 1929a). With carbohydrate concentrations of 5 to 15 per cent, particularly in replacement cultures, sufficient calcium fumarate is formed to cause the whole medium to gel.

TABLE 1

ZINC AND METABOLISM OF RHIZOPUS NIGRICANS[1]

	Glucose consumed, mg.	Fumaric acid formed, mg.	Per cent conversion	NH$_3$—N consumed, mg.	Total calcium in solution, mg.	Calcium due to fumaric acid, mg.	Per cent of calcium due to fumaric acid
No Zn..........	4,702	2,349	50.0	31.0	760	716	113[3]
0.6 p.p.m. Zn....	5,088[2]	452	8.9	82.1	338	220	71

[1] From Foster and Waksman (1939a).

[2] All available sugar. Zinc invariably induces notably faster consumption of carbohydrate.

[3] Excessively high due to imperfect neutralization of the acids by the CaCO$_3$. True value is approximately 100 per cent.

Aside from the matter of strain specificity (discussed below) probably the most critical single factor in the fumaric acid process is the effect of certain trace or heavy metals, notably zinc ion. Because organisms belonging to the genus Rhizopus synthesize such conspicuously large amounts of mycelium under favorable nutrient conditions, it is particularly easy to accentuate nutritional deficiencies such as zinc. Indeed, the only reason that any growth at all takes place in the absence of added zinc is because some zinc is present as an impurity in the medium (see Chapter 7; Foster and Waksman, 1939a). Usually any medium prepared from reagent-grade chemicals will be zinc-deficient, and addition of 0.2 to about 3 p.p.m. zinc exercises a profound acceleration and total increase in cell synthesis, and a corresponding decrease in fumaric acid accumulation. This is particularly true during the stages of active growth as long as assimilable N and minerals are present, and tends to be obscured by high yields of fumarate made in growth cultures after active cell synthesis has stopped. Table 1 demonstrates the remarkable influence of zinc on the physiology of *R. nigricans* No. 45.

The trace of zinc greatly increases the rate and total amount of growth as indicated by glucose consumption and NH$_3$ assimilation. At the same time it evokes a sharp reduction in the total amount and conversion rate of fumaric acid. Furthermore, the zinc culture contains appreciable amounts of organic acids that are not fumaric, whereas in zinc-deficient culture the acidity is due to fumaric acid almost exclusively. The specific effect of zinc is discussed in Chapter 7 and it suffices here to say that this element apparently functions as a catalyst (coenzyme?), enabling the organism to effect a more complete destruction of the glucose molecule and consequently its more efficient utilization as a source of energy and of carbon for cell synthesis. The following data calculated from the experiment in Table 1 demonstrate this effect. It is apparent

	Glucose carbon consumed, mg.	Carbon synthesized, into cell substance, mg.	*Cell substance C* / *Glucose C*
No Zn..............	1,881	279	14.8 per cent
Zn.................	2,035	739	36.3 per cent

from Column 3 that the zinc culture was 2.5 times more efficient in its utilization of the glucose carbon.

Other trace elements are important for growth and metabolism of *R. nigricans*. Iron is essential in next larger amounts; the effects are minor compared to the first named two elements. The effect of iron deficiency is not as spectacular as zinc, and there is good indication that the presence of this element diminishes the severity of the zinc effect, possibly an instance of ion antagonism. The ion effect can best be summarized by stating that zinc cultures containing added iron yield more fumaric acid than zinc cultures alone. As mentioned in Chapter 4, the zinc effect has an important bearing on the theory of shunt metabolism. Data exemplifying this point follow (from Foster and Waksman, 1939b).

	Glucose concentration			
	2.5 per cent		10.0 per cent	
	No Zn	1.2 p.p.m. Zn	No Zn	1.2 p.p.m. Zn
Glucose consumed, mg..........	2,369	4,752	4,530	9,795
Fumaric acid produced, mg.....	891	474	1,040	2,214
Conversion, per cent..........	37.6	10.0	22.9	22.6

Whereas 1.2 p.p.m. of zinc was sufficient to catalyze the conversion of the 2.5 per cent sugar largely to cell substance resulting in only 10 per cent fumarate conversion yield as compared to 37.6 in absence of zinc, it was unable to cause this effect with the higher sugar concentration, which, despite the zinc, gave more than twice the conversion yield in the lower sugar concentration. According to the idea of overflow metabolism the flow of split products from the more concentrated sugar solution could not be handled by the zinc-enzyme complex for the synthesis of cell material, and "overflowed," or was shunted, through the fumaric acid-forming channels.

Bernhauer and Thole (1936) obtained a zinc effect just contrary to general expectations and the above results. Addition of .005 per cent $ZnSO_4$ increased the yield of fumaric acid to 41.6 per cent on the basis of sugar consumed as compared to 20.7 in the control. However, the amount of zinc they used was evidently toxic to the organism for their strain of *R. nigricans* was inhibited by the zinc (0.86 g. mycelium vs. 1.10 g. in the no-zinc control). Hence these results are quite different from a deficiency experiment.

2. REPLACEMENT CULTURES

As in the case of the previously discussed metabolic processes, elimination of the growth processes facilitates an understanding of the mechanism whereby fumarate is formed from carbohydrate. Pregrown Rhizopus surface mycelium is extremely active and hardy in the formation of fumarate so that a surface pad will still produce fumarate after six to twelve consecutive sugar solution replacements (with neutralizing agent). Although numerous different factors may markedly influence the efficiency of fumaric acid formation during the growth stage, the mycelium is uniquely consistent in giving high conversion yields in the absence of assimilable nitrogen and minerals. For example, added zinc is without significant effect in replacement cultures. Furthermore, although the absence of neutralizing agents greatly diminishes growth rate and fumarate conversion yields occurring therein, the absence of neutralizing agent in replacement culture is not as critical as in the growth stage, it being possible to obtain conversion yields not too much smaller than in the presence of $CaCO_3$. Thirty-four per cent conversion yield has been reported under free acid conditions. Nevertheless the rate of carbohydrate consumption is significantly depressed.

An interesting example of the ability to form and accumulate free fumaric acid in total absence of neutralizing agent is that where preformed surface pads of *R. nigricans* No. 45, acting on a 10 per cent glucose solution, produced sufficient free fumaric acid to crystallize out in the culture vessel, in a total conversion yield of 22 per cent of the carbohydrate consumed (Foster and Waksman, 1939b; see also Ehrlich, 1919). At this point the pH of the liquid was 2.4, and the liquid was equivalent to a 1 per cent (0.086 M) solution of fumaric acid. This is the only instance on record where an organic acid accumulates to such an extent that the free acid crystallizes out spontaneously in the culture fluid. This is due, of course, to the low solubility of fumaric acid in water (0.7 per cent at 25°C.). As a final commentary on the neutralization aspect, it must be remembered that for most of the time (except for a short period during hand shaking) the surface cultures containing calcium carbonate are doubtless producing fumarate under conditions of high acidity owing to the layering of the acid in direct contact with the mycelium, as the acid is excreted from the cells.

There is a distinct relation between carbohydrate concentration and fumarate conversion efficiency, the latter being in inverse proportion to the sugar concentration. On the other hand, up to a certain point where osmotic effects doubtless become inhibitory, there is a direct relation between sugar and concentration, consumption increasing to a maximum at 15 per cent glucose (Table 2). An interpretation of this effect cannot

TABLE 2

CARBOHYDRATE CONCENTRATION AND FUMARIC ACID CONVERSION EFFICIENCY IN R. NIGRICANS REPLACEMENT CULTURES[1]

Initial glucose concentration, per cent	Glucose consumed, mg.	Fumaric acid formed, mg.	Conversion per cent
2.5	3,323	1,559	46.9
5.0	6,750	2,651	39.3
10.0	10,575	3,563	33.7
15.0	12,215	3,681	30.1
20.0	10,060	2,986	29.7
25.0	10,440	1,954	18.7
30.0	5,125	631	12.3
45.0	5,125	399	7.8

[1] From Foster and Waksman (1939a).

be stated except that the bulk of the consumed carbohydrate not converted into fumarate accumulates as ethyl alcohol. This may well be a good example of shunt metabolism in that the aerobic processes cannot keep pace with the increased supply of triose furnished anaerobically, and that during prolonged incubation and in particular under good aeration conditions these percentage values might become more nearly equal. Evidence for this is that oxygen was not severely limiting the absolute amount of fumaric acid formed up through 20 per cent glucose.

The physiological and biochemical activities of mycelium of many fungi, and particularly Aspergilli, on which most such work has been done, is markedly influenced by the previous growth history of the organism, as though the very enzymic composition of the cells varies according to the growth environment. Work on organisms of the genus Rhizopus indicates that the distinctive biochemical activities of these organisms are quite independent of the growth history. For example, either lactic acid- or fumaric acid-producing strains of Rhizopus can be cultivated so that no trace of fumaric or lactic acids are formed during growth, yet this very mycelium in replacement cultures will convert sugar actively and efficiently to the respective organic acids. The growth conditions referred to are a low C/N ratio and an adequate zinc content of the medium. Incidentally, the presence of zinc in sugar solutions in replacement cultures is without effect on the acid conversion—the zinc effect appears to be intimately associated with the synthesis of cell material, which, under these conditions, can not take place owing to absence of nitrogen and minerals.

3. STRAIN SPECIFICITY

As in the case of any sufficiently studied microbiological process this problem has become well recognized relative to fumaric acid. The classic example of variation of Aspergillus fumaricus has already been discussed. Strain differences in Rhizopus nigricans relative to their ability to grow on pyruvate as the sole source of carbon, and form fumaric acid, led to an interesting historical controversy. Gottschalk (1926) reported his strain would utilize calcium pyruvate as the sole source of carbon, and obtained a 32 per cent of theoretical yield assuming two moles of pyruvate would generate one fumarate. Small amounts of acetic and lactic acids were present, and on the basis of this experiment and without experimental verification, this investigator proposed the theory for fumarate formation for which there is ample evidence today and which is considered most probable (see below). The following year, Takahashi and Asai (1927) showed that acetate could be converted to fumarate by Rhizopus. However, the discoverer of fumaric acid in fungi, Ehrlich, and his coworker Bender were unable to get pyruvate utilization by their strain of R. nigricans under any conditions, including preformed mycelium. An interesting series of polemical notes by these investigators centers about this subject (Ehrlich and Bender, 1927a, b; Gottschalk, 1927, 1929). Gottschalk ascribed the disparity in results to strain specificity but Ehrlich avowed he used the identical strain. The issue finally quieted down after Gottschalk got negative results with a new strain of his original organism, and ascribed the whole incident to physiological degeneration for which, of course, there was ample precedent (viz., *Aspergillus fumaricus*).

Direct comparison of strains of Rhizopus from the standpoint of fumaric acid specificity came considerably later (Foster and Waksman, 1939b, c). In one case the specificity was associated with sexuality, the male or (+) race being a very active fumarate former and in high yields, whereas the female or (−) race never produced a trace. The designation male or female in this case refers to the fact that these organisms are heterothallic, hyphal fusion of the two being capable of forming, under proper conditions, the sexual spore or zygote.

Clear-cut specificity differences were demonstrated between the two highest yielding strains, *R. nigricans* No. 35 and No. 45, obtained in an extensive survey (Foster and Waksman, 1939b), and the physiological disparities were best shown in replacement cultures. Most significant were: (a) In No. 45, 99 per cent of the total acid formed was fumaric; in No. 35 fumaric accounted for only 55 per cent of the total acidity as indicated by calcium in solution (neutralized CaCO₃). Thus No. 35 produces substantial proportions of acid other than fumaric, whereas No. 45 does not. (b) The preformed mycelium of strain No. 45 produced significant amounts of fumarate (up to 20 per cent conversion yield) from glucose under anaerobic conditions whereas No. 35 formed none. Certain other minor differences were noted.

4. MECHANISM OF FORMATION OF FUMARIC ACID

The Russian investigators Butkewitsch and Federoff were the first to study the physiology of these organisms systematically, and, with Japanese investigators, provided experimental evidence for our understanding of one of the origins of this acid from sugar. Their particular strain, *Mucor stolonifer* (identical with *Rhizopus nigricans*), gave up to 36.7 per cent conversion yield of fumarate from glucose in 39 days and produced some succinic acid (10 per cent of fumaric acid yield). The pertinent observation was made that the conversion efficiency was not parallel to sugar consumption but increased as a function of age. Thus, though the overall yield at the end of the experiment (39 days) was 36.7 per cent, the conversion yields during successive individual 3-day intervals were as follows:

Conversion yield (per cent) over 3-day interval between							
15–18 days	18–21 days	21–24 days	24–27 days	24–30 days	30–33 days	33–36 days	36–39 days
18.5	17.2	51.2	56.9	35.4	74.2	71.1	—

This same observation has been made with submerged cultures, where yields on this basis sometimes exceed 100 per cent.

It is evident from these data that as the sugar supply became depleted fumarate apparently was formed at an accelerated rate. The culture solutions were found to contain appreciable quantities of ethyl alcohol, and it was established that ethanol formed from the carbohydrate in the initial stages of culture was itself later converted to fumaric acid. Thus, an inverse relation exists between the amount of alcohol and fumarate present in such cultures. Acetic acid also is found in small yields. A typical product balance is given in Table 3:

TABLE 3

PRODUCT BALANCE IN R. NIGRICANS SURFACE CULTURE[1]

Glucose consumed, g.	44.20
Mycelium, g.	1.92
CO_2, g.	18.58
Ethanol, g.	9.74
Acetic acid, g.	0.232
Fumaric and succinic acids, g.	4.08

[1] From Butkewitsch and Federoff (1930b). Thirty-two-day-old cultures.

Takahashi and Asai (1933) also observed high alcohol yields in Mucor cultures. When air was passed through the medium the alcohol yield dropped to one-half and acid formation doubled.

Preformed mycelium of *R. nigricans* furnished with alcohol and with acetate convert these substances into C_4-acids, mainly fumaric, with some succinic, in rather high yields, thus supporting the theory for origin of the C_4-acids via synthesis from two C_2 moles of acetic acid, i.e., the classical Thunberg-Wieland mechanism postulated for mammalian muscle. The sequence of reactions may be represented as follows:

Glucose → 2 Triose → 2 Pyruvic acid → $2CH_3CH_2OH$ → $2CH_3COOH$
                                   Ethanol   Acetic acid

$$\rightarrow \begin{array}{l} CH_2\!-\!COOH \\ | \\ CH_2\!-\!COOH \end{array} \rightarrow \begin{array}{l} CH\!-\!COOH \\ \| \\ CH\!-\!COOH \end{array}$$
   Succinic acid   Fumaric acid

The structural formula of fumaric acid is the *trans*-form:

$$\begin{array}{l} HC\!-\!COOH \\ \| \\ HOOC\!-\!CH \end{array}$$

The formula

$$\begin{array}{l} CH\!-\!COOH \\ \| \\ CH\!-\!COOH \end{array}$$

actually is that of maleic acid, the *cis*-isomer of fumaric acid. For the purpose of convenient graphic relations in the sequence of biochemical reactions the maleic structure is usually preferred to the true fumaric one.

The alcohol is formed by anaerobic reactions exclusively; Rhizopus organisms have already been described as strongly fermentative. See p. 310 regarding aerobic vs. anaerobic C_2. The conversion of alcohol to acetate may be envisioned as occurring in the classical manner:

$$CH_3CH_2OH \xrightarrow[-2H]{+O} CH_3CHO \xrightarrow[-2H]{+HOH} CH_3COOH$$

     Alcohol   Acetaldehyde   Acetic acid

The condensation of acetate to succinate may be described as follows:

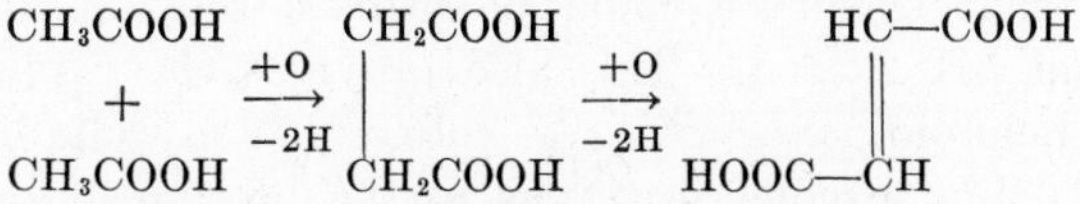

$$
\begin{array}{ccccc}
CH_3COOH & & CH_2COOH & & HC{-}COOH \\
+ & \xrightarrow[-2H]{+O} & | & \xrightarrow[-2H]{+O} & \| \\
CH_3COOH & & CH_2COOH & & HOOC{-}CH \\
\text{Acetic acid} & & \text{Succinic acid} & & \text{Fumaric acid}
\end{array}
$$

The details of this enzymatic reaction have never been elucidated experimentally since it was postulated by Thunberg and Wieland, whose names are always associated with this particular transformation. In recent years the use of isotopic carbon has permitted a more direct demonstration of acetate condensation to succinate in bacteria (Slade and Werkman, 1943).

The oxidation of succinate to fumarate is carried out by succinoxidase (succinic dehydrogenase) an ubiquitous enzyme and one of the major oxidation enzymes in biological systems. The oxidation is linked with an oxygen-activating system, namely cytochrome-C and cytochrome oxidase. A third component of this oxidation system is now known, a flavoprotein hydrogen carrier system that functions between the dehydrogenase and the oxidase. In the absence of molecular oxygen, organic H acceptors such as methylene blue can satisfy the succinoxidase system.

When R. nigricans mycelium is mixed with sugar anaerobically, all the steps described above which utilize molecular oxygen are, of course, blocked, and instead of being further oxidized the anaerobically formed alcohol simply accumulates as such. As seen later, a certain alternative reaction may occur in some strains.

Evidence favoring the above mechanism is: (a) the postulated intermediate always can be detected in rather significant amounts in fumarate-forming cultures, (b) the C_2-compounds disappear in sugar cultures with the concomitant formation of C_4-acids, (c) fumarate-forming organisms convert alcohol and acetate to fumarate in high enough yields to make the above reactions entirely feasible. Alcohol may be converted to fumarate in 70 per cent weight yield, and acetate to fumarate in about 30 per cent (Butkewitsch and Federoff, 1929b; Foster and Waksman, 1939a).

On the other hand, the behavior of succinate is seemingly inconsistent with the theory as hypothesized above. Addition of succinate salts to active Rhizopus surface cultures not only fails to yield fumarate, but the succinate is not utilized at all. Similar results are obtained with submerged mycelium. A further curious observation is that whereas alcohol-calcium carbonate mixtures are rapidly converted to fumarate when furnished to surface pad mycelium, no fumarate is formed from the same mixture by submerged mycelium aerated by agitation on a shaking machine. This anomalous behavior was clarified by Foster, Carson, and Davis (unpublished). Employing Warburg respirometer techniques it was shown that succinate could be utilized only at acid pH values, ranging from pH 2 to 4. This also provides the explanation for the anomalous behavior of surface vs. submerged mycelium in relation to alcohol. Calcium carbonate settles to the bottom of surface cultures, and small amounts of acid are present at the interphase between the mold pellicle and the alcohol solution, thus permitting the generation of fumaric acid from alcohol under the locally acid environment immediately contiguous to the mycelium, and out of range of the neutralizing agent. In shaken submerged cultures no such local acid zone exists owing to continuous neutralization by $CaCO_3$ in the agitated liquid. When, however, the experiment is done in absence of a neutralization agent, pH 2 to 4, maximum conversion yields of alcohol to fumarate are obtainable.

In these cases, permeability of the solute through the cell membranes is probably a function of pH. Succinic acid can penetrate only as the undissociated molecule, and although some alcohol is consumed at neutral pH, the fact remains that its considerably higher rate of utilization at pH 2 to 4 indicates that permeability is involved here also. Cogent evidence for this conclusion is provided by the fact that air-desiccated R. nigricans mycelium oxidizes succinate readily at neutral pH values whereas the undried fresh mycelium is inert towards this substrate (Foster and J. B. Davis, unpublished). Similar reasoning might explain the following results of Butkewitsch and Federoff (1930a):

Fumarate from sugar solution alone...................... 0.8 g.
Fumarate from succinate solution alone.................... 0.0 g.
Fumarate from sugar plus succinate....................... 3.0 g.

An acid layer probably was generated by conversion of the sugar, enabling succinate to be oxidized to fumarate, whereas this could not take place in neutral succinate solution alone.

These same workers found that their strain of fungus formed C_4-acid from calcium acetate solution in yields up to 29 per cent, the product consisting chiefly of succinate, whereas the action of the organism on acetate plus glucose gave a mixture with fumarate preponderating.

$$\text{Acetate} \rightarrow 13.4 \text{ per cent C}_4 \text{ yield} \begin{cases} 80.75 \text{ per cent Succinate} \\ 19.25 \text{ per cent Fumarate} \end{cases}$$

$$\text{Acetate and sugar} \rightarrow 25 \text{ per cent C}_4 \text{ yield} \begin{cases} 25.9 \text{ per cent Succinate} \\ 74.1 \text{ per cent Fumarate} \end{cases}$$

The interpretation of the Russian investigators is that metabolic products from the sugar act as H acceptors in the oxidation of succinate to fumarate. As pointed out above, organic-H acceptors may substitute for molecular oxygen in the succinoxidase system. In organisms of this type acetaldehyde would appear to be the only feasible hydrogen acceptor, the succinate oxidation thus competing with the oxidation of intermediate phosphoglyceraldehyde, acetaldehyde being the common oxidizing agent. How the oxidation actually proceeds in this case is not discussed. This interpretation cannot be considered as factual until further evidence is provided. Their particular strain was able to form oxalic acid slowly from succinate or acetate, but this property has not been reported for other fumaric acid organisms.

It is worthwhile to dwell a moment upon the significance of the Thunberg-Wieland condensation reaction in mold metabolism. Early thought to be the mechanism accounting for the origin of C$_4$-dicarboxylic acids in animal tissues, this reaction has not been given much attention since, and in recent years seemingly has been considered almost superfluous owing to several other well-established means of genesis of the vital C$_4$-dicarboxylic acids, for example, fixation of CO$_2$ by pyruvate, decarboxylation of α-ketoglutaric acid in the tricarboxylic acid respiratory cycle, and transamination of the amino acid, aspartic acid. One of the main reasons for discounting the Thunberg-Wieland reaction from a vital role in animal tissue is that the metabolism of C$_2$ compounds, viz., acetate, does not occur under normal physiological conditions. This C$_2$ + C$_2$ condensation would then be an incidental reaction at most, which possibly could come into play to regenerate C$_4$-acids should the other mechanisms be inoperative.

However, in contrast to animal tissues, the metabolism of the majority of fungi centers about C$_2$ compounds as the main pathway of metabolism; consequently their oxidation is expected to take place actively. There is ample reason for considering that C$_2$ fragments, ethanol, formed via anaerobic reactions, and acetate, via oxidative decarboxylation, are main channels of carbohydrate metabolism in fungi, and that they are further metabolized aerobically. The Thunberg-Wieland condensation is a key step in the aerobic utilization of the primary C$_2$ split products. From the standpoint of the economy of the organism the usefulness of these secondary aerobic oxidation mechanisms becomes evident from energy considerations. Alcohol formed from a gram mole of glucose liberates only 22 calories or only 3 per cent of the energy content of the carbo-hydrate molecule. Since the oxidation of C_2 compounds in biological systems is believed to proceed mainly through condensation accompanied by dehydrogenation, the importance of the Thunberg-Wieland reaction in increasing the efficiency of energy utilization and permitting abundant growth is self-evident.

Nevertheless, notwithstanding the attractiveness of a direct $C_2 + C_2$ condensation as the explanation of C_4 accumulation in fungi, the reader must recognize that acceptable proof for this reaction in fungi has not yet been advanced.   Even then it will be necessary to establish that this reaction accounts for the bulk synthesis of C_4 instead of small catalytic amounts for oxidative metabolism.   At the present writing it is impossi-ble to say that the accumulated C_4 does not arise as a result of the oxida-tion of C_2 via the tricarboxylic acid respiratory cycle described on p. 411 in Chapter 12.

The functioning of the C_2 condensation in molds characterized by accumulations of C_4-dicarboxylic acids is strongly indicated. From extensive experiments with organisms belonging to the Mucorales in particular, Butkewitsch and also Takahashi hold that C_2 condensation to C_4 is a property common to all organisms of this order.   In systems where no accumulations occur, the Thunberg-Wieland condensation is doubtless also at play, the C_4 being further oxidized, but few specific tests on this point are available (cf. Chapter 10).   One might suspect that this reaction is as universal among the fungi as the ability to produce alcohol (see Chapter 9).   In support of this idea is the fact that C_2 and C_4 compounds can almost invariably be found in association in fungus cultures grown on carbohydrates under stationary conditions.

INTERCONVERSIONS BETWEEN C_4-DICARBOXYLIC ACIDS

The nature and amounts of the C_4-dicarboxylic acids that may be found in a culture solution depends on cultural conditions, and the species and strain of the organism.   As pointed out above, R. nigricans No. 45 formed fumaric to the exclusion of other acids, whereas other strains generally form other acids.   Oxalacetic acid, on account of its very high chemical and biological lability, would not be expected to accumulate. Succinate and fumarate account for the bulk of the C_4-dicarboxylic acids formed in the majority of fungus cultures.

As fumaric acid-containing cultures of Rhizopus or Mucor age, the fumarate tends to disappear and malic acid, present in small quantities in the young cultures, is formed in increasing amounts.   The fluctua-tions which may occur in such cultures are illustrated by the following data of Bernhauer and Thole (1936) for R. nigricans on sugar medium:

Days	9	11	13	17
Total acids, per cent of theory[1]	76.6	89.4	92.1	83.6
Succinic acid,[2] per cent	4	4.2	3.9	4
Fumaric acid,[2] per cent	25.8	50.5	61.6	50.4
Malic acid,[2] per cent	14	17.2	19.1	25
Total C₄ acids,[2] per cent	43.8	71.9	84.5	79

[1] Theory = 64.5 per cent of glucose consumed.
[2] Per cent of the theory from glucose consumed.

The biochemical relationships between the C_4-dicarboxylic acids has become universally known through Szent-Györgi's elucidation of their function as hydrogen carriers, or catalysts, in the respiratory metabolism of all biological systems. The essence of their relations is represented as follows:

Oxidizable substrate   Oxidizable substrate

```
COOH           |         COOH            COOH           |         COOH
|              |         |               |              |         |
CO       +2H   →         CHOH  -HOH  CH        +2H      →         CH2
|        -2H    ←         |      →    ||        -2H      ←          |
CH2            |         CH2   +HOH  CH              |         CH2
|              |         |               |              |         |
COOH           |         COOH            COOH           |         COOH
Oxalacetic   Malicodehydrogenase  Malic   Fumaric   Succinoxidase   Succinic
  acid                          acid      acid                       acid
```

All of these transformations are enzymatically catalyzed. Succinoxidase has already been discussed. The conversion of fumaric to malic acid by addition of water to the unsaturated bond is effected by the enzyme fumarase. This enzyme is widespread in biological systems, probably including most, if not all, fungi, and forms and activates only fumarate and/or l-malic acid. Cell-free preparations of this enzyme acting on either fumaric or malic acid arrive at an equilibrium in which about 75 per cent of the total acid is malic and 25 per cent is fumaric. This equilibrium does not apply to systems containing living cells, as several other factors influence the balance in addition to the fumarase equilibrium constant, viz., other enzymes, permeability, diffusion, etc.

As indicated above, information on the C_4-dicarboxylic acid system functioning as respiratory catalysts is abundant for animal, yeast, and bacterial systems, but scanty for fungi. However, where studied, this system has proved to be vital for fungi. Most pertinent in this regard are the experiments of Ryan et al. (1944) using Neurospora crassa, a fungus not known to accumulate in the medium C_4-acids as a result of carbohydrate metabolism. Succinoxidase was present in the mycelium of this organism and succinic, fumaric, and malic acids all could almost completely reverse the inhibition of growth and respiration of the organism caused by iodoacetic acid. Iodoacetate is a well-known inhibitor of enzyme action, largely through its ability to combine avidly with sulfhydryl groups: free sulfhydryls are essential for the action of succinoxidase. Succinic acid alone increased the growth over that in unpoisoned controls in poorly aerated cultures, functioning presumably as an auxiliary oxidation (H-carrying) system. Emphasis was made of the fact that succinic acid could not be used as an energy source in the absence of sugar, strongly suggesting that the action of the C_4-acids is catalytic. Tausson (1941) also concluded that the C_4-dicarboxylic acids were vital for fungi, playing an important role in the synthetic processes of the cell.

In Chapter 8 it was noted that lactic acid-producing species of Rhizopus formed small amounts of fumaric acid, especially in aged cultures. See also Lockwood et al. (1936) and Ward et al. (1936). Sakaguchi et al. (1941, 1942) have compared fumarate formation by such a lactic acid Rhizopus and also by a fumaric acid Rhizopus. Each produced its main acid to the exclusion of the others when utilizing glucose as substrate. On the other hand, when ethyl alcohol or acetic acid is furnished to the preformed mycelium of both, abundant fumarate formation takes place from the fumarate and lactate organisms alike. Thus, the so-called lactic acid organism may be either that or a fumaric organism, depending on the substrate. Interestingly enough, although fumarate is formed from alcohol as the sole carbon source, this acid was not formed at all in the sugar cultures although a considerable accumulation of alcohol occurred together with lactic acid. This probably accounts for the appearance of fumarate in lactic cultures after aging, when the glucose has disappeared or is diminished. In keeping with a general rule, the attack on the initially formed alcohol is deferred until the sugar is depleted.

A curious finding was that considerable alcohol was formed in the conversion of acetate to fumaric acid by both organisms. No interpretation of this unexpected finding was offered but a likely mechanism may be represented as follows:

$$2 \text{ Acetate} \xrightarrow{-2H} \text{Succinic} \xrightarrow{-2H} \text{Fumarate} \xrightarrow{+HOH} \text{Malate} \xrightarrow{-2H} \text{Oxalacetate}$$
$$\downarrow {-CO_2}$$
$$\text{Ethyl alcohol} \xleftarrow{+2H} \text{Acetaldehyde} \xleftarrow{-CO_2} \text{Pyruvate}$$

FUMARATE FORMATION VIA CO_2 FIXATION

Strong evidence exists for the formation by *R. nigricans* of fumaric acid from glucose by a mechanism different than the $2C_2$ condensation.

The first evidence of this kind was the unexpectedly high yields of fumaric acids formed by preformed surface pads of *R. nigricans* when acting on glucose-CaCO$_3$ solution under anaerobic conditions (Foster and Waksman, 1939b). Up to 50 per cent of the aerobic yields were obtained anaerobically, indicating the presence of an alternative mechanism, e.g., one independent of oxygen. Another strain that was tested simultaneously formed no fumarate anaerobically and almost as much aerobically, illustrative of strain specificity and confirming the suggestion of two different fumarate-producing mechanisms. Further experimentation (data given in Table 4) showed that alcohol and CO$_2$ were the other major products present, plus small amounts of lactic acid. High yields

TABLE 4

ACTION OF RHIZOPUS NIGRICANS NO. 45 ON GLUCOSE SOLUTION UNDER ANAEROBIC CONDITIONS[1]

	Glucose culture[2]			Water control
	g.	mM.	mM. C$_2$	
Glucose consumed...............	1.494	8.33	16.66	
Fumaric acid....................	.320	2.76	5.52	None
Calcium in soln.................	.130	.....	.....	None
Calcium accountable as fumaric acid.........................	.110			
Ethyl alcohol...................	.582	12.65	12.65	
Lactic acid.....................	.090	1.00	1.00	
Volatile acid...................	Trace	.....	Total: 19.17	None
Weight conversion of glucose to fumaric acid, per cent..........	21.4			

[1] From Foster and Davis (1948).
[2] 50 ml of 3 per cent glucose.

of fumaric acid were formed and obviously at the expense of alcohol, for a theoretical alcoholic fermentation would have yielded 8.33 × 2 = 16.66 mM. alcohol. Furthermore, a balance based on C$_2$ indicates that the fumarate could not have arisen via the Thunberg-Wieland condensation as it does aerobically. According to this scheme 2.76 mM. fumaric acid requires 2.76 × 2 = 5.52 mM. C$_2$ for its generation. Altogether a total of 19.17 mM. C$_2$ was recovered as alcohol, lactate, and fumarate. However, the maximum C$_2$ available from the sugar fermented was only 16.66 mM., leaving an excess of 2.51 mM. C$_2$ unaccounted for. As there is no question as to the origin of the alcohol and the lactate, the fumarate origin is suspect, the only conclusion being that it does not arise via the assumed condensation of 2C$_2$.

If one assumes the formation of one mole of CO_2 accompanies each mole of alcohol, and computes the oxidation-reduction balance for this experiment, an excess of 5.52 milliatoms of oxygen is found. This means that an oxidized substance has entered the system without being correspondingly reduced.

A most reasonable conclusion is the fixation of CO_2 for the synthesis of fumaric acid via the Wood-Werkman reaction:

$$CO_2 + CH_3COCOOH \rightarrow HOOCCH_2COCOOH$$
$$\text{Pyruvate} \qquad\qquad \text{Oxalacetic acid}$$

By well-known secondary reactions the oxalacetate is converted to fumarate. This C_3 origin of fumarate is now compatable with the amount available from the sugar in Table 4. On this basis the balance is: C_3 available from sugar, 16.66 mM.; C_3 equivalency of

Alcohol	12.65 mM.
Lactate	1.00
Fumarate	2.76
Total	16.41

Experiments on the gas balance revealed that less than theoretical amounts of CO_2 were produced, indicative of reassimilation and also accounting for the O/R balance in excess of theory (Foster and Davis, 1948). All these facts are evidence supporting the conclusion that anaerobic fumarate formation involves CO_2 fixation via the Wood-Werkman reaction. The fixation enzyme oxalacetic decarboxylase was shown to be present in this fungus.

Direct evidence for this conclusion has been obtained by the use of the radioactive isotope of carbon (C^{11}). Radioactive CO_2 was furnished to *R. nigricans* aerobically and anaerobically acting on sugar; the isolated fumaric acid from both treatments after degradation was found to have C^{11} in the carboxy groups (Foster et al., 1941). The anaerobically produced fumarate contained a greater fraction (37 per cent) of the C^{11} assimilated than the fumarate produced aerobically (14.5 per cent). This probably may be explained by the fact that an alternative mechanism for aerobic fumarate synthesis exists, i.e., C_2 condensation. Anaerobically, fumarate formation can occur only by CO_2 fixation. Incidentally, the small amount of fumarate formed by a lactic acid Rhizopus is produced at least partially by CO_2 fixation in addition to C_2 condensation.

The indispensability of CO_2 for fungus growth has been noted several times (Rockwell and Highberger, 1927; see Chapter 12) and in some cases the growth rate is accelerated in proportion to the concentration of CO_2 up to 20 per cent of the atmosphere (Golding, 1940). Doubtless the

CO_2 permitted the synthesis of the C_4-dicarboxylic acid catalytic systems essential for respiratory metabolism. The experiment of Hes (1938) supports this idea; methylene blue reduction by *Aspergillus niger* mycelium in the presence of oxidizable substrate was greatly retarded in the absence of CO_2.

THEORETICAL ASPECTS OF FUMARATE MECHANISMS

The overall equation for fumarate formation from glucose via the C_2 condensation mechanism is:

$$C_6H_{12}O_6 + 3O_2 \rightarrow C_4H_4O_4 + 2CO_2 + 4H_2O$$

Theoretical maximum weight yield is therefore 64.5 per cent of carbohydrate consumed. Yields actually obtained with the best strains of Rhizopus under optimum conditions generally range around 50 per cent conversion both in surface and in submerged culture. According to this equation for aerobic fumarate formation the CO_2 to fumarate ratio is 0.758. Actual measurements show a significant disparity at times: thus ratios of 0.566, 0.627, and 0.609 have been observed (Wang, 1941). These data indicate an average CO_2 deficiency of 20.7 per cent of the theoretical total. It is obvious that the C_2 condensation theory could not account for all the fumarate produced in this case, and Wang accordingly proposed a $C_4 + C_2$ or a $3C_2$ split in the hexose carbon chain instead of the classical $2C_3$ split to account for his results. He failed to detect an overall CO_2 uptake by the organism using conventional chemical methods.

Barinova (1941) also supports the $C_4 + C_2$ split based on the fact that alcohol and the C_4-acids (fumaric and succinic) accumulated in equimolar ratios during the first few days, after which the alcohol disappeared via $2C_2$ condensation to C_4.

These anomalous results regarding fumarate formation, as well as similar disparities with respect to citric acid production by strains of *Aspergillus niger* (see Chapter 12), are at once clarified by the above discovery that bulk formation of a C_4-dicarboxylic acid from sugar by fungi can take place independent of oxygen and that it arises via fixation of carbon dioxide. The anomalies arise from the fact that physiological balances between carbohydrate consumed and CO_2 and organic acids produced were not consistent with values expected according to the mechanisms conventionally used to interpret their formation. These mechanisms all predicate an initial alcoholic fermentation and subsequent aerobic condensation of the C_2 moieties to C_4 and, in the case of citrate, of $C_4 + C_2$. Because of acid yields exceeding those possible by these schemes, mechanisms such as a direct $C_4 + C_2$ split of the hexose chain and even a closing of the C_6 chain have been postulated.

These novel theories need not be resorted to if one considers that all the available data can be reconciled to the fact that in various fungi two mechanisms for the synthesis of C_4-dicarboxylic acid can take place concomitantly, namely, $C_2 + C_2$ and $C_3 + C_1$. The C_1 is reutilized as a byproduct of the C_2 formation (see equations in Chapter 12). This is a logical explanation for the high yields of fumarate and citrate, and low CO_2 yields reported for certain strains. This idea was suggested on the basis of qualitative CO_2 fixation studies with C^{11} (Foster et al., 1941) in which the fixed CO_2 was located in the carboxyl groups of fumarate and citrate. The bulk formation of C_4 reported (Foster and Davis, 1948) now lends added weight to this idea.

Special note must be made of the fact that four other strains of Mucorales that produce fumaric acid aerobically did not produce fumarate anaerobically. This affords one explanation of strain specificity with regard to organic acid production by fungi, at least for fumarate and citrate, and possibly others. That is, strain specificity in part at least, depends on the possession of a bulk CO_2 fixation mechanism which supplements the regular C_2 condensation mechanism for synthesis of C_4- and C_6-acids. Different strains may possess this mechanism to varying degrees. Doubtless all exceptionally high-yielding strains will be found to possess a bulk CO_2 fixation mechanism. In the case of citric acid, it is well to keep in mind the possibility of bulk CO_2 fixation via oxalosuccinic acid.

A strictly chemical approach to this problem, especially under aerobic conditions, is extremely difficult to assess, and in the final analysis isotopic CO_2 studies afford the only absolute proof of CO_2 fixation. Factors rendering difficult, if not impossible, the detection of gross CO_2 uptake in fungus processes using conventional chemical (i.e., non-isotopic) methods are: (1) low partial pressures of CO_2 in normal cultures, possibly limiting the reassimilation to a very low if not immeasurable rate, (2) net *production* of CO_2 concomitantly from oxidation of substrate, and (3) reassimilation of respiratory CO_2 *in situ* before it has a chance to diffuse out of the relatively thick fungus cells.

Returning now to the anaerobic fermentation of glucose by *R. nigricans* No. 45, the three products generated, namely lactic acid, ethyl alcohol and fumaric acid, may be considered, biochemically at least, to represent a reduction of pyruvic acid in three states: (1) before decarboxylation, to lactic acid (2) after decarboxylation, to ethanol (3) after carboxylation, to fumaric acid (malic acid minus water).

INHIBITION OF ANAEROBIC FUMARATE FORMATION BY ELEVATED CO_2 TENSIONS

Foster and Davis (1949) observed that anaerobic fumarate formation by *R. nigricans* mycelium was suppressed when the volume of the closed experimental vessel was small (Warburg vessel) whereas in a large gas volume (desiccator) the same mycelium produced fumarate actively. The effect was traced to the accumulation of CO_2 generated by the alcoholic fermentation. Table 5 shows that elevated CO_2 tensions inhibit fumarate formation and that the effect is proportional to the CO_2 tension.

TABLE 5

CARBON DIOXIDE INHIBITION OF ANAEROBIC FUMARATE FORMATION BY R. NIGRICANS No. 45 MYCELIUM[1]

Initial CO_2 tension	Glucose consumed, mg./ml.	Fumaric acid formed, mg./ml.	Weight conversion of glucose to fumaric acid, per cent
Zero[2]	23.5	3.24	13.8
1 per cent CO_2	20.0	2.52	12.6
30 per cent CO_2	17.0	0.69	3.5
100 per cent CO_2	10.6	0	0

[1] From Foster and Davis (1949).
[2] The CO_2 concentration was zero throughout due to presence of alkaline absorbing agent.

The fumarate-forming mechanism was entirely suppressed in 100 per cent CO_2, glucose consumption being reduced somewhat more than 50 per cent. In 30 per cent CO_2 alcoholic fermentation was inhibited 27.5 per cent and fumarate production almost three times as much, 74.8 per cent. This was interpreted to mean that the fumarate-forming mechanism is more sensitive to CO_2 than any one of the dozen-odd enzymes concerned in alcoholic fermentation, for the sugar consumed is converted chiefly to alcohol and CO_2. The oxalacetate decarboxylase activity of desiccated *R. nigricans* mycelium was inhibited by high CO_2 tensions and it was suggested that CO_2 inhibition of anaerobic fumarate formation in living mycelium centers on the CO_2 fixation reaction itself, the Wood-Werkman reaction. Certain other aspects of CO_2 inhibition of growth and metabolism are discussed in Chapter 12.

FUMAROALANIDE

This interesting derivative of fumaric acid, a combination with alanine (fumaryl-*dl*-alanide or fumaromono-*dl*-alanide) was isolated in crystalline form from cultures of *Penicillium resticulosum* n.s. grown on glucose medium (Birkinshaw *et al.*, 1942). Its structure:

$$\text{HOOC·CH} = \text{CH·CO·NH} - \overset{\displaystyle \text{CH}_3}{\underset{\displaystyle \text{COOH}}{\text{CH}}}$$

Fumaroalanide

Total yield of the crude product was 3.3 g. from a total of 1750 g. glucose furnished to the mold. The substance m. 229° (decomp.) and was a hitherto unknown compound. The fact that the alanine portion was the inactive *dl*-form is a matter of interest inasmuch as the occurrence of *dl*-amino acids in nature is rare. Acid hydrolysis splits the compound to fumaric acid and *dl*-alanine.

INDUSTRIAL PRODUCTION OF FUMARIC ACID

The availability of organisms giving up to 50 to 55 per cent weight conversion of fumarate from sugar furnishes a source of relatively cheap fumaric acid. The principal commercial uses for this acid are for conversion to the *cis*-form, maleic acid, by heating in acid solution. Maleic acid is used chiefly in synthetic resins and in paints and varnishes (Doscher *et al.*, 1941). Magnesium and sodium salts of fumarate have a carthartic action similar to citrates, and may provide an outlet for this product (Locke *et al.*, 1942). It also has found an outlet in the field of synthetic detergents. Doubtless additional uses will become known as the cost of fumaric acid diminishes. However, new postwar developments in the production of maleic acid from benzene by catalytic oxidation may make it difficult for microbiological fumaric acid to compete.

The fumarate is produced from cheap carbohydrates by submerged growth of selected strains of *Rhizopus nigricans* in tanks (Kane *et al.*, 1943; Waksman, 1943). The culture is agitated and aerated mechanically during the fermentation. Limestone ($CaCO_3$) is added as a neutralizing agent, and calcium fumarate accumulates until incipient crystallization, which may occur in 48–72 hours. If the process is allowed to proceed further the whole mass sets to a solid gel. Free fumaric acid crystallizes out quickly from concentrated solutions of calcium fumarate owing to the much lower solubility of the free acid as compared to the salt. Contrary to recoveries in other microbiological processes where the acid-liberated organic product is soluble, and the calcium is separated as insoluble $CaSO_4$, sulfuric acid cannot be used and instead a mineral acid which yields a soluble inorganic calcium salt, such as HCl or HNO_3, is used, thereby enabling the insoluble fumaric acid to be separated.

SUCCINIC ACID

Traces of this acid almost certainly could, if the effort were made, be detected in culture filtrates of virtually all filamentous fungi in media containing more than small amounts of carbohydrate. The universality of CO_2 fixation by pyruvic acid justifies this statement, and the ubiquity of alcohol formation, furnishing the precursors of the C_2 condensation reaction, lends added emphasis.

On the other hand, relatively large accumulations of succinate are characteristic of the genus Fusarium as a whole. However, many other unrelated species in various genera have been reported to form this substance. Systematic research designed to find optimum conditions for formation and accumulation of succinic acid, such as in the case of fumaric acid, has never been carried out because of lack of practical value. In almost every case the succinic acid has been isolated incidental to other problems of interest. More often than not the cultures analyzed were quite old, a circumstance conducive to the formation of succinate from initially-formed alcohol via the Thunberg-Wieland condensation, especially after the carbohydrate supply is depleted or exhausted.

This acid was observed by Pasteur and his contemporaries to accompany alcoholic fermentation of sugar by species of Mucor and Rhizopus in the latter part of the last century. The occurrence of the succinic acid in these cultures in amounts approximating those in yeast fermentation was considered to be additional evidence for the identity of the physiological process of fermentation in the different systems. Although Pasteur himself was convinced that succinate was a direct product of carbohydrate breakdown in yeast fermentation, an insight confirmed a half-century later, the belief of Ehrlich (1909) that succinate originated from glutamic acid of the yeast cell protein* dominated the thinking on this subject until recent years when Kleinzeller (1941) showed that the amount of succinate formed from pyruvate and sugar was in excess of the total weight of the yeasts and moreover was in proportion to the CO_2 tension, indicating a CO_2 fixation by pyruvate, that is, another mechanism besides Ehrlich's. In fact, succinate formation in CO_2-free systems

* Ehrlich's mechanism:

$$\text{HOOC·CH}_2\text{·CH}_2\text{·CH(NH}_2\text{)·COOH} \xrightarrow{-\text{NH}_3} \text{HOOC·CH}_2\text{·CH}_2\text{·CO·COOH}$$

Glutamic acid α-Ketoglutaric acid

$$\xrightarrow{-CO_2} \text{HOOC·CH}_2\text{·CH}_2\text{·CHO} \rightarrow \text{HOOC·CH}_2\text{CH}_2\text{·COOH}$$

Succinic semialdehyde   Succinic acid

Ehrlich showed that glutamic acid added to yeast fermentation did generate succinic acid, though no experimental evidence for this scheme was advanced.

was negligible. Without doubt this also explains the origin of succinate in alcoholic fermentation by fungi, and probably accounts for at least a part of the succinate present in aerobic fungus cultures. This can be stated on the strength of the interconvertibility of the C_4-dicarboxylic acids in metabolism and the fact that the Wood-Werkman reaction has already been demonstrated in fungi and, furthermore, is ubiquitous.

In addition to organisms that belong to the order Mucorales, the Raistrick school has isolated succinate in minor yields from a variety of organisms belonging to other groups, including *Aspergillus terreus*, *Aspergillus sp.*, *Penicillium aurantio-virens*, *Clasterosporium* and *Fumago vagans* (Birkinshaw, 1937). Others could be mentioned.

In an extensive survey covering twenty-nine strains of Fusarium, Lockwood *et al.* (1938) found that succinic acid is formed in appreciable quantities in nineteen strains. One species, *F. martii*, gave about 18 per cent conversion of sugar to succinate, calculated from the figures for soluble calcium. Special note should be made of the association of C_2 compounds with succinic acid in these cultures, suggesting the origin of at least part of the C_4-acid via $2C_2$ condensation. Indeed, this association is rather general.

MALIC ACID

This acid would be of some commercial interest as a possible substitute or competitor for tartaric acid in baking powders. Though it has been detected and isolated in small amounts from a great many fungus cultures where it exists in mixture with a variety of other acids, probably because of the interconvertibility of the C_4-dicarboxylic acids, only in a few isolated instances has it been reported as the chief product of metabolism in the sense that appreciable conversion yields accumulate from sugar.

Bernhauer *et al.* (1932) isolated 2 g. of malic acid from a citric acid strain of *Aspergillus niger*, where its presence can be explained in terms of the mechanism of citric acid formation (Chapter 12). Associated with the malate was 500 g. citric acid, both produced from 975 g. sucrose. Yuill (1936) reported malic acid in considerable amounts accompanied by smaller quantities of succinic and fumaric acids in "waterlogged," i.e. subsurface, cultures of *Aspergillus flavus*. Chalk ($CaCO_3$) was present as a neutralizing agent. When the organism grew in a different manner, that is, in the characteristic surface pellicle form, the metabolism was markedly altered, for calcium gluconate was formed instead. This situation is rather comparable to that in Rhizopus regarding lactic and fumaric acids, as described by Kanel (1935) (see Chapter 8).

The only record of a substantial accumulation of malate as the chief product of sugar utilization is that by Schreyer (1931) for *Penicillium corymbiferum* in surface culture. About one-quarter the weight of glucose consumed was precipitable by alcohol in the form of the calcium salt of the organic acid. The malic acid could not be isolated pure in crystalline form but the following evidence makes it probable that the bulk of the organic acids consisted of *l*-malic acid: elementary analysis and melting point of the phenylhydrazide derivative (m. 218–222°), chemical properties of the calcium salt, and the microscopic appearance of the calcium salt crystals. Fractional precipitation of the phenylhydrazide yielded small amounts of products with other melting points, 193–197° and 176°, indicating that other organic acids were present in minor amounts. Failure to obtain the free *l*-malic acid in crystalline form was ascribed to the presence of these other acids.

ETHYLENEOXIDE-α,β-DICARBOXYLIC ACID

This is the only other C_4-dicarboxylic acid formed in substantial amounts by fungi. It has this structure:

$$\begin{array}{c} \text{HOOC—CH} \\ \diagdown \\ \quad\quad \text{O} \\ \diagup \\ \text{HC—COOH} \end{array}$$

and is known also as fumaryl-glycidic acid. It was discovered and isolated in crystalline form from cultures of two unrelated fungi, *Monilia formosa*, n. s. and *Penicillium viniferum* n.s., by Sakaguchi *et al.* (1939) and later from culture filtrates of *Aspergillus fumigatus* (Birkinshaw *et al.*, 1945). The former organisms produced the acid in yields up to 15 per cent of substrate consumed and from a variety of different substrates, both in growth and in replacement cultures, including sucrose, glucose, levulose, mannitol, sorbitol, arabinose, xylose, erythritol, 2:3-butylene glycol, glycerol, acetate, and alcohol. Small amounts of succinic, fumaric, and citric acids accompanied the new substance in the *M. formosa* cultures.

The origin of this acid is a matter of speculation although its formation from such diverse carbon sources suggests a simple common precursor which may be C_2, or $C_3 + C_1$ similar to the other C_4-acids, and which, as mentioned, accompany the new acid. Chemically, it is an intermediate oxidation step between fumaric and tartaric acids. In fact, ethylene-α, β-dicarboxylic acid, a levorotatory substance, $[\alpha]_D^{17} = -100°$, is converted to mesotartaric and *d*-tartaric acids by refluxing in aqueous solution. This hydrolysis can be followed polarimetrically.

The tartaric acids themselves are not known to accumulate in fungus cultures to any significant amount although they have been reported to be present in small amounts in a certain few cases. Because of their relation the other C$_4$-dicarboxy acids in fungus metabolism, one might expect that tartrate formation will eventually be discovered. Actually tartrate formation has been obtained by *Aspergillus niger* acting on ethyl alcohol as the sole carbon source (Bernhauer and Böckl, 1932). A mixture of tartrate and malate was obtained in 25 per cent yield. Presumably all these C$_4$-dicarboxylic acids originate in the same manner as fumaric acid.

OTHER DICARBOXYLIC ACIDS

Two other short-chain dicarboxylic acids are known products of fungus metabolism, both, chemically speaking, simple derivations of the C$_4$-dicarboxylic acids, by virtue of 1-carbon substituents on a methylene carbon of the C$_4$ chain. These are itaconic and itatartaric acids respectively, and are discussed in Chapter 13.

REFERENCES

Barinova, S. A. 1941. *Microbiology USSR* **10**, 716–729 (Chem. Abstracts **38**, 2990, 1944).
Bernhauer, K., and Böckl, N. 1932. *Biochem. Z.* **253**, 16–24.
Bernhauer, K., Böckl, N., and Siebenauger, H. 1932. *Biochem. Z.* **253**, 37–41.
Bernhauer, K., and Thole, H. 1936. *Biochem. Z.* **287**, 167–171.
Birkinshaw, J. H. 1937. *Biol. Revs. Cambridge Phil. Soc.* **12**, 357–392.
Birkinshaw, J. H., Bracken, A., and Raistrick, H. 1945. *Biochem. J.* **39**, 70–72.
Birkinshaw, J. H., Raistrick, H., and Smith, G. 1942. *Biochem. J.* **36**, 829–835.
Butkewitsch, W., and Federoff, M. 1929a. *Biochem. Z.* **206**, 440–456.
Butkewitsch, W., and Federoff, M. 1929b. *Biochem. Z.* **207**, 302–318.
Butkewitsch, W., and Federoff, M. 1930a. *Biochem. Z.* **219**, 87–102.
Butkewitsch, W., and Federoff, M. 1930b. *Biochem. Z.* **219**, 103–121.
Clutterbuck, P. W., Mukkopadhyay, S. L., Oxford, A. E., and Raistrick, H. 1940. *Biochem. J.* **34**, 664–677.
Doscher, C. K., Kane, J. H., Cragwall, G. O., and Staebner, W. H. 1941. *Ind. Eng. Chem.* **33**, 315–319.
Ehrlich, F. 1909. *Biochem. Z.* **18**, 391–423.
Ehrlich, F. 1911. *Ber.* **44**, 3737–3742.
Ehrlich, F. 1919. *Ber.* **52**, 63–64.
Ehrlich, F., and Bender, I. 1927a. *Z. physiol. Chem.* **170**, 118–133.
Ehrlich, F., and Bender, I. 1927b. *Z. physiol. Chem.* **172**, 317–318.
Foster, J. W., Carson, S. F., Ruben, S., and Kamen, M. D. 1941. *Proc. Natl. Acad. Sci. U. S.* **27**, 590–596.
Foster, J. W., and Davis, J. B. 1948. *J. Bact.* **56**, 329–338.
Foster, J. W., and Davis, J. B. 1949. *Arch. Biochem.* **21**, 135–142.
Foster, J. W., and Waksman, S. A. 1939a. *J. Bact.* **37**, 599–617.
Foster, J. W., and Waksman, S. A. 1939b. *J. Am. Chem. Soc.* **61**, 127–135.
Foster, J. W., and Waksman, S. A. 1939c. *Science* **89**, 37.
Golding, N. S. 1940. *J. Dairy Sci.* **23**, 891–898.
Gottschalk, A. 1926. *Z. physiol. Chem.* **152**, 136–143.

Gottschalk, A. 1927. *Z. physiol. Chem.* **172**, 314–316.
Gottschalk, A. 1929. *Z. physiol. Chem.* **182**, 311–312.
Hes, J. W. 1938. *Nature* **141**, 647.
Kane, J. N., Finlay, A., and Amann, P. F. 1943. U. S. Patent 2,327,191.
Kanel, E. 1935. *Microbiology USSR* **4**, 636–654.
Kleinzeller, A. 1941. *Biochem. J.* **35**, 495–501.
Locke, A., Locke, R. B., Schlesinger, H., and Carr, H. 1942. *J. Am. Pharm. Assoc.* **31**, 12–14.
Lockwood, L. B., Stubbs, J. J., and Senseman, C. E. 1938. *Zentr. Bakt. Parasitenk. Abt. II* **98**, 167–171.
Lockwood, L. B., Ward, G. E., and May, O. E. 1936. *J. Agr. Research* **53**, 849–857.
Raistrick, H., and Simonart, P. 1933. *Biochem. J.* **27**, 628–633.
Rockwell, G. E., and Highberger, J. H. 1927. *J. Infect. Diseases* **40**, 438–466.
Ryan, F. J., Tatum, E. L., and Giese, A. C. 1944. *J. Cellular Comp. Physiol.* **23**, 83–94.
Sakaguchi, K., Asai, T., and Munekata, H. 1941. *J. Agr. Chem. Soc. Japan* **17**, 19–22.
Sakaguchi, K., Asai, T., and Munekata, H. 1942. *Zentr. Bakt. Parasitenk. Abt. II* **105**, 161–165.
Sakaguchi, K., Inoue, T., and Tada, S. 1939. *Zentr. Bakt. Parasitenk. Abt. II* **100**, 302–307.
Schreyer, R. 1928. *Biochem. Z.* **202**, 131–156.
Schreyer, R. 1931. *Biochem. Z.* **240**, 295–325.
Slade, H. D., and Werkman, C. H. 1943. *Arch. Biochem.* **2**, 97–111.
Sumiki, Y. 1929. *Bull. Agr. Chem. Soc. Japan* **5**, 10–13, 13–15.
Sumiki, Y. 1931. *Bull. Agr. Chem. Soc. Japan* **7**, 62–63.
Takahashi, T., and Asai, T. 1927. *Proc. Imp. Acad. Japan* **3**, 86–89.
Takahashi, T., and Asai, T. 1933. *Zentr. Bakt. Parasitenk. Abt. II* **89**, 81–84.
Takahashi, T., and Sakaguchi, K. 1925. *J. Agr. Chem. Soc. Japan* **1**, 344.
Tausson, V. O. 1941. *Compt. rend. acad. sci. URSS* **31**, 373–376.
Thies, W. 1930. *Zentr. Bakt. Parasitenk. Abt. II* **82**, 321–347.
Waksman, S. A. 1943. U. S. Patent 2,326,986.
Wang, Y. 1941. *J. Shanghai Sci. Inst. N. S.* **1**, Abstracts 177–178 In English (*Chem. Abstracts* **37**, 3786 (1943)).
Ward, G. E., Lockwood, L. B., May, O. E., and Herrick, H. T. 1936. *J. Am. Chem. Soc.* **58**, 1286–1288.
Wehmer, C. 1918. *Ber.* **51**, 1663–1668.
Wehmer, C. 1928. *Biochem. Z.* **197**, 418–431.
Yuill, J. L. 1936. *Chem. Industries* **55**, 155.

CHAPTER 12

CITRIC ACID

$$
\begin{array}{l}
\text{CH}_2\text{—COOH} \\
\quad \diagdown \text{OH} \\
\text{C} \diagup \\
\quad \diagup \diagdown \text{COOH} \\
\text{CH}_2\text{—COOH}
\end{array}
$$

Probably more study has been devoted to this fungus process than any other function in mold metabolism, yet, curiously, there is probably less basic established fundamental knowledge regarding it than in most, if not all, the other major processes treated in this book. This paradox is true notwithstanding the fact that historically the citric process in fungi was one of the first to be discovered (still in the last century) and was immediately recognized to have important industrial potentialities.

In one respect, however, study of this process through the years has been an important factor in the development of the general field of mold metabolism, for from it has evolved much information relative to the *biological* aspects of mold metabolism, as well as methodology. By and large, this information has found applicability and ready acceptance in the study of other, later fungus processes, and to a large extent has been the reason for the rapid, successful advancement of knowledge in those segments of the field. Experience with the *biological* aspects of citric formation was purposely emphasized, for as indicated, specific knowledge and information of the biochemical aspects of the citric process itself has been very slow in forthcoming, and even today much of it can be obtained only by surmisal and by comparative biochemistry. In a sense, because much of the methodology and biological aspects of the field of mold metabolism did evolve from the citric process, perhaps this chapter dealing with a subject that has had so much teaching value for other processes, should have been an introductory one, preceding the chapters dealing with the organic acids. However, its location here is dictated by the relative complexity of the biochemical synthesis of citric acid and the fact that it fits orderly into the biochemical sequence outlined in Chapter 4. Because most of the biological principles and methodology have been covered in previous chapters, they will not be covered here.

Among the main points having general applicability in the study of mold metabolism and which largely emanated, directly or indirectly, from a half century's experience with the citric process, these may be mentioned: (a) high enough yields of carbohydrate dissimilation products, especially organic acids, are obtainable to make industrial processes economically feasible; (b) recognition of the fact that if a strain of a given species produces a certain metabolic product, the best chance for finding other organisms to carry out this process as well as the original strain or better is to examine other strains of the same species; (c) recognition of strain specificity (see Chapter 5); (d) physiological degeneration; (e) the proportions in which the several products of metabolism appear in the culture filtrates can be controlled and varied at will: (f) remarkable sensitivity of fungus metabolism to small alterations in any one of many environmental conditions, i.e., response variation, (g) replacement culture technique (Pilzdecke); (h) development of surface growth techniques, their principles and practice, and philosophy in the field of fungus metabolism. In a way, this latter probably has been a handicap to the development of unambiguous and reproducible findings in the field, and its long entrenchment has been due to the fact that only in the last few years has any significant success been obtained in securing citric acid in submerged shake cultures. That an aura was created about the idea that fungi were adapted only to surface type growth and metabolism is best indicated by the fact that more recent fungus processes like those resulting in fumaric, gluconic, kojic, and itaconic acids underwent very comprehensive and systematic development as surface processes; the same applied even to penicillin, though it was soon exploited by submerged culture. See Chapter 3 for a discussion of surface vs. submerged cultivation. There is no doubt that the whole development of the field of mold metabolism would have had an interestingly different evolution, had it been discovered 20 to 30 years ago that citric acid could be formed in appreciable amounts in submerged culture. It is only 16 years since the principles of submerged mold culture were exposed by Kluyver and Perquin.

From these as well as other considerations it may be said that in a sense, the field of mold metabolism in relation to carbohydrate at least, has grown up around the citric acid process.

HISTORICAL

The vast amount of work devoted to this process in the last half century is a direct result of the enormous commercial potentialities of citric acid. A second reason may be its physiological uniqueness as a biochemical process, but this certainly must have played a very minor role because even after this process in fungi was realized to have a striking parallelism to the respiratory events in mammalian (and plant) tissues it has been virtually neglected, notwithstanding the fine opportunity available for an enzymatic or physiological approach to citric origin in a system which synthesizes it to an exceedingly intense degree.

The German botanist, Carl Wehmer, discovered citric acid in cultures of fungi in 1893, not long after he discovered oxalic acid formation in fungi (Wehmer, 1893, 1897, 1912, 1913). The two original isolates were obtained from the air and resembled Penicillia, but this hitherto unknown property of citric acid formation induced him to create the genus Citromycetes, with two species, C. pfefferianus and C. glaber. Later, the eminent American mycologist, C. Thom, considered these organisms as true Penicillia, and Wehmer's genus designation has been abandoned. Wehmer demonstrated that citric acid-forming Penicillia could be isolated in abundance from the air of different localities, and also found it to be produced by P. lacteum and by the Phycomycete Mucor pyriformis (M. racemosus). While citric acid formation by Penicillia is known today to be a very common property for Penicillia, only rarely has this been reported for Phycomycetes. In the first reported experiments on Penicillia a 50 per cent weight conversion yield was obtained from sugar consumed, the accumulation of citric acid in the culture filtrate being the equivalent of an 8 per cent solution. The organisms were very sensitive to the presence of mineral acids and were retarded, but they were not, however, hindered by the free citric acid accumulating in the culture. Calcium carbonate was also utilized successfully as a neutralizing agent and gave the highest yields. Wehmer was impressed by the origin of this branched chain compound from the straight chain sugar molecule, but never studied the mechanism of its origin. He did, however, interpret the meaning of citric acid formation from the standpoint of the metabolism of the fungus in precisely the same way we consider it today, namely, as a manifestation of incomplete oxidation of carbohydrate, the citric acid (like oxalic acid previously studied by Wehmer) being an intermediate accumulation product in sugar oxidation. Oxygen was shown to be essential to the process.

Wehmer was very much alive to the utilization of this fungus citric process for practical industrial purposes, and he obtained broad patent coverage of his process, both in Germany and in several other countries. The reasons why Wehmer's process never did reach a commercial success despite the attractively high yields and relative speed of the process almost certainly were due to the failure to master the problem of contamination when done on a factory scale. Two factors doubtless were involved here: (1) Aside from the brewing industry, there were no large-scale pure culture fermentation industries at that time and the highly refined methodology and engineering equipment, design, and practice essential for factory scale operations were non-existent, (2) the organisms

Wehmer used could not tolerate a high enough initial acidity, and consequently the citric acid fungi were not furnished any selective advantage over contaminants. Furthermore, with regard to pH, $CaCO_3$ was considered essential during the growth in order to obtain maximum yields, through "fixing" the citrate (Wehmer, 1905–07). Aside from industrial applications, Wehmer's published laboratory work also reveals an underestimation of the concept of pure culture technique.

The situation today is quite different, and with the highly evolved and efficient microbiological technology available today (exemplified by penicillin and streptomycin production) the contamination problems very likely would not be so formidable an obstacle to the utilization of the Penicillia in citric acid production, especially in submerged culture. The major factors would be yields obtainable with a particular strain, and also the cost of the neutralizing agent together with the mineral acid required in the recovery stage to liberate free citric acid. All in all, a neutral aerobic fermentation today on an industrial scale is entirely feasible whereas this could hardly be said to be the case less than a decade ago.

One of the peculiar incidents typical of science is the fact that Wehmer, despite extensive work with various fungi on the citric process, never discovered that Aspergilli, especially *A. niger*, were potent citric acid-formers; in general our knowledge today indicates this property is more common and intense in these organisms than in Penicillia. In fact, Wehmer's experience with oxalic acid formation led him to believe the black Aspergilli were typified by oxalate metabolism, and Penicillia-like fungi by citrate metabolism. Probably this stems from the fact that the conditions under which he tested them (low acidity) were conducive to oxalate formation, as demonstrated so cogently by Currie in 1917.

Our whole modern concept of the citric process is based on this work of Currie, and in order to become conversant with this subject the reader is almost obliged to be familiar with this paper, which represents a mile-stone in the subject. Actually citric acid was already recognized to be formed in substantial amounts by the black Aspergilli (Zahorski, 1913; Thom and Currie, 1916), but Currie laid the broad foundations of current knowledge of this process. The outstanding discovery was that the *A. niger* was capable of growing abundantly at initial pH values of 2.5 to 3.5 and would accumulate high concentrations of free citric acid sufficient to lower the pH of the medium below 2.0. This was the lowest pH tolerance in a vegetative biological system known up to that time (since then the autotrophic bacterium *Sulfomonas thiooxidans* has been found to grow well at reactions approximating pH 0 (Starkey, 1925). Starkey (1943) described two fungi, *Acontium velatum* and an unidentified member of the Dematiaceae, which grew well in synthetic medium at pH 0.3.   *A. niger* grows just as well at higher pH values (4 to 5) but here little or no citric acid is formed, oxalic acid being formed almost exclusively (some strains also produced gluconic acid). Thus, by adjusting the initial pH of the medium the citric acid yield can be varied between zero and 50–60 per cent weight conversion of the consumed sugar.

The problem of strain specificity is very real in this work. Some strains are good gluconic acid-producers and poor citric-producers, and vice versa, and some are intermediate (Bernhauer, 1928a). Bernhauer (1926) was able to achieve a similar separation of citric acid formation in the case of strong gluconic acid-forming strains of *Aspergillus niger*. Here in the replacement phase peptone nitrogen, $CaCO_3$ and low inorganic N sources favored gluconic acid accumulation at the expense of citric.

The very low optimum initial pH at once eliminates most contamination problems for very few other microorganisms (air-borne types) can develop in such high acidity, although some fungi (Penicillia) do grow on and parasitize the *A. niger* surface mycelium.   It also makes sterilization simple, for at pH 2 to 3, merely steaming at 100° for 30 minutes suffices, whereas above 4.0–4.5 steam under pressure is required for sterilization with a safety factor, this necessitating special high-pressure equipment.   As in all cases of products of carbohydrate metabolism in fungi, and in accordance with ideas of shunt metabolism, maximum citric acid formation is favored by high sugar concentrations (10–15 per cent) and low N content of the medium.   In general NH_3-N is more favorable than NO_3-N, although urea also is favorable.

So long as the pH is kept low, citric acid is the only acid appearing; as the pH rises mixtures of oxalate, citrate and gluconate occur, and eventually only oxalate is formed at the higher pH values.

Selected strains of Aspergilli may accumulate citric acid from concentrated sugar media (15 per cent) to the stage where the culture filtrate represents a 7.5 to 10 or more per cent solution of the acid. One might judge that these high contents of citric acid would create such an extremely high hydrogen ion concentration (low pH) that the organism would become inhibited and that both growth and metabolism would be injured. Actually, these fungi grow well at pH 1.8 to 2.0, and the ionization of citric acid is such that very large increments in concentrations make only slight changes in pH values.

	Citric acid concentration, per cent			
	7.5	10	15	20
pH	1.7	1.6	1.5	1.4

One might expect that strains able to tolerate and form organic acids in the presence of high initial acidity might be superior acid-formers in the absence of the initial high acidity. This has been shown to be the case (Bernhauer, 1929). However, different strains reacted differently to the initial acidity caused by HCl and H_3PO_4. In general HCl is the preferred acidification agent in the citric acid process. Bernhauer also showed that consecutive transfer of a fungus (A. *niger*) through media of high acidity leads to increased acid-forming powers of the fungus. This has been confirmed by Doelger and Prescott (1934) who obtained a 3.5-fold increase in citric acidity after 15 consecutive transfers through acid mediums. The final value represented a 1.2 N solution of citric acid. Doubtless such results can be explained by selection of acid-tolerant variants. Strains initially characterized as weak citric acid-formers can be considerably strengthened by this technique (Bernhauer et al., 1941).

By the very demonstration of these high citric acid yields Currie's work invalidated Wehmer's concept of the reutilization of unneutralized citric acid. However, as brought out in the discussion of shunt metabolism in Chapter 4, the failure to attack as a source of energy and further convert the initially formed citric acid holds only insofar as the other preferred energy source is present in the medium, namely carbohydrate. Upon exhaustion of the sugar, the fungus now destroys the accumulated citric acid. This has been demonstrated in physiological experiments centering around respiratory quotients (Wang, 1940). The presence of sugar quickly stops the oxidation of citric acid. For this reason mainly, the industrial citric process is always stopped short of complete sugar utilization. On the other hand, if $CaCO_3$ is present so that the citric acid is present as citrate, the organism does not attack it upon exhaustion of the sugar. The acid is protected from decomposition in the calcium salt form. However, as discussed in Chapter 2, the pH picture in surface cultures is not clear-cut. Under homogeneous conditions where the pH factor may be evaluated unequivocally, it is known (Karow and Waksman, 1947, see also Chrzaszcz and Peyros, 1935; Frey, 1931) that high acidity-tolerant fungi are nevertheless favored by partial neutralization which increases the rate and amount of citric acid formed, though not the conversion percentage. In other words, sugar consumption and growth were accelerated. Thus, an unneutralized culture has 52.8 g. citric acid per liter; cultures one-fifth and one-third neutralized by $CaCO_3$ had 56.8 and 71.3 g. per liter, respectively. The pH was never allowed to rise above 3.5, this preventing oxalate formation. Curiously, when KOH, NaOH, or NH_4OH were used as neutralizing agents, oxalate was always formed.

When citric or oxalic acid are attacked by the fungus the eventual oxidation product is carbon dioxide. The former acid generally is decomposed in part to oxalic acid, this being further decomposed to CO_2 when the citric acid is largely exhausted. Currie formulated this metabolic sequence thusly:

$$\text{Sugar} \rightarrow \text{Citric acid} \rightarrow \text{Oxalic acid} \rightarrow CO_2$$

As discussed in Chapter 10, this does not mean that oxalate formation from sugar always proceeds via citrate; it means merely that the fungus can form oxalate from citrate.

In spite of the vast amount of work done on the citric process in many countries since Currie's 1917 paper, it appears not to be an exaggeration to say that aside from the general features outlined earlier, no major advances specific to the citric process were made until the feasibility of production of this acid in submerged cultures was demonstrated only within the past few years. As emphasized in the previous chapters, the vast amount of work is a clear indication of the industrial implications of this process, and doubtless was a direct consequence of the practical value of the process. The best evidence of this is the decided utilitarian slant to the great mass of the published work on this subject. Actually, mycological citric acid is a huge industry in many countries today, including several European countries, Russia, England, Japan (before the war) and the United States. An institute devoted to the development and improvement of this process exists in Russia. In the United States one company dominates production, furnishing approximately one-half of the 13,000 tons produced annually today. Eighty per cent of the total is fermentation citric acid. The rest is contributed by the citrus-fruit industry as a by-product from culled lemons, and a few smaller fermentation companies. In terms of monetary size, the microbiological production of citric acid ranks after industrial alcohol (excluding alcoholic beverages), acetone-butanol fermentation, penicillin and streptomycin production, and lactic acid fermentation. The main uses of citric acid are for medicinal products (65 per cent) and for foods (flavoring extracts, soft drinks, etc., 14 per cent); the remainder is used in candies, inks, silvering, dyeing, calico printing, engraving, etc. (Wells and Herrick, 1938).

All mycological production still is by the shallow pan surface process, although recent patents make it very likely that a shift to the more popular submerged method is imminent within a few years. At least, several companies are directing efforts toward that goal. Naturally, details of the commercial process are trade secrets involving special selected fungus strains, nutrient and environmental conditions, mechanical operations and contamination-proof practices, but it can be calculated that the output of the main supplier in the United States must necessitate constant cultivation of fungus mycelium in the range of 10 to 20 acres of surface growth. This, according to one estimation, involves the use of about 37,000 shallow pans measuring 2–3 inches in depth and 3 feet square (Wells and Ward, 1939).

It would be superfluous to cover here the extremely profuse literature contributed to this subject in the past three decades or so because for the most part no orderly development of the subject was made, an incredible lack of uniformity and reproducibility (from laboratory to laboratory) prevails, and even the informed student of the subject obtains only an impression of confusion as to the scientific meaning of these diverse results. Certainly, few scientific generalizations or principles of teaching or educational value may be derived from them. They serve one generalization, however—the circumstances under which high yields of citric acid are formed in the very numerous different laboratories and at different times are highly empirical, and in the main can only rarely be translated into other laboratories with reasonable duplication of results. Few laboratories ever work with the same strain or culture conditions, yet by trial and error testing, high yields have been obtained in numerous different laboratories. Laboratories from which much work on this subject has originated over a period of years are those of Bernhauer in Prague, Butkewitsch in Russia, and Chrzaszcz in Poland.

A concise but rather complete compilation of much of the literature on this work has been made recently (von Loesecke, 1945) with special emphasis on optimum conditions for maximum citric acid yields, i.e., the practical and production aspects of the process (see also Challenger, 1929; Prescott and Dunn, 1940). Bernhauer (1926) gives a comprehensive coverage of the physiology of the surface process. Obtainable from these articles are numerous references dealing with the nature and concentration of carbon source (carbohydrate), nature and amounts of nutrient minerals, cultural methods, media composition, pH, surface area of mycelial mat, air supply, temperature, process time, yields of citric acid, and commercial recovery.

The gist of all these studies may be epitomized by saying that empirically selected strains, usually *A. niger*, must be used, the initial pH of the medium ought to be 2.0–4.0, sucrose as a source of carbon (in the form of molasses, industrially) at initial concentration of 10 to 15 per cent, inorganic N or urea as a source of nitrogen, and KH_2PO_4 and $MgSO_4$ as the other main minerals added. Additional minerals required in smaller amounts are furnished as impurities in the water or in the sugar, but must be in correct balance (see later). A weight conversion yield of about 50 to 70 per cent of the sugar consumed may be obtained in a growth period of 5 to 10 days. After the mycelial mat has been formed, replacement solutions containing sugar, with or without certain predetermined supplementary nutrients, are converted to citric acid in about one-half that time. The citric acid in the culture filtrate may amount to a 10 to 15 per cent solution, and is recovered by conversion with lime to the calcium salt followed by crystallization as calcium citrate. The free citric acid may be prepared by treatment of a solution of the salt with the calculated amount of sulfuric acid, separating the insoluble $CaSO_4$, concentrating and crystallizing the acid.

Any process such as Zender's (1937, 1938) which in principle crystallizes the citric acid directly from the culture fluid without first conversion to the calcium salt, possesses a great economic advantage over the latter process because the cost of the lime and the sulfuric acid needed to liberate the free acid again is the largest material item in the process next to the carbohydrate. The small amounts of residual sugar which prevent crystallization of the acid may be fermented out by yeast, but this involves partial neutralization to about pH 4.0–4.5 to permit yeast activity, thus defeating the objective to a certain extent. The alcohol may be recovered as a byproduct (Fernbach *et al.*, 1925).

Apart from the establishment of the optimum routine factors such as nitrogen source, air supply, temperatue, etc., what are the really decisive factors in the initiation of a successful, uniformly reproducible production of citric acid with high yields, both in the laboratory for fundamental investigations and in the factory for commercial scale operations? Despite the mass of seemingly conflicting results in the literature, it is possible to make a few deductions on the basis of the literature, experience, and current knowledge. First and foremost by far, indeed, the very crux of success, depends on the strain of fungus used. Obviously, a high acidity-tolerant strain has a certain advantage in suppressing contamination and oxalate formation, but as described above, it is perfectly feasible today to conduct neutral fermentations.*
It is not sufficient merely to have a selected high-yielding strain—this is taken for granted—and the very abundant literature indicates these are not lacking nor particularly difficult to procure. The stumbling block is the translation of laboratory results to pilot plant or factory scale, owing to inevitable differences between the laboratory and larger scale operations despite every effort to replicate conditions exactly. Such difficulties in duplication must and ordinarily do mean that the differences are relatively minor in degree, but obviously are major in effect. The

---

* The term fermentation is used here in the colloquial sense, meaning the formation of some product by a microbiological process. The citric acid process is an oxidation, not a fermentation, in the Pasteurian or scientific sense.

gaseous atmosphere (air flow and distribution) may be one aspect, but the most common cause of the discrepancy is apparently the slight uncontrolled variables in the trace element composition of the medium in production units, and also a disturbance of the nutrient balance previously found to be optimum for the process. This may be caused by the cruder chemicals generally used in large scale, or by the tap water, or by the pipes and vessels, etc. with which the medium comes in contact. The extra time consumed during heating and cooling of large batches in sterilization may also cause trouble by creating changes in the medium.

In other words, this is one aspect of the "response variation" described in Chapter 4, and is the bane of commercial scale processes inasmuch as the most rigorous control of operations usually cannot entirely eliminate these significant fluctuations in performance of the fungus used; most often the plant yields are not as high as those obtainable in the laboratory with the same strain. All this is a reflection of the extreme sensitivity of the fungus to its nutritional environment to the point where differences in the environment would be inapparent were it not for the response variation of the fungus. Ordinarily, tap water, for example, contains enough iron to make it greatly inferior to distilled water for citric acid formation (Knobloch and Sellman, 1941; Perquin, 1938).

The sensitivity of citric acid-forming fungi to trace elements is just as marked as in other acid-forming fungi. The main point is that different strains react differently, that various levels of zinc or other trace elements evoke varying responses, and that a given level of an ion may enhance citric acid formation in one fungus and depress it in another strain. In other words, strain specificity of citric acid-forming fungi is exceedingly striking in connection with trace element nutrition. Zinc, iron, and manganese in proper proportions are the most critical trace elements, the proper proportions being dependent on a particular strain. Details and a number of examples of these effects are found in Chapter 7. (See also Foster, 1939; von Loesecke, 1945, Perlman *et al.*, 1946a; Perquin, 1938; Knobloch and Sellman, 1941.)

As the biological sensitivity of these organisms is much greater than the usual control efforts, the best solution, in fact the essence of the solution, is to circumnavigate these troubles by utilizing fungus strains which are relatively insensitive to the kinds of variables encountered. The enormous diversity among strains in response to environmental variables also includes some which are relatively less susceptible to nutritional environment than others. Strains of this type, relatively rare, and selected purposely for this character, are the key features in uniform and reproducible citric acid formation and almost certainly provide the basis for the most efficient commercial manufacture of citric acid.

As an example, one may cite the fact that while two different citric acid strains may behave alike on pure sucrose media, the citric acid yields by one may be far superior to the other when the sucrose is furnished in the form of molasses. Detailed published examination of the molasses problem in citric acid formation was first made by Karow (1942) (Karow and Waksman, 1947; see also Bernhauer et al., 1941) for a high yielding strain of *Aspergillus wentii* in submerged culture, and later by Perlman et al. (1946a and b) for *A. niger* strains. Compared to the corresponding amounts of synthetic sucrose medium which gave, under the (submerged) conditions employed, 50 to 67 per cent yields, the best molasses tested yielded only 3 to 20 per cent conversion. The critical features here proved to be the mineral content of molasses, which is variable from batch to batch. The ash from molasses added to an equivalent amount of sucrose depressed the yields to those expected of molasses, hence the inferiority of molasses stems from the mineral unbalance which disturbs the metabolism of the fungus. This effect manifests itself by increased cell synthesis and growth at the expense of citric acid formation. Treatment of molasses to remove impurities including the minerals, by absorption in series on activated carbon (two kinds: bone char and Suchar) and synthetic ionic exchange resins (Amberlite IR 4 and IR 1) restored the molasses (in basal medium) to a citric acid efficiency equivalent to pure sucrose. This is to be expected as this purification procedure generates a virtually pure sucrose solution from molasses. The cation impurities appear to be the agents responsible, and their removal with exchange resins yields threefold more citric acid (Perlman et al., 1946a and b). Even commercial grades of glucose and sucrose are improved by this treatment, though iron must be restored after the absorption. Another purification method applicable to molasses depends on precipitation of the harmful Fe and Mn with small amounts of potassium ferrocyanide in acid solution ($K_4Fe(CN)_6$).

The point demonstrated here is that this citric acid organism is an example of one highly sensitive to its mineral environment. Other fungi are known, though no published reports have appeared, which are not influenced so radically in their citric acid metabolism. Cost calculations indicate that the commercial production of citric acid involves such relatively insensitive fungus strains, for the use of pure sugar would be too expensive a raw material. If not, some purification step must be employed. Interestingly enough, different types of cane molasses vary considerably in their usefulness in this process; the best cane molasses apparently is, however, inferior to beet sugar molasses, as the latter is the preferred raw material for the citric acid industry. Presumably the types and amounts of mineral impurities in beet molasses are relatively inocuous to the particular fungus strain employed.

Not to be overlooked is the presence of toxic factors in molasses. This toxicity may actually retard growth and rate of sugar turnover. Also, it may specifically influence unfavorably the citric acid mechanism whereby reduced yields would be obtained. According to von Loesecke (1945) this feature dictates the use, in commercial practice, of beet molasses only from certain localities. Others are believed to be unsuitable owing to toxic effects on the organism.

SUBMERGED PRODUCTION OF CITRIC ACID

Through the years several reports have been made in which citric acid formation was demonstrated under what may be considered more or less submerged conditions. However, only in 1938, beginning with Perquin's work, have detailed systematic studies been available, and these studies represent the first real advances in the subject since Currie's work in 1917. The work of Perquin is published in Dutch and unfortunately has not received the attention it deserves. It cannot be overlooked by anyone interested in submerged citric acid production, for it deals systematically, qualitatively and quantitatively, with virtually all the factors influencing citric acid formation under these conditions, and is perhaps a model for subsequent work. In fact, at this date, work of Perquin, of Karow, and of Shu and Johnson (1948) are the only published comprehensive approachs to this practical development, although the essence of a submerged process is described in the Szücs patents (1944, 1948). Reference to the sporadic earlier attempts at submerged citric acid formation may be obtained from the above-mentioned works.

The outstanding feature of this technique is that some strains are adapted to forming citric acid abundantly but others (the majority) are not. Furthermore, the fact that an organism produces citric acid in high yields in surface culture does not mean it will perform similarly in submerged culture. In other words, strains effective in submerged culture are those selected for that property. The conditions are highly critical, so that a medium ideal for one organism may be poor for another organism, yet the latter may itself be a good producer under another set of conditions. For this reason, few generalizations may be made. A case in point: *A. wentii*, tested in the medium found by Perquin (1938) to be best for growth and citric acid production by *A. niger*, gave very sparse growth and little citric acid (Karow, 1942). Perquin's medium contained no added manganese, but must have had it as an impurity at about the proper level.   Yet when Karow added manganese, there was good growth but little citric acid produced, a feature also observed by Shu and Johnson (1947) for *A. niger*.   The latter authors revealed that the sensitivity to manganese is so extreme that special precautions must be taken to minimize the amount of this element carried into the medium in the spores used as inoculum (see Chapter 7).   This is an outstanding example of the extreme susceptibility of the citric acid-forming mechanism to slight alterations in nutrient environment.

In all cases, the mineral balance is highly crucial.   When imbalance prevails the result usually is greater synthesis of cell material at the expense of citric acid accumulation.   This sensitivity is reduced and in some cases largely eliminated under conditions where cell synthesis is sharply limited, as for example, in replacement cultures where one or more growth essentials is deficient or lacking altogether.   Thus, one finds in current aspects of this development (Perquin, Karow, Szücs) marked emphasis on the replacement phase (but see below).

A second major point is that the composition of the medium during the growth phase exercises a profound influence on the behavior of the organism in any given replacement medium.   This has been illustrated decisively by Bernhauer (1928b) for citric acid formation by *A. niger*, and by Kluyver and Perquin (1933) for kojic acid formation by *Aspergillus flavus*, and applies equally well to citric acid formers (see especially Perquin, 1938).   Bernhauer's results (1928b and d) are of special significance for they show strikingly that the *qualitative* metabolism of the preformed fungus (surface mycelium) acting on sugar solutions depends on the medium on which the mycelium was grown.   Thus, gluconic acid is produced almost exclusively when the mycelium was previously cultivated on a growth medium poor in nitrogen, regardless of the type of nitrogen.   The best N concentration was 0.01–0.03 per cent N.   On the other hand, citric acid was formed only when the mycelium had been cultivated on a medium relatively rich in nitrogen.   These results can only mean that the enzyme makeup of the mold is different and dependent upon the nitrogen content available during growth.   Now, even when the growth medium is relatively rich in nitrogen, the type of nitrogen is of paramount influence on the amount of citric acid formed in replacement medium.   Table 1 shows how striking this effect is with several different forms of nitrogen, the N content being the same throughout.   It is clear that only where nitrate-N is present during growth (NH_4NO_3, KNO_3, urea nitrate) were the citric acid yields high in replacement culture.   Clearly the nature of the growth medium is determinative of the subsequent physiological activity of the fungus.   It is interesting to note that the growth medium is without effect on subsequent fumaric or lactic acid formation from sugar by species of Mucorales. The accelerated turnover of sugar, both in rate and amount, which preformed cell material accomplishes during the replacement phase leads to a depletion or exhaustion of the cell material caused probably by gradual autolysis, or loss of vital organic and inorganic cellular components by enzymatic decomposition or by diffusion. This state can be minimized and the vigor of the mycelium prolonged by furnishing small amounts of selected nutrients which enable the organism to make very small increments in growth and at the same time build up or replenish the cell components actively participating in acid formation. Essentially, the added nutrients forestall autolysis and presumably regenerate coenzymes, enzymes, etc.

TABLE 1

INFLUENCE OF TYPE OF NITROGEN IN GROWTH MEDIUM ON CITRIC ACID PRODUCTION IN REPLACEMENT PHASE (SURFACE MYCELIUM)[1]

Nitrogen type	Per cent	Mycelial weight	Ca citrate	Sugar used	Conversion, per cent
NH₄NO₃.............	0.2	1.04	1.48	2.49	59
(NH₄)₂SO₄..........	.5	1.26	.36	2.29	16
KNO₃..............	.5	0.73	.84	1.27	66
NH₄Cl.............	.134	0.47	.29	1.23	24
NH₄H₂PO₄..........	.58	.98	.29	1.8	16
Urea..............	.15	.37	.14	1.63	9
Urea NO₃..........	.32	.91	1.33	2.45	54
Asparagin..........	.32	.59	.28	1.21	23
Glycocol..........	.4	.78	.10	1.48	7
Peptone..........	.54	1.03	.18	1.65	11

[1] From Bernhauer (1928d).

The optimum replacement medium varies according to the organism, but there is virtual unanimity as to the harmful effect of phosphate, and this element is omitted. The same holds true for magnesium ion, for some strains only. The following data illustrate the effects of these two elements, and is typical of them in replacement cultures of organic acid-forming fungi (Table 2).

It is clear that these elements influence sugar consumption to a minor degree compared to their effect on the formation of citric acid. As indicated above, the essence of Szücs patent is utilization of phosphate-free replacement medium. To illustrate the nature of a replacement medium, the following is that developed by Karow as being optimum for his organism (A. wentii): urea, 0.5; KH₂PO₄, 0–0.5 g./l.; pH, 3.5. pH values above 3.5 allowed oxalate to form. Perquin's strains of A. niger were, however, favored by small amounts of magnesium sulfate in the replacement medium, and so it is evident that the Mg requirement must be determined for each individual strain.

TABLE 2

INFLUENCE OF PHOSPHATE AND MAGNESIUM ON CITRIC ACID PRODUCTION IN REPLACEMENT PHASE OF A. WENTII (SUBMERGED CULTURE)[1]

KH_2PO_4, g./l.	Sucrose consumed, g./l.	Conversion to citric acid, per cent
0	130.7	42.2
.05	132.2	48.4
.1	131.7	37.8
.2	127.6	26.0
.5	135.2	20.0
$MgSO_4 \cdot 7H_2O$, g./l.		
0	130.4	47.6
0.25	113.4	29.1
0.5	116.4	36.8
1.0	116.4	25.0
2.0	114.4	29.0

[1] From Karow and Waksman (1947).

Notwithstanding the fact that the growth phase of the organism requires mineral nutrients for the synthesis of cell material the fact remains that, in general, for good citric acid-forming-mycelium, as well as good yields during the growth phase, the concentration of nutrient salts must be at a minimum compatible with a reasonable amount of growth. One interesting exception is described by Shu and Johnson (1948) where most rapid citric acid production by a strain of *A. niger* in submerged culture requires a concentration of phosphate in excess of the optimum value for growth. The effect is not due to buffering action as the pH falls rapidly to pH 2 in all cases (see section on mechanism). The high citric acid yields obtainable invariably are formed from the sugar after the active cell synthesis has slowed down or ceased. The large excess of sugar present in comparison with the other nutrients means that for all practical purposes the minerals were consumed early and the cell material then proceeds to produce citric acid from the excess available sugar. Kostyschew and Tschesnokov (1927) found that no citric acid is formed as long as the mycelium is taking up nitrogen from the medium. They believed that citric acid formation is connected with the absorption of nitrogen, and consequently with the structure of proteins in the fungus. These facts may be more acceptably interpreted on the basis of shunt metabolism, whereby glucose carbon is diverted to organic acid production when nitrogen limitation prevents cell synthesis, a point further supported by the fact that limitation of minerals causes the same result.

The following growth medium is that found by Karow (1942) to be optimal for *A. wentii* growth and citric acid formation. It is given here not because it will prove ideal for other citric acid fungi, but because it exemplifies the type of medium used. Sucrose, 150 g.; urea, 1 g.; $MgSO_4 \cdot 7H_2O$, 0.5 g.; KH_2PO_4, 0.08 g.; KCl, 0.15 g.; $MnSO_4 \cdot 4H_2O$, 0.02 g.; $ZnSO_4 \cdot 7H_2O$, 0.01 g.; distilled water, 1 liter. Holding the replacement phase at a lower temperature (20°C.) than the growth phase (28°C.) is said to lead to maximum output of citric acid (Kovats, 1946).

OXYGEN RELATIONS

Perquin demonstrated that pure oxygen atmosphere was decidedly superior to ordinary air for citrate formation in replacement culture conditions, and Karow employed 100 per cent oxygen throughout his studies. Interestingly, pure oxygen was more effective when used after air had been used for a few days than when it was used the entire period.

Citric acid is an oxidation acid and its formation involves the participation of molecular oxygen. The physical conditions under which it is formed in maximum yields cannot be assumed to be ideal without special attention being given to the problem. Even in shake flask cultures which usually are assumed to provide free access of air the oxygen supply may be deficient for the process as clearly demonstrated by Karow's results. Thus, in the shake flasks with ordinary cotton plugs the citric acid formation was 4.5 g./l.; in the shake flask through which air was being passed the yield was 6.4 g./l.; and in the flask in which pure oxygen was passed the yield was 23.7 g./l. This striking stimulation of pure oxygen may be a reflection of inadequate shaking and physical dispersion of the air to maintain a dissolution rate concomitant with the oxygen demand and removal from solution by the mold cells, and it may be that increased agitation and more efficient mixing would permit air to equal the results obtained with oxygen.

Further support for this possibility is provided by the work of Shu and Johnson (1948, discussed below) where yields of citric acid near the theoretical ceiling were obtained in *A. niger* shake cultures in ordinary air, without passage of supplementary air over or through the culture. They showed that rate and type of mechanical agitation exercised a marked effect on the results and their optimum shaking rate (on a rotary shaker) was decidedly higher than Karow's: 256 r.p.m. vs. 150 r.p.m.

Another indubitable criterion of oxygen insufficiency in the *A. wentii* air cultures is the abundance of alcohol generated, i.e., anaerobiosis (Karow and Waksman, 1947). Obviously pure oxygen would be superior in such cases, and no alcohol was noticeable in the oxygen cultures.

On the other hand, it cannot be ruled out that higher oxygen tension may yield superior results for some strains over others, other conditions being equal. Intrinsic differences in metabolic makeup could create this situation. In any case it has been amply demonstrated how critical the aeration problem is in this process.

WISCONSIN SUBMERGED PROCESS (SHU AND JOHNSON, 1948)

This is treated separately because it embodies what, on paper at least, appears to be the most efficient and feasible process development available. The yields are near the theoretical maximum, ordinary air atmosphere is adequate and the results are achieved in one-step growth cultures, replacement cultures being unnecessary for these high yields. The optimum concentrations of the various nutrients in the medium were ascertained and these media finally selected:

Medium A for cultivation of inoculum. The significance of this medium is the requirement for spores low in manganese content. Domino sucrose, 140.0 g./l.; Bacto Agar, 20.0; KH_2PO_4, 1.0; $MgSO_4 \cdot 7H_2O$, 0.25; NH_4NO_3, 2.5.

Trace metals: Cu^{++}, .48 mg./l., Zn^{++}, 3.8; Fe^{+++}, 2.2; Mn^{++}, <1.0.

Medium B, production medium: sucrose, 140 g./l.; KH_2PO_4, 2.5; $MgSO_4 \cdot 7H_2O$, 0.25, NH_4NO_3, 2.5; Cu^{++}, 0.06 mg./l.; Zn^{++}, 0.25; Mn^{++}, <1.0; Fe^{+++}, 1.3.

Fifty-milliliter quantities were used in 500-ml. Erlenmeyer flasks incubated at 25°C. on a rotary shaker at 250 r.p.m. Maximum yields of 72 g. anhydrous citric acid per 100 g. sucrose consumed were obtained in 9 days. There was a broad pH optimum for the organism, and unlike the surface process, initial pH values below 2.8 retarded growth and acid production. In general citric acid conversion yields were inversely proportional to mycelium weight. This was striking in the case of concentration of iron; within the limits tested growth was proportional to the Fe content of the medium and citric acid yields inversely proportional to the Fe content.

Despite the one-step nature of this process (i.e., growth culture) two distinct phases were nevertheless distinguished in these cultures, and in essence the principle of replacement has been accomplished in the growth cultures. This picture is rather typical of all acid-forming processes in fungi. Changes in the culture during cultivation are depicted in Fig. 1, where it is evident that there is an initial growth phase, where the sugar is used mainly for mycelium production with little acid formation, and an acid production phase which starts shortly after the beginning of acid production.   Here the mycelial growth has stopped due to exhaustion of nutrients and most of the sugar utilized was converted to citric acid. Calculated from Fig. 1, in the interval between the 140th and 240th

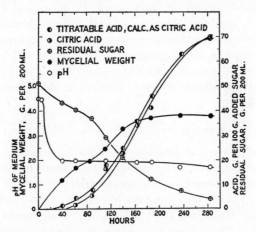

Fig. 1.—Chemical changes during citric acid production by *A. niger* (from Shu and Johnson, 1948).

hours 6.7 g. sucrose was used per 100 ml.   Assuming 100 per cent efficiency of conversion of the carbon of this sucrose into citric acid, an extremely unlikely efficiency, a maximum of 7.5 g. citric acid theoretically should have been produced, yet actually 9.9 g. was formed in addition to an appreciable amount of mycelial growth.   This means that an (nonreducing) intermediate substance(s) generated from the sugar is present in considerable quantities in the early stages, and converted to citric acid as the sugar supply becomes depleted.   This situation has its parallel in alcohol formation and later conversion to fumaric acid by *Rhizopus nigricans* (see Chapter 11).   In this work these intermediates were not further identified, but possibilities will be evident from the discussion to follow on mechanism of citrate formation.

FUNGI FORMING CITRIC ACID

Formation of this acid is known to be so widespread among fungi, expecially in the genera Aspergillus and Penicillium that any new strain tested may be found to possess this character.   Indeed, citric acid formation is probably one of the most widely distributed metabolic processes known in fungi, possibly a consequence of the universality of the tricarboxylic respiratory cycle.   The following list of fungus species of

which one or more strains has been reported to form citrate is taken
in part from Von Loesecke (1945) from which the original references
may be obtained: *Citromyces sp., C. pfefferianus, C. glaber, C. citrious,
Aspergillus carbonarius, A. glaucus, A. clavatus, A. cinnamomens, A.
fumaricus, A. awamori* Nakazawa, *A. awamori* var. *fumeus, A. aureus*
Nakazawa, *Penicillium sp., P. arenarium, P. olivaceum, P. divaricatum,
P. sangifluus, P. glaucum, Mucor sp.,* and *M. pyriformis.* The wood-
destroying basidiomycete *Coniophora cerebella* is also known to produce
citric acid during the decomposition of the wood (Birkinshaw *et al.,*
1940), and the plant parasite *Botrytis cinerea* also is a citric acid-former
(Chrzaszcz and Leonhard, 1936). Beyond a doubt numerous other
fungi form citric acid.

MECHANISM OF CITRIC ACID FORMATION

Two salient points are implicit in this discussion: (1) a branched-
chain compound is formed from straight-chain sugar molecules, (2) citric
acid is known to be formed from a great variety of carbon compounds of
varying chemical types and numbers of carbon atoms, including di- and
polysaccharides. Thus, C_2, C_3, C_4, C_5, C_6, C_7 compounds are known to
yield citric acid. These facts can only mean that all substrates, regardless of carbon chain length, are initially converted by the fungi to certain
key intermediates from which citric acid is synthesized, and that these
key intermediates are derivable from each of the carbon-type compounds
mentioned. Other conditions being satisfactory, failure of a compound
to yield citric acid very likely means that it is not convertible to the
citric intermediates, or at least not intensively enough. The situation
with respect to the intermediates is, in a sense, comparable to that when
one organism can grow on a variety of individual carbon compounds—the
typical components of cell material, lipides, carbohydrates, and proteins,
are synthesized from each individual substrate. This means that the
identical intermediate building blocks of these protoplasmic constituents must have been produced alike from each of the different carbon
substrates.

Thus, the fact that citric acid can be formed from gluconic or saccharic
acids does not imply that these are normal intermediates in the pathway
from sugar. They simply can be broken down to the key intermediate
in citric synthesis. These other acids in citric acid cultures represent
only another type of sugar metabolism proceeding concomitantly with
citric acid formation, and not necessarily intermediates in citric synthesis
from sugar any more than they are intermediates in oxalate formation
from sugar. There is some evidence that the conversion of gluconic
acid to citric acid may involve adaptive enzyme formation or some
mechanism of adaptation (Bernhauer, 1928c).

A point doubtless of metabolic significance, but as yet unexplained is the clearcut superiority of sucrose as a substrate for citric acid production as compared under comparable conditions with equivalent concentrations of glucose. These monosaccharides are readily utilized, but citric acid yields are appreciably lower than from sucrose. In some instances, fructose, and equimolar mixtures of glucose and fructose, have been reported as decidedly inferior to sucrose (Karow, 1942), but the comparative surface culture studies of Bernhauer (1928c) summarized in Table 3 show fructose and the fructose polymer inulin to be about as effective as sucrose.

TABLE 3

CITRIC ACID CONVERSION FROM DIFFERENT CARBOHYDRATES[1]

	Average	Highest value
Sucrose..............................	37.2%	46.5
Fructose.............................	36.9	44.5
Inulin...............	35.1	39.9
Glucose.............................	24.6	31.7
Glyceraldehyde.......................	23.9	30.2
Glycerol.............................	20.3	30.0
Maltose.............................	13.2	16.9
Xylose..............................	12.0	.5
Mannose.............................	5.6	11.5
Arabinose............'...............	5.4	8.7
Mannitol............................	4.1	7.7
Galactose...........................	1.8	6.2

[1] From Bernhauer (1928c).

Because sucrose is 50 per cent glucose, which by itself is considerably inferior, Bernhauer considered that the fructose portion of the sucrose molecule was much more efficient in generating citric acid than free fructose, thus compensating for the low yielding glucose portion of the disaccharide. The possibility was raised that this may be ascribed to the fact that fructose in the sucrose molecule is the gamma form. Another possibility is that the hexose may be phosphorylated when sucrose is split, in a manner similar to that in *Pseudomonas saccharophila* (Doudoroff *et al.*, 1943). In any case it is evident that a split of sucrose into its simple hexose constituents cannot account for the distinct superiority of this disaccharide in citric acid metabolism, and that the breakdown of sucrose evidently is not that simple in these organisms.

An interesting case of carbohydrate utilization for citric acid formation is one in which *Aspergillus japonicus* splits raffinose into fructose and melibiose, the fructose being converted to citric acid, the melibiose accumulating because the organism lacks the enzyme melibiase (Amelung, 1930).

The history of citric acid metabolism in fungi is strewn with theories purporting to be the biochemical mechanism of the origin of this substance from hexose sugars. A number of these theories are strictly of historical interest nowadays and no useful purpose is served in discussing them here. They are treated briefly elsewhere (Prescott and Dunn, 1940; von Loesecke, 1945), and for additional details the original references should be consulted. Credence today is given only to theories centering around synthesis of citric acid from the condensation of a C_4-dicarboxylic acid with a C_2-monocarboxy acid. Modern facts and hypotheses are in agreement that the synthesis can be represented roughly in the following graphic manner:

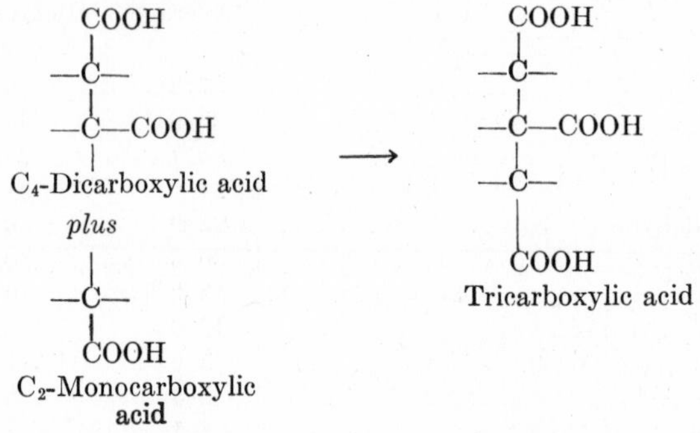

$$
\begin{array}{c}
\mathrm{COOH} \\
| \\
-\mathrm{C}- \\
| \\
-\mathrm{C}-\mathrm{COOH} \\
| \\
C_4\text{-Dicarboxylic acid} \\
plus \\
-\mathrm{C}- \\
| \\
\mathrm{COOH} \\
C_2\text{-Monocarboxylic} \\
\text{acid}
\end{array}
\qquad \longrightarrow \qquad
\begin{array}{c}
\mathrm{COOH} \\
| \\
-\mathrm{C}- \\
| \\
-\mathrm{C}-\mathrm{COOH} \\
| \\
-\mathrm{C}- \\
| \\
\mathrm{COOH} \\
\text{Tricarboxylic acid}
\end{array}
$$

Several different modifications of this principle have been proposed, each conforming to the above scheme but varying in regard to the specific dicarboxylic and monocarboxylic acids undergoing the condensation. These two acids, incidentally, are what were earlier referred to as the key intermediates in citric acid formation; often the term "precursors" is used to designate the intermediates immediately preceding the product. Further points of differences in the various theories based on this condensation idea center around the origin of the C_4 and C_2 acids which participate in citric synthesis. This will be discussed later.

In regard to the specific nature of the acids involved in the condensation reaction there are, in reality, only a few possibilities consistent with the requirements of the reaction; and, indeed, each of these possibilities has been proposed as the one immediately involved. For example, among the dibasic acids proposed have been succinic acid, oxalacetic acid, and l-malic acid, whereas the C_2 acid has been considered as acetic and also glycolic acid. The close structural similarity between these various theories and their protagonists is clear from the following:

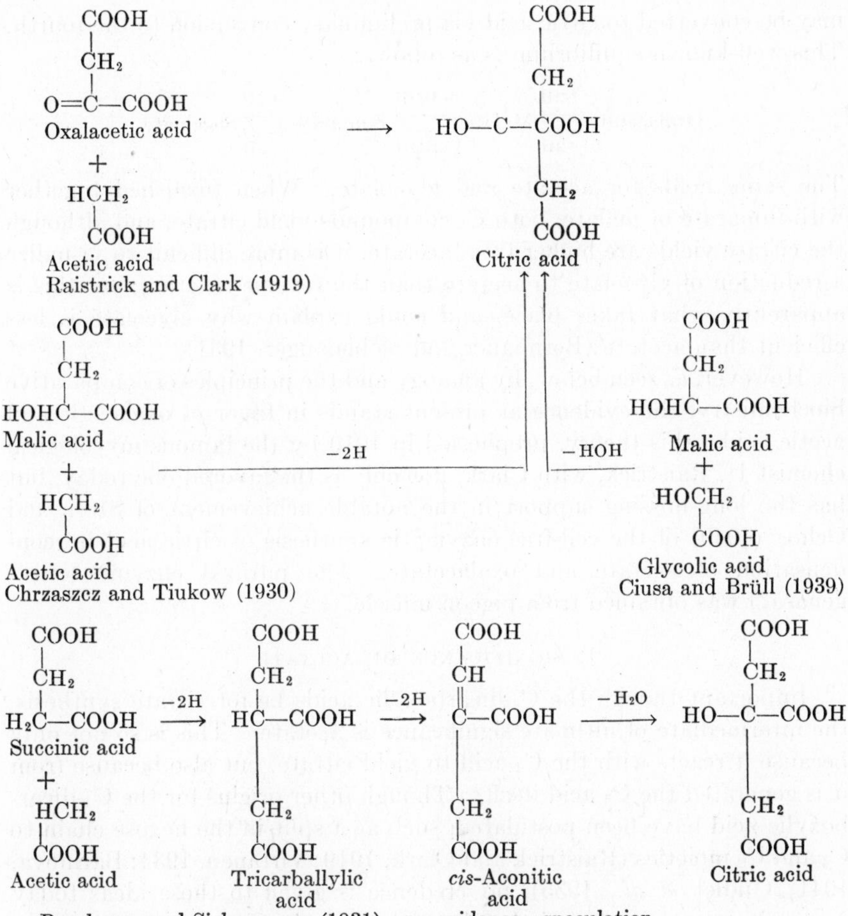

COOH
|
CH₂
|
O=C—COOH
Oxalacetic acid
+
HCH₂
|
COOH
Acetic acid
Raistrick and Clark (1919)

⟶

COOH
|
CH₂
|
HO—C—COOH
|
CH₂
|
COOH
Citric acid

COOH
|
CH₂
|
HOHC—COOH
Malic acid
+
HCH₂
|
COOH
Acetic acid
Chrzaszcz and Tiukow (1930)

—2H

—HOH

COOH
|
CH₂
|
HOHC—COOH
Malic acid
+
HOCH₂
|
COOH
Glycolic acid
Ciusa and Brüll (1939)

COOH
|
CH₂
|
H₂C—COOH
Succinic acid
+
HCH₂
|
COOH
Acetic acid

—2H ⟶

COOH
|
CH₂
|
HC—COOH
|
CH₂
|
COOH
Tricarballylic
acid

—2H ⟶

COOH
|
CH
‖
C—COOH
|
CH₂
|
COOH
cis-Aconitic
acid

—H₂O ⟶

COOH
|
CH₂
|
HO—C—COOH
|
CH₂
|
COOH
Citric acid

Bernhauer and Siebenauger (1931)—no evidence—speculation.

Actually the evidence available is not discriminating enough to permit a decision in favor of any one of the above possibilities. There are two reasons for this: (1) all the different possibilities have not been compared at the same time with the same strain of fungus; (2) the fungi, like all other biological systems, possess enzymes which make the C_4-dicarboxylic acids virtually interchangeable owing to the fact that from any one of them (oxalacetate, fumarate, succinate, malate) the other three are readily formed, the final equilibrium depending on which one is undergoing further transformation so as to drive the equilibrium in its direction. Thus, succinate, fumarate, malate, or oxalacetate, each may be converted into citrate when furnished to preformed mold mycelium under the appropriate conditions, but within the cells the other three may be converted to citric acid via preliminary conversion to the fourth. This well-known equilibrium is as follows:

$$\text{Oxalacetate} \underset{-2H}{\overset{+2H}{\rightleftharpoons}} \text{Malate} \underset{+HOH}{\overset{-HOH}{\rightleftharpoons}} \text{Fumarate} \underset{-2H}{\overset{+2H}{\rightleftharpoons}} \text{Succinate}$$

The same holds for acetate and glycolate. When furnished together with fumarate or malate, both C_2 compounds yield citrate, and although the citrate yields are higher from acetate, it is more difficult to visualize a reduction of glycolate to acetate than the reverse reaction; yet this is apparently what takes place, and could explain why glycolate is less efficient than acetate (Bernhauer and Siebenäuger, 1931).

However, as seen below, by analogy and the principles of comparative biochemistry, the evidence at present stands in favor of oxalacetic and acetic acids; this theory, prophesied in 1919 by the famous mycological chemist H. Raistrick, with Clark, not only is the favored one today, but has the long-missing support in the notable achievement of Stern and Ochoa (1949) of the cell-free enzymatic synthesis of citric acid by condensation of acetate and oxalacetate. The purified enzyme (citrogenase?) was obtained from pigeon muscle.

1. SIGNIFICANCE OF ACETATE

Important though the C_4-dicarboxylic acids be for citrate synthesis, the intermediate of ultimate significance is acetate. This is so not only because it reacts with the C_4 acid to yield citrate, but also because from it is generated the C_4 acid itself. Though other origins for the C_4-dicarboxylic acid have been postulated, such as a split in the hexose chain to C_4 and C_2 moieties (Raistrick and Clark, 1919; Virtanen, 1934; Barinova, 1941; Gudlet et al., 1935), no credence is given to these ideas today except in one case where it has been proved via $C_3 + C_1$ condensation (see below). The generally accepted mechanism (and there is some evidence in its support) involves the condensation of two acetates to yield succinate, which then is interconvertible with the other C_4-dicarboxylic acids. This condensation is known as the Thunberg-Wieland

$$\begin{array}{cc} CH_3COOH & CH_2COOH \\ + & \xrightarrow{-2H} \mid \\ CH_3COOH & CH_2COOH \\ \text{Acetic acid} & \text{Succinic acid} \end{array}$$

reaction after the physiologists who first secured evidence for its occurrence in mammalian muscle (Thunberg, 1920). Though the existence of such an enzyme has been in doubt for many years due mainly to lack of specific evidence demonstrating it, a large amount of circumstantial evidence makes its validity quite likely; in the last few years definite evidence has come forth supporting the Thunberg-Wieland hypothesis. In the field of fungus metabolism the invariable association of C_2 compounds (ethanol and acetate) and C_4 acids suggests a relation between the two, and, in particular, experiments with fumaric acid-producing fungi discussed in Chapter 11 created an extremely strong probability for conversion of acetate into C_4 acid in view of the high yields obtainable. Much other data of this type could be provided.

In recent years more direct evidence has been provided by means of isotopic carbon (C^{13}). Acetate with the carboxyl carbon and with both carbons labeled was converted into succinate by *Aerobacter indologenes* and *Escherichia coli* during glucose fermentation, and the succinate isolated from the first case contained the labeled carbon exclusively in the carboxyl carbons; the succinate isolated from the second case had the labeled carbon in both carboxyl and methylene carbons—a convincing piece of evidence for the acetate condensation mechanism. Furthermore, the reversibility of the reaction could be demonstrated by furnishing succinic acid with carboxyl carbons labeled and isolating acetic acid with its carboxyl carbon labeled (Slade and Werkman, 1943; Kalnitsky *et al.*, 1943).

This reaction was also incriminated in acetate oxidation by yeast where succinate and citric acid are obtained when acetate is the sole carbon source. This was first observed by Wieland and Sonderhoff in 1932 and has been confirmed several times since. For late reviews of this subject see Wood (1946), and Bloch (1947).

As indicated elsewhere in this book (Chapter 4), this reaction is of special significance in mold metabolism because alcohol and acetate are so universally intermediate products of metabolism in these organisms, and their further oxidation or conversion may well proceed via dehydrogenative condensation of acetate to succinate as the first step of oxidative dissimilation.

No discussion of the role of C_2 in the synthesis of C_4-dicarboxylic acids and citric acids is complete without incorporating the unequivocal evidence of Weinhouse and Millington (1947) using yeast to metabolize acetate with the carboxyl labeled with C^{13}. Distribution of labeled C in the products was entirely in agreement with the synthesis of the citrate via $C_4 + C_2$ (oxalacetate + acetate) condensation (see below). Furthermore, C_4 was found to have arisen by $C_2 + C_2$ condensation to yield succinate, etc. Seventeen per cent of the acetate was recovered as citrate. The remainder was oxidized to CO_2 and water via the tricarboxylic acid cycle. In either case the primary C_6 condensate is probably *cis*-aconitic acid. Their results may be interpreted on the basis of two pathways whereby *cis*-aconitate is metabolized: one is hydration to citric acid, to the extent of 17 per cent in this yeast work; the other is hydration to the isomer of citric acid, isocitric acid, which then undergoes degradation according to the usual Krebs' cycle via oxalsuccinic acid, α-ketoglutaric acid and succinic acid. This C_4, after conversion to oxalacetic acid now condenses again with acetate yielding C_6, and the cycle is continued, accounting for the oxidation of 83 per cent of the consumed acetate. In reality, then, there are two competing reactions for the condensation product, aconitate (see p. 411 for chemical cycle). These events are virtually identical with those occurring in animal tissues and the precepts of comparative biochemistry validated in yeast and muscle almost certainly explain the events in fungi.

The varying yields by any one fungus strain, or between two strains may, then, be interpreted on the basis of shunt metabolism: more or less of the C_6 condensate (*cis*-aconitate) being hydrated to citrate, the remainder being shunted through the oxidation cycle and resulting in that much less yield of citrate.

With citric acid fungi there is no doubt that C_2 compounds, in particular ethanol and acetate, can be converted into C_4 acid and citrate as well. As indicated above, none of the evidence purporting to establish that acetate condensation in the primary reaction is really definitive, and logic, analogy, and comparative biochemistry are used to provide support for the beliefs expressed above.

Chapter 9 mentions some of the evidence supporting the idea that when citrate is formed from sugar it passes through the C_2 stage, which, by itself can be shown to be converted to citrate. As a matter of fact, alcohol was reported to yield citrate as far back as 1904 (Mazé and Perrier). First and foremost in support of this theory has been the Polish school under Chrzaszcz, starting in 1930 (Chrzaszcz and Tiukow; see also Chrzaszcz *et al.*, 1932; Chrzaszcz and Zakomorny, 1936a, b; Chrzaszcz and Leonhard, 1936). Penicillia and Aspergilli produced succinic, fumaric, oxalic, malic, and citric acids from acetate, from which evidence one may well surmise that acetate condensation takes place. Similar support for this theory was also provided by Bernhauer at the German University in Prague (Bernhauer and Thelen, 1932; Bernhauer and Siebenäuger, 1931) and since that time the idea has gained general credence. Additional literature on the role of acetate in citric formation in fungi is obtainable elsewhere (Wells *et al.*, 1936).

It is not surprising that different strains of fungi vary in the efficiency of their conversion of C_2 to citrate; this was extensively shown by Bernhauer and Böckl (1932a). The C_2 condensation theory connotes that the citric acid fungi, which are popularly considered to be strong oxidative organisms, possess mechanisms which generate the acetate utilized for citrate synthesis. This has been repeatedly demonstrated for the vast majority of fungi which cause an alcoholic fermentation to a greater or lesser degree depending on the strain. (See Chapter 9.) As a rule, small amounts of alcohol generally accompany C_4 or C_6 (citric) acid formation in fungi, especially when the aeration conditions are not ideal. It is not necessary to assume that alcohol itself is the specific C_2 precursor of acetate, for the latter could originate via oxidative decarboxylation of pyruvate formed in the manner of the classical fermentation schemes. The oxidative decarboxylation of pyruvate is well known for bacteria, but has not been demonstrated in fungi. This is not to say that results have been negative, but rather that it has not been studied enzymatically, and is merely assumed to take place in some few reports (see below).

On the other hand evidence is available favoring the decarboxylation of pyruvate to acetaldehyde and CO_2, the aldehyde then undergoing further oxidation to acetate, etc. Most pertinent are the studies of Bernhauer and Thelen (1932) who employed Neuberg's method of trapping acetaldehyde as it was formed intracellularly during sugar metabolism by the addition of sodium bisulfite. Bisulfite forms in insoluble addition compound with aldehydes, thus "fixing" the aldehyde and preventing its further conversion. In this case strains of *A. niger* characterized normally as strong acid-formers produced much lower than normal yields, and, in fact, organic acid formation was almost entirely blocked. From this one may infer that acetaldehyde (via oxidation to acetate) is a precursor of the C_4 and citric acids. And yet one has evidence to the contrary to contend with. Tomlinson (1937) found several species of Penicillia and Aspergilli that all produced alcohol, but there appeared to be no relation between alcohol fermentation ability and citric acid-forming ability. Thus more citric acid was formed aerobically than the rate of alcohol formation in a nitrogen atmosphere could account for. These results must be considered in rendering final judgment as to the citric mechanism, but not inconsistent with these observations is the conclusion that the C_2 precursor of citrate in these organisms, namely acetate, is generated not via alcohol or acetaldehyde, but directly via oxidative decarboxylation of pyruvate (see Chapter 9; also below). Also, results with acetaldehyde trapping agents could be explained by a diversion of the equilibrium whereby pyruvate is fermentatively decarboxylated, hence draining off pyruvate otherwise directed towards citrate formation via oxidative decarboxylation.

The remarkable influence of strain specificity in interpreting action of fungi is manifested once more in relation to trapping experiments. Another strain of *A. niger* fails to behave like the one mentioned above in the presence of bisulfite (Rippel and Wiangke, 1941). Here under anaerobic conditions ethanol was formed in abundance from sugar

(30.9 per cent), yet only traces of acetaldehyde were recovered in fixed form (it would be expected to be low in view of the high alcohol yield). Dimedon was not successful owing to its toxicity. It is also said to be destroyed by *A. niger* (Bernhauer and Schön, 1928). However, it is useful as a trapping agent in other fungi, especially Fusaria. It is evident that positive results with this technique are much more meaningful than negative results and caution must be exercised in interpreting negative trapping experiments. These bisulfite experiments and possible interpretations are discussed in Chapter 9.

It has been pointed out previously (Chapter 10) that acetate is not often detectable in sugar cultures of fungi, particularly Aspergilli, but this cannot be used as an argument against its formation as an intermediate because it is further converted with such rapidity that it normally never accumulates in detectable amounts. This is evident from the extremely rapid rate with which added acetate is attacked by fungi aerobically. A valuable experiment on this issue is that by Chughtai *et al.* (1947) who showed that appreciable quantities of acetate are present inside the cells of *A. niger* though none could be detected in the external glucose medium. This shows that acetate is, indeed, the likely rapidly metabolized key intermediate in fungus physiology. To be precise about the origin of acetate and the presence of alcohol in sugar cultures of most acid-producing fungi, it is likely that the alcohol serves only indirectly as a precursor of acetate (and C_4 and C_6 acids). Under the aerobic conditions usually favorable for acid formation the acetate is most likely formed from pyruvate directly (see p. 310 and the following scheme). When oxidation conditions are not optimum (more the rule than the exception) acetaldehyde may be formed faster than it can be oxidized, and at once becomes reduced to alcohol in the manner customary for alcoholic fermentation. Then, when oxidation conditions are restored, and especially when acetic acid formation via pyruvate decarboxylation ceases owing to depletion of the sugar supply, the alcohol is now attacked, oxidized via dehydrogenation to acetaldehyde which then goes to acetate, etc. The alcohol in this system is then a secondary side reaction, probably not entering the metabolic stream to a major degree until the carbohydrate supply is exhausted. This well-known situation in molds may be called the "alcohol excursion" (see p. 310).

```
                 AEROBIC      CO₂ + Acetic acid (Acetyl phosphate)
              -2H          ↗              ↑ -2H
Hexose ————————→ Pyruvate ---------------------------------------
                          ↘              | +HOH
  Alcohol   ⎰ ANAEROBIC    CO₂ + Acetaldehyde
  excursion ⎱                    +2H ↕ -2H
                                  Alcohol
```

It should be appreciated that there has been some opposition to the idea of preliminary C_2 formation in citric acid formation, but the weight of comparative biochemical evidence from bacterial, yeast, and animal tissues, and in addition studies with C_4 acid formation in Mucorales and in Fusaria has in recent years become overwhelming. Proof against a role of acetate in the process is limited, and indeed, has not received confirmation. The Russian worker Butkewitsch in particular has opposed the acetate condensation theory of citrate synthesis in fungi, notwithstanding the fact that our acceptance of the role of C_2 condensation in succinic and fumaric acid synthesis is based largely on work from his laboratory. Butkewitsch's principal opposition is that preformed fungus mycelium which is acting on acetate and forms citrate has a high content of reducing substances, later identified as glucose and fructose, and that there was a certain parallelism between reducing power of the mycelium towards Fehling's solution and citric acid-forming powers. Furthermore, there was no apparent relation between the amount of acetate disappearing and the citrate formed; the action of the acetate was believed to be solely that of protecting the decomposition of the citric acid formed. The mycelium carbohydrate theory was given added emphasis by the fact that appreciable yields of oxalate are obtainable from the mycelium on alkaline solution in the absence of any added carbon source (Butkewitsch et al., 1934a, b, and c; Butkewitsch, 1934).

The idea that dissimilation of various carbon sources by fungi is preceded by a primary synthesis to cellular carbohydrate before subsequent degradation has cropped up frequently during the development of mold metabolism. The Raistrick school has also advanced ideas along this line. This concept is detailed in Chapter 16, where it is concluded that all in all there is no need to resort to such a theory.

In this particular case the general significance of Butkewitsch's idea is lost because his results were not confirmed in a fungus actively producing citrate and oxalate from acetate (Chrzaszcz and Zakomorny, 1936a and b). Also, the lack of relation between acetate consumed and citrate formed merely means that other pathways of acetate utilization exist (oxalate formation, for example) and furthermore, that the citrate once formed may be subject to decomposition. Though oxalate may be formed from mycelium alone, ostensibly from the content of reducing substances, the fact remains that citrate is not formed under these conditions, acetate being necessary. Finally, it has been established that the amounts of acids and CO_2 formed by A. niger acting on acetate exceed the loss in mycelial weight, indicating the mycelium theory alone could not account for the observed results.

Chrzaszcz and Zakomorny (1936b) have shown that the addition of small amounts of sugar and malate promotes the utilization of acetate and citrate formation. One may presume that the breakdown products of the sugar may function as hydrogen donors or acceptors in the dehydrogenation reactions involving acetate, and also that the sugar may furnish C_4 for condensation with acetate (see below). Free malic and acetic acids were toxic to *A. niger* mycelium, but when 0.5 per cent sodium malate and 0.5 per cent sugar both were added to a calcium acetate solution, more citrate was formed than was formed from 2 per cent sugar solution alone. The citrate yield was equivalent to about 50 per cent of the acetate consumed. This high yield is rather strong evidence for the direct participation of acetate in citrate synthesis and to a certain extent supports the malate and acetate condensation theory proposed earlier (1930) from Chrzaszcz' laboratory. As seen above, the malate may well be converted intracellularly by simple dehydrogenation into oxalacetate prior to the condensation.

One may further adduce that acetate condensation is the key mechanism in citrate synthesis from the fact that certain Mucorales, the group characteristics of which are generally accepted as displaying the Thunberg-Wieland condensation to yield the C_4-dicarboxylic acid accumulations so often found in these organisms, carry the condensation one step further to the citric acid stage. *Mucor* sp. and *M. piriformis* have been identified in this respect (Wehmer, 1897; Das-Gupta *et al.*, 1940). In a sense, then, all the Mucorales which carry the oxidation of acetate only to the C_4 state, are effecting a less complete oxidation of acetate than those organisms which carry the acetate condensation one step further to citrate. Further illustrating this point is the important experiment in which a citric acid mold produced C_4 and citric acids from the potassium and sodium salts of acetate, but when the acetate is in the form of the calcium salt, the $C_4 + C_2$ condensation apparently is blocked and only C_4 acids are formed (malate and succinate) (Chrzaszcz and Tiukow, 1930). The role of these acids in the respiratory cycle of fungi will be discussed later.

Throughout this discussion the precursor of the carboxylic acid has been referred to as acetic acid. In all probability, and in agreement with modern concepts of intermediary metabolism, the compound is not acetic acid *per se*, but acetyl phosphate, $CH_3COOPO_3H_2$. This point is discussed on p. 310, Chapter 9.

Incidentally, the tricarballylic acid mentioned as a possible intermediate in citrate synthesis by Bernhauer and Siebenaüger (1931) is so mentioned only because it is a chemical possibility. In reality no evidence whatsoever exists for its intermediate formation as the primary condensate of $C_4 + C_2$; furthermore, it is not even known if this compound can be attacked and further converted by citric acid fungi; and, finally, these authors themselves consider this theory only speculation and support the malate-acetate condensation mechanism.

2. EVIDENCE AGAINST THE C_2 MECHANISM

Granting full acceptance of the idea of citrate genesis via $C_4 + C_2$ condensation, and the origin of the C_4 component itself by $C_2 + C_2$ condensation, there still remains, apart from the Butkewitsch school belief, an imposing array of experimental evidence seemingly incompatible with this mechanism. The evidence is based mainly on yields of products obtained from the amount of carbohydrate consumed, which appear in excess or are otherwise inconsistent with the above ideas. One will recall that this same situation was met in relation to fumaric acid and oxalic acid systems. Assuming the above mechanism to occur, it takes 1.5 moles of hexose to obtain the three C_2 molecules which condense to citrate. From each triose (pyruvate) generated from the hexose, one C_2 moiety results, and CO_2 is lost. On this basis it is easy to compute that the maximum yield of citrate obtainable is 71.1 per cent of the hexose decomposed. In the case of sucrose, the anhydride of two hexoses, the theoretical yield is slightly higher, 74.9 per cent. Several studies in the literature report yields in excess of these figures, hence requiring a reconsideration of the theory.

In each case the excessive citrate yields obtained have led the respective authors to abandon the preliminary C_2 formation and acetate condensation idea; and in some cases, alternative theories have been proposed which could explain the high citrate yields chemically speaking, but for which there has not been advanced a bit of reasonable experimental support. The Russian workers apparently were the first to contend with the yield anomaly, and, as a consequence, with the fact that apparently the citrate was formed without loss of carbohydrate-carbon in the form of CO_2 via pyruvate decarboxylation. Theories were proposed in which neither decarboxylation, pyruvate, nor the usual anaerobic fermentation scheme figured. In one case, the hexose chain was postulated to undergo an aldol condensation to a five-membered ring via gluconic acid, this ring, with a one-carbon side chain, opening opportunely to yield citric acid after oxidation (Butkewitsch and Gaevskaya, 1935). In another case, while adopting the principle of $C_4 + C_2$ condensation, the C_4 was visualized as resulting from a direct break in the glucose chain, thus avoiding loss of CO_2 via pyruvate decarboxylation (Gudlet et al., 1935; see p. 369). These ideas cannot be accepted within the domain of comparative biochemistry. Other yield anomalies are known: 75 per cent (Bernhauer et al., 1932); 77 per cent (in Table 11 of Chrzaszcz and Peyros, 1935; Shu and Johnson, 1948); 87 per cent (Clutterbuck, 1936); and in one case (Zhuravskiĭ, 1939), the yields were so high, and CO_2 evolution so small that the reaction was envisioned as a conversion of sucrose to citrate without loss of CO_2 with consequent invalidation of the idea of the central role of C_2: $2C_6H_{12}O_6 + 3O_2 \rightarrow 2C_6H_8O_7 + 9H_2O$. What CO_2 was evolved was considered as "respiratory" CO_2, as contrasted to CO_2 originating from fermentative pyruvate decarboxylation. To be borne in mind is the fact that these figures are really minimum with regard to carbohydrate utilized. Doubtless some small amounts of other acidic by-products are generated along with the citrate, and almost certainly some oxidative assimilation or growth also occurs. In either case additional C_3 or C_2 fractions would be consumed, making the total products derived from C_2 even higher than the above citric acid figures indicate.

Of interest was Zhuravskiĭ's observation that the R.Q.

$$\left(\frac{CO_2 \text{ (evolved)}}{O_2 \text{ (consumed)}} \right)$$

was always less than unity, and was always smallest when citric acid formation was most vigorous, i.e., CO_2 liberation was not concomitant with citrate formation as required by the theories of Chrzaszcz and Bernhauer.

The only detailed treatment of this subject in English is that of Wells et al. (1936) of the United States Department of Agriculture and certain of their critical data are presented in Table 4. According to the alcoholic fermentation theory the citric acid to CO_2 ratio could not exceed 1.45:1, yet in this work it approached 4:1. Also clearly at variance with the theory, are the 87 per cent conversion yields (theory = 71.1). The data strongly indicate that decarboxylation and CO_2 loss do not occur and the authors concluded that "the usual alcoholic breakdown of glucose plays no part in the formation of citric acid by molds."

3. CARBON DIOXIDE ASSIMILATION

With the facts available today, and with the aid of comparative biochemistry it is possible to reconcile all these anomalous results with the C_2 condensation theory. That is, the $C_4 + C_2$ condensation idea appears to be still valid, and the alcoholic fermentation scheme to generate the C_2 for that reaction still takes place as visualized by Chrzaszcz and by Bernhauer, the point of difference being in the mechanisms of formation of the C_4 reactant in the system. The data oblige one merely to accept the idea that more than one mechanism forming the C_4 intermediate is at play in some citric acid fungi, especially in the ones yielding anomalously high conversions from sugar. The $C_2 + C_2$ condensation has been shown to occur and the second mechanism was first apparent when it was shown that *A. niger* placed on a sugar solution in the presence of CO_2 labeled with radioactive carbon (C^{11}) produced citric acid, which upon isolation proved to be radioactive, proving beyond a doubt that CO_2 fixation had taken place and that at least some of the fixed carbon

TABLE 4

PRODUCT BALANCE OF A CITRIC ACID STRAIN OF A. NIGER[1,2]

Age, days	CO_2, g.	Myce-lium, g.	Glucose used, g.	Citric acid,[3] g.	Citric acid CO_2	Glucose used for citric acid and CO_2[4]	Conversion yield of citric acid, per cent
4	0.67	0.375	2.64	1.61	2.40	2.11	76.3
7	1.55	.676	8.78	5.82	3.75	6.66	87.4
10	2.19	.825	12.12	8.50	3.88	9.74	87.3

[1] From Wells, Moyer and May (1936).
[2] In 75 ml. of 19.45 per cent glucose medium.
[3] From Ca salt recovered.
[4] Calculated by deducting from total glucose consumed, the glucose equivalent of mycelium and small amounts of other soluble by-products.

was converted to citrate (Foster *et al.*, 1941). Chemical degradation of the radioactive citrate indicated that the labeled C was mainly, if not all, in the carboxyl groups, and later the fixed carbon (C^{14}) was proved to be equally distributed in all the carboxyl groups (Martin and Wilson, 1949).

Demonstration of a bulk formation of fumaric acid by *Rhizopus nigricans* via CO_2 fixation (Foster and Davis, 1948; see Chapter 11) provides an additional pattern emphasizing the probability that other fungi, such as high-yielding citric acid strains, utilize the CO_2 fixation in bulk in the synthesis of citric acid. This mechanism is in addition to the $2C_2$ condensation. In the same manner as the fumaric acid fungi, the well-known strain specificity of *A. niger* cultures with respect to citric acid-forming abilities may well depend on the degree to which CO_2 fixation occurs insofar as it ends up as citrate. The highest yielders probably will be found to carry out both mechanisms to a marked degree concomitantly. A highly developed CO_2 reutilization at once explains why CO_2 formation has been found to be less than theory predicts. For example, the nearly complete conversion of carbohydrate to citrate with the very small amounts of CO_2 formed, as described by Zhuravskiĭ (1939), merely reflects the reassimilation of almost all the CO_2 liberated from those pyruvate molecules which had undergone decarboxylation. This reutilization is visualized as occurring via condensation with pyruvate molecules which did not undergo decarboxylation, i.e., via the Wood-Werkman reaction. The perfect reaction may be expressed thusly:

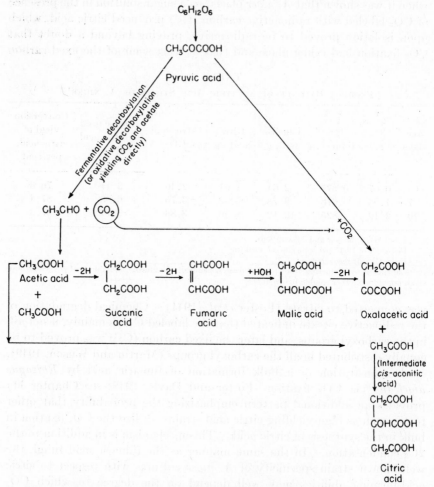

The net result of these reactions may be represented as:

$$C_6H_{12}O_6 + 3O \rightarrow C_6H_8O_7 + 2H_2O.$$

Citric acid

Carbon dioxide fixation via oxalacetate accounts for the labeling only of the middle and one end carboxyl of citric acid. Fixation in all three carboxyls (Martin and Wilson, 1949) must be due to one or more additional CO_2 assimilation reactions. In all probability these reactions are: the carboxylation of succinic acid yielding α-ketoglutaric acid (Ajl and

Werkman, 1948), and the carboxylation of α-ketoglutaric acid yielding oxalosuccinic acid (Ochoa, 1945) (see scheme below). In reality then these fixation reactions are the reverse of decarboxylations in the tricarboxylic acid respiratory cycle. These latter mechanisms have not yet been tested on fungi. The equal distribution of C^{14} observed in the *A. niger* citrate synthesis probably is a coincidental resultant of the numerous simultaneous metabolic reactions occurring at different rates.

There is no reason to believe at present that the events in the synthesis of the tricarboxylic acids in fungi are any different from those in other biological systems. To complete the picture on the basis of comparative biochemistry, mold citric acid in itself probably is not the direct condensation product of $C_4 + C_2$, but rather represents the hydration product formed from the intermediate *cis*-aconitic acid. In reality then, citric acid is a dead-end offshoot from the main cyclic metabolic pathway, the central figure of which is the primary C_6 condensate, *cis*-aconitic acid. This is brought out in the scheme below. This is the mechanism whereby sugar split-products (C_4 plus acetate) escape oxidative breakdown to CO_2 and water. When citric acid itself is further oxidized by the fungus, it may be visualized as proceeding via the classical Kreb's tricarboxylic acid respiratory cycle, well known for other systems, but not yet studied in fungi. Despite assumptions that aconitate is the primary condensation product, it is a fact that with a pigeon enzyme citrate itself is the condensate (Stern and Ochoa, 1949).

The *cis*-aconitic acid actually can be further converted in two different ways by hydration, depending on the orientation of the OH and H during the time of addition. The following scheme shows that addition of water in one way yields citrate and this occurs presumably under circumstances where the latter cannot be further attacked, for one reason or another. The addition of water in the other way yields isocitric acid, which then is the first step in the oxidative breakdown of the tricarboxylic acids, for its dehydrogenation yields oxalosuccinic acid which in turn is decarboxylated to succinic acid, regenerating the C_4 system.

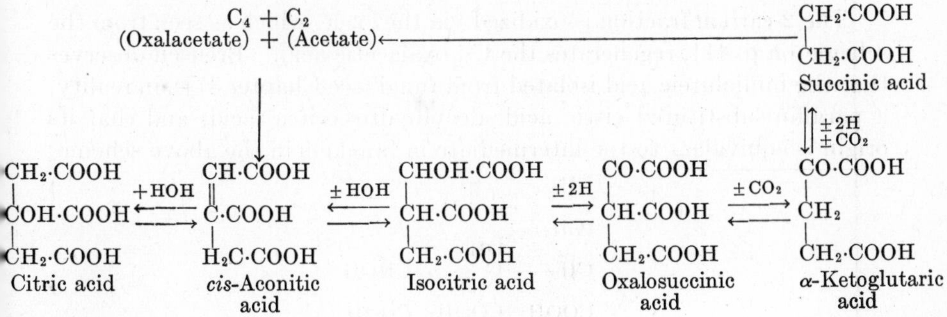

These also are the events found by means of C^{13}-labeled acetate in yeast, as described on p. 401 (Weinhouse and Millington, 1947). For an up-to-date critical review of this whole matter in mammalian tissues and in bacteria see Wood (1946).

Curiously enough, the role of aconitic acid in intermediary metabolism with special reference to the genesis of citrate was proposed in the case of *A. niger* some years before the citric cycle in muscle was clarified as we know it today. Thus, aconitic acid was shown to be converted in 25 per cent yield to citric acid by preformed *A. niger* mycelium, and furthermore the reverse was demonstrated: citrate furnished as the sole carbon source yielded aconitate (Bernhauer and Böckl, 1932b). No other work with aconitate and fungi is available.

GENERALIZED SIGNIFICANCE OF THE FINAL CONDENSATION REACTION

Breusch (1948) suggests that the oxalacetic acid condensation reaction (enzyme = citrogenase) in the oxidation of citric acid via the tricarboxylic acid respiratory cycle may be only one manifestation of a generalized mechanism for oxidation of any fatty acid R-COOH. The first stage, well-known, is simple oxidation to the β-keto acid which then condenses with oxalacetic acid, generating citric acid and a fatty acid with two less carbons:

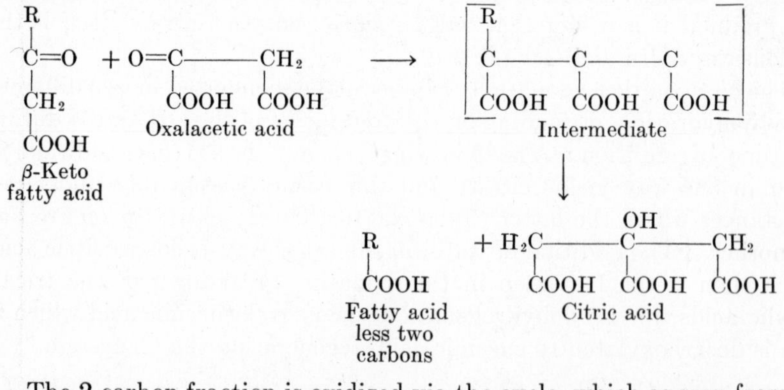

The 2-carbon fraction is oxidized via the cycle, which as seen from the scheme on p. 411, regenerates the C_4, oxalacetic acid. Breusch observes that the minioluteic acid isolated from fungi (see Chapter 3) is, in reality, a paraffin-substituted citric acid, decylhydroxycitric acid, and that its origin is equivalent to the intermediate in brackets in the above scheme:

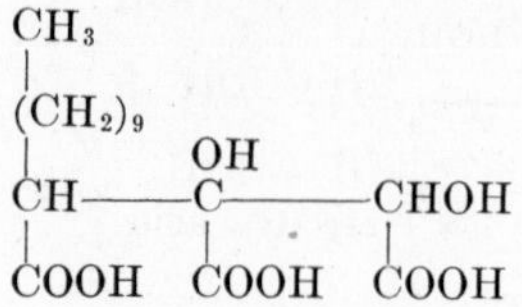

OTHER ASPECTS OF CO_2 AND MOLD METABOLISM

Regarding other general features of carbon dioxide reutilization by fungi, the reader is referred to Chapter 11. As pointed out there, the Wood-Werkman reaction in *Rhizopus nigricans* is strongly inhibited by high CO_2 tensions (see also Foster and Davis, 1949). Certain findings in the literature dealing with *A. niger* and citric acid formation might be readily interpreted on this basis if one takes the license afforded by comparative biochemistry to assume that this inhibitory reaction would also apply to fungi of the Aspergillus type. For example, high CO_2 atmospheres markedly inhibit the growth of *Penicillium roquefortii* and other fungi (for literature see Golding, 1940), and *A. niger* (Kuhn, 1938). Of special interest is the CO_2 inhibition of citric acid formation by *A. niger* cultures (Zhuravskiĭ, 1939; Karow, 1942). Data recalculated from Table 8 of Karow's thesis show that although growth and sugar consumption were retarded by 15 per cent CO_2 when compared to no-CO_2 controls, citric acid formation was inhibited to a considerably greater degree (Table 5):

TABLE 5
CO_2 INHIBITION OF A. WENTII[1]

Age of culture, days	Reduction in sucrose consumption by 15 per cent CO_2, per cent	Reduction in citric acid formation by 15 per cent CO_2, per cent
3	10	27
4	16	47
5	27	50
6	10	30

[1] Recalculated from Karow (1942).

Based on the foregoing, a likely explanation is inhibition of the CO_2 fixation reaction via the Wood-Werkman mechanism. Karow also observed that growth of the fungus on agar plates was not inhibited by CO_2 when the pH of the plates was 6.5, but distinct inhibition was obtained at pH 2.5. The parallelism to results with CO_2 inhibition of *Rhizopus nigricans* (Foster and Davis, 1949) is again apparent, and indicates that bicarbonate ion does not have the same action as CO_2 itself. Bicarbonate ion cannot, of course, exist at pH 2.5. Possibly permeability is the factor at play here, as it is in certain other systems where bicarbonate and CO_2 are not interchangeable biologically (Osterhout and Jacques, 1930; Steeman-Nielsen, 1946).

No discussion of CO_2 and *Aspergillus niger* would be complete without mention of the work by the celebrated Russian physiologist A. F. Lebedev.

Employing this heterotrophic fungus as a tool and in a brilliant example of inductive analysis and scientific insight, Lebedev concluded that it (and by extrapolation, other heterotrophs) assimilates carbon dioxide. The full import of this conclusion becomes apparent when one realizes this work was done more than 30 years ago—two decades before isotopic carbon and the discovery of the Wood-Werkman reaction! Only recently has this contribution been exhumed from the inaccessible Russian journal in which it was published in 1921, and republished in English (*Am. Rev. Soviet Med.* **5,** 17–27, 1947–1948).

Other work which presaged current knowledge of the role of CO_2 in heterotrophic metabolism and which has been strangely overlooked came from the studies of A. Rippel and coworkers on fungi (Rippel and Bortels, 1927; Rippel and Heilmann, 1930). Numerous workers previously had established the indispensability of CO_2 for growth of bacteria and fungi but the careful quantitative studies of the above authors revealed that not only is CO_2 required, but that concentrations in excess of those in air (0.03 per cent) give maximum results. The effect is essentially one on rate of growth because after growth commences, the CO_2-deficient cultures generate their own CO_2. The CO_2 deficiency effect is proportional to the pH of the medium, as evidenced by the following data for *A. niger:*

pH of medium	0.3	0.5	0.7	1.5	2.0	3.4	5.6
Mycelial weight in CO_2-free cultures as per cent of CO_2-containing control	15.7	27.0	31.8	61	81	86	84

The growth response as a function of CO_2 concentration (Fig. 2) impressed Rippel and Heilmann as being similar to that for the usual

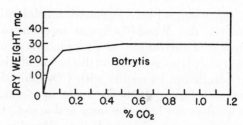

Fig. 2.—Growth response of Botrytis as a function of CO_2 concentration (from Rippel and Heilmann, 1930).

nutrients and they stated that CO_2 was not merely a stimulating substance as conventionally supposed, but rather a nutrient, and that this property in heterotrophs relates their metabolism to autotrophs.

.The lowly mold has indeed laid the foundation for profound concepts in general biology.

CITRIC ACID DECOMPOSITION BY FUNGI

This subject has been mentioned in connection with oxalate formation from citrate (Chapter 10) and has also been discussed earlier in this chapter in connection with its reconversion to *cis*-aconitic acid and degradation via the classical Krebs respiratory cycle. While this may account for some of the citrate consumption, other mechanisms must be at play, to judge from the results of Challenger *et al.* (1927). The following compounds were isolated after *A. niger* mycelium was allowed to act on citrate: acetonedicarboxylic acid, malonic acid, acetone, and glycolic acid.

The sequence leading to these products was visualized as follows:

```
COOH          COOH      COOH
|             |         |
CH2           CH2       CH2  → CO2 + H2O
|             |         |
COH—COOH  →   CO   →    COOH
|             |         Malonic acid
CH2           CH2       +
|             |         CH3      CH2OH     CHO       COOH
COOH          COOH      |     →  |      →  |      →  |
Citric acid   Acetone-  COOH     COOH      COOH      COOH
              dicarboxylic Acetic  Glycolic Glyoxylic Oxalic
              acid      acid     acid      acid      acid
              ↓ −2CO2
              CH3
              |
              CO
              |
              CH3
              Acetone
```

Baba and Sakaguchi (1942) discovered two strains of *A. niger* which produce citric acid at a high rate from *l*-xylose, but also two organic acids new to mold metabolism: glutaric and glutaconic acids. The authors suggest that these C_5 dicarboxylic acids might arise from initially-formed citric acid via α-ketoglutaric acid:

```
COOH         COOH     COOH    COOH
|            |        |       |
CH2          CO       CH      CH2
|            ‖        ‖       |
C—OH   →     CH2  →   CH  →   CH2
| \          |        |       |
|  COOH      CH2      CH2     CH2
CH2          |        |       |
|            COOH     COOH    COOH
COOH
Citric acid  α-Keto-  Glutaconic Glutaric
             glutaric acid      acid
             acid
```

Speaking of acids new to mold metabolism, Chrzaszcz and Leonhard (1936) found propionic acid formed along with citric acid by *Botrytis cinerea* acting on lactate as the sole carbon source. The origin of propionic acid, hitherto unknown in the fungi, was supposed to occur as follows, though no evidence was produced:

$$CH_3CHOH\ COOH \rightarrow CH_3COCOOH \rightarrow CH_3CHO + CO_2$$

Lactic acid   Pyruvic acid   Acetaldehyde

$$\left.\begin{array}{l} CH_3CHO \\ CH_3CHOH\ COOH \end{array}\right\} \xrightarrow{\text{Dismutation}} \begin{array}{l} CH_3COOH \\ \text{Acetic acid} \\ + \\ CH_3CH_2COOH \\ \text{Propionic acid} \end{array}$$

In essence, the dismutation consists of an oxidation of the aldehyde by the lactic acid functioning as hydrogen acceptor, which becomes reduced to propionate. It is to be doubted that propionate formation is that simple, for several intermediate unknown steps probably are involved, according to the latest beliefs regarding propionic acid formation in bacteria.

The examples cited in this section illustrate an extremely important point in mold metabolism. There is a tendency to view and to characterize fungi with regard to their metabolism only while utilizing carbohydrates (hexoses) as the carbon and energy source. There must be a hitherto unsuspected tremendous variety of other metabolic products and versatility in metabolism which would be revealed by the study of these organisms on numerous other kinds of substrates. In other words, the ability to carry out many new kinds of metabolic transformations is latent in known fungi.

REFERENCES

Ajl, S.J. and Werkman, C. H. 1948. *Proc. Natl. Acad. Sci. U.S.* **34**, 491–498.
Amelung, H. 1930. *Z. physiol. Chem.* **187**, 171–172.
Baba, S., and Sakaguchi, K. 1942. *Bull. Agr. Chem. Soc. Japan (Abstracts)* **18**, 93–94.
Barinova, S. A. 1941. *Microbiology USSR* **10**, 716–729 (*Chem. Abstracts* **38**, 2990, 1944).
Bernhauer, K. 1926. *Biochem. Z.* **172**, 324–349.
Bernhauer, K. 1928a. *Biochem. Z.* **197**, 278–286.
Bernhauer, K. 1928b. *Biochem. Z.* **197**, 287–308.
Bernhauer, K. 1928c. *Biochem. Z.* **197**, 309–326.
Bernhauer, K. 1928d. *Z. physiol. Chem.* **177**, 102–106.
Bernhauer, K. 1929. *Biochem. Z.* **205**, 240–244.
Bernhauer, K., and Böckl, N. 1932a. *Biochem. Z.* **253**, 16–24.
Bernhauer, K., and Böckl, N. 1932b. *Biochem. Z.* **253**, 25–29.
Bernhauer, K., Böckl, N., and Siebenäuger, H. 1932. *Biochem. Z.* **253**, 37–41.
Bernhauer, K., Knobloch, H., and Iglauer, A. 1941. *Biochem. Z.* **309**, 151–178.
Bernhauer, K., and Schön, K. 1928. *Biochem. Z.* **202**, 164–179.
Bernhauer, K., and Siebenäuger, H. 1931. *Biochem. Z.* **240**, 232–244.

Bernhauer, K., and Thelen, H. 1932. *Biochem. Z.* **253**, 30–36.

Birkinshaw, J. H., Findlay, W. P. K., and Webb, R. A. 1940. *Biochem. J.* **34**, 906–916.

Bloch, K. 1947. *Physiol. Revs.* **27**, 574–621.

Breusch, F. L. 1948. *Advances in Enzymol.* **8**, 393–394.

Butkewitsch, V. S. 1934. *Biochem. Z.* **272**, 371–375.

Butkewitsch, V. S., and Gaevskaya, M. S. 1935. *Compt. rend. acad. Sci. USSR* (N.S.) **3**, 405–408 (See C. A.).

Butkewitsch, V. S., Menzshinskaya, E. V., and Trofimova, E. T. 1934a. *Biochem. Z.* **272**, 290–307.

Butkewitsch, V. S., Menzshinskaya, E. V., and Trofimova, E. T. 1934b. *Biochem. Z.* **272**, 364–370.

Butkewitsch, V. S., Menzshinskaya, E. V., and Trofimova, E. T. 1934c. *Biochem. Z.* **276**, 446–452.

Challenger, F. 1929. *Ind. Chemist* **5**, 181–184.

Challenger, F., Subramaniam, V., and Walker, T. K. **1927**. *J. Chem. Soc.* 200–208.

Chrzaszcz, T., and Leonhard, K. 1936. *Biochem. J.* **30**, 1947–1952.

Chrzaszcz, T., and Peyros, E. 1935. *Biochem. Z.* **280**, 327–336.

Chrzaszcz, T., and Tiukow, D. 1930. *Biochem. Z.* **229**, 343–357.

Chrzaszcz, T., Tiukow, D. T., and Zakomorny, M. 1932. *Biochem. Z.* **250**, 254–259.

Chrzaszcz, T., and Zakomorny, M. 1936a. *Biochem. Z.* **285**, 340–347.

Chrzaszcz, T., and Zakomorny, M. 1936b. *Biochem. Z.* **285**, 348–355.

Chughtai, I. D., Pearce, A. A., and Walker, T. K. 1947. *Nature* **160**, 572.

Ciusa, R., and Brüll, L. 1939. *Ann. chim. applicata* **29**, 3–11.

Clutterbuck, P. W. 1936. *J. Soc. Chem. Ind. London* **58**, 55–61.

Currie, J. N. 1917. *J. Biol. Chem.* **31**, 15–37.

Das-Gupta, G. C., Saba, K. C., and Guha, B. C. 1940. *Ind. News Ed. J. Indian Chem. Soc.* **3**, 6474.

Doelger, W. P., and Prescott, S. C. 1934. *Ind. Eng. Chem.* **26**, 1142–1149.

Doudoroff, M., Kaplan, N., and Hassid, W. Z. 1943. *J. Biol. Chem.* **148**, 67–75.

Fernbach, A., Yuill, J. L., and Rowntree & Co., Ltd. 1925. Brit. Patent 266,414, Oct. 26.

Foster, J. W. 1939. *Botan. Revs.* **5**, 207–239.

Foster, J. W., Carson, S. F., Ruben, S., and Kamen, M. D. 1941. *Proc. Natl. Acad. Sci. U. S.* **27**, 590–596.

Foster, J. W., and Davis, J. B. 1948. *J. Bact.* **56**, 329–338.

Foster, J. B., and Davis, J. B. 1949. *Arch. Biochem.* **21**, 135–148.

Frey, A. 1931. *Arch. Mikrobiol.* **2**, 272–309.

Golding, N. S. 1940. *J. Dairy Sci.* **23**, 891–898.

Gudlet, M. A., Kirsanowa, V., and Makarowa, V. 1935. *Proc. Inst. Sci. Res. Food Ind. Leningrad* **3**, No. 1, 45–65.

Kalnitsky, A., Wood, H. G., and Werkman, C. H. 1943. *Arch. Biochem.* **2**, 269–281.

Karow, E. O. 1942. Production of Citric Acid in Submerged Culture. Thesis, Rutgers Univ.

Karow, E. O., and Waksman, S. A. 1947. *Ind. Eng. Chem.* **39**, 821–825.

Kluyver, A. J., and Perquin, L. H. C. 1933. *Biochem. Z.* **266**, 82–95.

Knobloch, H., and Sellman, R. 1941. *Biochem. Z.* **309**, 105–150.

Kostyschew, S., and Tschesnokov, W. 1927. *Planta* **4**, 181–200.

Kovats, J. 1946. *Przemysl Chem.* **2**, 122–128 (C. A. **42**, 3129, 1948).

Kuhn, F. 1938. *Zentr. Bakt. Parasitenk. Abt. II* **98**, 430–444.

Martin, S. M., and Wilson, P. W. 1949. *Soc. Am. Bact.*, Abstracts 49th. Gen. Meeting pp. 45–46.

Mazé, P., and Perrier, A. 1904. *Compt. rend.* **139**, 311–313.

Ochoa, S. 1945. *J. Biol. Chem.* **159**, 243–244.

Osterhout, W. J. V., and Jacques, A. G. 1930. *J. Gen. Physiol.* **13**, 695–713.

Perlman, D., Dorrell, W. W., and Johnson, M. J. 1946a. *Arch. Biochem.* **11**, 131–143.

Perlman, D., Kita, D. A., and Peterson, W. H. 1946b. *Arch. Biochem.* **11**, 123–129.

Perquin, L. H. C. 1938. Bijdrage tot de kennis der oxydatieve dissimilatie van *Aspergillus niger* van Tieghem. Thesis, Delft.

Prescott, S. C., and Dunn, C. A. 1940. Industrial Microbiology, McGraw-Hill, N. Y., pp. 368–369.

Raistrick, H., and Clark, A. B. 1919. *Biochem. J.* **13**, 329–344.

Rippel, A., and Bortels, H. 1927. *Biochem. Z.* **184**, 237–244.

Rippel, A., and Heilmann, F. 1930. *Arch. Mikrobiol.* **1**, 119–136.

Rippel, A., and Wiangke, H. 1941. *Arch. Mikrobiol.* **12**, 124–127.

Shu, P., and Johnson, M. J. 1947. *J. Bact.* **54**, 161–167.

Shu, P., and Johnson, M. J. 1948. *Ind. Eng. Chem.* **40**, 1202–1205.

Slade, H. D., and Werkman, C. H. 1943. *Arch. Biochem.* **2**, 97–111.

Starkey, R. L. 1925. *J. Bact.* **10**, 135–163.

Starkey, R. L. 1943. *J. Bact.* **45**, 509–519.

Steeman-Nielsen, E. 1946. *Nature* **158**, 594–596.

Stern, J. R., and Ochoa, S. 1949. *J. Biol. Chem.* **179**, 491–492.

Szücs, J. 1944. U. S. Patent 2,353,771, July 18.

Szücs, J. 1948. U. S. Patent 2,438,136, March 23.

Thom, C., and Currie, J. N. 1916. *J. Agr. Research* **7**, 1–15.

Thunberg, T. 1920. *Skand. Arch. Physiol.* **40**, 1–91.

Tomlinson, T. G. 1937. *New Phytologist* **36**, 418–434.

Virtanen, A. I. 1934. *J. Bact.* **28**, 447–460.

Von Loesecke, H. W. 1945. *Chem. Eng. News* **23**, 1952-1959.

Wang, T. 1940. *J. Shanghai Sci. Inst. Sect. IV* **5**, 61–90 (C. A. **36**, 6194, 1942).

Wehmer, C. 1893. Compt. rend. 117, 332–333; Beiträge zur Kenntnis Einheimische Pilze, Hanover, No. 1.

Wehmer, C. 1897. *Chem. Ztg.* **21**, 1022–1023.

Wehmer, C. 1905–1907. In Lafar's Handbuch techn. Mykologie, Jena, 2nd. iv, 242.

Wehmer, C. 1912. *Chem. Ztg.* **36**, 1106–1107.

Wehmer, C. 1913. *Chem. Ztg.* **37**, 373–379.

Weinhouse, S., and Millington, R. H. 1947. *J. Am. Chem. Soc.* **69**, 3089-3093.

Wells, P. A., and Herrick, H. T. 1938. *Ind. Eng. Chem.* **30**, 255–262.

Wells, P. A., Moyer, A. J., and May, O. E. 1936. *J. Am. Chem. Soc.* **58**, 555–558.

Wells, P. A., and Ward, G. E. 1939. *Ind. Eng. Chem.* **31**, 172–177.

Wieland, H., and Sonderhoff, R. 1932. *Ann.* **499**, 213–228.

Wood, H. G. 1946. *Physiol. Revs.* **26**, 198–246.

Zahorski, B. 1913. U. S. Patent 1,066,358.

Zender, J. 1937. U. S. Patent 2,072,919.

Zender, J. 1938. U. S. Patent 2,121,064.

Zhuravskii, G. I. 1939. *Microbiology USSR* **8**, No. 3–4, 414–430 (*Chem. Abstracts* **35**, 484, 1941).

CHAPTER 13

ITACONIC ACID

The thesis, already repeatedly emphasized, that systematic scientific work on a particular type of fungus metabolism depends on its commercial potentialities and practicability was never better exemplified than with itaconic acid production by fungi. Discovered in 1929 by the Japanese investigator Kinoshita, this unsaturated* dicarboxylic acid, methylene succinic acid,

$$CH_2=C-COOH$$
$$CH_2-COOH$$

received no more than incidental study until the spectacular development of the synthetic plastics field focused attention upon those raw materials having specialized properties for particular purposes. Thus, Hope (1925) described in a patent a nonshatterable glass in which two layers of glass were cemented to a thin sheet of cellulose acetate by means of polymerized dialkyl itaconate esters. Other polymers of itaconate esters characterized by special properties such as brilliance, hardness, clarity, and refractive index, etc., are known and are particularly suited for the manufacture of lenses, artificial jewelry and numerous common objects.

Polymerization of the itaconate esters occurs readily as, in reality, itaconic acid is a substituted methacrylic acid of which huge amounts are consumed in synthetics (Plexiglas, Lucite, Crystallite). Potential application to the field of synthetic detergents is also a definite possibility.

Until just a few years ago the only commercial source of itaconic acid was from citric acid by pyrolysis. Concentrated aqueous solutions of citric acid are distilled *in vacuo* at 230° or over, giving a mixture of citraconic,

$$CH_3·C-COOH,$$
$$HC-COOH$$

and itaconic acids or their anhydrides (Scheuing and Walach, 1939). However desirable itaconic acid is for resins, it could scarcely be manufactured from citric acid and compete successfully on a cost basis with the analogous methacrylic acid currently widely used since methacrylic

* Fumaric acid is the only other unsaturated acid produced during carbohydrate dissimilation by fungi.

419

acid is a low cost item, being synthesized from chlorohydrin and also from the pyrolysis of lactic acid, a whey fermentation by-product of the dairy industry.

Since the realization of the potentially huge market for low cost itaconic acid, organized series of investigations have been carried out in two laboratories in this country, both projects based on Kinoshita's observation that a fungus could convert substantial amounts (24 per cent) of cheap carbohydrate to this valuable product. One extensive series of investigations was done in the Northern Regional Research Laboratories of the United States Department of Agriculture at Peoria, Ill. and the other in industry (Chas. Pfizer & Co., Brooklyn), and there is ample reason for considering that substantial success has been achieved.

Kinoshita (1929) isolated his organism, a green Aspergillus, from the sour juice of dried salted plums, and, on the basis of this biochemical property hitherto unknown for a microorganism, he named it *Aspergillus itaconicus* n. sp. In view of the well known physiological heterogeneity among different strains of morphologically identical fungi, the wisdom of this designation is open to question. Indeed this organism is considered by Thom and Raper (1945) to be identical with *A. varians* described by Wehmer in 1899, but they retain Kinoshita's species designation. On account of its being so closely related in physiological response as well as in several of its structural characters, these mycologists classify this organism as belonging to the large and common *A. glaucus* group, although as an extreme form. In view of its origin, this organism was especially adapted to media of high osmotic pressures and developed well in media of 20 per cent sugar concentration, which inhibits most ordinary unadapted fungi. In fact, this organism failed to grow well at all on the usual fungus media, requiring 20–30 per cent sugar solutions or 2 N salts solution. *A. itaconicus* also formed substantial quantities of mannitol. In this type of medium the hyphae were thickened several fold and their surface was covered with a rather thick layer of a hemi-cellulose type of polysaccharide (Kinoshita, 1937). After isolation as the calcium salt, the acid was identified (1931) as the anilide and dibromide derivatives as well as by catalytic hydrogenation to methyl succinic acid. Boiling itaconic acid solutions in strong KOH gave mesaconic acid in 76 per cent yield. Itaconic acid could be synthesized from pyrotartaric and malonic acids.

When $CaCO_3$ was added to the medium, both calcium citrate and calcium gluconate could be isolated, but these acids were not found in the absence of the carbonate. This led Kinoshita to postulate that itaconic acid formation from sugar involved a primary formation of citric acid which was further converted to itaconic acid via *cis*-aconitic acid.

$$\overset{\text{OH}}{\underset{\text{H}_2\text{C·COOH}}{\text{HOOC·CH}_2\text{·C·COOH}}} \quad \xrightarrow{-\text{H}_2\text{O}} \quad \overset{\text{HOOC·CH}_2\text{·C·COOH}}{\underset{\text{HC·COOH}}{\parallel}} \quad \xrightarrow{-\text{CO}_2} \quad \overset{\text{HOOC·CH}_2\text{·C·OOH}}{\underset{\text{CH}_2}{\parallel}}$$

Citric acid   *cis*-Aconitic acid   Itaconic acid

Since these two supposed intermediate acids were not found in acid media, it was concluded that they are converted to itaconate faster than they are generated from sugar.

About 15 years later, Kinoshita's strain, which had been deposited in the famous European fungus collection of the Centraal Bureau voor Schimmelcultures in Baarn, Holland, was tested at Peoria, and, though still possessing the distinctive appearance and tolerance of very high salt concentrations according to the description of Kinoshita, possessed the ability to form only traces of itaconic acid, despite several modifications of the medium (Moyer and Coghill, 1945). Presumably the organism had undergone physiological degeneration through prolonged laboratory cultivation.

The traditional philosophical attitude towards so-called academic research, to the effect that a scientific finding seemingly inconsequential when made, may eventually have enormous theoretical or applied value was never better borne out than in this particular situation. With a potential industrial-scale fermentation in the making, the only isolate of *A. itaconicus* in existence, namely a culture derived from Kinoshita's parent strain, had lost its itaconic acid-producing powers. Seemingly no organism or type organism was available for development, except for an observation made in 1939 by Calam *et al.*, as part of an extended survey of metabolic products of fungi spanning some 20 years at the London School of Hygiene and Tropical Medicine. In a routine coverage of six different strains of *Aspergillus terreus*, these authors noted that one strain only formed itaconic acid, the others forming a variety of substances, in particular, other dicarboxy acids—oxalic, succinic, fumaric. No mention was made of the potential significance of this discovery as a possible means of manufacturing a raw product for synthetic resins, and one may presume that this work was considered to have academic significance only. Possibly the advent of the war prevented further exploitations. Calam *et al.* were unable to subscribe to Kinoshita's hypothesis that citric acid is an intermediate in itaconate formation. Acetic, pyruvic, malic and citric acids, alone and in various combinations were furnished to preformed pellicles of this organism, and, although some small amount of itaconate was formed from malic acid, the yield was only one-sixth that from glucose tested as a control, from which the weight conversion yield was 11.8 per cent. Citric acid also yielded some, about one-tenth that from glucose. In evaluating these possible precursors, it would have been well to test glucose plus citrate and glucose plus malate.

Beyond these two rather cursory approaches to the mechanism of itaconic acid formation by fungi, nothing has been reported in the literature at this writing.

Three years after this report a patent application covering itaconic production by submerged cultures of *A. terreus* was filed (Kane *et al.*, 1945), and quite evidently was based on the observation of the British workers who had worked only with surface cultures of *A. terreus*. This patent will be discussed later.

The bulk of our information pertaining to itaconate production, also from *A. terreus* and presumably based on the lead of the English, comes from the USDA workers at Peoria. Their work dealt exclusively with surface cultures and though of extreme interest academically, may be preempted as an industrial process by the patent covering the submerged process.

QUANTITATIVE ESTIMATION OF ITACONIC ACID IN MOLD FILTRATES

The principle dates back to Koppescher in 1876 and involves measurement of the amount of bromine absorbed by the unsaturated itaconic acid. Friedkin (1945) has developed it to make it especially suitable for culture filtrates of fungi by virtue of the observation that glucose, the principal interfering substance in the medium, does not react with Br_2 at pH 1.2 whereas itaconic acid does equimolecularly. Thus, culture media initially containing 15 per cent glucose do not disturb the method, and where the sugar concentration is less than 5 per cent, the Br absorption can be made safely even at somewhat higher pH values.

The sample is brought to pH 1.2 with H_3PO_4—H_2SO_4 buffer, a measured amount of bromine water added, and after standing 15 minutes in a closed vessel KI was added and the liberated iodine titrated with standard thiosulfate solution. The difference from a bromine blank represents Br_2 absorption due to itaconic acid. The specificity under the conditions is very good, the following likely present substances, including the unsaturated aconitic acid, giving no interference: glucose, fumaric, succinic, lactic, citric, malic, tartaric, oxalic, acetic acids, and gluconolactone. Replicates show an average deviation from theoretical of 1.5 per cent.

STRAIN SELECTION

In addition to the traditional manner of comparing, in routine, *A. terreus* strains and selecting the strongest itaconic organism for further microbiological study, the Peoria group employed a technique which surely will henceforth become a standard approach in the development of new industrial fermentations, and for further improvement of already-operating fermentation industries, namely, artificial mutations as a means of stepping up the potency of the most potent organism available (see Chapter 6).

As Calam *et al.* already showed, and as ordinary familiarity with microbiological biochemistry indicates, not all strains of *A. terreus* form itaconic acid, and among those which do there is great variation in the intensity of this process. Incidentally, no other species apart from Kinoshita's organism is known to produce itaconic acid. This does not mean a unique kind of specificity but rather that this acid has not been sought from other fungi, since the *A. terreus* lead furnished by the English workers has followed true so effectively. As interest in this acid has developed only in the past 5 years, it is expected that it will in time be found in other fungi.

Two surveys of *A. terreus* strains, one of thirty cultures in the NRRL stock culture collection (Moyer and Coghill, 1945), the other of 308 strains isolated from soil samples collected from widely different geographical points (Lockwood and Reeves, 1945) led to the selection of two strains, Nos. 265 and 1960, each of which was studied systematically from a microbiological production point of view. No. 1960, a soil isolate, was a considerably better itaconate producer than 265 which gave a maximum of 29 per cent weight conversion of glucose and which also produced other acids up to 20 per cent of the amount of itaconate. Only No. 1960 will be discussed here, as, in the main, the principles and development were quite similar with No. 265, details of which can be found in Moyer and Coghill (1945). Furthermore, 1960 was extended to the pilot plant stage (Lockwood and Ward, 1945).

Out of 308 soil isolates of *A. terreus*, eleven gave itaconic acid yields exceeding 45 per cent of theory (theory = one mole itaconic acid per mole glucose consumed = 72 per cent); and No. 1960, originating from a soil sample from Texas, gave the biggest yield of all, 51 per cent (i.e., 36.7 per cent weight yield g. itaconic acid per g. glucose consumed).

The outstanding feature of the itaconate process is the low pH optimum for growth and acid formation by this organism, pH 2.1–2.2; in this respect it is the only counterpart of citric acid formation by *Aspergillus niger* and kojic acid formation by *A. oryzae*. The pH is extremely critical, for acid formation takes place only within a very narrow pH range. A difference of 0.2 pH unit means the difference between maximum itaconate yields and none (Fig. 1). This action is specific for the acid forming process, as growth (mycelial weight) progressively increases with pH rise, obviously at the expense of itaconic acid formation.

At these low pH values the organism has a rather high $MgSO_4 \cdot 7H_2O$ requirement (4.75 g./l.), and since it will not grow at all with only 0.25 g./l., it may be inferred that this salt endows a tolerance to acidity that is particularly useful as high concentrations of itaconic acid accumulate, although this organic acid itself functions as a buffer on the acid side.

The trace element nutrition of *A. terreus* 1960 also was studied. Aluminum ion is toxic, but this toxicity is overcome entirely by mag-

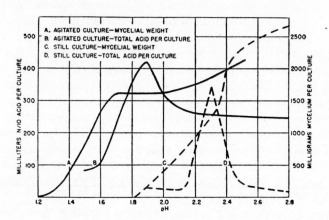

Fig. 1.—Critical effect of pH on itaconic acid formation by *Aspergillus terreus* (from Lockwood and Nelson, 1946).

nesium ion; hence, at the concentrations of $MgSO_4 \cdot 7H_2O$ employed, aluminum toxicity does not interfere. The importance of Al toxicity lies in the potential use of aluminum pans for pilot plant production by the surface process. Iron and zinc ions naturally are required for growth (see Chapter 7), and at pH 2.0 in a medium deficient in these elements, their addition results in increased itaconic acid production. The individual ions are not additive in this action, and when the pH is raised to 3.0 or higher, they give the traditional effect of greatly increasing synthesis of mycelium at the expense of itaconic acid formation with consequent small yields. At a very low pH, 1.7, where growth alteration was insignificant, iron was more effective than zinc, weight for weight, in augmenting itaconic acid formation.

SURFACE CULTIVATION ON PILOT PLANT SCALE

Using *A. terreus* No. 1960, in excess of 30 per cent weight conversion yields from glucose in 12 days have been reported (Lockwood and Ward, 1945). The batches were conducted in shallow aluminum pans, employing the information obtained from laboratory experimentation. The following medium was developed for this purpose:

Glucose monohydrate (commercial)	165 g.
$MgSO_4 \cdot 7H_2O$	4.4 g.
NH_4NO_3	2.5 g.
NaCl	0.4 g.
$ZnSO_4 \cdot 7H_2O$	0.0044 g.
HNO_3 (0.42 sp. gr.)	1.6 ml.
Conc. corn steep liquor	4.0 ml.
Initial pH	~2.0
Water	1.0 l

After about 12 days, the culture filtrate is concentrated by evaporation on a steam bath with constant stirring till a slurry of fine itaconic acid crystals appears. After complete crystallization at room temperature, the itaconic acid crystals are separated and water-washed in a basket centrifuge. A second crop of crystals may be obtained by further concentrating the mother liquor which retains about 20 per cent of the original, but a superior method appears to be by extraction with n-butanol. At 28° a 1 per cent aqueous solution of itaconic acid shows a water/butanol distribution coefficient of 0.469. The acid crystallizes readily from the concentrated butanol.

This overall process yielded 50 per cent itaconic acid recovery based on the theoretical obtainable from the glucose consumed, i.e., about one-half mole itaconate per mole sugar consumed, equivalent to a 36 per cent yield, weight for weight of sugar consumed. On the basis of sugar supplied, of which some was left unconsumed, the weight recovery was 25 per cent—the real economic yield.

Based on prices current at that preinflation time (1945), Lockwood and Ward estimate the raw material cost per pound of itaconic acid recovered to be $0.22. Individual costs were glucose 5.3 cents per lb., corn steep liquor 2.5 cents per lb. and salts, 0.4 cents per lb. The cost of the itaconic acid is primarily that of the glucose. When one considers that labor and overhead, both rather high in a surface process, have yet to be included, the likelihood of itaconic acid produced by this process being cheap enough to compete with synthetic methacrylic acid in resins is rather remote; it may well be displaced by the submerged process described below.

ARTIFICIAL MUTATIONS OF A. TERREUS

The well-known and generally accepted aspects of ultraviolet irradiation with the object of securing induced mutations have been applied to A. terreus with moderate success in initial experiments (Hollaender *et al.*, 1945; Raper *et al.*, 1945 and Lockwood *et al.*, 1945). Principles and techniques of this type of work are discussed in Chapter 6. Apart from a large variety of morphological, cultural and other biochemical mutants obtained, considerable alteration with respect to itaconic acid-producing capacity was encountered. The following summarizes briefly the main features of this work, which employed *A. terreus* 265 as the parent.

Out of 217 isolates tested after exposure to irradiation, seventeen were morphologically and culturally indistinguishable from the parent, but differed in acid forming powers. Four could produce no acid whatsoever and thirteen were superior by a rather small percentage to the parent culture. Comparative biochemical data on the best mutant is given in the following tabulations:

	Parent and mutant comparison						
	Glucose consumed, g.	Total acid ml. of N/10	Itaconic acid ml. of N/10	Itaconic acid, g.	Purity	Itaconic[1] acid yield.	Mycelial wt., g.
Parent, non-irradiated........	11.4	445	411	2.67	92.2%	32.4%	1.927
Mutant No. 32D-S-4-2.........	11.4	468	468	3.06	94.2	37.2	1.703

[1] Based on a theoretical yield of 72 per cent by weight, i.e., one mole itaconic acid per mole glucose.

A second strain, No. 32D-55-4-1, is stated to form up to 20 per cent more acid than the parent, without change in the purity.

Yield increments from 32.4 to 37.2 per cent represents an efficiency increase of 15 per cent over the parent, an important difference in a process where the yield has a theoretical ceiling. By purity is meant the percentage that itaconic acid comprises of the total formed. It is evident that small amounts of other acids accompany itaconic in the parent, and that even less are formed in the mutant. Several other mutants (15) gave purity analyses exceeding 100 per cent. Since itaconic acid was measured by Friedkin's bromine absorption method, this merely means that other unidentified unsaturated acids were formed, i.e., other bromine-absorbing substances. Where the purity is less than 100 per cent, this means naturally that other saturated acids are present. As indicated above, there was no relation between morphological and cultural appearance and the ability to form itaconic acid, although in general those mutants characterized by limited yellow floccose growth with sparse sporulation formed little acid. Another biochemical group of seventeen cultures was characterized by the fact that the purity was 100 per cent, i.e., itaconic acid was the only acid formed.

Yuill recently reported (1948) that appreciable amounts of kojic acid accompanied the itaconic acid in culture filtrates of a unnamed Aspergillus. The ratio between the two acids varied with the temperature of incubation, itaconic acid preponderating at higher temperatures. Up to 20 per cent weight conversion of glucose utilized to itaconate was obtained.

ITATARTARIC ACID

Only in one case has the extra acidity in the mutant cultures been studied, viz., No. 265S14, an ultraviolet mutant (Stodola et al., 1945). The saturated acids were separated by fractionating the methyl esters in vacuo, yielding two fractions, one boiling at 129–134° and one at 151–154° at 2–3 mm. pressure. The lower boiling fraction was identified as itatartaric acid, a homologue of tartaric acid, and hitherto unknown in microbial metabolism or in nature.

$$CH_2OH—C(OH)—COOH$$
$$|$$
$$CH_2—COOH$$
Itatartaric acid

This acid apparently exists only in the salt form and as the lactone, which actually was the higher boiling fraction, in amount roughly equal to the free acid (salt). Evidently the free acid does not exist as such. The yields of this new fermentation product were rather appreciable, amounting to 5.8 per cent of the total acidity in the culture. The chemical similarity of itatartaric acid to itaconic acid is obvious.

While this irradiation program on strain No. 265 was under way, the survey of natural soil isolates described above was also in progress (Lockwood and Reeves, 1945) and yielded strain 1960, which, therefore, by direct isolation from nature was superior even to the best mutant obtained from strain 265. However, the point is clear: artificial mutation has been employed successfully to enhance itaconic acid-producing efficiency, and similar success should be obtainable with 1960.

SUBMERGED PRODUCTION OF ITACONIC ACID

The only information on this point is the survey of cultural conditions by Lockwood and Nelson (1946) and the cursory description in a patent issued to Kane et al. in 1945. The former work dealt with A. terreus NRRL 1960 in shake flask cultures, and is, in essence, the counterpart of the study of surface cultures by Lockwood and Reeves (1945). Already pointed out is the very narrow limits of pH essential for maximum itaconate yields; a sharp reduction occurs by small changes in pH on either

side.   The pH optimum is 1.8, as compared to 2.2 for surface culture.
As in surface culture, the reduced yields favor the marked mycelial
development which occurs with rise in pH (Fig. 1).

Addition of sodium chloride to a Na- and Cl-deficient medium
markedly accelerates mycelial growth, with sharp reduction in yields of
acid.   Unlike surface cultures, there was no response to added zinc;
another marked difference was the amount of $MgSO_4 \cdot 7H_2O$ required for
maximum yields— 0.75 g./l. submerged vs. the abnormally high 4.5 g./l.
in surface culture.

In general, the concentration of nutrients required for the submerged
process were less than for surface, due probably to elimination of diffusion
gradients in the former.   An interesting effect, observed frequently in
fungus metabolism, is that itaconate yields are inversely proportional
to the amount of inoculum (Table 1).

TABLE 1

EFFECT OF AMOUNT OF INOCULUM[1,2]

Inoculum, No. of pellets/culture	Conversion yield, per cent	Mycelial wt., g.
1	40.4	1.296
2	40.4	1.144
3	32.8	1.207
4	28.6	1.245
5	20.1	1.477
8	11.8	1.490
16	15.4	1.625
40	10.1	1.655
100	13.4	1.488

[1] From Lockwood and Nelson (1946).
[2] *A. terreus* NRRL1960; 125 ml. culture; 8 g. glucose consumed in each case.

The only feature of the process as described in the Kane *et al.* patent
which is distinctive from the submerged process familiar to any person
skilled in the art is the use of "selected fungus strains."   *A. terreus* is
the only specific organism mentioned and about 25 per cent weight conversion yield (35 per cent of theory) was obtained in 7 days.   Exceptionally
high concentrations of nitrate salts (15 g./l. of $NaNO_3$ or $Ca(NO_3)_2$)
were used, evidently so that residual cation would buffer against development of too great acidity as itaconic acid accumulated, although other
reasons may exist.

This patent is astonishingly broad in its coverage of organisms.   Thus,
while only *A. terreus* (and, historically, *A. itaconicus*) is known to produce
itaconic acid, and this obviously was the only organism the patentees

used, the curious claims granted cover submerged production of itaconic acid by any "mold selected from the group of genera consisting of Myxomycetes, Schizomycetes and Eumycetes." Competent fermentation authorities feel that should itaconic acid production be discovered for a new organism, the Kane *et al.* patent would not hold up in interference owing to the non-specific, sweeping, broad coverage of organisms. In other words, how can a patent be issued to cover a property not now known to exist in microorganisms other than the two species of Aspergilli mentioned?

In any case, the yield performance in submerged culture at least approximates those of surface culture, and in much shorter time, with much less labor and overhead involved per production quota. The itaconic acid fermentation is not yet conducted on full industrial scale, although this is imminent. Production is, however, on such a scale that barrel lots of itaconic acid are available for pilot plant experimentation regarding various possible applications.

REFERENCES

Calam, C. T., Oxford, A. E., and Raistrick, H. 1939. *Biochem. J.* **33**, 1488–1495.
Friedkin, M. 1945. *Ind. Eng. Chem., Anal. Ed.* **17**, 637–638.
Hollaender, A., Raper, K. B., and Coghill, R. D. 1945. *Am. J. Botany* **32**, 160–165.
Hope, E. 1925. U. S. Patent 1,644,131.
Kane, J. H., Finlay, A. C., and Amann, P. F. 1945. U. S. Patent 2,385,283 to Chas. Pfizer and Co., Sept. 18.
Kinoshita, K. 1929. *J. Chem. Soc. Japan* **50**, 583–593.
Kinoshita, K. 1931. *Acta Phytochim. Japan* **5**, 271–287.
Kinoshita, K. 1937. *Acta Phytochim. Japan* **9**, 159–187.
Lockwood, L. B., and Nelson, G. E. N. 1946. *Arch. Biochem.* **10**, 365–374.
Lockwood, L. B., Raper, K. B., Moyer, A. J., and Coghill, R. D. 1945. *Am. J Botany* **32**, 214-217.
Lockwood, L. B., and Reeves, M. D. 1945. *Arch. Biochem.* **6**, 455–469.
Lockwood, L. B., and Ward, G. E. 1945. *Ind. Eng. Chem.* **37**, 405–406.
Moyer, A. J., and Coghill, R. D. 1945. *Arch. Biochem.* **7**, 167–183.
Raper, K. B., Coghill, R. D., and Hollaender, A. 1945. *Am. J. Botany* **32**, 165–176.
Scheuing, G., and Walach, B. 1939. German Patent 678,985, July 26.
Stodola, F. H., Friedkin, M., Moyer, A. J., and Coghill, R. D. 1945. *J. Biol. Chem.* **161**, 739-742.
Thom, C., and Raper, K. B. 1945. A Manual of the Aspergilli. Williams and Wilkins, Baltimore, 373 pp.
Wehmer, C. 1899. *Botan. Centr.* **80**, 460–461.
Yuill, J. L. 1948. *Nature* **161**, 397.

CHAPTER 14

KOJIC ACID

An exaggerated importance has always been attached to this product of fungus metabolism, seemingly far out of line in relation to the host of other chemical substances known to accumulate in mold cultures. The reason is easy to see: attractively high conversion yields of carbohydrate to kojate are obtainable, both in surface and in submerged cultures, and the potentialities for development on a commercial scale were therefore excellent. These hopes and the emphasis have been in vain, however, for, up to now, no industrial use or application has been found for kojic acid. Nevertheless, this misguided interest lingers, and one always finds undue interest in this compound in treatises on fungus metabolism despite the fact that innumerable other compounds are equally deserving from a strictly comparable biochemical point of view.

One feature of this substance does, however, warrant an emphasis perhaps not due many other metabolic products of fungi: kojic acid is a simple cyclic pyrone compound. The opportunities to study mechanisms of ring closures or cyclic compounds of any sort are few in biochemical systems, and the present instance is one in which large amounts are formed quickly and in a perfectly controllable and reproducible system. Further discussion in this point is given below.

Kojic acid was a compound unknown to organic chemistry before its isolation by the Japanese investigator Saito in 1907 from steamed rice on which *Aspergillus oryzae* had grown. The acid was extracted with ether and was obtained in crystalline form as colorless needles. Saito showed it was distinct from other common organic acids formed by fungi, having the empirical composition $C_{12}H_{14}O_8$; on the basis of the melting point (152°) and a characteristic red coloration with ferric chloride, the new compound was incorrectly identified as β-resorcyl carbonic acid. Limitation of material prevented further study. Traetta-Mosca (1914) also isolated an acid from cultures of *A. glaucus* growing on fructose, sucrose, and glycerol, and at first thought it to be the γ-lactone of trihydroxy-hexadiene acid, but in a subsequent work (1921) he concluded it was a hydroxymethyl hydroxy γ-pyrone. Today it is almost certain that Traetta-Mosca's compound actually was kojic acid. The eminent Japanese biochemist, T. Yabuta, now Director of the Agricultural

Chemistry Institute of Tokyo Imperial University, resumed study of this compound in 1916. Yabuta coined the name kojic acid from the fact that it was first isolated from the traditional fermenting rice of the Orient, "koji." In fact, it was originally called koji acid. Molecular weight determinations showed the empirical composition to be one-half that formerly given. He prepared amounts adequate for extensive chemical study, and in 1924 assigned the correct structure as follows:

$$
\begin{array}{c}
O \\
\parallel \\
C \\
\diagup \quad \diagdown \\
HOC \qquad CH \\
\parallel \qquad \parallel \\
HC \qquad C{-}CH_2OH \\
\diagdown \quad \diagup \\
O
\end{array}
$$

Kojic acid (5-hydroxy-2-hydroxymethyl-γ-pyrone)

Additional detailed organic chemistry and derivatives of kojic acid may be found in Yabuta (1930), Armit and Nolan (1931) and Barham and Smits (1934). Kojic acid has been synthesized chemically starting with acetobromoglucose (Maurer, 1934).

ORGANISMS PRODUCING KOJIC ACID

Upwards of a score of different species of fungi are known to produce kojic acid from carbohydrates and it is worthy of note that with one exception, all belong to the genus *Aspergillus*. The exception is *Penicillium dalae* (Birkinshaw *et al.*, 1931).

Among the Aspergilli known to produce the acid are *A. oryzae, A. effusus, A. flavus, A. parasiticus, A. tamarii, A. glaucus, A. candidus, A. nidulans, A. gymnosardae, A. awamori, A. clavatus, A. fumigatus, A. giganteus, A. luteo-virescens*, and several unidentified species. The preponderant specificity of Aspergilli with respect to kojic acid formation probably is apparent rather than real. The remarkable heterogenieity of metabolic types among this group, the universal occurrence of other metabolic organic acids crossing all taxonomic barriers constructed on morphology, and the fact that already other organisms are known to form this, as well as closely related compounds, render any special significance to the Aspergillus-kojic acid association extremely unlikely. The most likely explanation is that numerous other species of Aspergilli were tested after the original discovery that *A. oryzae* produced it. A systematic survey of Penicillia, and possibly other fungi, doubtless would show this property is more widespread than is realized at present. An even more rigorous association was believed to hold for kojic acid and the *A. flavus-oryzae* group of fungi. Most species of the group tested formed

432 CHEMICAL ACTIVITIES OF FUNGI

some of the acid, a feature claimed to be suitable as a diagnostic test for this group of Aspergilli, i.e., an Aspergillus forming kojic acid most likely would be of the *flavus-oryzae* group (Birkinshaw *et al.*, 1931). However, as this property has now been demonstrated for Aspergilli belonging to almost all of Thòm and Raper's (1945) thirteen species groups of Aspergilli, this idea no longer has any serious significance.

Unlike virtually all the organic acids formed by fungi via carbohydrate dissimilation and which commonly are accompanied by one or more acids, little information is available as to other organic acids characteristic of kojic acid-forming fungi. The British mycologist Yuill has recently noted (1948) one of the few instances where kojic is formed in admixture with another acid—itaconic acid—by an unnamed species of Aspergillus (see Chapter 13). Kojic acid has also been found accompanied by gluconic, citric and oxalic acids in cultures of a strain of *Aspergillus oryzae* (Sakaguchi, 1931).

In addition to the fungi mentioned already, certain bacteria are known to produce kojic acid. Unidentified species of acetic acid bacteria (and one authentic species, *Bacterium xylinoides*), isolated from Japanese fruits, produce kojic acid from mannitol and fructose in small yield (Takahashi and Asai, 1933), and another acetic acid bacterium, *Gluconobacter liquefaciens*, produces the homologous oxidation product of kojic acid, comenic acid, from galactose (Takahashi and Asai, 1936).

Comenic acid

Other biochemical relationships will be discussed later.

QUANTITATIVE ESTIMATION OF KOJIC ACID

As mentioned above, kojic acid gives a characteristic deep cherry-red color with $FeCl_3$, and the color, being proportional to the concentration of kojate, may be employed for a colorimetric quantitative estimation (Tamiya, 1927; Corbellini and Gregorini, 1930). However, a number of complications potentially may arise when this test is applied to culture filtrates. Various other metabolic products of fungi, especially phenolic compounds and α-hydroxy acids, are known to form colored complexes with iron, and precipitates may be formed by insoluble compounds of iron with organic and inorganic (phosphates) components of the filtrate;

other colored metabolic substances may also be present. However, the iron red-coloration test is an extremely sensitive presumptive qualitative test for the presence of kojic acid, being able to detect a 1:200,000 solution of the acid. It is quite likely that some of the diffusible red pigments observed about fungi growing on agar media is due to kojic acid formed by the organism, reacting with iron in the medium to give the characteristic red coloration, even though the iron may be present only as an impurity. Although the Fe test is given by 3-hydroxypyrones, the presence of any but kojic acid in fungus cultures is exceedingly remote.

Birkinshaw and Raistrick (1931) observed that during the iodometric analysis for glucose in culture filtrates containing kojic acid, iodoform was unexpectedly encountered. They showed the latter originated from the kojic acid and worked out a quantitative method for kojate based on iodine absorption in alkaline solution. Per mole of kojic acid oxidized, one mole each of oxalic acid, iodoform, formic acid, and hydroxyacetic acid results according to the following proposed mechanism:

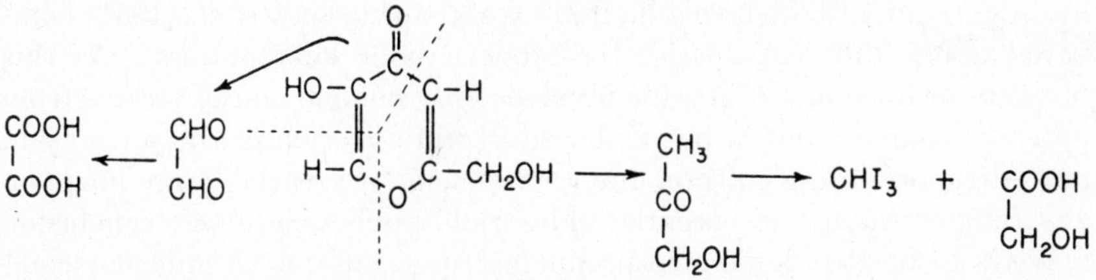

One mole of kojic acid consumes 10 I, and for completion of the reaction a fourfold excess of iodine is required and a reaction time of 90 minutes. However, under different conditions one mole of kojic acid consumes only four atoms iodine (Airoldi and Bionda, 1942). As residual dextrose in the medium also consumes iodine, allowance is made for the glucose determined polarimetrically.

Kojic acid reduces Fehling's solution, hence complicates the ordinary sugar determination. May et. al. (1931) point out that if the kojic acid content is less than 3 g./1. it does not interfere seriously with the sugar determination by ordinary copper reduction methods. Otherwise the sugar must be run after separation of kojic acid as copper kojate or a copper correction employed for the amount of kojic acid present.

Although lacking a free carboxyl group, kojic acid is a very weak acid owing to its phenolic nuclear hydroxy group. It is a weaker acid than carbonic acid as it may be precipitated by carbon dioxide from concentrated solutions of its sodium salt. It may be extracted with ether from acidified solutions and weighed directly provided interfering acids are negligible.

Kojic acid forms insoluble salts with heavy metals, of which copper kojate has a solubility of less than 5 p.p.m. in distilled water, and is most useful for the gravimetric determination of the acid, being highly specific. The kojate is precipitated from neutralized solutions with dilute calcium acetate. The precipitation must be carried out under carefully standardized conditions else copper coprecipitates as the basic copper salts of kojic acid and acetic acid (Barham, 1939). The copper kojate precipitate consisting of light-green rhombic crystals has been claimed variously to have zero, one-half, and one molecule of water of crystallization, on the basis of copper oxide content. The best evidence indicates that the salt itself is anhydrous with a CuO content of 23.01 per cent, and though precipitated as the anhydrous salt, it contains varying small amounts of strongly adsorbed water (Barham, 1939).

PRODUCTION OF KOJIC ACID BY FUNGI

Unlike all the processes previously discussed, no systematic study has been undertaken to obtain or develop superior strains of kojic acid-forming fungi, although to a limited extent Birkinshaw et al. (1931) compared a few different species for relative kojic acid powers. As this problem in its simplest aspects involves only comparison of strains from different sources, and in particular substrain selection of the progeny of any single promising culture, and as these efforts invariably are made on any fungus product of potential industrial application, a safe conclusion appears to be that kojic acid-producing fungi are not of sufficient commercial interest to warrant strain selection studies. The validity of this observation will at once be transparent should kojic acid suddenly find industrial application.

However, as one might expect, great differences exist among the organisms known to produce kojic acid. Some form only traces whereas others may convert over half of the consumed sugar into this product. In some cases material amounts of other metabolic products accumulate, whereas in others kojic acid is formed to the virtual exclusion of other metabolic products, except carbon dioxide and cell material.

With a single exception, to be discussed in detail below, all studies have dealt with surface cultures, again a signal indication of lack of commercial interest in kojic acid. Use of submerged cultures in the work of Kluyver and Perquin (1933) was designed largely for the elucidation of various fundamentals of the methodology of mold metabolism (see Chapter 2).

A large variety of factors influencing kojic acid formation have been studied in many organisms by various authors (May et al., 1931; Barham and Smits, 1936; Tamiya, 1927, 1938; Di Capua, 1933; Katagiri and

Kitaadra, 1929). These deal mainly with optimum conditions such as optimum pH, mineral concentration, nature and amount of carbohydrate, temperature, heavy metal nutrition, and so forth, and, not being of general or fundamental significance, need not be discussed here. In fact, conditions worked out in great detail for one kojic acid-producing fungus are almost certainly worthless for a different species or even for a different strain of the same species. Indeed, it would be a rare thing to be able to reproduce the results with the identical strain and identical conditions (ostensibly) in a different laboratory.

Nevertheless, certain aspects of the cultural studies do have a general significance. A great variety of different carbon compounds have been converted to kojic acid by different organisms: hexoses, pentoses, sugar alcohols, glycerol, other organic acids, etc. The significance of this feature is discussed below in relation to mechanism of formation of kojic acid. Yields as high as 50 to 65 per cent on the basis of sugar consumed are obtainable (Katagiri and Kitahara, 1933; Kluyver and Perquin, 1933; May et al., 1931).

In keeping with all other fungus processes yielding compounds from carbohydrate dissimilation, a limited nitrogen nutrition of the organism is conducive to highest yields of kojate (Kinoshita, 1927; Kluyver and Perquin, 1933; Tamiya, 1927). A common reason for this phenomenon underlies all these different fungus activities and is discussed in Chapter 4. Essentially the same conclusion has been reached where, instead of using small amounts of readily assimilable N (or eliminating it entirely in replacement cultures), like NH_4NO_3, a difficulty utilizable source of N is used, such as cobaltamine salts $[(Co(NH_3)_5 \cdot H_2O)Cl_3]$ (Kinoshita, 1927) but this still lacks confirmation (Challenger et al., 1929).

Consideration of pH relations of this process must embrace two points: (1) optimum pH for growth of the organism producing kojic acid, and (2) optimum pH of the kojic acid process independent of the growth of the organism, i.e., dissimilation vs. assimilation. Doubtless there will be strain differences in pH tolerance for growth; but, like other acid forming processes, the optimum pH for the dissimilation of sugar to kojic acid is strongly on the acid side, in the neighborhood of pH 2 to 3 (Katagiri and Kitahara, 1929; Barham and Smits, 1934; Tamiya, 1927). It is recalled from Chapter 2 that pH experiments on acid formation in surface culture are subject to serious question because neither the initial pH of the medium nor the pH of a representative sample of medium during growth reflect the true pH conditions under which the organism is metabolizing, namely, a strongly acid layer immediately contiguous to the surface pad. The clearest experiments on this point are those of Kluyver and Perquin (1933) with submerged cultures of *Aspergillus flavus* under replacement conditions, showing that at pH 1.9 the conversion of sugar to kojic acid was 78.0 per cent of theory (theory = 80.7 per cent, assuming one mole kojic acid per mole glucose), whereas only a slight reduction in acidity, namely to pH 2.2, (i.e., about 50 per cent reduction in hydrogen ion concentration) lowered the conversion to 49.6 per cent of theory. Important from a practical viewpoint is the fact that the total sugar turnover at the more favorable conversion percentage was only about one-half what it was at pH 2.2. So far, the production of this and itaconic acid are the only fungus processes in which the optimum pH is as extreme as that in the classical citric acid fermentation.

Other facts obtained by these authors under the ideal conditions of submerged culture are:

(a) The highest kojic acid yields occur in replacement cultures devoid of nitrogen.

(b) There is a definite initial carbohydrate concentration which is optimum, in this case 10 per cent. It is to be stressed that this ideal concentration lasts a very short time, as the sugar is consumed.

(c) An abundance of air is essential lest the organism go into alcoholic fermentation. Addition of an accessory hydrogen carrier, pyocyanin, aids in suppressing the strong alcoholic fermentation tendencies, thereby resulting in regular definite increases in kojic acid yields, amounting to as much as 15 per cent over controls.

(d) Small amounts of mycelium in the replacement solution give higher conversion yields than large amounts of mycelium, which consume more sugar but give appreciably lower yields.

(e) Suitable buffer capacity is essential to maintain the optimum pH in the face of accumulations of large amounts of kojic acid, as demonstrated in this tabulation:

Phosphate Buffer at pH 2.0	Kojic Acid, Per Cent of Theory
$\frac{1}{8}$ Molar	48.9
$\frac{1}{16}$	45.9
$\frac{1}{32}$	35.2
$\frac{1}{136}$	26.8

(f) The nature of the medium on which the mycelium is grown is of crucial importance for the kojic acid-producing ability in replacement solutions, i.e., the composition of the cell material used, is critical. Only cells grown on mineral media gave significant yields; cells grown on organic media (malt extract) produced no kojic acid in replacement solutions (sugar and phosphate). Data and a discussion of this point are given in Chapter 2.

An interesting case of stimulation of the kojic acid process by a nonbiological substance, ethylene chlorhydrin, has been reported now for some 17 years (May *et al.*, 1932) but apparently has never been tested in other laboratories. A series of forty diverse organic chemicals was tested and one, ethylene chlorhydrin, had a decided accelerating affect on growth and kojic acid formation by *Aspergillus flavus*. Although there was a slight (app. 5 per cent) increase in conversion rate of sugar to kojic acid, the main effect was one of accelerating the physiological activities in an overall sense, as sugar consumption, cell synthesis, CO_2 production, and total kojic acid production was increased per unit time compared to controls (see Table 1). This effect seems to be a nonspecific one, and would be well-worth while testing in other fungus processes, especially as ethylene chlorhydrin also has stimulating powers regarding vegetative growth of certain plants. Conceivably this chemical enhances permeability.

TABLE 1

EFFECT OF ETHYLENE CHLORHYDRIN[1]

Ethylene chlor-hydrin, Mg./l.	Sugar consumed, g.	Mycelial dry weight, g.	Kojic acid produced, g.	Conversion, per cent
0	8.6	0.278	3.56	41.5
1	8.7	.284	3.72	42.8
10	9.2	.312	4.30	46.8
100	10.8	.414	4.96	45.9

[1] From May, O. E., *et al.* (1932).

MECHANISM OF FORMATION OF KOJIC ACID

The striking structural similarity of glucose and kojic acid has led many investigators (Yabuta, 1924; Kinoshita, 1927; Haworth, 1929) to postulate a direct conversion of the former to the latter by various fungi by the processes of dehydration and oxidation, represented as follows:

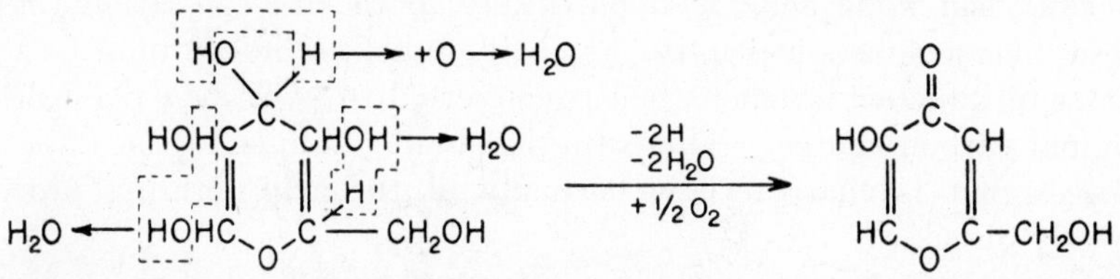

However, the relationships which seem obvious to the organic chemist need not impute that biology carries out these reactions in this way, and, as a matter of fact, there is not a bit of evidence to support this idea in spite of Maurer's (1934) synthesis of kojic acid from a glucose derivative. As seen later, the similarity between these two structures appears to be purely coincidental, and does not imply that one generates the other.

An outstanding feature in connection with mechanisms is that kojic acid is formed from a wide variety of different carbon sources, of heterogeneous chemical types. The following list is not intended to be complete, but it does give an idea of the diversity of the carbon sources convertible into kojic acid: starch, inulin, dextrin, sucrose, maltose, lactose, trehalose, glucose, fructose, mannose, galactose, rhamnose, arabinose, xylose, dihydroxyacetone, glyceraldehyde, inositol, mannitol, sorbitol, dulcitol, erythritol, glycerol, sodium glycerophosphate, ethanol, quinic acid, gluconic acid, and glycolic acid.

Aside from the fact that compounds with fewer carbon atoms than kojic acid do yield kojic acid, the chemical reasoning employed above to interpret the origin of kojate via dehydration and oxidation of glucose might lead one to expect pyromeconic acid from the pentose arabinose:

$$
\begin{array}{cc}
\begin{array}{c}
\text{CHOH} \\
\diagup \quad \diagdown \\
\text{HOHC} \qquad \text{CHOH} \\
| \qquad\qquad | \\
\text{H}_2\text{C} \qquad \text{CHOH} \\
\diagdown \quad \diagup \\
\text{O}
\end{array}
&
\begin{array}{c}
\text{O} \\
\parallel \\
\text{C} \\
\diagup \quad \diagdown \\
\text{HC} \qquad \text{COH} \\
\parallel \qquad\qquad \parallel \\
\text{HC} \qquad \text{CH} \\
\diagdown \quad \diagup \\
\text{O}
\end{array}
\\
\text{Arabinose} & \text{Pyromeconic acid}
\end{array}
$$

but instead, kojic acid is formed. Similarly, the dehydration theory would have comenic acid resulting from gluconic acid, but kojic acid does. Finally, the formation of kojic acid from fructose is incompatible with the persistence of the pyranose ring, since, if it were not ruptured it should yield 3-hydroxy-2-hydroxymethyl-γ-pyrone, and not kojic acid (the 5-hydroxy compound). Thus, the fact that different carbohydrates do not yield the corresponding "dehydrated" compound, and that compounds, sugar and non-sugar, with two to seven carbon atoms all can yield kojic acid, lead inevitably to the interpretation that all these diverse substances must first be metabolized in common to a precursor of kojic acid, which then is converted to kojic acid regardless of original carbon source. This situation is not unique to the kojic acid process, but is characteristic of many of the acid forming processes already discussed.

From this point on, nothing conclusive can be said of the kojic acid mechanism except that there are numerous theories and they are virtually all contradictory. Two main categories may be recognized.

(a) The common precursor produced from all carbon sources (except glucose) is glucose, which then is converted to kojic acid via simultaneous dehydration and dehydrogenation. The glucose may accumulate as intracellular polysaccharide and constitutes a reserve from which kojate is formed via glucose (Tamiya, 1932; Birkinshaw *et al.* 1931). It has indeed been demonstrated, but it certainly is not unexpected, that a kojic acid-strain of *A. flavus* does synthesize a starchlike substance utilizing xylose as carbon source (Barham and Smits, 1934). Gould (1938) has examined this reserve polysaccharide theory with totally negative results. He harvested mycelium of *A. tamarii* grown on various carbon sources and presumably rich in stored polysaccharide, washed the mycelium, dried and ground it, and utilized the powdered material as the carbon source in a medium now inoculated with living *A. tamarii*. No trace of kojic acid could be found in any of the cultures. This experiment in itself, being negative, is not absolute proof contrary to the polysaccharide hypothesis, as other nutritional factors may have intervened owing to the use of whole mycelium, but failure to get positive results renders the theory of questionable credibility. It must be remembered that the main premise of this theory, namely dehydration of the sugar pyranose structure to kojic acid, has not one bit of positive evidence to support it, and considerable theoretical evidence against it (see above).

(b) The common precursor produced from all carbon sources is not glucose, but a C_3 or C_2 fragment which undergoes condensation with itself to form kojate. Evidence for this idea seems strongest for the C_3 fragment dihydroxyacetone, and acetaldehyde has been proposed as the potential C_2 precursor or intermediate. Not only is there some basis for this theory on account of the rather high conversion yields from dihydroxyacetone, but on the grounds of comparative biochemistry the idea has plausibility. This triose is a key intermediate in carbohydrate metabolism and can therefore easily be accounted for in the dissimilation of any carbohydrate. Secondly, recognizing that a fungus will develop on C_2, C_3, C_4, C_5, and C_7 compounds and synthesize its multifarious cell components, including the polysaccharides and pentoses fundamentally a part of protoplasm, it is virtually mandatory to conclude on the basis of present day knowledge that the triose dihydroxyacetone or its isomeric equilibrium product, glyceraldehyde, are formed as a key intermediate in these syntheses. Third, numerous analogous conversions of triose (and C_2) intermediates to metabolic end products are known (see Chapter 4). Thus the triose may end up as glycerol or lactic acid. The C_2 may end as ethanol or acetic acid. On the other hand, these intermediary fragments may undergo synthesis to C_4 compounds (acetylmethylcarbinol, succinic acid) or to C_6 compounds (citric, aconitic). Thus, kojic acid formation is merely one additional mechanism fungi have for disposing of rapidly formed triose, entirely analogous to the other well known systems. Fourth, in general the conditions conducive to high kojate yields are those least favorable to cell synthesis, i.e., the principles of shunt metabolism are involved. Unless the hexose chain were split, cell synthesis would not compete with kojic acid formation. Finally, even though the C_3 (or C_2) fragments are formed from hexose, it is not essential that the former, produced from non-hexose substances, first be synthesized to cellular carbohydrate which then yields the triose again for kojate synthesis. The triose could, of course, be converted directly to kojate without the preliminary excursion to hexose. Kojic acid could then be looked upon as a triose condensation product alternative to hexose.

The Italian investigators Corbellini and Gregorini (1930) were the first to propose a triose condensation in the genesis of kojic acid. The strength and value of their idea lies in their utilization of the precepts of comparative biochemistry, for the experimental evidence is superficial and rests largely on the fact that glycerol consumption by *A. flavus* leads to kojic acid. As glycerol oxidation is bound to generate a triose, the latter was assumed to play a key role in synthesis of kojate. Dihydroxyacetone ($\rightleftharpoons$ glyceraldehyde) and a further hypothetical oxidation product, also C_3, 1,3-glyceroldialdehyde, both aldehydes, were presumed to condense in a manner entirely analogous to Neuberg's aldol condensation of acetaldehyde by the enzyme carboligase in the biological genesis of acetylmethylcarbinol. Dehydration of the condensation product then leads to kojic acid. The type reaction may be expressed as $R_1CHO + R_2CHO \rightarrow R_1COCH(OH)R_2$ and in this case is presumed to be

However attractive the comparative biochemistry of this idea, it cannot yet be taken seriously for a number of reasons: (1) neither dihydroxyacetone nor the dialdehyde were tested for their ability to undergo these reactions through the agency of the organisms, (2) none of the three claimed intermediates was detected, and (3) the dialdehyde and the condensation product are purely hypothetical as far as biological systems are concerned and they are not known to occur.

Soon after, dihydroxyacetone was definitely incriminated in kojate synthesis by Challenger *et al.* (1931) and Katagiri and Kitahara (1933). It was shown that glyceraldehyde was formed as an intermediate in glycerol oxidation by *A. oryzae*, and it was actually isolated and identified (as derivatives). Furthermore, dihydroxyacetone furnished as the sole carbon source gave up to 55 per cent of theoretical yields of kojic acid, a figure impressively close to the 65 per cent obtained from glucose at the same time. In view of the fact that no other substrates of the numerous ones employed (except, of course, di- and polysaccharides which generate the simple hexoses) lead to such high yields, there is a certain logic for incriminating that simple split product of hexoses.

May *et al.* (1931) involve 1-hydroxyacetyl-3-formyl-3-hydroxyacetone as the immediate precursor of kojic acid, the former resulting from 2- and 3-C split products. However, as stated earlier, regardless of the attractiveness of a reaction from the organic chemistry point of view, the presence of enzymes in biological systems at once creates possible mechanisms that are not the most apparent to the organic chemist. Until this postulated intermediate can be shown to generate kojic acid in fungus cultures in high yields, and until it can be detected as an intermediate in kojic synthesis from sugar, it cannot be regarded seriously.

As in virtually all fungus processes dealing with carbohydrate dissimilation, the formation of alcohol by kojic acid-forming fungi raises the question of its (or acetaldehyde, its precursor) being an intermediate in the synthesis of the 6-carbon acid. Birkinshaw *et al.* (1931) were among the first to present this issue, and, in particular, because kojic acid-producing fungi seemed to have a marked tendency toward alcoholic fermentation. As discussed in Chapter 9, alcoholic formation is extremely widespread among fungi; hence, on this basis alone there is no more reason for associating C_2 with kojic acid synthesis than there is associating it with lactic acid formation by *Rhizopus*. Unless shown otherwise, it may mean merely that the organism can decarboxylate pyruvic acid as well as perform other biochemical reactions with sugar split products. As a matter of fact, Gould (1938) was unable to block kojic acid production by *A. tamarii* by the presence of sulfite or dimedon, agents which fix acetaldehyde in the form of addition products in the medium. If kojate formation were suppressed, and if acetaldehyde fixation products were detected, this would be fair evidence for involvement of C_2 in kojic acid synthesis. However, Gould observed no reduction in kojate formation and no fixation products resulted. Added phosphate was without effect on kojate formation from glucose, xylose, and glycerol in replacement cultures.

Even though acetaldehyde fixation can be demonstrated (Katagiri and Kitahara, 1929) with kojic acid cultures, this is rather universal among the fungi, and only when the fixation or trapping of the aldehyde leads to blockage of kojic formation can it be concluded that C_2 fragments are normal intermediates in kojate synthesis from hexose. Otherwise, it means only that the organism can carry out an alcoholic fermentation (specifically, decarboxylate pyruvic acid).

On the other hand, one is faced with the fact that kojic acid can actually be formed from ethyl alcohol, although this is by no means true for all kojic acid fungi (Tamiya, 1932; Katagiri and Kitahara, 1933). Sakaguchi (1932) found that alcohol added to glucose cultures of A. oryzae increased kojic acid formation over controls, and more recently Barnard and Challenger (1946) have given this matter some detailed attention. Their culture of A. oryzae formed up to 16.7 per cent yields of kojic acid (from ethanol) on a carbon-carbon basis. The action took place both in growth and replacement cultures, but was very slow as compared to events in the usual sugar cultures. Two per cent ethanol solutions were optimum, whereas no kojic acid was formed from 4 per cent alcohol although acetaldehyde was found in abundance. The addition of sodium sulfite reduced kojate formation from alcohol, but did not inhibit its formation completely. The reduction would be expected, for any utilization at all of alcohol, regardless of its fate, would have to be via its oxidation product, viz., acetaldehyde.

Deducible from these experiments is that alcohol can yield kojate, but there need not be a direct relation or reason to believe that this is the pathway in kojate formation from sugar. Alcohol is merely one more of the many substrates yielding the acid, and, because the organism can synthesize its cell constituents from alcohol, is evidence of its being able to synthesize carbohydrate, dihydroxyacetone, or the other intermediates common to the other substrates, and from which kojate is formed. Probably the most effective proof of participation of C_2 in kojate synthesis from carbohydrate would be suppression of the latter in the presence of acetaldehyde-fixing agents, and Gould's negative experiments on this point render this mechanism possibility an unlikely one at this time.

An additional attack on the mechanism of formation of kojic acid may be had by studying the reversal of this process, namely the mechanism of the breakdown of this compound. It is neither unreasonable nor unlikely that the primary split products of kojic acid are the immediate precursors in the reverse process, its synthesis. Kojic acid has been little studied in this respect but it is a biologically reactive substance on three counts: (1) it can be destroyed by *A. flavus* after being formed (Corbellini and Gregorini, 1930), (2) it has antibiotic activity against a variety of microorganisms (see below) and (3) it can be fermented to ethyl alcohol by yeast (Traetta-Mosca, 1914). If the last is true and it occurs in high yields, the alcohol presumably originated from pyruvate which in turn must have originated from a triose generated from kojic acid and which obviously must correspond to the triose precursor of pyruvate in sugar fermentation, i.e., dihydroxyacetone or its equilibrium isomer glyceraldehyde. Here, indeed, would be light on the mechanism of kojate origin, but experimental confirmation of alcohol fermentation of kojic acid is lacking.

Implications of Kojic Acid

Its significance from the standpoint of comparative biochemistry in relation to other mold processes has already been stressed, the experimental evidence for synthesis of a cyclic compound via C_3 condensation being particularly interesting. Similar types of 3-hydroxypyrones exist in nature, and they may be similarly synthesized in nature: flavonols such as quercitin and anthocyanins such as callistephin (Challenger *et al.*, 1929). Included here (May *et al.*, 1931) also may be chelidonic acid (2,6-dicarboxy-1,4-pyrone) which amounts to 2 per cent of leaves of lily-of-the-valley, meconic acid (2,6-dicarboxy-3-hydroxy-1,4-pyrone) which occurs as 4 per cent of opium, and maltol (3-hydroxy-2 methyl-1,4-pyrone) which occurs in pine needles and in the bark of the larch tree. Also pointed out is that pyrones react readily with NH_3 to yield pyridones, which may relate to synthesis of pyridine bases in nature.

A considerable body of information relating to the organic chemistry of kojic acid and of numerous derivatives has been built up (see Barham and Smits, 1934 for review) with the object of discovering properties which would enable kojic acid to compete economically with other raw products in commercial practice, particularly in the field of synthetic dyestuffs and resins, and drugs, especially those of the β-eucaine type, of value as local anesthetics. Kojic acid gives solid derivatives with a large series of aldehydes via a mechanism similar to resin formation:

$$\text{2 Kojic acid moles} + \text{RCHO} \xrightarrow{-H_2O} \text{Kojic acid} - \overset{\overset{\textstyle H}{|}}{\underset{\underset{\textstyle R}{|}}{C}} - \text{Kojic acid}$$

Exemplifying previous comments, another attempt to anticipate a commercial application of kojic acid is demonstrated by studies (Rayman, 1941) showing it can be produced by fungi (*A. flavus*) from a cheap bulk-available material like oat hulls.   In this case the high pentosan content is the carbohydrate source, being acid-hydrolyzed to the pentose xylose, which is known to yield kojic acid.

Since 1945 (Foster and Karow) many authors have found that kojic acid accounts for the antibacterial properties of culture filtrates of various fungi.   It is of particular interest that the acid is unique among the host of antibiotics known, in that it is more strongly inhibitive to gram negative bacteria than to gram positive (Foster and Karow, 1945). A statement pertaining to this remarkable specificity, long overlooked by workers in the field of antibiosis, was made by Reed and Bushnell as early as 1934 (cited in Barham and Smits) even before Dubos' work opened up the field of antibiotics.

Speaking of comparative biochemistry, γ-pyrones, and antibacterial activity, the structural chemical similarity between kojic acid and another

Patulin (Woodward and Singh, 1949)

well-known antibiotic substance of fungus origin, patulin (clavacin) is worthy of attention.

REFERENCES

Airoldi, R., and Bionda, G.   1942.   *Ann. chim. applicata* **32**, 385–390.
Armit, J. W., and Nolan, T. J.   1931.   *J. Chem. Soc.* 3023–3031.
Barham, N. H.   1939.   *Ind. Eng. Chem., Anal. Ed.* **11**, 31–33.
Barham, N. H., and Smits, B. L.   1934.   *Trans. Kansas Acad. Sci.* **37**, 91–113.
Barham, N. H., and Smits, B. L.   1936.   *Ind. Eng. Chem.* **28**, 567–570.
Barnard, D., and Challenger, F.   1946.   *Biochem. J.* **40**, ixii.
Birkinshaw, J. H., Charles, J. H. V., Lilly, C. H., and Raistrick, H.   1931.   *Trans. Roy. Soc. London* **B220**, 127–138.
Birkinshaw, H. J., and Raistrick, H.   1931.   *Trans. Roy. Soc. London* **B220**, 139–152.
Challenger, F., Klein, L., and Walker, T. K.   **1929.**   *J. Chem. Soc.* 1498–1505.
Challenger, F., Klein, L., and Walker, T. K.   **1931.**   *J. Chem. Soc.* 16–23.
Corbellini, A., and Gregorini, B.   1930.   *Gazz. chim. ital.* **60**, 244–256.
Di Capua, A.   1933.   *Gazz. chim. ital.* **63**, 296–302.
Foster, J. W., and Karow, E. O.   1945.   *J. Bact.* **49**, 19–29.
Gould, B. S.   1938.   *Biochem. J.* **32**, 797–802.
Haworth, W. H.   1929.   Constitution of Sugars.   Longmans Green, New York.
Katagiri, H., and Kitahara, K.   1929.   *Bull. Agr. Chem. Soc. Japan* **5**, 38–47.
Katagiri, H., and Kitahara, K.   1933.   *Mem. Coll. Agr., Kyoto Imp. Univ.* No. 26, 1–29.

Kinoshita, K. 1927. *Acta Phytochim. Japan* **3**, 31–51.

Kluyver, A. J., and Perquin, L. H. C. 1933. *Biochem. Z.* **266**, 68–81, 82–95.

Maurer, K. 1934. *Ber.* **63B**, 25–34.

May, O. E., Moyer, A. J., Wells, P. A., and Herrick, H. T. 1931. *J. Am. Chem. Soc.*, **53**, 774–782.

May, O. E., Ward, G., and Herrick, H. T. 1932. *Zentr. Bakt. Parasitenk. Abt. II* **86**, 129–134.

Rayman, M. N. 1941. *Iowa State Coll. J. Sci.* **16**, 122–124.

Saito, K. 1907. *Botan. Mag. Tokyo* **21**, 7–11.

Sakaguchi, K. 1931. *J. Agr. Chem. Soc. Japan* **7**, 748–762.

Sakaguchi, K. 1932. *J. Agr. Chem. Soc. Japan* **8**, 264–265.

Takahashi, T., and Asai, T. 1933. *Zentr. Bakt. Parasitenk. Abt. II* **88**, 286–295.

Takahashi, T., and Asai, T. 1936. *Zentr. Bakt. Parasitenk. Abt. II* **93**, 248–252.

Tamiya, H. 1927. *Acta Phytochim. Japan* **3**, 51–173.

Tamiya, H. 1928. *Acta Phytochim. Japan* **4**, 77–213.

Tamiya, H. 1932. *Acta Phytochim. Japan* **6**, 1–129.

Thom, C., and Raper, K. B. 1945. A Manual of the Aspergilli. Williams and Wilkins, Baltimore, 373 pp.

Traetta-Mosca, F. 1914. *Ann. chim. applicata* **1**, 488–492.

Traetta-Mosca, F., and Preti, M. 1921. *Gazz. chim. ital.* **51**, (II) 269–277.

Woodward, R. B., and Singh, G. 1949. *J. Am. Chem. Soc.* **71**, 758–759.

Yabuta, T. 1916. *J. Chem. Soc. Tokyo* **37**, 1185–1233; 1234–1269.

Yabuta, T. 1924. *J. Chem. Soc.* **125**, 575–587.

Yabuta, T. 1930. *J. Agr. Chem. Soc. Japan* **6**, 516–525.

Yuill, J. L. 1948. *Nature* **161**, 397.

CHAPTER 15

GLUCONIC AND OTHER SUGAR ACIDS

A Frenchman, Molliard, discovered gluconic acid in cultures of filamentous fungi in 1922 when he observed that citric and oxalic acids present in the culture filtrate of *Sterigmatocystis nigra* (*Aspergillus niger*) quantitatively could not account for the total acidity of the solution. *d*-Gluconic acid was detected, isolated and identified by a variety of tests, cinchonine salt, phenylhydrazide, elementary analysis of calcium salt; the formation of a "sugar-acid" was thus established for the fungi. Actually gluconic acid had been a well-known product of metabolism of the acetic acid bacteria (genus Acetobacter) since the latter part of the last century, and lately by members of the genera Pseudomonas and Phytomonas (Lockwood *et al.*, 1941).

d-Gluconic acid is an important industrial and pharmaceutical chemical; consequently, like other processes of practical interest, both the bacterial and mold production of this acid have received much study with the ultimate object of evolving the most efficient process. Such study has led to elucidation of many points of theoretical and scientific interest, as well as practical application. The relation of this compound to its parent substance glucose is as follows:

$$
\begin{array}{cc}
\mathrm{CH_2OH} & \mathrm{CH_2OH} \\
| & | \\
\mathrm{(CHOH)_4} & \mathrm{(CHOH)_4} \\
| & | \\
\mathrm{CHO} & \mathrm{COOH} \\
\text{Glucose} & \text{Gluconic acid}
\end{array}
$$

As in the case of metabolic products of other fungi, paramount determinants of the performance of the culture are strain specificity and cultural conditions. Molliard's work was confined to only one strain, but he was able to show decisively that by controlling the composition of the medium the organism could be induced to form exclusively gluconic acid, citric acid, oxalic acid, combinations thereof, or form virtually no organic acids. Thus, in a so-called balanced medium, with all constituents in adequate amounts for maximum growth, only a trace of organic acids was found. Diminishing the nitrogen and mineral content to $\frac{1}{25}$ the normal supply gave gluconic acid exclusively, and in maximum yield; reduction of the nitrogen supply only resulted in appearance of

446

citric acid alone; lowered phosphorus content gave a mixture of citric and oxalic acids, whereas when potassium was limiting, oxalic acid alone was formed. Later, Molliard (1924) decided that it was chiefly the low nitrogen which favors gluconate formation, whereas low minerals allowed oxalate to preponderate.

The main features of Molliard's nutritional conclusions, particularly the favorable effect of low minerals, were confirmed by the Russian worker, Kardo-Syssojeva (1933), who employed a strain of *A. niger* giving weight conversion yields of glucose to gluconic acid in excess of 100 per cent (theory = 108.8). Since low mycelial weight was always obtained in the low mineral medium in which maximum gluconic acid yields were obtained, it is evident that the latter was formed at the expense of cell synthesis. The effect of alterations in N content of the medium was found to be a function of the degree of acidity. Thus, low nitrogen favored gluconate formation in non-acid media, i.e., presence of $CaCO_3$, but in acid media gluconic acid formation was favored by *high* nitrogen content. This same organism, under other conditions, gave 60 per cent weight conversion yields of citric acid.

The nitrogen effect was confirmed by Bernhauer (1928a and b) who demonstrated that the N nutrition of the organism during growth determined the nature of its acid-forming metabolism in replacement cultures with sugar solution. Mycelium grown on low N media mainly produced citric acid in the second phase, a profound metabolic change comparable to the influence of pH on citric vs. oxalic acid formation by fungi (Chapter 12). Similar results were obtained by Perquin (1938) using shake cultures.

Other things being equal, the presence of a neutralizing agent is always conducive to highest gluconate yields. Generally, calcium carbonate is the preferred neutralizing agent. It must always be borne in mind that if a high acidity exists, either initially or later through organic acid formation, particularly with Aspergillus, and notably *A. niger*, citric acid tends to accumulate (Butkewitsch, 1924). On the other hand, the chances are that an *A. niger* strain whose metabolic nature is such that it does not form gluconate in $CaCO_3$-containing media, will form oxalate.

It is not to be concluded that these acids are formed totally independent of each other. While conditions usually can be found that will allow one acid to accumulate to the virtual exclusion of others, or preponderate, mixtures of the acids in varying degrees are more often encountered. This is particularly true of gluconic, citric, and oxalic acids. Often the ratios may change; for example, gluconic acid may appear early in the incubation period, followed by its disappearance and subsequent formation of citric and/or oxalic acids. It is known that gluconic acid furnished as the sole energy source can be broken down and converted to citric and oxalic acids by fungi.

Two years after Molliard's discovery it became recognized that gluconate formation was a character of an extremely large number of different fungi, and, in particular, species of Aspergilli and Penicillia, although this may be due to the fact that large numbers of species belonging to these genera have been tested, as compared to others. Beginning with Butkewitsch's (1923, 1924) detection and isolation of calcium gluconate from *Citromyces glaber* (Penicillium), this acid has been found in numerous different species, although, as usual, by far the largest amount of study has been devoted to strains of *A. niger*. Following are some of the species found to form gluconic acid: *A. cinnamomeus, A. fuscus, A. fumaricus, A. wentii, A. luchuensis, A. oryzae,* and large numbers of different strains of *A. niger*. Even larger numbers of Penicillia have been identified with this property: *P. glaucum, P. luteum-purpurogenum* var. *rubisclerotium, P. purpurogenum, P. luteum, P. chrysogenum, P. oxalicum, P. notatum, P. resticulosum, P. griseofulvum, P. brevicaule, P. africanum, P. citrinum, P. trzebinski.* Also *Polyporus vaporius, Mucor plumbeus, Dematium pullulans, Fumago vagans, Fusarium lini* (Falck and Kapur, 1924; Wehmer, 1928; May *et al.*, 1927; Schreyer, 1931; Perwozwansky, 1930; Angeletti and Cerruti, 1930; Birkinshaw and Raistrick, 1931; Sakaguchi, 1932; Knoblock and Mayer, 1941; Nord and Engel, 1938.) It is evident that the ability to form gluconic acid is extremely widespread among fungi, and it crosses widely separated genus boundaries.

The first systematic physiological study of this process was done by the prolific German mold physiologist K. Bernhauer (1926) (Bernhauer and Wolf, 1928) using the method for quantitative estimation of gluconic acid previously worked out by Butkewitsch. This depends upon recovering and weighing the calcium salt of gluconic acid which is precipitated from aqueous solution by addition of three volumes of 90–95 per cent ethyl alcohol. Pure calcium gluconate may be obtained by recrystallization from warm 30 per cent alcohol. Bernhauer's strain of *A. niger* produced no citric acid, either in acid, neutral, or alkaline media. The latter was found to favor higher accumulations, particularly when calcium oxide was used as a neutralizing agent. Up to 76 per cent conversion yields were obtained in 5 to 7 days with 10 to 40 per cent glucose solutions. Following Butkewitsch's lead, Bernhauer also applied the replacement technique ("Methodik der fertigen Pilzdecken") to this process and demonstrated that preformed *A. niger* surface pads converted glucose to gluconic acid with undiminished vigor through four successive replacements. This principle was later adopted in a commercial process for gluconic acid production (see Re-use of Mycelium).

Similar systematic studies directed toward refinement of conditions essential for maximum gluconic acid yields were performed (May *et al.*, 1929) with the object of developing a commercial surface process for manufacture of gluconic acid using a selected strain of *P. luteum purpurogenum var. rubrisclerotium* cultivated in shallow aluminum pans arranged shelflike in a closed chamber. This organism was the best gluconic acid producer out of 172 different organisms tested (May *et al.*, 1927). A survey by Schreyer (1931) showed that nine out of twenty-five fungi produced gluconate.

Yields of 55–75 per cent were obtained by May *et al.* from 20–25 per cent sugar solution in 14 days. In a tray with a surface to volume ratio of 0.25–0.30, the economic optimum, one square meter of mycelium produced 4–4.5 kg. gluconic acid during that time. Actually much higher yields are obtainable with higher surface to volume ratios but the total sugar turnover becomes very small in such shallow layers of medium. In one experiment a ratio of 0.16 gave 30 per cent conversion, while a ratio of 1.0 gave 82 per cent. Development of the surface process was quickly abandoned in favor of a submerged process (see Gluconic Acid in Relation to Oxygen).

Strain Specificity

Data on this all-important feature are available for *A. niger* strains only. In one surface study (Bernhauer and Wolf, 1928) nine different strains were tested in media made acid ($M/35$) with HCl or H_3PO_4. Growth of some strains was stimulated and some repressed. Gluconic acid formation was uniformly suppressed, citric acid appearing in every case. Another survey covering forty-two strains of *A. niger* tested in submerged culture showed that 34 out of the total gave 70–90 per cent conversion yields of glucose to gluconic acid (Knoblock and Mayer, 1941). Calcium carbonate was present in these cultures.

Strain stability with respect to gluconic acid formation has not been the subject of much study up to now, although it can scarcely be questioned that this feature plays as much a role in this process as in the several others already known. Doubtless some gluconic acid-producing strains are more stable than others, so that the progeny of any one single spore colony show variation in this property, low yielders eventually overgrowing the potent ones after more or less prolonged cultivation on artificial media. This physiological degeneration in gluconic acid forming powers has already been observed by May *et al.* (1927) during development of the industrial scale surface process utilizing *P. luteum purpurogenum var. rubrisclerotium.* In order to maintain the consistently high yields obtained initially, single colony progeny had to be continuously isolated and tested for gluconic acid production, and the desirable ones selected for further use. Physiological variation may go the other way: it will be recalled that Wehmer's (1928) *Aspergillus fumaricus* degenerated with respect to fumaric acid-forming ability, and instead, acquired the ability to produce gluconic acid, especially in submerged culture (Thies, 1930). See also Coulthard *et al.* (1945) regarding notatin.

GLUCONIC ACID IN RELATION TO OXYGEN

Inspection of the chemical formulas of glucose and gluconic acid makes it evident that the latter is a simple oxidation product of the former, the relation being chemically expressed as follows: $CH_2OH(CHOH)_4CHO + \frac{1}{2}O_2 \rightarrow CH_2OH(CHOH)_4COOH$. It is also evident that once an organism with an inherently high ability to form gluconic acid has been selected, and once the nutritional and other cultural factors conducive to gluconic acid formation have been defined, the efficiency with which the organism will oxidize glucose to gluconic acid depends exclusively upon oxygen. It has already been emphasized (Chapter 2) that, on account of the physical nature of microbial cultures, the high cell density, the enormous, simultaneous oxygen demand of all cells, and the limited solubility of oxygen in water (culture fluid), full oxygen saturation of the biological system is extremely difficult to achieve. From these considerations one might expect that a process so directly a function of oxygen as the glucose $\rightarrow$ gluconic acid system might find the oxygenation problem a real one where the issue is oxidation *at maximum rate*. This is exactly the issue in an industrial process, which, because the organism, cultural conditions, and sugar supply used all have been ascertained as ideal, simplifies itself essentially to securing maximum oxidation rates of concentrated sugar solutions.

Investigators at the United States Department of Agriculture at the By-Product Laboratory in Ames, Iowa have developed step by step a commercial submerged process for gluconic acid production which stands as a model approach for the development of any microbiological process. The principle problem encountered relates to efficient aeration, and this particular study (Wells *et al.*, 1937) is one of the best treatises available in the field of microbiology on the features and solution of aeration problems. A number of papers by these and other United States Department of Agriculture workers deal with other aspects of the process. The main points will be covered here; details can be found in the original papers (May *et al.*, 1934; Herrick *et al.*, 1935; Moyer *et al.*, 1937; Moyer *et al.*, 1940; Porges *et al.*, 1940; Porges *et al.*, 1941). See also Perquin (1938) for shake flask culture studies.

The early work used *P. chrysogenum* cultivated in submerged conditions by passing air through gas washing bottles with sintered glass false bottoms. Incubation of the vessels was done in a pressure autoclave; the rate of glucose consumption and its conversion to gluconate proved to be a direct function of the air pressure up to 3 atmospheres, but the process took about 8 days. Later a horizontal rotating (long axis) cylindrical fermenter* was devised which permitted mechanical agitation of the culture meanwhile being aerated by a stream of sterile air, maintained under any desired air pressure. A strain of *A. niger* (No. 67) proved superior for this work, and under optimum aeration conditions in the presence of calcium carbonate was capable of giving almost theoretical yields of gluconic acid from concentrated sugar media. The data in the following three tables quantitatively demonstrate the separate effects of the three individual components making up the aeration complex; mechanical agitation (rotation), air flow, and air pressure. These are particularly interesting examples for they apply to a strict oxidation process uncomplicated by alternative oxygen consuming reactions typical of other metabolic systems.

One additional factor is crucial, but this was not studied: dispersion of air in liquid. Actually, this is to some extent a function of the mechanical agitation, but in particular it refers to some mechanical means of comminuting the air bubbles which enter the culture fluid. (See Chapters 2 and 18.)

TABLE 1[1]

TANK ROTATION RATE[2]

Rotations per min.	Hours	Glucose consumed	Gluconic acid produced	Gluconic acid yields based on	
				Glucose consumed	Glucose available
		g.	g.	per cent	per cent
4.5	26	208	203	89.7	37.7
6.1	26	251	254	93.0	47.7
8.5	26	353	374	97.4	69.4
10.2	26	388	418	98.9	77.4
13	23	390	420	98.8	77.8

[1] From Wells, *et al.* (1937).
[2] Conditions: Pressure, 30 lbs/sq. in.
    Air flow, 400 ml./min.
    Volume, 3200 ml.
    Temp., 30°
    Glucose available, 495 g.

* This type fermenter is not practicable for industrial fermentations, the vertical stationary type with impeller agitation being universally employed.

Table 1 shows that the rate and total amount of glucose consumed increases with rotation rate up to 10 r.p.m.; and, of particular importance, that more gluconic acid was formed from each unit of glucose consumed at the higher rotation rates than at the lower ones. This can only mean that the gluconic acid forming enzyme system was not saturated, and that sugar was being decomposed by alternative routes, probably involving rupture of the carbon chain (glycolysis?).

Table 2 demonstrates the interesting point that under the conditions used, the smallest air flow, 200 ml./minute, was adequate to permit the highest conversion efficiency of glucose to gluconic acid, but was not adequate to oxidize the glucose at the maximum rate. The total glucose oxidized increased as the air flow increased.

TABLE 2[1]

AIR FLOW[2]

| Air flow, ml./min. | Glucose consumed | Gluconic acid produced | Gluconic acid yield based on | |
			Glucose consumed	Glucose available
	g.	g.	per cent	per cent
200	248	269	99.5	49.8
400	310	317	93.7	58.8
800	349	360	94.7	67.8
1200	410	420	94.2	77.9
1600	413	429	95.4	79.5

[1] From Wells, et al. (1937).
[2] Conditions: Pressure, 30 lbs./sq. in.
    Rotation, 13 r.p.m.
    Volume, 3200 ml.
    Temp., 30°
    Time, 18 hrs.
    Glucose available, 495 g.

In Table 3 is shown the effect of oxygen tension, secured by increasing the air pressure. The consumption of glucose is strikingly accelerated by elevated air pressures, up to 3 atmospheres pressure. The efficiency of gluconic acid formation was accelerated to a lesser degree.

It is self-evident, and experience has amply shown, that the various physical factors instrumental in facilitating access of oxygen to cells in submerged cultures are integrated, and that alterations in any one change the minimal requirements of the others to produce a desired effect. For example, according to Table 1, thirteen rotations per minute resulted in maximum rate of glucose utilization at 30 lbs. air pressure and 400 ml./minute air flow. If the air flow in this experiment had been 800 or 1200 ml./minute it is likely that maximum glucose utilization would be obtained with fewer rotations per minute. This point is particularly noticeable in propellor agitated fermentations in stationary vessels where the fineness of the air bubbles is critical in securing maximum oxygenation effects. A small rate of air flow is even more effective than a massive air flow provided the former is finely comminuted and dispersed adequately throughout the medium. Thus, for an oxidation process the ideal conditions would be a state where so much air is whipped into the liquid that the whole mass aquires the appearance of a foam. This principle as applied to gluconic acid has been patented; the mold grows in the foam of the aerated liquid stirred with a high-speed agitator. Conversion yields of 90 per cent in 48 to 60 hours are obtained (Currie et al., 1933).

TABLE 3[1]

AIR PRESSURE[2]

Pressure		Glucose consumed	Gluconic acid produced	Gluconic acid yield based on	
lbs/sq. in.	kg./sq. cm.			Glucose consumed	Glucose available
		g.			
5	0.35	178	173	89.1	32.1
15	1.05	257	258	92.1	47.9
30	2.11	336	351	96.0	65.1
45	3.16	429	454	97.1	84.2

[1] From Wells, et al. (1937).
[2] Conditions: Air flow, 1200 ml./min.
   Rotation speed, 13 r.p.m.
   Medium volume, 3200 ml.
   Temp., 30°
   Time, 18 hrs.
   Glucose available, 495 g.

NEUTRALIZING AGENTS

Several previous workers have demonstrated the favorable influence of the presence of a neutralizing agent for optimum conversion of glucose to gluconic acid. In refining their development of the industrial process, the United States Department of Agriculture group has studied this feature in detail. The utilization of concentrated sugar solutions (25–30 per cent glucose) by the fungus is incomplete if no $CaCO_3$ is present, owing to development of an unfavorably low pH in the medium; it is also incomplete if sufficient $CaCO_3$ is present to neutralize all the gluconic acid formed, because of crystallization of the high concentration of calcium gluconate which deposits on the hyphae, retards diffusion, and in general almost immediately retards the progress of sugar oxidation. Sufficient calcium gluconate may form to cause the whole culture to set in the form of a stiff gel, similar to what occurs in lactic and fumaric acid processes. Calcium gluconate is soluble to the extent of 4 g./100 ml water at 30°. However, it forms supersaturated solutions readily so that generally 13 to 15 per cent solutions can be obtained without crystallization. Also, in the presence of impurities such as are in a culture medium, the solubility may be even higher. Particularly is this so in the presence of glucose, owing to mutual solubility. Solutions containing about 15 per cent glucose generate enough calcium gluconate to give crystallization. Fermentation of 20–30 per cent sugar solutions has certain advantages from the standpoint of gluconic acid output per hour from any fermentation apparatus.

Prevention of crystallization in such media may be accomplished in two ways:

(1) By limiting the amount of $CaCO_3$ so that the final amount of salt formed just falls short of crystallization concentration. This was achieved with 26 g. of $CaCO_3$ per liter of 15.5 per cent glucose medium, equivalent to 102.1 g. gluconic acid. While the limited amount of $CaCO_3$ represses crystallization, thereby facilitating removal of the culture liquid from the vessel and separation of the mycelium prior to recovery of calcium gluconate, it does not permit the accumulation of much excess free gluconic acid, because even a small concentration of free gluconic acid greatly retards the reaction glucose → gluconic acid and the process rather quickly expires. The optimum pH for this reaction is about 5.0. A small excess of free gluconic acid reduces the pH to 3.2, virtually stopping sugar utilization. Reference to Fig. 1 showing these relationships will also bring out that rate of sugar oxidation was accelerated as the pH was gradually lowered from the initial 6.8 to about 5.0, the optimum, a sort of antocatalytic process. It is noteworthy that the oxidation effected by the living cells has a pH optimum at about 5.0 whereas 6.0 is the optimum for the cell-free enzyme carrying out the same transformation (see Mechanism). In fact, at pH 5 the enzyme activity is considerably below the maximum. This apparent discrepancy between the cell-free enzyme and the intact mycelium probably means that although the external pH is 5.0, the internal cellular pH, where the transformation actually occurs, is more nearly the optimum for the enzyme action, i.e., 6.0.

Note should be made that the above pH optimum has been ascertained only for this organism, *A. niger No.* 67, and that different strains and particularly different species might be characterized by an entirely different pH optimum.

(2) By addition of boron compounds such as borax ($Na_2B_4O_7 \cdot 10H_2O$) or boric acid (H_3BO_3). Boron compounds have long been known to form soluble stable complexes with polyhydroxy compounds, and, in fact, have been used for some time to maintain stable solutions of calcium gluconate in pharmaceutical preparations. The USDA workers found this principle applies when either borax or boric acid is added to the mold process where a sufficiently high sugar concentration is oxidized, yielding enough calcium gluconate to crystallize ordinarily, but does not owing to the boron now present. This remarkable stabilizing effect

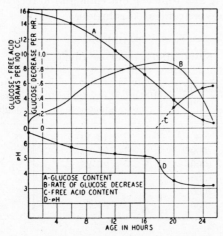

FIG. 1.—Relation between pH changes and gluconic acid production by *Aspergillus niger* (from Gastrock *et al.*, 1938).

of boron on gluconate crystallization is evident from Table 4, where 0.25 mg. boron per 100 cc. completely prevents crystallization at 45 hours that otherwise occurred in only 13 hours in the absence of boron. Here there is no need to limit the amount of $CaCO_3$ present. Under these conditions the crystallization threshold of calcium gluconate was about 2.5 times greater for the boron culture than the control (34.5 g. glucose consumed vs. 13–14 g.).

The antiseptic qualities of boron compounds are well known also, and it was found that certain fungi, otherwise, ideal for this work have such a low boron tolerance as to render them useless in cases as described. *A niger* No. 67 with which the USDA people did most of their developmental work was found to be quite sensitive (400 p.p.m. B), whereas another strain with equally good glucose oxidation properties required 2,000 p.p.m. B for inhibition. Obviously, boron resistance could be increased by strain selection or adaptation procedures (see Chapter 18). Also, sensitivity seems to be higher during germination and early growth stages, hence boron stabilizers are added after the culture is fairly well grown.

GLUCOSE CONCENTRATION

Although considerable emphasis is placed on higher concentrations, the physiologically optimum concentration is approximately 11 to 12 per cent. Concentrations higher than this are oxidized at progressively slower rates. However, from the economic standpoint of most efficient operation, higher concentrations may be used owing to the advantages of savings in starting and replacement time and in recovering the calcium gluconate from more concentrated solutions.

TABLE 4

STABILIZING EFFECT OF BORIC ACID[1]

Original glucose in 100 ml., g.	Boron added, p.p.m.	Glucose consumed in 100 ml. at crystallization of Ca gluconate, g.	Age of culture at crystallization of Ca gluconate, hours
20	0	13–14	13
30	500	21–22	25
30	1000	27–28	28
35	1500	30–31	38
35	2000	33	42
35	2500	34.5	None at 45

[1] From Moyer, *et al.* (1940).

RE-USE OF MYCELIUM

The final refinement in the development of the industrial application of the gluconic acid process by the USDA workers relates to elimination of the lag period before maximum rate of glucose oxidation to gluconic acid. The lag was appreciably shortened by use of pregerminated spore inoculum (a 6-hour-saving) and also by including in the inoculum vegetative mycelium obtained by dispersing the entire fungus pad consisting of mycelium and spores grown in surface liquid culture.

An even more important improvement utilizes the principle first demonstrated by Bernhauer (1926) for surface cultures: full grown mycelium continues to oxidize glucose to gluconic acid with undiminished vigor through several successive replacements of sugar-containing solutions. This is equally true for submerged cultures and has been found to give glucose oxidations at maximum rate through thirteen successive liquid replacements, the highest number tried. This semicontinuous process doubtless could be continued through an indefinite number of replacements, and such cultures have proved to be peculiarly immune to contaminations. Figure 2 exemplifies this semi-continuous process through four successive replacements. The only breaks in the conversion of glucose to gluconic acid at maximum rate are the very short intervals occupied by the replacement operations. The replacement solutions always contain high sugar concentrations, 15–30 per cent, and $CaCO_3$ and borax, and may or may not require accessory mineral and nitrogen nutrients. For prolonged replacement experiments, the presence of the latter is essential to maintain the vitality of the mycelium by permitting generation of some new growth. It has been estimated that in any fermenter the semicontinuous process gives 45 per cent more gluconic acid per hour over a prolonged period than the conventional single batch method.

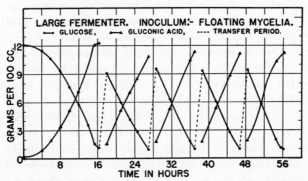

FIG. 2.—Gluconic acid formation by one lot of *A. niger* mycelium in successive replacements of sugar solutions (from Porges *et al.*, 1940).

Two techniques have been devised for reutilization of the mycelium on a pilot plant scale:

(a) Floatation technique. At the conclusion of the initial (growth) process, when glucose consumption has been completed, the air pressure is released suddenly, allowing the mycelium to float owing to air bubbles trapped in the thick mycelium, which expand and rise carrying the mycelium with them under the sudden pressure drop. Ninety per cent of the mycelium is in the top 20 per cent of the solution, and the lower 80 per cent, consisting of substantially clear liquid, is drained off from the bottom. The tank is next recharged with a sterilized volume equal to that drained off and containing 1.25 times the final ingredient concentrations desired, owing to dilution by the 20 per cent remaining in the tank. Glucose oxidation to gluconic acid begins immediately and at maximum rate as soon as optimum aeration conditions are restored.

(b) Centrifugation technique. Later, a means of draining off essentially all the culture filtrate was devised, thus enabling a 25 per cent increase in output. This involves collecting the mycelium in a sterile basket centrifuge, connected through a closed system to the fermenter. The mycelium is resuspended in fresh sterile replacement solution by back flushing of the centrifuge, transferred by air pressure to the fermenter, and the charge is brought up to volume. The practicability of this technique awaits testing under industrial conditions. Further details of this mechanical setup may be found in Porges *et al.* (1941).

MECHANISM OF FORMATION OF GLUCONIC ACID. GLUCOSE-AERODEHYDROGENASE (GLUCOSE-OXIDASE)

The conversion of glucose to gluconic acid is a simple oxidation of the aldehyde grouping to a carboxyl group. This conversion is about the simplest biochemical transformation a hexose can undergo due to fungus action (but compare simple reduction of fructose to mannitol). Doubtless this explains why the exact mechanism is known in some detail, and indeed, this is probably the only carbohydrate transformation carried out by fungi which is unequivocal and fully understood. The transformation can be effected by a cell-free enzyme, on which there has accumulated a considerable body of knowledge.

Just three years after Molliard's discovery of gluconic acid in *A. niger* cultures, Müller (1926) reported a cell free enzyme preparation from *A. niger* which consumed oxygen in the presence of glucose. In subsequent papers (1928, 1929, 1936) Müller extensively studied this enzyme, which he showed took up molecular oxygen during gluconic acid formation. He named it glucose-oxidase. Actually, as early as 1904 Maximov prepared an acetone precipitate of *A. niger* press juice which absorbed oxygen and produced CO_2. The CO_2-forming ability was lost much faster than the O_2 absorption and Maximov concluded that his preparation contained an oxidase which was independent of zymase activity. He further observed that addition of glucose increased the O_2 uptake and concluded that glucose activates an oxidase. This crucial statement and experiment, which formed the basis of the gluconic acid mechanism, had been overlooked for 25 years before Müller's work. Müller provided much general and fundamental information regarding the preparation and properties of this enzyme, and it has been extended in considerable biochemical detail, especially by Franke and coworkers (1937, 1939, 1944). Much additional information pertaining to this enzyme was provided by the discovery of the English group of workers that a powerful antibiotic substance present in cultures of penicillin-producing and other fungi was identical with the glucose oxidizing enzyme of Müller (Coulthard *et al.*, 1942, 1945; Hirsch, 1943; Roberts *et al.*, 1943; Keilin and Hartree 1946, 1948a).

The following discussion is based largely upon the work of the above mentioned authors. Müller and Franke obtained the enzyme in the press juice of *A. niger* mycelium. The mycelium is allowed to starve for about 6 hours to exhaust intracellular carbohydrate and the excess liquid expressed with a hand press. The mycelium is ground in a mortar with pure quartz sand and diatomaceous earth, then pressed in a Buchner press at 300 atmospheres. From 300 g. mycelium 100–150 cc. press juice is obtained. A second crop may be obtained by regrinding the tissue. The enzyme is precipitated from the press juice with 96 per cent alcohol, alcohol-ether (2:1) or acetone, by adding the juice to the solvent dropwise. Treating the precipitate with water leaves about one-half the material as insoluble inert matter which is removed by centrifugation. Dialysis of the active solution results in no loss of activity, but in a substantial loss of solids ($\sim$ 40 per cent). The enzyme is finally precipitated by solvents, dried by washing with absolute alcohol followed by ether, and stored over H_2SO_4. The aqueous solution can also be lyophilized. One to three grams dry enzyme are obtained from 100 ml. original press juice. Further purification may be achieved by absorption on kaolin or aluminum oxide, elution and precipitation with $(NH_4)_2SO_4$. This procedure yields a concentrate 250 to 600 times more active than the original press juice solids.

Concentration of crude enzyme solutions at slightly elevated temperatures often is accompanied by an up to fourfold increase in enzyme activity. Active mycelial preparations can be obtained by dehydrating minced mycelium directly with a large volume of dehydrating agent (alcohol-ether, 2:1, 3 liters/140 g. mycelium). After standing a short while, the mycelium is washed with ether and dried *in vacuo* over H_2SO_4. From 140 g. squeezed fresh mycelium, 30 g. of the "Dauer" preparation was obtained.

The enzyme also occurs free in the culture filtrate of fungi producing it and was first isolated from *Penicillium notatum* culture filtrates as an antibiotic agent variously known as notatin, penicillin B, and penatin. It may be precipitated from the concentrated medium by acetone or by tannic acid followed by acetone extraction of the tannic acid. It may also be precipitated with Reinecke salt followed by acetone extraction. Due probably to the fact that the cell material contains much proteinacious materials as impurities as compared to the culture filtrates, particularly in the synthetic Czapek-Dox medium in which the extracellular enzyme was formed, material obtained in this manner is much purer than that obtained from the mycelium by the methods of Müller and Franke. A final purification by precipitation with 80–83 per cent saturated ammonium sulfate yields a canary yellow precipitate which is dissolved in water, dialized in the cold, and precipitated with acetone at 0°.

The enzyme is a flavoprotein which can be resolved into the riboflavin prosthetic group and inactive protein in the presence of acetic acid, yielding the typical greenish fluorescence of riboflavin. The enzyme has the typical absorption spectrum of a flavoprotein with maxima at 270–280, 375–380, and 450–460 A. It is therefore a typical "yellow enzyme" in the sense of Warburg. As in other flavoproteins, the prosthetic group is alloxazine-adenine-dinucleotide (riboflavin-phosphate-phosphate-ribose-adenine) (Keilin and Hartree 1946, 1948a). Since it is not possible to split notatin into inactive protein and prosthetic group and recombine them to form the active enzyme, Keilin and Hartree demonstrated the identity of the prosthetic group by the neat expedient of adding boiled notatin to the active protein of d-amino acid oxidase, which can be split free from its prosthetic group that is known to be alloxazine-adenine-dinucleotide, and which can be reconstituted to form active enzyme. Restoration of the activity of d-amino acid oxidase protein by addition of notatin rather conclusively proved the nature of the prosthetic group of the latter.

In the presence of glucose and oxygen the glucose is converted to gluconic acid with the concomitant uptake of one atom of oxygen. One mole of hydrogen peroxide is formed per mole of sugar oxidized. Quantitative studies revealed the following stoichiometric relations for this reaction:

$$CH_2OH(CHOH)_4CHO + H_2O + \tfrac{1}{2}O_2 \longrightarrow CH_2OH(CHOH)_4COOH + H_2O_2$$

Glucose — Gluconic acid — Hydrogen peroxide

This equation is satisfied only by the pure enzyme itself at pH 5.6, the optimum for the enzyme action, for in this situation the H_2O_2 is not further decomposed. With living cells the presence of catalase destroys the H_2O_2 so that the overall equation becomes

$$C_6H_{12}O_6 + \tfrac{1}{2}O_2 \longrightarrow C_6H_{12}O_7$$

It is the hydrogen peroxide which accounts for the powerful antibacterial activity of the enzyme. The enzyme itself is devoid of this activity. A dilution of 10^{-9} produces an inhibitory concentration of H_2O_2 for *Staphylococcus aureus*. In the presence of catalase, which destroys the peroxide as rapidly as it is generated, no antibacterial activity is detected. Incidentally, any hydrogen peroxide generating enzyme system is strongly antibacterial for the same reason, for example, xanthine oxidase from milk, a flavoprotein oxidizing hypoxanthine to xanthine and uric acid with simultaneous formation of hydrogen peroxide (Green and Pauli, 1943).

Impure enzyme preparations may contain catalase which makes it impossible to detect H_2O_2 formation. However, catalase action may be poisoned by H_2S, HCN, sodium azide, etc., permitting H_2O_2 to accumulate. The enzyme is not absolutely specific for glucose although the oxidation rate is by far greatest for this sugar. Some difference of opinion exists as to the other sugars oxidized. Most of the preparations oxidize d-xylose and mannose; and, although d-galactose has been reported in some cases, the possibility exists for other enzymes as impurities or even two separate types of sugar oxidases (Müller, 1940) although this has been questioned (Franke, 1944). There can be no question that different sugars are oxidized by the various fungus preparations. The issue is whether these oxidations are carried out by the identical enzyme which oxidizes glucose, or by different contaminating enzymes, specific for other sugars. Galactose oxidation to a small fraction of the glucose rate has been reported for glucose oxidase preparations by most authors concerned with this subject (see also Ogura, 1939), yet what probably was the most highly purified preparation yet obtained did not oxidize galactose. One might presume therefore that a galactose oxidase, difficult to remove, accompanies the glucose oxidase, but Keilin and Hartree (1948) have shown that positive results with galactose are due to glucose present as an impurity from the lactose hydrolysis used to prepare galactose. With this virtually pure enzyme, mannose and xylose were the only other sugars oxidized, and these at a rate only about 1 per cent that of glucose. No other biological substances are oxidized.

If the organism is cultivated on carbon sources other than glucose, little or none of the enzyme is formed, except on mannose and galactose. This is therefore an instance of adaptive enzyme formation. Mannose-grown cells do not possess any more enzyme oxidizing mannose than do glucose-grown cells, but contain the same amount of glucose-oxidase as glucose-grown cells. Thus, either mannose is oxidized to mannonic acid or is first converted to glucose by means of an isomerase during its utilization.

Fructose grown cells also contain glucose oxidase, but no enzyme oxidizing fructose; despite twenty passages through fructose the enzyme obtained from *P. chrysogenum* is completely specific for glucose (Keilin and Hartree 1948a). Molliard earlier (1924) had observed that addition of fructose to glucose media increased the amount of glucose oxidase formed, and that even in pure fructose medium, glucose oxidase was formed to one-third the extent it was in glucose medium. Here again, one is led to suspect that the fructose is metabolized via glucose.

Because endogenous respiration is cyanide-sensitive owing to the function of cytochrome, whereas glucose oxidase, lacking heavy metal catalysis, is cyanide insensitive, it is possible to secure intracellular oxidation of glucose to gluconic acid by cyanide poisoned mycelium of *P. chrysogenum* (Keilin and Hartree, 1948a).

MECHANISM OF ACTION OF GLUCOSE OXIDIZING ENZYME

From the facts that his preparation oxidized glucose in the presence of oxygen but not in its absence (H_2 atmosphere), and that he was unable to detect glucose oxidation anaerobically in the presence of potential hydrogen acceptors like methylene blue, quinone, potassium ferricyanide, etc., Müller considered his enzyme to be an oxidase as contrasted to a dehydrogenase, hence the name glucose oxidase. Ample evidence has now been collected, mainly by Franke and coworkers (also see Coulthard *et al.*) quite definitely showing that the enzyme is not an oxidase in the classical sense, and actually is a dehydrogenase capable of oxidizing glucose to gluconic acid independently of oxygen provided suitable hydrogen acceptors are available. While not denying the existence of such a glucose dehydrogenase, Müller (1940, 1941) maintains the existence of two glucose → gluconic acid enzymes in fungi, one (oxytropic dehydrogenase) requiring oxygen for its action i.e., as H acceptor, the other (anoxytropic dehydrogenase) being able to utilize oxidation-reduction dyes as H acceptors. The evidence for this is not strong (Franke, 1944) and the existence of an oxygen-requiring glucose dehydrogenase has never been confirmed whereas the anaerobic utilizability of alternative H acceptors has been abundantly confirmed. The reason for Müller's failure with alternative hydrogen acceptors is not clear.

Five main lines of evidence indicate a dehydrogenase activity for the gluconic acid enzyme as opposed to an oxidase activity, and, perforce, the term glucose-oxidase must be abandoned. The name glucose aerodehydrogenase is now used, connoting dehydrogenation activity with the ability to utilize oxygen as H acceptor forming H_2O_2, as contrasted to the glucose dehydrogenase of mammalian tissue which does not oxidize glucose to gluconic acid aerobically, until cytochrome C, cytochrome oxidase and cozymase are added (Harrison, 1931). The former apparently requires no coenzyme or hydrogen carrier and is similar in this respect to the dozen-odd other known flavoproteins. Thus the essential functional distinctiveness of the latter in relation to the former is that Harrison's enzyme does not activate oxygen and requires some intermediary H carrier such as methylene blue or the cytochrome system to transfer the hydrogen to oxygen. Hydrogen peroxide is not formed. However, both enzymes yield gluconic acid from glucose.

The five reasons why the fungus enzyme is not an oxidase are:

(1) Oxygen can be replaced by typical organic hydrogen acceptors such as quinone, several indophenol indicators, methylene blue, toluyl blue, thionine, pyocyanine, saffranin T, and cytochrome.

(2) The enzyme is insensitive to heavy metal poisons such as H_2S, HCN, NaN_3, NH_2OH, CO. True oxidases are heavy metal proteins and are inhibited by such poisons.

(3) Strong specificity for a single substrate. This is characteristic of dehydrogenases, whereas oxidases are more or less generic in their substrates.

(4) The enzyme is a flavoprotein. All known flavoproteins are dehydrogenases.

(5) The enzyme is inhibited by a variety of narcotics which characteristically inhibit dehydrogenases: chloralhydrate, ethyl urethane, phenylurethane, nitrile, sulfite, etc.

OTHER PROPERTIES OF GLUCOSE AERODEHYDROGENASE

Aerodehydrogenase has an isoelectric point at pH 4.4 and is precipitated in active form from aqueous solutions by acetone, methanol, dioxane, ether-alcohol, etc. Phosphate is without effect on the activity of the enzyme. Kinetically, the uptake of $\frac{1}{2}O_2$ per mole glucose obeys the monomolecular reaction and the Michealis constant K (concentration of substrate giving half maximum oxidation rate) = 0.026 M. The sugar concentration at which the oxidation is optimum is 0.5 M. Rate of enzyme action is accelerated about twofold in pure oxygen as compared to air, the effect being aggravated by a temperature rise, as evident from the following tabulation:

$$O_2/Air \text{ activity ratio at } \frac{20°}{1.55}, \frac{30°}{1.95}, \frac{40°}{2.16}.$$

The enzyme demonstrates increased activity as a function of temperature in air, with a Q_{10} of 1.1 to 1.6, and is quickly destroyed at 73°. The optimum pH is 6.0, the maximum 10, and the minimum 2.8. If glucose oxidation by the enzyme is started at pH 7 to 8 the reaction becomes autocatalytic as the pH is lowered to the optimum by the generation of free gluconic acid. The enzyme has no action whatsoever on certain substances undergoing oxidation very readily by true oxidases, viz., phenol, pyrocatechin, hydroquinone, p-phenylenediamine. Keilin and Hartree (1948b) have developed an accurate and highly sensitive manometric method for glucose determination based on oxygen uptake catalyzed by glucose oxidase. The method measures glucose instantly as it is formed in solution, hence is an excellent means of studying kinetics of enzyme reactions which liberate glucose. In order that the observed O_2 uptake will be a true measure of glucose, all the hydrogen peroxide must be used up. This may be done with catalase or by coupled oxidation in which the H_2O_2 formed at once reacts with added alcohol, oxidizing it to the aldehyde.

According to Lwoff and Toupizina (1938) gluconic acid formation by *A. niger* is inhibited by 15×10^{-5} *M* sodium fluoride, a concentration which also severly damaged the physical nature of the mycelium.

HEXONIC ACIDS BESIDES GLUCONIC

By inference from the oxidative action of the various preparations of glucose aerodehydrogenase on different sugars as described above, one may assume the formation of the corresponding galactonic acid, mannonic acid, etc., although these were not isolated. Nevertheless there is ample evidence that a corresponding oxidation of mannose and galactose can be accomplished by certain fungi when they are furnished those carbohydrates as sole carbon sources, or even in the presence of other carbohydrates. Thus, up to 70 per cent conversion of *d*-mannose to *d*-mannonic acid has been formed in 11 days by selected strains of *A. niger* in the presence of $CaCO_3$ (Knoblock and Mayer, 1941). A similar oxidation of galactose to galactonic acid is carried out in high yield by the same organism, and it also forms gluconic acid from glucose. The calcium salts of these acids crystallize out in the medium as the concentration increases, and are readily isolated and identified.

The behavior of this organism toward di- and polysaccharides was also studied. From sucrose, gluconic and citric acids were formed, the former from the glucose moiety and the latter from fructose. Fructose furnished alone yielded citric acid. Lactose and rhamnose each yielded both gluconic and galactonic acids, from the corresponding sugar moieties, whereas starch and maltose gave gluconic acid exclusively. *Penicillium luteo-purpurogenum* var. *rubrisclerotium*, the same organisms used in the early studies of the U.S.D.A. workers for gluconic acid production, converts *d*-mannose to *d*-mannonic acid in appreciable yield (9 per cent) but was inactive toward *d*-galactose (Angeletti and Cerruti, 1930). This, as well as the inactivity of glucose oxidase against galactose, indicates separate identities for the enzymes oxidizing glucose (mannose), and galactose.

PENTONIC ACIDS

Hayasida (1938) has shown that preformed pads of *Fusarium lini* oxidize the pentoses xylose and *l*-arabinose to xylonic and arabonic acids respectively, the latter being isolated and identified. On account of the analogy of these oxidations to that carried out by glucose aerodehydrogenase, the enzyme responsible for the pentose oxidation was renamed aeropentosedehydrogenase. The enzyme was not, however, isolated, nor was glucose tested at the same time. It may well be that different flavoproteins are involved here, exerting high specificity of substrate, just as in the case of the several known flavoproteins.

GLUCURONIC ACID, $COOH(CHOH)_4CHO$

Report of the occurrence of this acid in sugar cultures of *Ustulina vulgaris* (Wunschendorff and Killian, 1928) are unauthentic owing to the fact that the acid was not isolated, nor the manner of identification given. The only other report is by the Japanese, Itto (1933), who obtained glucuronic acid together with several other acids including gluconic acid, from *Penicillium* sp. α-D-galacturonic acid is obtained via fungus action not by oxidation of galactose, but by hydrolysis of pectin, of which this uronic acid comprises a substantial portion in the form of the polyuronide. The galacturonic acid is readily crystallizable without other treatments by digesting pectin with the pectin enzymes of many different fungi (Rohm and Haas, 1945) (see chapter 17).

SACCHARIC ACID, $COOH(CHOH)_4COOH$

This dicarboxy sugar acid has been isolated as the potassium acid salt from glucose cultures of *A. niger* (Challenger *et al.*, 1927b) and identified by neutralization equivalent, potassium content, and thallium content of the corresponding thallium salt. Yields were not specified and the speculation was made that saccharic acid was an intermediate in the formation of citric acid from glucose (Challenger *et al.*, 1927a). No credence is given this idea today. The only other available record of the formation of saccharic acid by microorganisms describes its formation from glucose by two yeasts, *Anthomyces Renkaufii* and *Amphiernia rubra* (Grüss, 1926).

GLUCOSONE, $CH_2OH(CHOH)_3 \cdot CO \cdot CHO$

This dehydrogenation product of glucose has been isolated in 8 per cent yield from glucose and in 13–17 per cent yields from sucrose, maltose, and starch by action of *Aspergillus parasiticus* and *A. flavus* (Walker, 1932; Bond *et al.*, 1937). Washed fungus pads were used under plasmolysis conditions, i.e., carbohydrate solutions containing toluene, bromobenzene, or chloroform. Glucosone can function as a carbon source for several other fungi.

REFERENCES

Angeletti, A., and Cerutti, C. F. 1930. *Ann. chim. applicata* **20**, 424–433.

Bernhauer, K. 1926. *Biochem. Z.* **172**, 313–323.

Bernhauer, K. 1928a. *Biochem. Z.* **197**, 278–286.

Bernhauer, K. 1928b. *Biochem. Z.* **197**, 287–308.

Bernhauer, K., and Wolf, H. 1928. *Z. physiol. Chem.* **177**, 270–279.

Birkinshaw, J. H., and Raistrick, H. 1931. *Trans. Roy. Soc., London,* **B220**, 331–354.

Bond, C. R., Knight, E. C., and Walker, T. K. 1937. *Biochem. J.* **31**, 1033–1040.

Butkewitsch, W. 1923. *Biochem. Z.* **136**, 224–37.

Butkewitsch, W. 1924. *Biochem. Z.* **154**, 177–179.

Challenger, F., Subramaniam, V., and Walker, T. K. 1927a. *J. Chem. Ind.* 200–208.

Challenger, F., Subramaniam, V., and Walker, T. K. 1927b. *Nature* **119**, 674.

Coulthard, C. E., Michaelis, R., Short, W. F., Sykes, G., Skrimshire, G. B., Standfast, A. F. B., Birkinshaw, J. H., and Raistrick, H. 1942. *Nature,* **150**, 634–635.

Coulthard, C. E., Michaelis, R., Short, W. F., Sykes, G., Skrimshire, G. B., Standfast, A. F. B., Birkinshaw, J. H., and Raistrick, H. 1945. *Biochem. J.* **39**, 24–36.

Currie, J. N., Kane, J. H., and Finlay, A. 1933. U. S. Patent No. 1,893,819.

Falck, R., and Kapur, S. N. 1924. *Ber.* **57**, 920–923.

Franke, W. 1944. *Ann.* **555**, 111–132.

Franke, W., and Deffner, M. 1939. *Ann.* **541**, 117–150.

Franke, W., and Lorenz, F. 1937. *Ann.* **532**, 1–28.

Gastrock, E. A., Porges, N., Wells, P. A., and Moyer, A. J. 1938. *Ind. Eng. Chem.* **30**, 782–789.

Green, D. E., and Pauli, R. 1943. *Proc. Soc. Exptl. Biol. Med.* **54**, 148–150.

Grüss, J. 1926. *Jahrb. wiss. Botan.* **66**, 109–182.

Harrison, D. C. 1931. *Biochem. J.* **25**, 1016–1027.

Hayasida, A. 1938. *Biochem. Z.* **298**, 169–178.

Herrick, H. T., Hellback, R., and May, O. E. 1935. *Ind. Eng. Chem.* **27**, 681–683.

Hirsch, J. 1943. *Istanbul Seririyati,* **25**, No. 8.

Itto, G. 1933. *J. Agr. Chem. Soc. Japan* **9**, 552–562.

Kardo-Syssojeva, E. 1933. *Biochem. Z.* **266**, 337–351.

Keilin, D., and Hartree, E. F. 1946. *Nature* **157**, 801.

Keilin, D., and Hartree, E. F. 1948a. *Biochem. J.* **42**, 221–229.

Keilin, D., and Hartree, E. F. 1948b. *Biochem. J.* **42**, 230–238.

Knoblock, H., and Mayer, H. 1941. *Biochem. Z.* **307**, 285–92.

Lockwood, L. B., Tabenkin, B., and Ward, G. E. 1941. *J. Bact.* **42**, 51–61.

Lwoff, S., and Toupizina, G. M. 1938. *Compt. rend. acad. sci. (USSR)* **21**, 307–311.

Maximov, N. A. 1904. *Ber. deut. botan. Ges.* **22**, 225–235.

May, O. E., Herrick, H. T., Moyer, A. J., and Hellback, R. 1929. *Ind. Eng. Chem.* **21**, 1198–1203.

May, O. E., Herrick, H. T., Moyer, A. J. and Wells, P. A. 1934. *Ind. Eng. Chem.* **26**, 575–578.

May, O. E., Herrick, H. T., Thom, C., and Church, M. B. 1927. *J. Biol. Chem.* **75**, 417–421.

Molliard, M. 1922. *Compt. rend.* **174**, 881–883.

Molliard, M. 1924a. *Compt. rend.* **178**, 41–45.

Molliard, M.   1924b.   *Compt. rend.* **178**, 161–163.

Moyer, A. J., Umberger, E. J., and Stubbs, J. J.   1940.   *Ind. Eng. Chem.* **32**, 1379–1383.

Moyer, A. J., Wells, P. A., Stubbs, J. J., Herrick, H. T., and May, O. E.   1937.   *Ind. Eng. Chem.* **29**, 777–782.

Müller, D.   1926.   *Chem. Ztg.* **50**, 101.

Müller, D.   1928.   *Biochem. Z.* **199**, 136–170.

Müller, D.   1929.   *Biochem. Z.* **205**, 111–143.

Müller, D.   1936.   *Ergeb. Enzymforsch.* **5**, 259–272.

Müller, D.   1940.   *Naturwissenschaften* **28** 516.

Müller, D.   1941.   *Enzymologia* **10**, 40–47.

Nord, F. F., and Engel, W.   1938.   *Biochem. Z.* **296**, 153–170.

Ogura, Y.   1939.   *Acta Phytochim. Japan* **11**, 127–144.

Perquin, L. H. C.   1938.   Bijdrage tot de kennis der oxydativen dissimilatie van *A. niger* (van Tieghem).   Dissertation, Delft.

Perwozwansky, W. W.   1930.   *Zentr. Bakt. Parasitenk. Abt II* **81**, 372–392.

Porges, N., Clark, T. F., and Aronovsky, S. I.   1941.   *Ind. Eng. Chem.* **33**, 1065–1067.

Porges, N., Clark, T. F., and Gastrock, E. A.   1940.   *Ind. Eng. Chem.* **32**, 107–111.

Roberts, E. C., Cain, C. K., Muir, R. D., Reithel, F. J., Gaby, W. C., Van Bruggen, J. T., Homan, D. M., Katzman, P. A., Jones, L. R., and Doisy, E. A.   1943.   *J. Biol. Chem.* **147**, 47–58.

Rohm and Haas Co.   1945.   U. S. Patent No. 2,370,961, March 6.

Sakaguchi, K.   1932.   *J. Agr. Chem. Soc. Japan* **8**, 264–265.

Schreyer, R.   1931.   *Biochem. Z.* **240**, 295–325.

Thies, W.   1930.   *Zentr. Bakt. Parasitenk. Abt. II* **82**, 321–347.

Walker, T. K.   1932.   *Nature* **130**, 582.

Wehmer, C.   1928.   *Biochem. Z.* **197**, 418–432.

Wells, P., Moyer, A. J., Stubbs, J. J., Herrick, H. T., and May, O. E.   1937.   *Ind. Eng. Chem.* **29**, 653–656.

Wunschendorff, M., and Killian, C.   1928.   *Compt. rend.* **187**, 572–574.

CHAPTER 16

CARBOHYDRATES PRODUCED BY FUNGI

Several carbohydrates have already been discussed in relation to the cell walls of fungi in Chapter 3. A large number of other chemically diverse carbohydrates, many discovered for the first time and so far known to occur only in fungi, have been isolated from fungi, where they exist presumably in the mycelium. In almost every case however, the carbohydrate can also be isolated from the culture solution, and in a number of instances in sufficiently large amounts so as to necessitate consideration of them as by-products of metabolism of the glucose or other sugar provided in the medium as energy source.

The argument of occurrence in the culture liquid vs. the mycelium is irrelevent in view of the fact that in the final analysis the mycelium is producing the carbohydrate, and the degree to which a distribution sets itself up between mycelium and culture liquid is dependent on the solubility of the carbohydrate and its permeability through the cell walls. For the most part carbohydrates may accumulate in large quantities in the culture filtrate, given the right conditions. Nevertheless, it goes without saying that the same material could be isolated from the cell material, just as citric or fumaric or any organic acid usually found in the liquid in large amounts can also be recovered from the mycelium.

Doubtless some carbohydrate synthesis is essential for the growth and normal functioning of the cells, e.g., ribose compounds, glucoproteins, hexosamine of chitin, and probably others as yet unknown, and these reach an irreducible minimum in normal mycelium. On the other hand, under appropriate conditions, principally luxury carbohydrate nutrition, a fungus may produce more than its own weight of some simple or complex carbohydrate, and this synthesis may be caused to fluctuate within wide limits without impairment to the organism. This situation is entirely analogous to organic acid production by fungi according to the theory of shunt metabolism and for this reason is treated here as a separate chapter, as the organic acids are. The enzyme makeup of these organisms is such that instead of channeling substrate sugar split products to organic acids, they are instead condensed to various carbohydrates specific to the organisms. The latter are, then, products of overflow carbohydrate nutrition, metabolically equivalent to organic acid production and fat production.

Though fat production also is a manifestation of this same concept, purely as a matter of convenience this subject is not treated in a separate chapter by itself equivalent to acids and carbohydrates. The fact of the insolubility of fats and their retention in the cells seemingly makes it more convenient to consider them in connection with the chemical composition of cell material (Chapter 3) instead of with the other products which for the most part accumulate outside the cells. Nevertheless, the student ought to keep in mind the fact that metabolically the accumulation of fat, organic acids, and carbohydrates are all equivalent. They may be thought of as different manifestations of shunt or overflow (luxury) carbohydrate nutrition. These differences are the result of the differences in intrinsic enzyme constitution of the organisms. Refer to Chapter 4 for a discussion of the "reserve product" idea and shunt metabolism.

It is safe to say that some kind of carbohydrate synthesis can be demonstrated in any fungus in which it is sought. The limited chemical studies on this fraction already have revealed a diversity of carbohydrate synthesis among the fungi. Though all the studies discussed in the following pages deal almost exclusively with isolation of only one carbohydrate from a culture, the reader is reminded that these merely represent the chief carbohydrate present in the culture. Rarely are quantitative or qualitative studies of the entire carbohydrate fraction of fungi performed. Indeed, there is only one which has come to the notice of the author—that by the Japanese Takata (1929) on *Aspergillus oryzae*. His breakdown of the carbohydrate fraction is as follows: per cent of dry mycelium, mannitol 4.01, glucosamine 1.72, mannose trace, glucose 0.63, levulose trace, trehalose 2.30, alcohol-soluble polysaccharide 4.08, glycogen 3.01, amylose (starch) 1.38, carbohydrates in phosphatides 0.51, carbohydrates in proteins 2.00, alkali-soluble membrane substance 9.13, chitin 3.18.

POLYHYDROXY ALCOHOLS

For convenience the polyhydroxy alcohols will be included here, although, strictly speaking, they are not sugars. Their close relation has, however, merited the term "sugar alcohols" for them.

1. GLYCEROL

This is the simplest polyhydroxy alcohol. Its formation in small amounts is extremely wide-spread among fungi. Its formation by Mucorales and Fusarium in large yields is discussed in Chapter 9. As examples of other fungi from which glycerol has been extracted (culture filtrates) may be cited *Helminthosporium geniculatum, Clasterosporium sp.*, *Aspergillus wentii*, and *Aspergillus sp.* (Birkinshaw *et al.*, 1931b; Birkinshaw and Raistrick, 1931). The mechanism of its formation may be considered identical with that in yeast fermentation: reduction of 3-glyceraldehyde phosphate to 3-glycerolphosphate followed by phosphatase action splitting off the phosphate.

2. *i*-ERYTHRITOL, $CH_2OH(CHOH)_2CH_2OH$

This tetrahydroxy compound is of frequent occurrence in algae and lichens, but has only rarely been demonstrated in fungi. Zellner (1910) isolated it from spores of the corn smut *Ustilago maydis* and Oxford and Raistrick (1935) from the mycelium of *Penicillium brevi-compactum* and from mycelium and culture filtrates of *P. cyclopium*. Erythitol could not be demonstrated in other strains. The erythritol amounted to as much as 0.7 per cent of the dry mycelium, a minimum figure because the isolation procedure was not quantitative, nor was the culture filtrate worked up.

3. MANNITOL, $CH_2OH(CHOH)_4CH_2OH$

This common sugar-alcohol occurs in many plants and in higher fleshy fungi. It was first demonstrated in *A. niger* by the Frenchman Bourquelot in 1892. Obaton (1929) made one of the most detailed studies of the formation of mannitol in *A. niger*, finding it rose to a peak of 10 per cent of the dry mycelial weight in 48 hours, then was rapidly used up, for, by 72 hours the content was only 3.8 per cent. The ability of the fungus to utilize mannitol was demonstrated by its rapid growth when this substance was the sole carbon source. Less mannitol was formed in acid medium than in neutral, and maximum formation was always associated with a luxury consumption of sugar; depletion and exhaustion of available sugar led to rapid consumption of the initially present mannitol (shunt metabolism; storage products; see Chapter 4).

Another detailed study of mannitol production by fungi is by the Raistrick group working with an unnamed white species of Aspergillus (Birkinshaw *et al.*, 1931b; Coyne and Raistrick, 1931). Yields of mannitol approached 50 per cent of the glucose utilized. Such large amounts of this very soluble substance would not be expected to be retained by the mycelium, and the mannitol was recovered from the culture filtrates. Raistrick and Young (1931) developed a useful polarimitric analytical method for mannitol based on the high positive optical rotation in the presence of 6 per cent borax solution. Mannitol was produced in substantial yields from glucose, mannose, galactose, xylose, and arabinose as single carbon sources. No mannitol was formed from fructose, which was utilized very poorly by the mold. These results are at variance with mannitol formation by bacteria, where mannitol is formed only from fructose, by reduction. In view of the diverse carbon sources yielding mannitol, Coyne and Raistrick postulate a breakdown to a common intermediate and resynthesis to a reserve polysaccharide which is broken down yielding the immediate precursor of mannitol. It would seem premature to exclude fructose as the intermediate on Coyne and Raistrick's data alone, especially in view of the bacterial mechanism. Fructose ought to be tested in the presence of other hydrogen donors and under varying oxygen tensions. It may be that a hydrogen donor is essential for the reduction process

$$
\begin{array}{ccc}
CH_2OH & & CH_2OH \\
| & +2H & | \\
CO & \longrightarrow & CHOH \\
| & & | \\
(CHOH)_3 & & (CHOH)_3 \\
| & & | \\
CH_2OH & & CH_2OH \\
\text{Fructose} & & \text{Mannitol}
\end{array}
$$

and that the fructose, obviously oxidized with difficulty to judge from the poor growth it supported, may function as H acceptor under proper conditions. Failing this possibility, a new precursor would then have to be postulated. A direct reduction of glucose to the analogous alcohol sorbitol has never been discovered in fungi.

Yamasaki and Simomura (1937) proposed glycerol as a direct precursor of mannitol because of the 20–30 per cent yields obtained from the triose by *Aspergillus glaucus* strains. They propose a 2-C_3 assymetric condensation accompanied by an oxidative dehydrogenation as follows:

$$
\begin{array}{ccc}
CH_2OH & & CH_2OH \\
| & & | \\
HCOH & & CHOH \\
| & & | \\
HCOH & -2H & CHOH \\
| \;\; H & \longrightarrow & | \qquad + 66.2 \text{ kcals.} \\
2H \leftarrow \;\; H & + & HOCH \\
| & & | \\
HOCH & & HOCH \\
| & & | \\
HOCH & & CH_2OH \\
| & & \\
CH_2OH & & \\
\text{2 Glycerol} & & d\text{-Mannitol}
\end{array}
$$

This energy-yielding process supports the activities of the fungus. There is no evidence that this simple reaction takes place, and in view of the great variety of different carbohydrate products known to be formed by fungi from glycerol and other carbon-chains of various lengths, presumably via glyceraldehyde synthesis to hexose, this instance need not be considered a special case until proved. The observed facts could just as well be interpreted as a condensation to a hexose, by enzymatic or Lobry de Bruyn rearrangement to fructose or mannose and reduction to mannitol. The role of glycerol here would then be the same as in the pentoses mentioned above—they both furnish the triose intermediate for the synthesis. On the other hand, the theory of the Japanese could by the same token explain mannitol formation from different hexoses and pentoses—they all generate the suggested precursor glycerol.

Another high mannitol-yielding fungus is *Byssochlamys fulva*, the heat-resistant ascomycete of considerable economic importance as a cause of spoilage in the processed fruit canning industry. It converts 30 per cent of the glucose consumed to mannitol (Raistrick and Smith, 1933).

POLYSACCHARIDES

1. PENTOSANS

Polymers of C_5 carbohydrates are probably as widely distributed among the lower fungi as they are in higher plants, but little work has been done on this subject. Dox and Niedig (1911) demonstrated 0.86–1.17 per cent pentosans in three Aspergilli and three Penicillia by distillation of the mycelium with 12 per cent HCl, for conversion to furfuraldehyde, which was weighed as the phloroglucide. (See also Norman, *et al.*, 1932.) Each of the organisms was grown on glucose medium. Pentose synthesis in fungi is illustrated also by the universal occurrence of ribose in nucleic acids, nucleotides, etc.

2. HEXOSANS

A great multiplicity of these substances are known in fungi, and, doubtless as more of the vast numbers of different fungi are examined chemically, additional hexosans will be discovered. Several hexosans (glucans, glucosans, dextrans) are well-known in which the hexose residue is exclusively *d*-glucose units. These will be treated separately:

(a) Glycogen

True glycogen is well-known in yeast and in many fungi. Ordinarily its presence is detected qualitatively by crushing fungus cells and microscopically observing the characteristic red-brown coloration of glycogen with dilute iodine solution. From an unnamed white Aspergillus Birkinshaw *et al.* (1931b) isolated glycogen or a closely allied substance.

Glycogen makes up 36.7 per cent of the total weight of sclerotia of the cotton root rot parasite *Phymatotrichum omnivorum*, from which Ergle (1947) isolated it in chemically pure form and found its chemical and physical properties identical with true glycogen. The glycogen exists in free (10.1 per cent) and in bound (26.6 per cent) form in the sclerotia. The free glycogen is readily extracted with hot water, and bound glycogen is insoluble in hot water, but is soluble in hot 35 per cent KOH. The latter was suggested to be combined with lipides and protein. Glycogen was also present in the mycelium.

(b) Mycodextran

This hexosan was described first by Dox and Niedig (1914a and b), who isolated it from mycelium of *Penicillium expansum* and *Aspergillus niger*. On cooling the hot water extracts of the dry mycelium, a flocculent precipitate was obtained, which, after several reprecipitations, gave no color reaction with iodine. *d*-Glucose was the sole product of hydrolysis. Mycodextran is not attacked by the ordinary amylolytic enzymes. The mycodextran content increased with age even in well autolyzed cultures, i.e., this carbohydrate was not preferentially utilized under starvation conditions, an unusual situation. The mycodextran content of *P. expansum* mycelium after 3, 5, and 7 days was 0.9, 4.7, and 7.3 per cent respectively.

Other glucan-type polysaccharides giving no color with iodine, but apparently different from mycodextran, have been isolated from *Fumago vagans* and *Penicillium digitatum*. The latter had a high optical rotation (Birkinshaw and Raistrick, 1931; Birkinshaw *et al.*, 1931a; see also Norman and Peterson, 1932).

A dextran-type polysaccharide isolated from *Penicillium javanicum* by Ward *et al.* (1935) was considered to be the same as that from *P. digitatum* by Birkinshaw, *et al.* (1931a) and also similar to the mycodextran of Dox and Niedig. Still another polyglucose of this type was isolated and named sclerotiose after *Penicillium sclerotiorum* (Albericci *et al.* 1943). Like mycodextran, it gives no color with iodine. When the organism is grown on Czapek-Dox medium at neutral pH, 10 per cent of the dry mycelial weight consisted of sclerotiose, whereas mycelium from acid medium contained only 2.8–3.0 per cent.

(c) Starch (Mold-Starch, Fungus-Starch)

Typical plant starch, giving the intense blue color with iodine and hydrolyzed by the usual diastatic enzymes, is formed by many filamentous fungi. It can easily be detected by blue coloration of the mycelium when iodine is added to the reverse side of a surface pad. The starch also exists free in the medium and may be "soluble" starch or may be intracellular starch liberated by autolyzing cells.

Boas (1916) observed microscopically that the iodine-stained blue color was localized as incrustations on the cell walls and it was dissolved by boiling. Chrzaszcz and Tiukow (1929) found the stained starch to be located in various places within the cells in a cross-section of a surface mycelial pad. In some strains of Penicillia the starch was located in cells in one region of the pad, and in different regions in other cells. Some cells had the starch diffusely throughout the interior, while in others the starch was localized in granules. In either case photomicrographs show that cells in large areas of the pad formed none or little starch, excellent evidence for the thesis advanced in Chapter 2 explaining the inhomogeneity of metabolism of different portions of the typical surface mycelial pad.

Early workers (Cramer, 1894; Wehmer, 1913; Boas, 1916, 1917, 1919, 1922; and Schmidt, 1935) studied various aspects of starch formation by various fungi and found it produced from a variety of single carbon sources, sugar and non-sugar, with the production favored in strongly acid media and at somewhat elevated temperature (33°C.).

The first isolation of starch from filamentous fungi apparently was by Cramer (1894), who extracted it from spores of Penicillium glaucum grown on white bread. The yield was 17 per cent of the weight of the spores. Because of the blue coloration with iodine Cramer named this material "spore starch."

Hida (1934) found that nine out of twenty-two A. niger strains were starch producers, but only in strongly acid media (pH < 2.2). The optimum conditions for starch synthesis were not the same as those for growth. He concurred with an early view of Boas, since rejected, that the accumulation of starch is due to the high-acidity inhibition of diastic enzyme activity, which normally destroys the starch. This explanation is rather dubious, for it assumes that the internal pH of the cells is identical with the external. The extensive studies of Chrzaszcz and Tiukow (1929) on forty-five species of Penicillium, twenty-two of which produced mycelial starch to varying degrees, led to a more credible interpretation of starch accumulation. They found that their organisms could be divided into two groups: the starch formers, which form smaller amounts of organic acids than the second group, the non-starch formers, which were strong acid formers. The starch and the organic acids both were regarded as playing the role of reserve foodstuffs. (See shunt metabolism; reserve storage products, Chapter 4.) This idea fits in well with the concept of shunt metabolism, according to which the organic acids and the starch would be considered overflow shunt products of luxury carbohydrate nutrition, the particular enzyme makeup of the organisms determining which, and to what proportion. Starch, then, is analogous not only to accumulation of organic acids, but also fat production, excess Raistrick type pigment production, etc. In this sense starch formation is a reflection of the physiological potentialities of the organism, a normal physiological process according to Chrzaszcz and Tiukow, proceeding at maximum rate in strongly acid environment, and not a poisoning effect of the low pH. Chrzaszcz and Tiukow advance the argument that starch formation is a more primitive property of the fungi than the more recently evolved mechanisms for organic acid formation.

(d) Levulan

Kopeloff and Kopeloff (1919) discovered that spores of *Aspergillus sydowi* contain an enzyme which produces a levulan gum in concentrated sucrose solutions. The gum has been isolated and identified as a levan consisting exclusively of levulose residues and indistinguishable from the levan synthesized by bacteria. As is the case of bacteria, the fungus levan is produced only from sucrose and not from invert sugar, indicative that a "nascent" levulose or other active split product (phosphorylated derivative?) of the sucrose is the required unit for levan synthesis. The levan of *Bacillus mesentericus* consists of 2:6-anhydrofructofuranose units, and is formed only from substrates containing this unit in a terminal position, i.e., sucrose and raffinose, but not melezitose (Hibbert *et al.*, 1931). The fungus levan may be identical with this, but it has not been studied structurally.

(e) Galactans (Polygalactoses)

Dox and Niedig (1914b) observed that after the mycodextran had precipitated out of the hot water extract of *A. niger*, the supernatant set into a transparent jelly upon further cooling. The responsible polysaccharide was isolated, gave no color with iodine, consisted entirely of galactose residues upon hydrolysis, and was named mycogalactan.

The other galactans have been reported by the Raistrick School (Clutterbuck *et al.*, 1934; Haworth *et al.*, 1937; Clutterbuck, 1936). One, produced by *Penicillium charlesii*, is called galactocarolase, and its chemistry has been extensively investigated. The other, rugulose, produced by *P. rugulosum*, is merely mentioned by Clutterbuck (1936). Galactocarolase occurs as a mixture with a polymannose in the culture filtrates from which it is recovered by acetone precipitation from the concentrated filtrate. The mixture is separated by fractional precipitation with absolute alcohol and the purified polygalactose has a rotation of $[\alpha]5790 = -84.3°$. Molecular weight determination and methylation studies show that galactocarolose has a minimum chain length of 9–10 units of β-galactofuranose mutually linked through the 1:5 positions.

(f) Mannans (Polymannoses)

One such polysaccharride referred to above is mannocarolose, from *P. charlesii* culture filtrates. It is considerably more resistant to acid hydrolysis than the accompanying galactocarolose, and yields *d*-mannose residues exclusively (Clutterbuck *et al.*, 1934; Haworth *et al.*, 1935a). Chemical investigations revealed that the basic chain length is 8–9 units of *d*-mannose linked through the 1:6 positions. According to Haworth *et al.* (1935a) this is a unique molecular structure for a polymannose though it has since been found to be that in the mannans of yeasts (Garzuly-Janke, 1940). In this latter work, using a crude qualitative test, mannan could not be detected in the cells of sixty-eight different filamentous fungi tested.

3. Complex Polysaccharides

This includes those polysaccharides whose units consist of more than a single substance. Three are well-known in the fungi:

(a) Luteic Acid

Luteic acid, obtained in culture filtrates of two different strains of *Penicillium luteum*, when the organism grows on a variety of single carbon sources including glucose, fructose, galactose, mannose, xylose, arabinose, glycerol, succinic acid, and citric acid (Raistrick and Rintoul, 1931; Birkinshaw and Raistrick, 1933; Anderson *et al.*, 1939). Luteic acid is a colloidal, levorotatory material of high molecular weight, the salts of which form very viscous solutions. On acid hydrolysis glucose and malonic acid ($HOOCCH_2COOH$) are liberated in a 2:1 molar ratio; the compound probably is a malonylester of a polyglucose. One carboxyl group of the malonic acid is free, giving the polysaccharide acidic properties. The malonic acid is split out by mild alkaline hydrolysis giving a neutral levorotatory polysaccharide, luteose, while an acid hydrolysis gives glucose as the sole product. Luteose is isolated in purified form from the alkaline reaction mixture by addition of Fehling's solution. The malonyl groups are removed as a soluble complex and luteose forms an insoluble copper complex. The molecular weight value obtained by osmotic pressure measurements corresponded to eighty-four glucose units. These are glucopyranose residues united by 1:6-β-glucosidic linkages.

(b) Varianose

Varianose, obtained in culture filtrates of *Penicillium varians* (Haworth *et al.*, 1935b). The chain length corresponds to eight hexose members and a molecular weight of 1300. Constituents of the polysaccharide obtained by acid hydrolysis are the hexoses d-glucose, d-galactose, and d-idose or l-altrose in molar ratios of 1:6–8:1.

(c) Capreolinose

This is produced by *Penicillium capreolinum* and is the most complex polysaccharide known in the fungi. Its hydrolysis products are mannose, glucose, galactose, and malonic acid (Clutterbuck, 1936).

4. GUMS

The numerous high-molecular-weight hydrophilic polymers produced universally by fungi and other microorganisms lend, upon drying, extremely tough and resistant properties to the cellular mass. During the first world war a method was developed in Germany for manufacture of a leather substitute from tanned membranes of bacteria and fungi (*Mucor biodin*) (Herzog, 1915). Sanborn (1934, 1935, 1936) has been active in this country in attempting to exploit those properties of the dried membranes of microorganisms for industrial application. The polysaccharide "gums" in some cases produce transparent membranes when pressed and dried thin.

Polysaccharides of pathogenic fungi are described by Nickerson (1947).

All the foregoing evidence make one all-important point evident: fungi can synthesis any one of a great variety of simple hexoses from any one of a great variety of hexoses, pentoses, alcohols, and organic acids, a fact recognized as far back as 1920 by the Russian, Kostyschew, who demonstrated glucose production and liberation into the medium by *A. niger* from substrates as diverse as tartaric acid, glycerol, quinic acid, mannitol, and lactic acid. Kostyschew states that sucrose also was formed but no details were given and no other report of sucrose synthesis by a fungus is known.

All this can only mean that diverse substrates are broken down to a common intermediate which then is synthesized to a hexose (or pentose) sugar according to the particular enzyme makeup of the organism.

RAISTRICK SCHOOL THEORY OF POLYSACCHARIDES AS METABOLIC INTERMEDIATES

The great variety of different polysaccharides synthesized by fungi, each specific to certain organisms, has led the group of workers under the leadership of H. Raistrick at the London School of Hygiene and Tropical Medicine to evolve an interesting theory as to the role of these substances. They offer the hypothesis that, regardless of substrate, a particular polysaccharide is synthesized, and the other metabolic products characteristic of the organisms are produced from it as a forerunner. The substrate source of carbon is visualized as being degraded to

. . . relatively simple molecules containing only a few carbon atoms which are then built up to form carbohydrates of the peculiar pattern required by the organism, acting as a template, much in the manner that ingested proteins are broken down in the animal body to the constituent amino-acids, which are then used for synthesizing the proteins specific for the organism (Birkinshaw and Raistrick, 1933, p. 375).

The characteristic metabolism products of the organism are then produced from its own particular polysaccharide by a series of chemical actions, reductions, oxidations, condensations, and hydrolyses.

The chief evidence used in support of this concept is the chemical similarity between certain complex organic acids produced by *Penicillum charlesii* and the galactofuranose (polygalactose) polysaccharide obtained from the same organism. There are two C_9 acids, carolic acid and carolinic acid, and two C_{10} acids, carlic acid and carlosic acid.

. . . The acids have been shown to be derivatives of tetronic acid, the C_9 acids having the general formula A, the C_{10} acids the formula B.

Acids produced by P. charlesii

Galactofuranose

A comparison with the structure of galactofuranose (C), or better still with that of the corresponding lactone obtained by oxidation of the methylated material with bromine (D), indicates the close similarity of structures B and D. This close relationship makes it appear probable that this polysaccharide is an intermediate in the microbiological synthesis of these acids. (Clutterbuck, 1936, p. 60T.)

This hypothesis is presented here in detail to stimulate the reader toward similar kinds of reflections in this field. The evidence for this theory is exceedingly scanty and even dubious, and a great deal of more direct evidence, including its applicability to other species, would be required to gain credence for it. Nevertheless, formulations of this type coming from authorities in the field are highly valued for the challenges they present to the critical reader and research worker, and the field of mold metabolism could profit from considerably more of this interpretive approach and imaginative thinking.

The theory of shunt metabolism seemingly is at variance with this theory, for the former holds the carbohydrates to be end-products of condensation rather than metabolic intermediates. Yet, in the same manner that organic acids and fats, similar end-products, may be partially or entirely further converted, so may the carbohydrates. The value of the shunt metabolism concept is its generalized applicability. However intriguing and attractive the polysaccharide theory is, its weakness lies in the lack of general applicability so far, and in the fact that of the multifarious products of mold metabolism known, few bear chemical similarity to a parent carbohydrate as depicted above.

REFERENCES

Albericci, V. J., Curtin, T. P., and Reilly, D. 1943. *Biochem. J.* **37**, 243–246.
Anderson, C. G., Haworth, W. N., Raistrick, H., and Stacey, M. 1939. *Biochem. J.* **33**, 272–279.
Birkinshaw, J. H., and Raistrick, H. 1931. *Trans. Roy. Soc. London* **B220**, 331–354.
Birkinshaw, J. H., and Raistrick, H. 1933. *Biochem. J.* **27**, 370–375.
Birkinshaw, J. H., Charles, J. H. V., and Raistrick, H. 1931a. *Trans. Roy. Soc. London* **B220**, 153–71.
Birkinshaw, J. H., Charles, J. H. V., Hetherington, A. C., and Raistrick, H. 1931b. *Trans. Roy. Soc. London* **B220**, 355–367.
Boas, F. 1916. *Biochem. Z.* **78**, 308–312.
Boas, F. 1917. *Biochem. Z.* **81**, 80–86.
Boas, F. 1919. *Ber. deut. botan. Ges.* **37**, 50–56.
Boas, F. 1922. *Zentr. Bakt. Parasitenk. Abt. II* **56**, 7–11.
Chrzaszcz, T., and Tiukow, D. 1929. *Biochem. Z.* **207**, 39–52.
Clutterbuck, P. W. 1936. *J. Soc. Chem. Ind.* **55**, 55T–61T.
Clutterbuck, P. W., Haworth, W. N., Raistrick, H., Smith, G., and Stacey, M. 1934. *Biochem. J.* **28**, 94–110.
Coyne, F. P., and Raistrick, H. 1931. *Biochem. J.* **25**, 1513–1521.
Cramer, E. 1894. *Arch. Hyg.* **20**, 197.
Dox, A. W., and Niedig, R. E. 1911. *J. Biol. Chem.* **9**, 267–269.
Dox, A. W., and Niedig, R. E. 1914a. *J. Biol. Chem.* **18**, 167–175.
Dox, A. W., and Niedig, R. E. 1914b. *J. Biol. Chem.* **19**, 235–237.
Ergle, D. R. 1947. *J. Am. Chem. Soc.* **69**, 2061–2062.
Garzuly-Janke, R. 1940. *Zentr. Bakt. Parasitenk. Abt. II* **102**, 361–365.
Haworth, W. N., Raistrick, H., and Stacey, M .1935a. *Biochem. J.* **29**, 612–621.

Haworth, W. N., Raistrick, H., and Stacey, M. 1935b. *Biochem. J.* **29**, 2668–2678.

Haworth, W. N., Raistrick, H., and Stacey, M. 1937. *Biochem. J.* **31**, 640–644.

Herzog, R. D. 1915. U. S. Patent No. 1,141,545.

Hibbert, H., Tipson, R. S., and Brauns, F. 1931. *Can. J. Research* **4**, 221–239.

Hida, T. 1934. *J. Shanghai Sci. Inst.* **1**, 85–116.

Kopeloff, N., and Kopeloff, L. 1919. *J. Agr. Research* **18**, 195–209.

Kopeloff, N., Kopeloff, L., and Welcome, C. J. 1920. *J. Biol. Chem.* **43**, 171–187.

Kostyschew, S. 1920. *Z. physiol. Chem.* **111**, 236–245.

Nickerson, W. J. 1947. Biology of Pathogenic Fungi. Chronica Botanica Co., Waltham, Mass., pp. 163–165.

Norman, A. G., Peterson, W. H., and Houtz, R. C. 1932. *Biochem. J.* **26**, 1934–1935.

Obaton, F. 1929. *Rev. gen. botan.* **41**, 282–292, 365–387, 424–512, 622–636.

Oxford, A. E., and Raistrick, H. 1935. *Biochem. J.* **29**, 1599–1601.

Raistrick, H., and Rintoul, M. L. 1931. *Trans. Roy. Soc. London* **B220**, 255–268.

Raistrick, H., and Smith, G. 1933. *Biochem. J.* **27**, 1814–1819.

Raistrick, H., and Young, W. 1931. *Trans. Roy. Soc. London* **B220**, 173–208.

Sanborn, J. R. 1934. *Ind. Eng. Chem.* **26**, 532–533; 1935. U. S. Patent No. 2,026,253; 1936. *Ind. Eng. Chem.* **28**, 1189–1190.

Schmidt, D. 1935. *Biochem. Z.* **158**, 223–252.

Takata, R. 1929. *J. Soc. Chem. Ind. Japan* **32**, Suppl. Binding 245–247.

Ward, G. E., Lockwood, L. B., May, O. E., and Herrick, H. T. 1935. *Ind. Eng. Chem.* **27**, 318–322.

Wehmer, C. 1913. *Ber. deut. botan. Ges.* **31**, 257–268.

Yamasaki, I., and Simomura, M. 1937. *Biochem. Z.* **291**, 340–348.

Zellner, J. 1910. *Monatsh.* **31**, 617–634.

CHAPTER 17

NITROGEN METABOLISM OF FUNGI

GENERAL

It is not unexpected that great diversity as well as versatility exists among the fungi with respect to ability to utilize various forms of nitrogen as the sole source for cell synthesis. Robbins (1937) has codified much information on this subject and coordinated various aspects of it. He observes that fungi studied up to now fall rather neatly into four groups with respect to the sources of nitrogen they are able to use. His delineations are tabulated thusly:

	N source utilizable			
	N_2	NO_3	NH_3	Organic N
Group I	+	+	+	+
Group II	−	+	+	+
Group III	−	−	+	+
Group IV	−	−	−	+

This arrangement denotes an ascending relation from N_2 through organic N. In the sequence N_2, NO_3, NH_3, and organic N, utilizability of any one type of N connotes utilizability of each type subsequent to it in the series. Organisms capable of utilizing N_2 or NO_3 are more versatile than those utilizing only NH_3 or organic N. Organisms utilizing only the last named (Group IV) represent a high degree of specialization, and from an evolutionary point of view, probably have evolved from Group III through loss of function, i.e., loss of ability to utilize ammonia. Similarly, Group III may have evolved from Group II, and Group II from Group I. In nature these lost functions do not necessarily represent a disadvantage from the standpoint of survival, as ample amounts of each type of nitrogen exist in soil and water, the habitats of these groups. As seen below, it is most likely that N_2 and NO_3 are converted to NH_3 and organic N during utilization by fungi, hence, in one sense, direct assimilation of the latter may be considered a more efficient means of nutrition than having to generate them from N_2 and NO_3.

NITROGEN FIXATION

The ability to utilize gaseous nitrogen as the sole source of nitrogen for cell synthesis has been claimed for a great variety of different fungi ever since bacterial N fixation was reported near the turn of the century. Critical examination of all the available evidence indicates that clear-cut nitrogen fixation at best is a property of very few species of fungi, these being mycorrhizal or near-mycorrhizal types. In earlier years the claims were widespread (see Duggar and Davis, 1916 for representative literature review), but lately the claims have been much more conservative. In cases of small fixation, especially over long incubation periods, considerable skepticism is apt to meet reports of fixation unless rigorous controls are adopted to rule out possible complications in this type of work. According to the authorities Burris and Wilson (1945), principal sources of errors are those involved in sampling, in the inadequacy of the Kjeldahl method for the measurement of certain types of fixed nitrogen, and in the low sensitivity of the usual chemical methods of analysis. Differences obtained when small aliquots are analyzed appear much larger (fallaciously) when multiplied by the factor for the entire culture. Similarly, small amounts of certain types of ring N compounds (pyrimidine, azo, nitro, nitroso, azoxy compounds, etc.) which may be present as impurities in the medium at the start, or introduced in the inoculum, may be converted during growth of the fungus to forms of N compounds now measurable by the Kjeldahl method, hence giving an apparent fixation. This is the type of error apparently involved in claims for the N fixation by germinating seeds (see Vita, 1937 for review). Regarding sensitivity, the only absolute criterion is the use of isotopic nitrogen (N^{15}, "heavy" nitrogen).

One feature that is seemingly an important source of error in a number of studies on this subject is the fact that the air contains a variety of different forms of fixed N, present, to be sure, in exceedingly minute quantities, but nevertheless subject to concentration in the form of fungus mycelium which takes them up from solution as rapidly as they dissolve. The equilibrium will then constantly be in the direction of solution from the air. Many different kinds of naturally-occurring substances are volatile, and traces of ammonia and other N compounds doubtless are present in the normal atmosphere. The air of laboratories is bound to be contaminated with various types of chemical fumes and products of combustion of natural gas from laboratory burners. Smoke of any kind, including tobacco smoke, also is a source of error. These factors may not appear significant, but in many cases the N fixed has been reported to be on the order of only a few milligrams over periods of 20 to 60 days, over which period this amount of N could easily be concentrated from impurities in the atmosphere by the cultures.

The extensive work of Schober (1930) represents one of the most careful and exhaustive of the many studies on N fixation by saprophytic fungi. Six strains of *Aspergillus niger* and one of *Citromyces* were claimed to fix N, the highest amount fixed being 4 mg. N in 48 days, this enabling synthesis of 180 mg. dry weight of mycelium. However, several other workers tested many different strains of *A. niger* and other species, including Schober's original strains, only with negative results for fixation (Roberg, 1932; Allison *et al.*, 1934; Schroder, 1931).

One cannot summarily reject claims for N fixation by these saprophytes exclusively on the grounds that results cannot be repeated. A great many instances of strain specificity with respect to virtually every phase of fungus metabolism have been cited in the preceding chapters in this book, and it is not impossible that strain specificity might be at play here, too. Conceivably strains fixing N may rapidly be lost owing to variation and selection of fixed N-users when cultivated on the usual N-containing laboratory media. According to Kasselbach (1931), this is what happened to Schober's cultures during cultivation on malt agar. However, Roberg passed the strains through soil and failed to restore the alleged N fixing ability of these strains, numbering altogether twenty-one. Catalysts such as molybdenum, tungsten, etc., were without effect. In any case, regardless of the intrinsic difficulties of the problem, the burden of furnishing unequivocal proof is that of the investigator claiming a fixation, and in only a few cases has this been done in acceptable fashion.

Saida in 1901 apparently furnished the first strong evidence for N fixation by fungi, using *Phoma betae*, a fungus related to mycorrhizal forms but actually not one. Fixation up to 10.5 mg. was observed in 100 ml. medium over $2\frac{1}{2}$ months.

While N fixation cannot be accepted as a generalized property of fungi, most workers regard that certain species of mycorrhizal fungi probably do fix nitrogen. Mycorrhizal fungi are those living symbiotically in nodules in the roots of a great variety of plants. Fungi from plants of the families *Ericaceae* and *Orchidaceae* have been implicated in N fixation. Sterile seedlings of these plants make very limited growth in a nitrogen-free medium. Inoculation with the homologous fungus symbiont now permits the plant to prosper, presumably by utilization of atmospheric nitrogen. Nitrogen fixation studies are done on pure cultures of these fungi. Ternetz in 1907 provided cogent evidence for fixation by five species of the endophyte *Phoma radicis* isolated from different host plants, and indicated according to the plant genus, viz.,

P. radiciis Oxycocci, *P. radiciis Andromedae*, *P. radiciis Vaccini*, *P. radiciis Tetralicus* and *P. radiciis Ericae*. Fixation was variable according to the species but a total of 7 to 15 mg. was fixed. These organisms are less vigorous than the aerobic N-fixing bacterium, *Azotobacter chroococcum*, which fixed 127.9 mg. N in comparison. But the fungi consumed considerably less glucose, and per gram glucose consumed were even more efficient than *Azotobacter*. Thus the first three species of *Phoma* listed above fixed 18.08, 10.92, and 22.14 mg. N per gram glucose used, compared to 10.66 for the *Azotobacter* control.

Careful work by subsequent investigators has lent much credence to this discovery, the results of Duggar and Davis (1916) being most extensive in this regard. Here *Phoma betae* was employed with positive results. A number of other saprophytes were tested: *Aspergillus niger*, *Penicillium expansum*, *P. digitatum*, *Glomerella gossypii*, *Macrosporium commune*, but the fixation of 1 to 2 mg. commonly observed for these organisms is considered within experimental error. However *Phoma betae* fixation of N_2 under the same conditions was 3.0 to 7.8 mg./100 ml. medium. This clearly is beyond any likely experimental error and is strong evidence for fixation. Other workers have obtained similar results with species of *Phoma* (Rayner, 1922). The exceedingly rigorous experimental setup of Jones and Smith (1928) is worthy of note. They obtained definite fixation after exercising extraordinary precautions, including cultivation of *Phoma radiciis callunae* in a N_2-free atmosphere for comparison with growth in a N_2-containing atmosphere. The latter always contained more fixed N. Yields were small, in one experiment 3.84 mg. N was fixed by a 50 ml. culture over 28 days. Glucose consumption was slight, 0.13 g., but on a gram basis the fixation was 29.5 mg., which clearly places this organism in a class with *Azotobacter*.

The second group of endophytes shown to fix nitrogen are *Orcheomyces*, symbionts of the orchid plants (Wolff, 1926). In these experiments the total amount of N fixed was small, 0.35 to 0.87 mg./100 ml. culture, but the accuracy of the nitrogen determination, which was done by nesslerization, was considered to be such as to make the above figures clearly valid. Per gram of glucose utilized the fixation calculates out to be 13.3 and 9.76 mg. respectively, again in the range of *Azotobacter*. Certain aspects of N fixation by fungi are reviewed by Senn (1928).

The ultimate criterion of nitrogen fixation in fungi has recently been established by University of Wisconsin Workers who showed that a species of Phomopsis (*Phoma casuarinae*) assimilates labeled nitrogen (N^{15}) (Tove *et al.*, 1949).

Considering the fact that numerous different bacteria, actinomycetes and algae are known to fix atmospheric nitrogen, it is not unexpected that fungi should carry out this feat, and the rather general availability now-adays of isotopic nitrogen for experiments of this type should throw much light on this question in the near future. This technique will be of especial value in checking claims for saprophytes previously reported to fix borderline amounts of nitrogen.

There is no reason for not believing that N_2 fixation in fungi is different from that process in N_2 fixation in bacteria, where it is known that the N_2 is converted to NH_3, which in turn is utilized for formation of the amino acids of primary importance in protein synthesis and transamination, namely glutamic and aspartic acids (Burris and Wilson, 1947). Thus, as indicated in the introduction of this chapter, regardless of what the form of nitrogen assimilated, it eventually becomes NH_3 in the intermediary metabolism of the cells, for purposes of protein synthesis.

AMMONIUM AND NITRATE NITROGEN

The great majority of filamentous fungi studied in the laboratory can be cultivated on synthetic media consisting of glucose, minerals, either NH_4^+ or NO_3^- nitrogen, and in numerous cases certain vitamins. Several of the classical media for cultivation of fungi recognized the widespread ability of this group of organisms to grow on simple media of this type. The media bearing the names of Raulin, of Pfeffer, and of Czapek are cases in point. In general, filamentous fungi do not have complex nitrogenous requirements such as one finds among the bacteria, though many exceptions to this statement exist. It may be that amino acids are required by some, owing to inability to synthesize that particular compound, but, furnished that, inorganic nitrogen may still be utilizable for cell synthesis. Many fungi are known which cannot be cultivated on synthetic media and it may be that the malt extract, yeast extract, etc., furnish organic nitrogen requirements of the organism, but the chances are that some specific unknown growth factors are involved. As seen below, this does not mean that fungi cannot utilize various amino acids as the sole source of nitrogen. It means that in most cases the likelihood exists that specific amino acids are not *required* as the nitrogen source. Nevertheless, there are some instances definitely where ammonia or nitrate nitrogen are not utilizable, although certain amino acids are. Thus Schade (1940) found that the water molds *Apodachlya brachynema* and *Leptomitus lacteus* would not use inorganic N but did use alanine, leucine, glycine or asparagine, the last two in the presence of acetate as carbon source. Here then is an example of Robbins' Group IV. (See section on Organic N.)

The ability to utilize nitrate N represents a greater versatility on the part of a fungus than ammonia N, for all nitrate users can use ammonia, but not vice versa. Most notable among the non-nitrate users are certain members of the Mucorales, particularly the genus Rhizopus, and especially the common laboratory tool, *R. nigricans*. Many others exist also, for example, the Chytridiacious fungus, *Rhizophlyctis rosea*, which uses organic and NH₃-N but not NO₃ (Stanier, 1942). Other examples are *Rhizopus oryzae* and *Ceratostomella ulmi*. On the other hand, many species of the genus *Mucor* use nitrate N and some not. Obviously Czapek's medium, one designed for cultivation of fungi in general, and widely used, would have greater applicability were the nitrogen source NH₄NO₃ instead of NaNO₃ as originally prescribed. On the other hand, most fungi do utilize nitrate, and here are included the ubiquitous forms in the genera *Aspergillus, Penicillium, Fusarium*, and numerous other *Fungi Imperfecti*.

Though most fungi can utilize either NO_3-N or NH_3-N when each is supplied alone, a great deal of interest has centered around the question of which form is preferentially utilized when both are present, as in the form of NH_4NO_3. The evidence is definitely in favor of the idea that NH_3-N is preferentially utilized in the presence of NO_3-N, but this behavior is subject to modification depending on the organism employed, on the previous cultivation history of the organism and on the cultural conditions. Working with *Aspergillus oryzae* Sakamura (1930) concluded, as had other workers previously, that the terms ammoniophile and nitratophile applied first in 1889 (Laurent) are only relative, and any one organism can be both depending on conditions. Use of these terms, then, has only limited validity.

The most common path of events is that ammonium ion is absorbed first and rapidly to the virtual exclusion of nitrate, until the former is exhausted, whereupon nitrate assimilation then takes place. It is quite definite that ammonia is selectively utilized. In the absence of organic acid production from carbohydrate, this means that the pH of the culture fluid drops in the early stages as the anion accumulates (HNO_3) and later rises as the anion is consumed. This is the socalled "physiological" acidity, as contrasted to organic acids.

Definite evidence exists that the prevailing pH can exercise a decisive influence and, indeed, is probably the most important factor in utilization of NH_3 vs. NO_3 out of a mixture of the two, and even on NH_3 utilization itself (Klotz, 1923). For example, *A. niger* preformed pads acting on NH_4NO_3 at very low pH values (1.89) selectively utilized NO_3, reversing the pH picture from that described above, because here residual cation accumulated (NH_3) causing the pH to rise to 8.2 after 112 hours incubation (Bach and Desbordes, 1933).

In another strain of *A. niger* (Itzerott, 1936; Bünning, 1936), the critical pH value for nitrate vs. ammonia uptake was 3.0 in a solution of NH_4NO_3. Above pH 3.0 only ammonia was used; below pH 3.0 only nitrate was used. When the ammonia was depleted, nitrate utilization took place slowly at the higher pH values. Utilization of ammonia was markedly reduced below pH 3.0, but was nevertheless assimilated concomitantly with NO_3. Nitrate uptake, proceeding best at pH < 3.0, apparently was independent of nitrate reduction in this organism, the latter proceeding best at pH 7.5.

Preferential utilization of amino acids out of a mixture of amino acids and nitrate nitrogen is indicated for a penicillin-producing strain of *Penicillium notatum* (Dimond and Peltier, 1945), yet ammonia was utilized in preference to peptone, acetamide, and glycine (Boas and Leberle, 1919; Zaleski and Pjukow, 1914). In view of the fact that these organic N sources have to be broken down to liberate the N as NH_3 for synthesis of proteins, etc., it is perhaps not surprising that NH_3 available directly in inorganic form would be utilized easier and faster, i.e., preferentially.

Differential absorption of NO_3^- vs. NH_3 had also been claimed to be influenced by the trace element nutrition of the organism, particularly iron, copper, and manganese (Sakamura, 1934, 1935; Currie, 1917). The Japanese worker has in this case stressed the idea of nitratophilic vs. ammoniophilic. Other workers have failed to confirm this (Itzerott, 1936) and the feeling is that the trace element effect of Sakamura is due to effects on the acidity of the medium, thereby affecting NO_3 uptake only indirectly. This subject is discussed in Chapter 7.

Rippel (1931) made a detailed examination of N source selection by four different fungi and makes the categorical conclusion that under the usual cultivation conditions (initial pH 4-6) *A. niger* does not assimilate the nitrate ion of NH_4NO_3 until the NH_4^+ ion is entirely consumed. The pH was found to be a most critical factor in N selection in the form of NH_4^+, NO_3^- and organic N. The critical pH value ranged from 3.8 to 4.6 for the different organisms. For example, *A. niger* on a mixture of NH_4NO_3 and asparagine (or peptone or yeast extract) first assimilated NH_4^+, then NO_3^- and then the organic N after inorganic N was exhausted. *A. oryzae* assimilated all three forms of N below pH 4.25, but NO_3^- was not assimilated above this pH value. *Penicillium schneggii* and *Mucor silvaticus* on the other hand did not utilize NO_3^- under any conditions, even in the absence of NH_4^+. Asparagine was used regardless of pH but NH_4^+ was assimilated only at pH values above 3.8-4.6, and not below.

Generally speaking, pH may be a controlling factor in membrane permeability and this is well known to be the case in connection with the utilization of various substances by many different microorganisms, including fungi. *A priori* one is tempted to interpret the events relating to ammonia vs. nitrate utilization on these grounds, i.e., NO_3 is assimilated only as the undissociated HNO_3 molecule, at low pH values, and NH_3 as the undissociated NH_4OH molecule at higher pH values. However at pH 5.0–5.5 ammonia already is virutally completely dissociated, and ammonia is readily assimilated even at much lower pH values. It may well be that selective permeability does play a role in the relative utilization of organic nitrogenous compounds. Though pH alters both the charge on membranes and also determines the ionic state of solutes, both of which may be critical in determining permeability rates of any particular substance, the idea has been advanced that the charge on the intracellular colloids of the fungus also plays a role in selective utilization of nitrate and ammonia insofar as pH is concerned (Rippel, 1931; Itzerott, 1936; Bünning, 1936) and some evidence supports it, particularly the fact that the critical pH for nitrate absorption corresponds roughly to the isoelectric point of cell colloids. Itzerott and Bünning claim to have demonstrated that permeability could not be the critical factor in nitrate assimilation by showing that the mycelium takes up and stores nitrate below pH 3.0, but later gives up some of the stored nitrate to the medium again, at which time the pH is well above 3.0. Thus the membrane is permeable to nitrate at high and low pH values, and could not, presumably, account for the pH effect on nitrate. However, de Boer (1940) found no evidence of nitrate accumulation by *A. niger*, indicating strain or cultural differences.

Boas (1919a) affirmed that dissociation was a critical factor in assimilability of a nitrogen source and that the most highly dissociated substances would be assimilated before less dissociated ones. In view of the fact that dissociation may be critically influenced by pH, this concept is pertinent to the one under discussion.

The amphoteric nature of the cell colloids has been established by dye uptake. The isoelectric point of fungus intracellular colloids was thus first determined by Robbins (1924) to be pH 5.0 for *Rhizopus nigricans* and 5.5 for *Fusarium lycopersici*. Bünning (1936) also used dyestuff assimilation in *A. niger* as a guide to nitrate absorption especially as a function of pH. Below pH 3, anion dyes and also nitrate were assimilated and stored, while cation dyes were taken up and stored above pH 3. The anion dyes diffused out when placed in solutions at higher pH values.

The charge on amphoteric colloids inside the cells is subject to alteration according to the external pH of the medium. Thus the higher the hydrogen ion concentration (lower pH) in the medium, the more hydrogen ion in the cell contents. This situation is analogous to metallic ion absorption as a function of concentration described in Chapter 3. By means of pH indicators Bünning reported these relationships between external and internal pH of *A. niger:*

pH of Medium (External)	Mycelium pH (Internal)
>8.0	7.0–7.5
6.5–7.0	5.0
2.5–3.0	4.4

Maddihassan (1930) found the internal pH of *Fusarium* cells to be 6.1. In the final analysis therefore, according to this theory, the absorption powers of the cell colloids depends on the pH of the latter, which in turn are controlled by the pH of the medium. When the colloids are at a pH above 4.4 no absorption of nitrate or anion dyes occurs. At low pH values (higher H^+ concentration) the amphoteric colloids acquire a positive charge and absorb anions (nitrate) while at higher pH values a negative charge is acquired and cations absorbed. This subject still needs considerable more experimental clarification.

Notwithstanding the attractiveness of the colloid absorption theory of explanation of the pH effect on nitrate assimilation, it would be premature to exclude selective permeability as a factor, and until more conclusive evidence is furnished the colloid theory cannot be accepted without objections. For example, the release of stored nitrate, the experiment Itzerott and Bünning place so much stress on as purporting to show that permeability is independent of pH, seemingly is a rather inconclusive one on which to build this theory. The amounts released were rather small, and took place in 8- to 12-day old cultures where autolysis or numerous other factors may have intervened. Incidently, a whole book devoted to the subject of nitrate assimilation by *Aspergillus repens* has been published (Desbordes, 1936). See also Regnier *et al.* (1946) on ammonia utilization.

MECHANISM OF NITRATE UTILIZATION

In view of the fact that NO_3-N eventually ends up as amino N in cell proteins, it must undergo reduction; the exact nature of events involved depends apparently on strains and cultural conditions. This problem is the same as that facing plant physiologists some years ago, as NO_3-N is the preferred nitrogen source for higher plants. Recognizing the same problem in the easily handled fungi, plant physiologists studied the phenomenon in *Aspergillus niger.* Kossowicz (1914) detected NH_3 formation when the organism was acting on NO_3^-, but this work has been criticized because of the failure to take into account the possibility of NH_3 formation by autolysis. Later work has established conclusively that nitrate is converted to ammonia and that the transformation probably, as expected, takes place via nitrite formation. Ritter (1916) obtained nitrite from nitrate so long as the medium remained alkaline, and in general any condition retarding the synthesis and utilization of amino acids intracellularly by the fungus, led to the accumulation of both NO_2^- and NH_3 from NO_3^- (Klein et al., 1926). Mentioned in particular were alkalinity and anaerobiosis. In the case of the latter the accentuated nitrate reduction results from the fact that NO_3 becomes the only hydrogen acceptor in the metabolism of this otherwise aerobic organism.

Ammonia accumulation also is critically influenced by the pH of the medium. At pH 1.6 to 2.6, surface pads of Aspergillus repens acting on $NaNO_3$ in a sugar-salts medium produced almost equivalent amounts of NH_3 from the NO_3 which disappeared, but the ammonia was not reutilized for growth and accumulated in the medium. At pH 4.4 and above the ammonia did not accumulate as it was assimilated and led to marked increase in weight of the fungus pad. This action was interpreted on the basis of diffusion of NH_3 but not the dissociated form, i.e., NH_4^+. Above pH 4.4 free NH_3 exists and can penetrate in to the cells. Below this pH the ammonia is trapped as dissociable NH_4Cl, hence, once excreted is not reutilized. This surely is peculiar to the strain of fungus used, as the great majority of Aspergilli readily utilize NH_3 from strong acid solution.

The intermediary formation of nitrite from nitrate was studied in detail by the celebrated Russian plant physiologist Kostytschew and Tswetkowa (1920). Washed surface pads of A. niger and Mucor racemosus accumulated nitrite in a nitrate solution only in the absence of carbohydrate. The presence of carbohydrate rapidly reduced nitrite to ammonia owing to the abundance of hydrogen available for the reduction by this organic donor. Added NO_2^- was also rapidly reduced to NH_3. Similar results were obtained with numerous species of Mucor (Hagem, 1910). Thus it is most likely that the following steps are involved in nitrate utilization:

$$NO_3^- \rightarrow NO_2^- \rightarrow NH_3 \rightarrow \text{Amino acids} \rightarrow \text{Protein}$$

The stage intermediate between NO_2 and NH_3 has been a matter of some question. Theoretically hydroxylamine (NH_2OH) would be expected to be an intermediate but tests for this substance as well as hydroxamic acid were always negative in the studies in Kostytschew and Tswetkowa. Lemoigne and coworkers showed that nitrite was detectable in NH_4NO_3 cultures only in the first few days, then it disappeared and hydroxylamine accumulated. Maximum concentration of NH_2OH attained was 1 mg./liter of culture. Unusually high concentrations of NH_4NO_3 favored the accumulation of NH_2OH, which disappeared in very old cultures. Hydroxylamine could also be demonstrated in cultures containing $NaNO_3$

as the sole N source and also with $(NH_4)_2SO_4$ as the sole N source. This means that hydroxylamine not only is formed by reduction of NO_3^- or NO_2^- but also by oxidation of ammonia. *A. niger* was found to grow well on NH_2OH as the sole source of N over the concentration range of 0.4–1.0 g/1.

Culture filtrates of *A. niger* rapidly reduced nitrite to hydroxylamine. This reduction was not enzymatic because it was not eliminated by boiling. The washed mycelium itself had only weak reducing powers, not unexpected in the absence of a hydrogen donor. Strong biological reducing chemicals, like glutathione, cysteine and ascorbic acid are known to reduce nitrite to hydroxylamine, and the filtrate doubtless contains such substances. Nitrites are utilizable as the sole N source by fungi and accumulate ammonia (Labrouse 1931; Sakaguchi and Chang, 1934) except when the medium is highly acid, in which case the HNO_2 is toxic, due perhaps to its rapid interaction with amino groups of cell proteins and amino acids (see Chapter 6). Lemoigne *et al.* (1935–1938) and Wirth and Nord (1943) postulate that amino acid synthesis in *A. niger* proceeds via reduction of the oximes of α-keto acids. This mechanism had been postulated by Virtanen to occur in nitrogen fixing bacteria, but recent evidence by the Wisconsin group using N^{15} makes this theory unlikely and favors direct participation of the completely reduced nitrogen molecule, namely NH_3 (Wilson and Burris, 1947). There was no other evidence for the occurrence of this reaction in fungi, the idea being only conjectural. Nevertheless Virtanen and Csáky (1948) have shown that *Torula utilis* generates oxime N from nitrate.

The fact that a hypothetical intermediate, in this case NH_2OH, can be used as a source of N by fungi does not in itself constitute proof that consumption of NO_3 procedes via NH_2OH, though the bulk of evidence favors it. Hydroxylamine is very unstable, and may not be used as such at all, growth being made instead at the expense of the spontaneous reaction products, which are about 50 per cent ammonia (Segal and Wilson, 1948).

The oxidation of ammonia to hydroxylamine by *A. niger* very likely may be taken as evidence for the existence of the reverse of this reaction, as biological reactions in general are reversible, given the appropriate conditions. From a chemical point of view, hydroxylamine must be intermediate between nitrite and ammonia. As seen above, considerable evidence for this in fungi already exists (see also Steinberg, 1939c), but its demonstration in other biological systems would strengthen the validity of the idea for fungi in their utilization of nitrates. Woods (1938) has provided favorable evidence by showing that the bacterium *Clostridium welchii* reduces each nitrate, nitrite, and hydroxylamine to ammonia with hydrogen gas. Another instance, this one bearing on the oxime conjecture of Lemoigne, stems from Quastel's (1947) studies on bacterial nitrification. For half a century hydroxylamine had been sought in vain as the logical intermediate in bacterial oxidation of NH_3 to NO_2^- but unsuccessfully because added hydroxylamine is so toxic for Nitrosomonas. If it is formed it is further converted to nitrite so quickly that it is not detectable. Quastel found that the hydroxylamine could be detoxified by furnishing it in the form of pyruvic oxime; the hydroxylamine then was rapidly nitrified, thereby rather definitely incriminating hydroxylamine as a biological intermediate between ammonia and nitrate, and vice versa. This subject is mentioned because it has a bearing on Lemoigne's oxime hypothesis, but the synthesis of amino acids in fungi via oximes has no experimental foundation, and from available evidence in all probability does not take place. Also, the fact that *A. niger* can oxidize ammonia to hydroxylamine does not of course mean that it is an autotroph because this does not comprise its sole source of energy, carbohydrates still being essential for growth. There are no autotrophic fungi known.

Steinberg (1937) has shown that when *A. niger* is furnished nitrate nitrogen as compared to other forms of nitrogen, it has a higher requirement for molybdenum and that omission of molybdenum from nitrate media led to sharp reduction in growth, but was without effect in ammonia or urea media. Considerable evidence was accumulated on the basis of his work as well as data from higher plants that molybdenum is required as an activator of nitrate reductase, in the sense of being a coenzyme. In reality then, nitrate assimilation depends upon molybdenum. This subject is discussed in detail in Chapter 7. Steinberg (1939a) in a review of fungus growth in synthetic media, cites the work of Hagem (1910) in which nitrate assimilation bore a relation to the type or carbon source. Several species of *Mucor* utilized either ammonia or nitrate with glucose, but only nitrate with glycerol. Two of the organisms, *M. spinosus* and *M. sphaerosporus*, required nitrate with mannitol as the carbon source. A dependency of kind of nitrogen assimilated on the carbon source has been reported for *Cladosporium herbarum* (Demmler, 1933) and for *A. niger* (Steinberg, 1939b) and may well be more generalized than hitherto recognized. Also Kossowicz (1912) found that *Cladospora herbarum* would not utilize glycine- nor hippuric acid N with cane sugar, and *Penicillium crustaceum*, *P. brevicaule* and *Aspergillus glaucus* did not use hippuric. All four used both, however, with dextrose or mannitol. Insufficient information is available to allow an interpretation of this curious response, although in some cases (not *A. niger*) growth factor impurities might account for these results. See pp. 495–496 for discussion.

Still another factor rather markedly affecting the utilization of inorganic N is the presence of organic acids in the medium, discovered by

Leonian and Lilly (1940) and confirmed by Burkholder and McVeigh (1940). Dealing mainly with *Phycomyces blakesleeana*, but also with other Mucorales, it was shown that ammonium nitrogen was utilized much more extensively if a small amount (0.1–0.2 per cent) of an organic acid such as fumaric, succinic, lactic, tartaric, etc., was present. A free carboxyl is apparently responsible, for aspartic acid behaved similarly, while asparagine did not. However, other neutral compounds were not tested. The synergistic effects of this type were rather striking, succinate for example causing a 1000 per cent increase in fungus growth on $(NH_4)_2$-SO_4, the succinate obviously not being necessary as a carbon source because an excess of carbohydrate was present. Succinate had no effect on aspartate utilization. Synergistic effects between different kinds of nitrogen were also noted; ammonia and aspartate have already been cited—both increase the growth over either alone. Synergism in growth effect was also noted with mixtures of amino acids, and the same holds true for peptone vs. individual amino acids in oxidation studies with certain fungi (Wolf and Shoup, 1943). Leonian and Lilly stress the importance of a "free" carboxyl group in "activating" the inorganic N source in inducing enhanced growth. Perhaps the effect is one of more rapid passage through the cell wall (i.e. permeability) but also to be considered is that the organic acids are rapidly absorbed and converted to certain metabolic intermediates, possibly α-keto acids, which then would permit a more rapid uptake and entrance of NH_3 into the metabolic stream. All the organic acids which showed the enhancing effect are intermediates in the tricarboxylic acid respiratory cycle or which could be readily converted to such. This means that pyruvate, oxalacetate, and α-ketoglutarate, all known pathways of entrance of NH_3 into cell synthesis, would be plentifully available. In view of the profound influence of pH on utilization of inorganic N discussed in the foregoing, this factor may have played a role in these results as the organic acids apparently were added as free acids.

Organic Nitrogen Sources

It is not the objective of this book to compile a review of all the different kinds of nitrogen sources utilizable by fungi for growth. Our purpose is to treat those aspects of nitrogen nutrition which have a bearing on the physiology of the organisms involved, or which deal with transformations the nitrogen compound undergoes through the agency of fungi.

Amino Acids and Related Substances

Virtually all fungi grow faster and probably more abundantly with complex organic materials as the nitrogen source than with simple inorganic nitrogen, and for this reason fungi are carried in stock on media such as peptone-glucose, malt-extract, etc. If carbohydrate is present, this can be interpreted on the basis of the fact that numerous biochemical molecules are assimilated and utilized intact, resulting in a great saving in energy and carbon that otherwise has to be expended in the synthesis of such compounds starting from inorganic nitrogen. Unfortunately there are not available direct experiments on this point, but one may offer as an analogy a case where *A. niger*, though able to synthesize its own biotin in glucose-mineral salts medium, nevertheless assimilates preformed biotin present in yeast or liver extracts (Foster and Allen, 1948) and a similar situation has been shown for *Trichophyton album* (Schopfer and Blumer, 1942). It seems not unreasonable to assume similar events take place with respect to at least some of the amino acids, and experiments of Robbins and Ma (1945) with *Trichophytan menta-grophytes* support this concept. This dermatophyte could use any one of fourteen amino acids as a nitrogen source, there being no evidence for any indispensable amino acids. Combinations were always better for growth, due doubtless to direct assimilation. Yet another possibility is created by the fact that a synthetic casein hydrolysate prepared from pure amino acids in the appropriate proportions was not as effective as the hydrolysate, suggestive of the presence of some non-amino acid growth accessory. Since twelve of the B vitamins were added to the basal medium, and trace elements were not limiting, another type of growth stimulator in casein hydrolysate was indicated. One is led to inquire as to the possibility of a peptide being the active factor in the hydrolysate. In the same way that amino acids may be assimilated directly into protein syntheses and thus enable the organism to develop more efficiently, so must consideration be given to the idea that peptides may function similarly, and be assimilated directly. Examples of physiologically active peptides are known: glutathione, strepogenin (Sprince and Woolley, 1944), and folic acid peptide derivatives, pteroyl di- and triglutamic acid are examples. The peptide strepogenin, a growth stimulant for hemolytic streptococci, is released during acid or enzymatic hydrolysis of proteins including casein, and is relatively acid resistant; and substances of this type might well be stimulating to fungus growth in an otherwise adequate medium, and may well permit one to interpret rationally results like those of Robbins and Ma.

Lycomarasmin is a tripeptide containing asparagine produced by *Fusarium lycopersici* and is the tomato wilting substance accounting for the pathogenicity of this organism (Plattner and Clausson-Kaas, 1945a and b). Lycomarasmin also inhibits the growth of *Lactobacillus casei*, and both tomato and bacterial toxicity are reversed by strepogenin

(Woolley, 1946).   The toxic effects of lycomarasmin can be reproduced by the synthetic peptide serylglycylaspartic acid and reversed by both strepogenin and serylglycylglutamic acid.   The latter tripeptide has strepogenin activity for *L. casei*.   The exact structure of strepogenin is not known at this time.   Lycomarasmin consists of asparagine, glycine and α-hydroxyalanine (Woolley, 1948).   The latter rare unstable compound also occurs in ergotamine, the alkaloid produced by the ergot fungus *Claviceps purpurea*.

$$\underset{\text{Lycomarasmin}}{\underset{\displaystyle \text{HOOC—CH—NH—CO—CH}_2\text{—NH—}}{\overset{\displaystyle \text{H}_2\text{NOC—CH}_2}{|}}} \quad \underset{\displaystyle \text{COOH}}{\overset{\displaystyle \text{CH}_3}{\underset{|}{\overset{|}{\text{C—OH}}}}}$$

In the absence of an extra source of carbon the picture of amino acid utilization is complicated by the breakdown of the nitrogenous constituents for carbon and energy also.   As indicated at the beginning of this chapter, fungi unable to utilize other sources (inorganic) of nitrogen are able to thrive on organic nitrogen, including complex mixtures such as extracts.   Examples have already been given in the form of *Apodachlya brachynema* and *Leptomites lacteus*.   *Basidiobolus ranarum* and *Saprolegnia parasitica* (Leonian and Lilly, 1938) and *Ophiobolus graminis* (Fellows, 1936) and *Trichophyton mentagrophytes* are further examples of fungi requiring organic nitrogen.   A point to observe here is that so far as is known, no fungus has a natural absolute requirement for a specific amino acid in the sense that it lacks the ability to synthesize this particular amino acid meanwhile synthesizing all the other cellular constituents.   Thus, amino acid utilizing fungi synthesize all their nitrogen constituents from the amino acid.   If a particular amino acid were an absolute requirement, the organism would require an extra nitrogen supply to synthesize the other cellular components.   There is no record of a requirement for amino acids similar to those among the lactic acid bacteria, for example.   Exceptions to this are of course those instances of artificial mutants where amino acid-less strains of fungi are obtained.

Much of the earlier work on the ability of an organism to utilize various forms of nitrogen nowadays must be re-examined in the light of accumulated knowledge of vitamins and other growth factors.   The inability of an organism to develop on a form of nitrogen in a synthetic medium does not necessarily mean that the particular nitrogen compound was not assimilable; it may rather mean that certain vitamins also essential for growth were lacking and that their need was unperceived in· "pre-vitamin" times.   For example, the parasitic fungus causing take-all of wheat, *Ophiobolus graminis*, utilized only casein, albumin, peptone, and nucleic acid as sources of N and none other of forty-three other pure nitrogen compounds, organic and inorganic (Fellows, 1936). This indeed is strange considering that some of the pure substances tested were constituents of these complex N sources. We know today that these complex materials contain all kinds of growth factors, and the pure compounds most likely none. Further work showed that the usual mineral-dextrose synthetic medium containing nitrate was satisfactory if small amounts of concentrates containing growth factors were added (Padwick, 1936), and then it was discovered that only biotin and thiamine were essential to secure good growth of the parasite on the synthetic media with simple nitrogen sources (White, 1941). It is evident that there is much to be on guard against in interpreting nitrogen utilization studies. As indicated above, it may be that a good deal of the work on nitrogen nutrition on fungi done before 1935, especially with relation to pure compounds in synthetic media, will have to be scrutinized carefully to insure the reliability of the results in the light of modern nutrition concepts.

Steinberg's careful studies (1942a) on the amino acid nutrition of *A. niger* are highly instructive on the subject. Table 1 shows the amount of growth made on the respective amino acids as the sole source of nitrogen. In each case 50 ml. 5 per cent sucrose-salts medium was used (the nitrogen level was 665 mg. N per liter), each test lasting 4 days.

TABLE 1

AMINO ACIDS AS N SOURCES FOR A. NIGER[1]

	Mg.		Mg.
dl-α-Alanine	1156	*dl*-Norleucine	114
d-Arginine	1252	*dl*-Phenylalanine	371
l-Aspartic acid	1325	*l*-Proline	1111
l-Cystine	71	*dl*-Serine	609
d-Glutamic acid	1293	*dl*-Threonine	647
Glycine	1235	*l*-Tryptophane	636
l-Histidine	121	*l*-Tyrosine	196
l-Hydroxy proline	1147	*dl*-Valine	292
l-Iodogorgic acid	0	Cysteine	12
dl-Isoleucine	246	α-Amino-*n*-butyric	605
l-Leucine	374	Ornithine	1017
d-Lysine	16	β-Alanine	19
dl-Methionine	437	Lanthionine	92
		Cystine (optically inactive)	99

[1] From Steinberg (1942a). Figures represent dry mycelial weight.

It is evident that the short-chain amino acids as a group are superior sources of nitrogen, though the heterocyclic proline and hydroxyproline are almost as good.   Special note may be made of the fact that the sulfur-containing amino acids are poor nitrogen sources.   Certain amino acids, in particular cysteine, were inhibitory to growth even in the presence of NH_4NO_3, and also inhibited the utilization of other amino acids when present in the same medium.   When glycerol was used as a source of carbon instead of sucrose, the response pattern of the individual amino acids was quite different.   Only ten of thirty-one amino acids were utilizable as sources of carbon for this fungus, most of the ten giving negligible growth.   The best carbon sources were l-proline, d-glutamic acid and l-aspartic acid, which gave one-quarter to one-fifth the amount of growth per gram of carbon available as did a sucrose control.   Hydroxy-proline was only one-sixth as good as proline.   However, these values merely indicated relative rates of utilization rather than absolute utiliza-bility, as the experiments were stopped in 4 days.   It is quite likely more growth would have occurred in these amino acids with longer incubation. Nevertheless, it is of particular interest that alanine, cystine, glycine, histidine, isoleucine, leucine, lysine, methionine, norleucine, phenylalaine, serine, threonine, tryptophane, tyrosine, valine, and asparagine could not be utilized at all as a carbon source or only negligibly so.   The picture was about the same when the amino acids were used as both carbon and nitrogen sources.   In mixtures, a synergistic effect on carbon utilization was observed.   Thus proline, glutamic acid and ornithine in admixture was four-fold better for carbon utilization than proline alone, the best single one.

Steinberg observed that the assimilability of the α- amino monocar-boxylic acids by $A.$ $niger$ decreased as the length of the carbon chain increased (Table 2).

TABLE 2

ASSIMILABILITY AND LENGTH OF CARBON CHAIN

	Yield on N Source, Mg. Dry Wt.
Glycine, 2C	1,235
Alanine, 3C	1,116
α-Amino-n-butyric, 4C	605
α-Amino-n-valeric, 5C	81
Norleucine, 6C	114

Steinberg considers proline, glutamic acid, and ornithine as "primary" amino acids for $A.$ $niger$, that is, the first-formed amino acids in cell synthesis.   From these, other primary amino acids, alanine, arginine, aspartic acid, glycine, and glutamic are synthesized; and the other amino acids, the "derived" amino acids, are those synthesized from the "pri-mary" ones.   Comparative biochemistry makes it necessary, however, to consider aspartic and glutamic acids as "primary" amino acids until shown otherwise in a decisive fashion.

In fungi one finds than any one of a number of different amino acids or related compounds permit satisfactory growth in the presence of glucose. We have here, then, a situation where the amino acid is used as a source of nitrogen for the synthesis of all the nitrogenous cellular constituents rather than a direct incorporation of the amino acid into the protein architecture. Modern concepts of amino acid synthesis make it almost mandatory to postulate that in fungi the amino acid synthesis proceeds via utilization of ammonia and some α-keto acids, so that one can only interpret the utilization of organic nitrogenous substances by a fungus as a means of obtaining ammonia for cell synthesis. In cases where nitrate or both nitrate and ammonia cannot be utilized, and yet the organic N eventually is converted into ammonia for resynthesis by the organism, one can only assume that the inorganic N is not accessible to the cells whereas organic N is. A definite conclusion is not possible at this time, but probably permeability plays some role here: Organic N compounds are permeable, are attacked and the NH_3 utilized intracellularly. Inorganic NH_3 probably never reaches the interior of the cells.

Demonstration of ammonia formation from amino acids or related compounds is in most cases an easy matter when the test is conducted in the absence or with small amounts of an extraneous carbon source. Not enough carbon is available for the fungus to combine with the NH_3 to synthesize cell proteins, etc. As a result the NH_3 accumulates and can easily be detected in the medium.

In view of the widespread occurrence of vitamin deficiencies in fungi, it would be most surprising indeed were there not many naturally-occurring amino acid-deficient fungi. Considering the prominent occurrence of amino acid-less bacteria, as well as the fact that amino acid-less fungi can be obtained as artificially induced mutants, one may safely predict that amino acid-deficient fungi will eventually be reported after a search for them has been made.

The extensive trials of Leonian and Lilly (1938) on amino acid utilization are pertinent here. Twenty-five species of thiamine-requiring fungi were tested for their response to various amino acids. Other things being equal, *Coprinus lagopus, Nyctalis asterophora, Pilaira moreaui,* and *Pluerotus corticatus* grew well when an amino acid mixture was present but did not grow on NH_4NO_3 as a nitrogen source. Ten of the twenty-five required factors other than amino acids and thiamine, probably vitamins in view of the small amount of added yeast extract which would support their growth. Some indication of an absolute requirement for an amino acid, but still not proved unequivocally, was demonstrated for *l*-cystine in the case of four species: *Saprolegnia mixta, Achlya conspicus, Isoachlia monilifera,* and *Aphanomyces camptastylus.* These organisms failed to grow in a basal synthetic medium containing thiamine and an amino acid mixture, until *l*-cystine was added. It may be that these organisms prefer an organic source of sulfur to the sulfate present in the medium, for they may not be able to reduce sulfate. As will be seen later, some organisms of the water mold group to which the above belong behave like that (see Hockenhull, 1948). Another species, *Saprolegnia parasitica* grew only if either *l*-cystine or *dl*-leucine were present. A related species of water-mold, *Blastocladia pringsheimia* fails to grow when three-quarters of the amino acids in peptone or casein are furnished in pure form (Cantino, 1948) which suggests unidentified growth factors other than amino acids, though possibly this indicates a specific amino acid requirement. Fourteen other organisms could use any one of a number of amino acids for growth, from which it may be concluded these amino acids are not required *per se,* but, in conformation to the above ideas, function merely as available sources of nitrogen. Other non-specific amino acid effects have been reported for *Trichophyton interdigitale* (Mosher *et al.,* 1936), for *Phycomyces blakesleeanus* (Leonian and Lilly, 1940; Schopfer, 1935), and for *Allomyces arbuscula, A. javanicus, A. moniliformis* and *A. cystogenus* (Wolf and Shoup, 1943). In general these works show that some amino acids are more useful than others, but no overall relationship between the various organisms and amino acids is evident. It may be pointed out that certain amino acids are known to have specific stimulating effects on penicillin production by *Penicillium chrysogenum* (see Chapter 19). Two other extensive studies (Tamiya and Usami, 1940; Steinberg, 1942a) are informative on the subject of amino acid utilization. The Japanese showed the following relative degrees of usefulness of individual amino acids for *Aspergillus oryzae;* in this case the compounds were used both as N and C sources, the results being therefore not exactly comparable to the foregoing discussion: isoleucine > alanine, leucine > glutamic acid > arginine > phenylalanine, histidine, tryptophane, valine, proline > glycine, serine, asparagine > lysine. Now, when respiration with preformed mycelium was taken as the index of utilizability, quite a different order was obtained: alanine > isoleucine; phenylalanine, tryptophane > leucine, serine, valine > proline, histidine, glycine > arginine, glutamic acid > asparagine > lysine.

This type of discrepancy between oxidation studies and growth studies on the same compounds has been observed also for carbon compounds with *A. oryzae* (Tamiya, 1932), also in the case of acetate and NH_3 utilization by *Leptomitis lacteus* (see next section) and probably, when tested sufficiently, will be found to be more of a general phenomenon than now realized.   Why should a compound which is rapidly oxidized be less efficient for growth than a slowly oxidized substance?   Possibly the answer lies in the fact that a competition exists for intermediary breakdown products between oxidation enzymes and assimilation enzymes, substrates generating intermediates especially amenable to the oxidative system of the organism being utilized mainly through this system; the compound ends up mainly as CO_2 and H_2O (and NH_3).   In a sense, potential cell building material is shunted away from assimilatory channels, particularly under resting cell conditions when accessory nutrients are lacking, resulting in depressed or less efficient growth. Another conception and perhaps an even more substantial one is that the primary breakdown products of the substrate are molecules of a type not efficiently utilizable in the synthetic or assimilatory reactions of the cell.   A great deal of intermediary "reshaping" of the compound might be necessary in order to generate an appropriate building block, the substance being subject to oxidative attack all the time due to the slowness or difficulty of the reshaping process.   On the other hand, a compound not oxidized rapidly allows more opportunity for the assimilatory mechanisms to utilize the intermediates.   It is possible to visualize certain oxidation reactions taking place which would not permit growth owing to the unsuitability of the product of the oxidation for assimilation or growth.   Thus, hydroquinone might easily be oxidized by a fungus to quinone

Hydroquinone   Quinone

the latter not being further attacked at all.   In general homo- or heterocyclic ring compounds with side chains function in this manner during biological attack.   The ring lends a stability to the chain so that the alterations are relatively slight.   Prominent in this type of behavior are the amino acids histidine, tryptophane, and tyrosine (see later), though the idea probably extends to other ring compounds.   Up until recent years the idea had been prevalent that the primary value of a compound for growth of an organism is the energy it obtains during the dissimilation.   Conclusions stemming from studies on oxidative assimilation in bacteria (Giesberger, 1936; Van Niel, 1940; Clifton, 1946) have been the grounds for a shift to the idea that generation of raw materials or suitable building blocks is more important, those building blocks entering spontaneously into the assimilation scheme and utilizing only a small amount of the available energy for these syntheses. The great bulk of energy is lost during progressive shaping or "chipping off" of the substrate to fashion the building block, most of these reactions being oxidative, i.e., exothermic. Thus the amount of assimilation that could occur for any compound is a direct function of the maximum amount of building blocks which could be produced from a given substrate and utilized by the particular enzyme makeup of the organism; this is in contrast to the amount of energy the organism is capable of liberating and utilizing from that substrate.

Steinberg (1942a) correlated utilizability of amino acids by *A. niger* with molecular structure. Alanine, arginine, aspartate, glutamate, glycine, hydroxyproline, ornithine, and proline all were equally as good N sources as inorganic N (NH_4NO_3), whereas the N of serine, threonine, and tryptophane was only 50 per cent utilized. All the sulfur-containing amino acids were very poor N sources, cysteine even being inhibitory. The only amino acids which were efficiently utilized as carbon sources were proline, aspartate, and ornithine. It is evident that the particular species, and doubtless even strain specificity, determines what particular amino acids are useful as N or C sources.

Incidentally, the inhibitory effect of cysteine on *A. niger* recalls the inhibitory action of hydroxyproline, threonine, and methionine on *Trichophyton mentagrophytes* (Robbins and Ma, 1945) and also on *T. gypseum, T. purpureum, Epidermophyton floccosum,* and *Microsporium canis* (Robbins and McVeigh, 1946). Some inhibition was evident at 1:20,000 concentration of *l*-hydroxyproline, and growth was virtually prevented at 1:800. Other examples are known. The hydroxyproline inhibition evidently is of the competitive type, with proline, for addition of as little as 0.001 mg. *l*-proline already gave a detectable beneficial effect in the presence of 1 mg. hydroxyproline. The mechanisms of amino acid inhibition in fungi are unknown, but to judge from comparable effects in bacterial metabolism where amino acid inhibitions manifest themselves as media became simplified and synthetic, we may in general say a large excess of a particular amino acid may competitively block the function of others in the metabolism of the organism. Thus these inhibitions are relieved in complex media where the blocked amino acid is present in amounts sufficient to compete effectively with the "blocker" in metabolism, i.e., neutralizes the inhibitor.

Steinberg showed that utilization of an amino acid as an N source depended on the presence of an α-amino group and of α-, β-, and carboxyl hydrogen. A substitution in the molecule for α-, β-, or carboxyl H, or a reduction of the carboxyl group, or a shift of —NH$_2$ from the α- to the β- carbon atom reduced or eliminated assimilability of the nitrogen of that compound.

ASPARTIC ACID, BIOTIN AND CO$_2$

One of the functions of biotin is as a coenzyme in the fixation of CO$_2$ in living systems via the Wood-Werkman reaction:

$$CO_2 + CH_3COCOOH \underset{\text{Oxalacetic decarboxylase}}{\overset{\text{Biotin }+}{\rightleftharpoons}} HOOCCH_2COCOOH$$

Pyruvic acid   Oxalacetic acid

A considerable portion of the oxalacetic acid so produced is aminated to yield aspartic acid which is utilized for protein synthesis.

$$HOOCCH_2COCOOH + NH_3 \xrightarrow[-O]{+NH_3} HOOCCH_2CHNH_2COOH$$

Aspartic acid

Biotin is required by *Torula cremoris* for growth, and aspartic acid has a biotin-sparing effect, i.e., less biotin is required when aspartic acid is furnished in the medium. This (Koser *et al.*, 1942) means that this amino acid is a product of biotin metabolism. This was the first observation which led to clarification of the mechanism of biotin action via CO$_2$ fixation to yield the precursor of aspartic acid. Other functions of biotin also are known.

OXIDATION OF AMINO ACIDS

Studies of this type on fungi have been scanty compared to what has been done on bacteria. Using manometric methods Wolf and Shoup (1943) compared four different species of the water mold Allomyces for utilization of peptone and various pure amino acids, as indicated by oxygen consumption. Species differences were observed, *A. arbuscula* for example, being able to oxidize more amino acids than any of the others, glycine and tyrosine being the only ones unattacked out of nine tested. Aspartic and glutamic acids were the only ones utilized by all four, a fact possibly bearing on the key role of these two amino acids in the transamination and protein synthesis. A suggestion was made that the greater versatility of *A. arbuscula* in utilizing food stuffs might be correlated with the predominance of this species in nature as compared with other forms of Allomyces, an intriguing possibility. This organism also utilizes more carbon sources than the others.

Of special interest in the inability of the other three species to attack the amide of aspartic acid, asparagine. Asparagine in general is one of the most readily utilizable nitrogen sources for fungi and is commonly employed for this purpose. As a matter of fact, Leonian and Lilly (1940) point out that aspartic is an even better source of N than asparagine for numerous Phycomycetes and that in view of the fact that synthetic aspartate is available, while asparagine in natural, use of the former in nutrition studies eliminates disadvantages intrinsic to the latter, which always is contaminated with vitamins.

Penicillium notatum Q176, the strain employed in commercial production of penicillin, was found to oxidize twenty-two different amino acids at different rates, alanine, glutamic acid, and proline being the most rapidly utilized (Wolf, 1948). $L(-)$ Cystine was not attacked at all, and, indeed, was inhibitory to endogenous respiration in the concentration used (0.01 M). $L(+)$ Cysteine was slowly attacked, and it may be that the organism is unable to split the disulfide linkage of the cysteine. These sulfur-containing amino acids are believed by some workers to stimulate penicillin production in a synthetic medium. It will be noted that a fission product of the ring structure of penicillin, penicillamine, is $d,-\beta,\beta$-dimethyl cysteine. Wolf ascribes a special significance of proline and glutamic acid in the nutrition of penicillin-producing fungi because they are oxidized at the highest rate by Q176 and were found (Halpern *et al.*, 1945) to promote penicillin formation by *P. chrysogenum* 832. This relation would seem to be rather nebulous in view of the fact that most fungi, including non-penicillin producing Penicillia, doubtless would attack these amino acids, secondly, inferences from strain to strain are hazardous; and third, because the weight of penicillin formed is so small in comparison to the turnover of amino acids, such a small part of any amino acid precursor would be converted to penicillin that a high rate of utilization would not be indicative of conversion to penicillin, as even the slowly oxidized amino acids could suffice to furnish the required amount of precursor.

The manometric studies of Schade and Thimann (1940) on amino acid oxidation by *Leptomitus lacteus* is one of the most instructive on this subject. *dl*-Alanine is oxidized with an R.Q. of 1.0 and $Q_{O_2} = 21$. The NH_3 liberated per O_2 consumed $= 0.343$, data consistent with the breakdown of this amino acid with the following balance; $CH_3CHNH_2COOH + 3O_2 \rightarrow 3CO_2 + 2H_2O + NH_3$. The substance is therefore deaminated and oxidized completely. Leucine behaves curiously: in the first place only the *l*-isomer is attacked, the *d*-, and norleucine being immune. Though all the leucine is consumed, it is not oxidized completely in the manner of alanine. In fact only 10 per cent of the theoretical oxygen uptake expected for complete oxidation was obtained. The R.Q. $= 0.64$, theory $= 0.80$. $NH_3/O_2 = 0.084$, theory $= .133$. The observed value is decidedly lower than the ratio obtained in buffer alone without leucine, 0.138. Evidently the ammonia which would have been excreted has been reabsorbed or assimilated, for there is less ammonia present than in controls. All the data conform to an oxidation of leucine to a product of the same composition of alanine which is then assimilated as cell material or which is synthesized from products of leucine. The assimilated material would have the same state of oxidation as carbohydrate (i.e., CH_2O) and in this sense is analogous to assimilation products of carbon compounds in general. The utilization of leucine is represented as

$$C_4H_9CHNH_2COOH + 4\tfrac{1}{2} O_2 \rightarrow (C_3H_2NO_2) + 3H_2O + 3CO_2$$
$$\text{l-Leucine} \qquad\qquad \text{Assimilated}$$
$$\text{product}$$

Theoretical R.Q. = 0.67, found, 0.64.

This is oxidative assimilation in much the same sense as applied to carbon compounds (see Chapter 4). This might also be interpreted as growth since N is available and minor elements are available intracellularly, except for the fact the nitrogen of alanine is not assimilated in the same manner. Thus, a portion of leucine is assimilated because its breakdown generates the appropriate building blocks adaptable to incorporation into the cell assimilation, whereas this is not the case with alanine. (See discussion in previous section.)

An interesting discrepancy between growth and assimilation was uncovered in this work. *L. lacteus* cannot utilize NH_3 for growth with acetate or any other source of carbon, but can utilize glycine as a source of N under these conditions. However, under resting cell conditions in buffer in which acetate is being oxidized, added NH_3 as NH_4Cl is consumed, i.e., assimilated. Similarly, in the case of amino acids being oxidized and which yield ammonia, viz., alanine and glycine, this ammonia is reassimilated if an extra oxidizable carbon source is present. Thus we have the paradoxical state where ammonia can be utilized by the organism under oxidative assimilation conditions but not under the usual growth conditions. Impermeability is not the reason why ammonia is not used under growth conditions because the cell is permeable to ammonia as evidenced by the fact that when it grows on amino acids, NH_3 passes out of the cells. This is, then, an instance where ammonia utilization is linked directly to assimilation as a process distinct from growth, for the utilization occurs only when a carbon source is undergoing a true oxidative assimilation, and parallel with that. Presumably the final assimilated nitrogenous material is similar if not identical with that from leucine.

ENZYMATIC STUDIES ON AMINO ACID UTILIZATION

1. *l*-AMINO ACID OXIDASE

This enzyme attacks the natural (*l*-configuration) amino acids according to the general equation

$$RCHNH_2COOH + \tfrac{1}{2}O_2 \rightarrow RCOCOOH + NH_3.$$

This enzyme has been well studied through the years in animal tissues and in bacteria, but only lately has it been demonstrated in fungi. Knight (1948) examined several different penicillin-producing fungi, among others, as the following list shows; and active enzyme was obtained from all: *Penicillium notatum* 832 and 172, *P. chrysogenum* 1951-B25, X1612, and Q176, *P. expansum*, *P. sanguineum*, *Aspergillus niger*. The theoretical balance between O_2 uptake and NH_3 formed was established, thus conforming to the equation given above. Mycelium obtained on shakers gave erratic enzyme activity when used as such, and the following procedure was found to give dry preparations which retained the amino acid oxidase activity at least 10 days. Water-washed mycelium is stirred quickly into acetone at $-20°C$. in dry ice-acetone bath and stirred for 3 minutes, then washed once with acetone at $9°C$. and dried in a vacuum desiccator at room temperature. After grinding to a fine powder, the material is stored at $4°C$. The enzyme attacked fourteen *l*-amino acids in the relative order of speed as given in Table 3, which for comparison shows the relative rates of attack of *d*-amino acids by *d*-amino acid oxidase prepared from Neurospora by Horowitz (1944) and discussed below.

TABLE 3

l- AND *d*-AMINO ACID OXIDASES IN FUNGI (*l*-Amino acid oxidase)[1]

Each value is for 50 mg. powdered acetone mycelium of *P. chrysogenum* 1951–B25.
Relative rates are referred to *l*-alanine which in 80 minutes showed 58 cmm. O_2 uptake.

Substrate	Relative Rate
l-Alanine	100
l-Methionine	92
dl-Methionine	86
dl-Alanine	85
dl-α-Amino-*n*-butyric acid	79
dl-α-Amino-*n*-valeric acid	64
dl-α-Amino-*n*-capric acid	48
dl-Valine	28
l-Cystine	17
l-Glutamic	16
l-Aspartic	12
l-Proline	12
l-Leucine	7
l-Tryptophane	7
Glycine	5
l-Phenylalanine	4

Relative rate of oxidation of amino acids by *d*-amino acid oxidase of Neurospora.[2] Mean rate of oxidation of *dl*-methionine = 107 mm.[3] O_2 per hour per gram wet mold. All amino acids were tested in a final concentration of $3.03 \times 10^{-3}\ M$ in terms of one optical isomer.

[1] From Knight (1948).
[2] From Horowitz (1944).

TABLE 3.—(*Continued*)

Substrate	Relative Rate
dl-Methionine	100
dl-Phenylalanine	85
Norvaline	85
Citrulline	81
Arginine	80
α-Amino-*n*-butyric	74
Leucine	66
Norleucine	52
Glutamic	41
Isoleucine	38
d(−) Alanine	33
dl-Aspartic	29
Alanine	26
Valine	26
α-Amino-*n*-caprylic	22
Lysine	14
dl-N-Methylleucine	13
dl-α-Aminophenylacetic	About 9
dl-Tryptophane	About 5
dl-Ornithine	About 4
Serine	0
Threonine	0
Proline	0
β-Alanine	0
dl-β-Amino-*n*-butyric	0
dl-α-Amino-*n*-methylbutyric	0
dl-α-Amino-*n*-ethylbutyric	0
dl-β,β-Dimethyl-α-amino-*n*-butyric	0
dl-N,N-Dimethylleucine	0
dl-Leucylglycine	0
Glycine	0

The difference in specificities of *l*- and *d*-amino acid oxidase from fungi is evident by the absence of any regular sequence in rate of attack of the different amino acids which were used in both experiments. The alanine is attacked fastest of all the amino acids by *l*-amino acid oxidase, yet the *d*-isomer of this amino acid is far down the list with the *d*-amino acid oxidase. Other disparities are conspicuous, though methionine is high in both cases. Addition of the *d*-isomer inhibited *l*-amino acid oxidase activity on the corresponding *l*-isomer, presumably via competitive inhibition. Various poisons also inhibited the enzyme at suitable concentrations: ammonium sulfate, copper sulfate, 2,4-dinitrophenol, capryl alcohol, benzoic acid, and iodoacetic acid.

The composition of the cultivation medium with respect to N source had no significant effect on *l*-amino acid content of the mycelium so long as the N source was organic. However, the presence of $(NH_4)_2SO_4$, either as the sole N source or in addition to organic N (corn steep liquor), resulted in a decisive lowering of mycelial enzyme activity to one-tenth to one-fifth of the normal. This may be indicative of the need of some sort of adaptation by exposure to amino acids during the growth period in order for the organism to develop the enzyme to its most powerful extent. *l*-Amino acid oxidase worked, though sluggishly, under anaerobic conditions using methylene blue as a hydrogen acceptor. The enzyme has been prepared in cell-free form from *P. chrysogenum* Q176. In a manner similar to Wolf (1948), Knight observed that the highest penicillin-producing strains of *Penicillium* had higher *l*-amino acid oxidase activity, but any further attempt to ally the two properties is very premature, considering the limited data available. Incidentally, *l*-amino acid oxidase activity in *Neurospora crassa* could not be demonstrated by the acetone method. Horowitz (1944) also showed that acetone destroys *d*-amino acid oxidase in *Neurospora*.

As stressed in the forgoing sections, when fungi utilize one or more amino acids as a source of N, deamination and liberation of the N as NH_3 for intracellular synthesis of amino acid or proteins takes place. *l*-Amino acid oxidase is doubtless the enzyme at work in this regard when the natural amino acids are involved.

2. *d*-AMINO ACID OXIDASE

Horowitz (1944) made the interesting observation that the artificial mutants of *Neurospora crassa*, methionineless, leucineless and arginineless strains respectively, could utilize racemic mixtures (*dl*) of the respective amino acids as absolute amino acid requirements for growth with the same efficiency that the naturally-occurring or *l*-forms were used. Because the methionineless and leucineless mutants also were able to utilize the corresponding α-keto acid analogues, a conversion of the *d*-amino acid into the *l*-form which exists in the mold protein exclusively, was considered probable by oxidative deamination of the former to the α-keto acid, followed by resynthesis of the *l*-isomer. The presence in Neurospora of a strong *d*-amino acid oxidase forming the corresponding α-keto acid was demonstrated. One atom of oxygen was required for deamination of a mole of *d*-amino acid. In the case of *d*-methionine, the formation of the corresponding α-keto-γ-methiolbutyric acid was established. The enzyme is obtainable as a water solution prepared as a supernatant after centrifuging the paste obtained by grinding mycelium in a mortar with sand. This preparation was free from *l*-amino acid oxidase activity. An apparent identity with *d*-amino acid oxidase of kidney is indicated by the fact the methionine is the most readily attacked of all the *d*-amino acids. The relative rates of attack are shown in Table 3. *P. chrysogenum* Q176 *d*-oxidase is similar (Emerson *et al.*, 1949).

Certain amino acids are not oxidized by the enzyme (see Table 3) and one, *dl*-isovaline (α-amino-α-methyl butyric acid) actually inhibits *d*-methionine oxidation competitively, as indicated by its dependence on the concentration of methionine. The failure to oxidize isovaline probably is due to the fact that it is impossible for this compound to form the imino structure which is intermediate in the deamination process. The overall deamination reaction is identical with that for *l*-amino acid oxidase given above. However, deamination is actually a two-step process, the first step an oxidation (dehydrogenation) yielding the imino compound; the second step is an exchange reaction between the imino group and the oxygen of water. Both *d*- and *l*-amino acid oxidases are enzymes having isoalloxazine (riboflavin)-adenine-dinucleotide as a coenzyme, and hydrogen peroxide is the product of the action. Since catalase is always present, this latter is immediately split to H_2O and O, so that the overall reaction actually is that given earlier (p. 504).

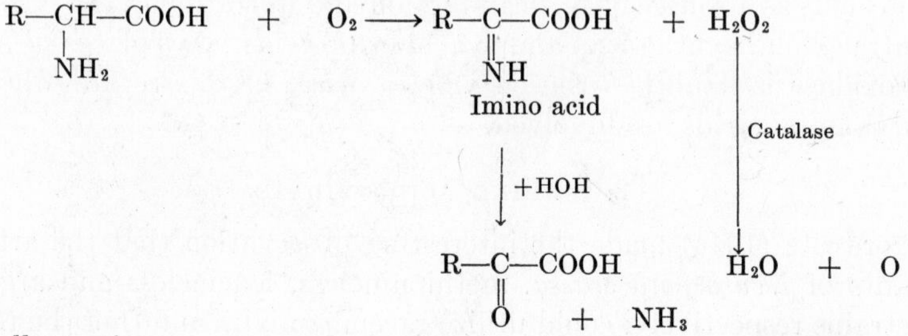

$$R-\underset{\underset{NH_2}{|}}{CH}-COOH \ + \ O_2 \longrightarrow R-\underset{\underset{NH}{||}}{C}-COOH \ + \ H_2O_2$$

Imino acid

Catalase

$+HOH$

$$R-\underset{\underset{O}{||}}{C}-COOH \qquad H_2O \ + \ O$$
$$+ \ NH_3$$

Overall reaction:

$$R-\underset{\underset{NH_2}{|}}{CH}-COOH \ + \ O \longrightarrow R-\underset{\underset{O}{||}}{C}-COOH \ + \ NH_3$$

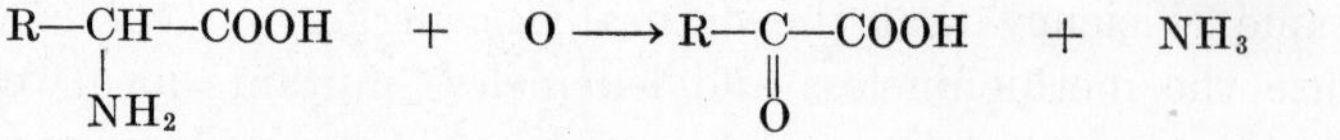

The activity of the mold *d*-amino acid oxidase is markedly dependent on the chain length in the homologous series of straight chain, mono-aminomonocarboxylic acids (Table 4).

TABLE 4

CHAIN LENGTH AND NEUROSPORA *d*-AMINO ACID OXIDASE ATTACK[1]

Amino Acid and No. of Carbons	O_2 Uptake per 15 Min., mm.[3]
dl-Alanine, 3	9.4
dl-α-Amino-*n*-butyric, 4	17.2
dl-Norvaline, 5	21.4
dl-Norleucine, 6	16.9
dl-α-Amino-*n*-caprylic, 7	6.2

[1] From Horowitz (1944).

Maximum activity is on a 5-carbon chain, dropping off rapidly on either side of that number. It is difficult to accept the presence of an enzyme like d-amino acid oxidase in an organism without assuming a function for the enzyme in the survival or metabolism of the organism. In this case difficulty arose owing to the fact that the d-amino acids are not known to play a part in Neurospora metabolism. The mold might encounter racemic amino acid mixtures in nature, or it may produce them in case of attack and utilization of proteins; in either case, the d-oxidase would have functional value, but not an indispensable role, for the wild type synthesizes all its amino acids from glucose and inorganic N. According to Horowitz, if the enzyme serves a useful purpose at all, it will be in connection with products of the mold's own metabolism, that is, assymetric synthesis of amino acids. In the amino acid deficiency mutants, the function is clear, as described above.

Products of Amino Acid Breakdown

This subject has been studied far less extensively with fungi than with bacteria, but enough data is available to indicate a parallelism in the action on amino acids by these two groups of organisms.

1. Deamination with formation of α-keto- and α-hydroxy acids

Wirth and Nord (1943) cultivated *Fusarium lini* on 2 per cent dl-alanine-salts medium and after 16 days isolated 80 mg. pyruvic acid which had accumulated in the medium as the 2,4-dinitrophenylhydrazone. It will be recalled (Chapter 9) this organism displays a natural deficiency of cocarboxylase which prevents it from utilizing pyruvate formed during carbohydrate utilization. In this case 1.63 g. alanine had disappeared (i.e., both d- and l-forms used) and 176 mg. dry mycelial weight formed. Hydrogen peroxide was detected only in traces, and it is rapidly decomposed by the catalase these organisms contain (Hayasida, 1938).

The facts were interpreted according to the general reactions given above for the d- and l-amino acid oxidases, both of which ostensibly are at play here.

$$CH_3CH(NH_2)COOH + O_2 \longrightarrow CH_3CHCOOH + H_2O_2$$

dl-Alanine

$$CH_3COCOOH + NH_3$$
Pyruvic acid

The H_2O_2 detected could have of course arisen via other reactions (for example, glucose oxidase), and the authors point out the possibility of the hydrolytic deamination of the alanine instead of oxidative deamination, yielding lactic acid, which then could be dehydrogenated to pyruvate. The matter was not settled except to show the formation of a keto acid (unidentified) and H_2O_2 when lactate was furnished as the sole carbon source.

An interesting case is described by Otani and Ichibara (1925) in which both optical forms of alanine (d,l-) are converted to lactic acid by *Oospora lactis* but in each case only (d-) (or +) lactic acid was produced. On the other hand there exists the type of isomer specificity in which yeast utilizes only the (+) form of alanine, leaving behind the (−) form (Ehrlich, 1906). The conversion of both optical forms to products of one optical form, and a likely mechanism has been discussed under *l*-amino acid oxidase and is treated further under phenylalanine below.

Aspergillus oryzae cultivated on synthetic media with the individual amino acids as the sole source of nitrogen converts (Uemura, 1937, 1939) the amino acids into the corresponding α-keto acids. Those involved and the products isolated were *l*-leucine ⟶-α-ketoisocaproic acid, *l*-glutamic acid ⟶ α-ketoglutaric acid, *l*-tyrosine ⟶ *p*-hydroxyphenylpyruvic acid, *l*-phenylalanine ⟶ phenylpyruvic acid. Thirty different strains of *A. oryzae* all carried out the last transformation. The conversions all conform to the generalized equation for oxidative deamination of amino acids as given earlier. Also obtained from the leucine filtrate was leucinic acid, the α-hydroxy analogue of the amino acid. Similarly, tyramine, acetaldehyde, and succinic acid were obtained from the tyrosine cultures.

The above deamination reactions in the overall form are:

$$\underset{\text{Leucine}}{\underset{CH_3}{\overset{CH_3}{>}}CH\cdot CH_2\cdot \underset{NH_2}{CH}\cdot COOH} \xrightarrow{+\frac{1}{2}O_2} \underset{\alpha\text{-Ketoisocaproic acid}}{\underset{CH_3}{\overset{CH_3}{>}}CH\cdot CH_2\cdot CO\cdot COOH + NH_3}$$

$$\underset{\text{Leucine}}{\underset{CH_3}{\overset{CH_3}{>}}CH\cdot CH_2\cdot \underset{NH_2}{CH}\cdot COOH} \xrightarrow{+H_2O} \underset{\text{Leucinic acid}}{\underset{CH_3}{\overset{CH_3}{>}}CH\cdot CH_2\cdot CHOH\cdot COOH + NH_3}$$

$$\underset{\text{Glutamic acid}}{COOHCH_2CH_2CHNH_2COOH} \xrightarrow{+\frac{1}{2}O_2} \underset{\alpha\text{-Ketoglutaric acid}}{COOHCH_2CH_2COCOOH + NH_3}$$

Tyrosine   *p*-Hydroxyphenylpyruvic acid

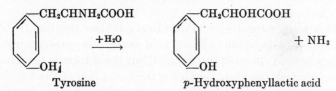

$$\text{Phenylalanine} \xrightarrow{+\frac{1}{2}O_2} \text{Phenylpyruvic acid} + NH_3$$

Phenylalanine — CH₂CHNH₂COOH

Phenylpyruvic acid — CH₂COCOOH

It is important to stress at this time, and considerable evidence will be provided later to support it, that an amino acid may be broken down concurrently in more than one way in any given culture so that different products are formed. In a sense this is analogous to the formation of gluconic, oxalic and citric acids from sugar, for example, by fungi.

Oospora lactis (in newer classifications this is *Geotrichum candidum*, Skinner, *et al.*, 1947) has been singled out for detailed study of amino acid utilization owing to the fact that this asporogenous yeastlike fungus is virtually a universal inhabitant of cheeses. Sometimes it is an indicator of unsanitary conditions for it is considered to cause off-flavors and odors in cheese, but on the other hand its constant presence in certain types of cheese of good quality indicates it may contribute to the characteristic flavor and aroma qualities. These functions are due to the proteolytic activities of the organism and amino acid breakdown products, which in proper proportions probably are the substances responsible for the distinctive aromas of certain cheeses. Presumably, when limited, these reactions benefit a cheese; when excessive, they constitute spoilage. Two groups of workers have characterized the action of *G. candidum* (*O. lactis*) on amino acids as being mainly hydrolytic deamination (Ehrlich and Jacobson, 1911; Kotake *et al.*, 1925). Here again the interesting problem of optical isomerism is revealed. Thus, high yields of *d*-*p*-hydroxyphenyllactic acid were obtained from *l*-tyrosine, this being, incidentally, the first time the pure *d*-isomer of this compound had been prepared in the field of chemistry (1911).

Tyrosine — CH₂CHNH₂COOH, —OH

p-Hydroxyphenyllactic acid — CH₂CHOHCOOH, —OH

$$\text{Tyrosine} \xrightarrow{+H_2O} \textit{p}\text{-Hydroxyphenyllactic acid} + NH_3$$

Small amounts of *p*-hydroxyphenyl alcohol (tyrosol) were also obtained, obviously via a different type of breakdown (see below), and several other fungi including *Penicillium sp.*, *Dematium pullulans*, Mycoderma, carried out these kinds of reactions. The relative intensity of these two reactions evidently is a function of strain, and probably conditions, for *Monilia candida* tested comparably converted tyrosine one-half to the *p*-hydroxyphenyllactic acid and one-half to *p*-hydroxyphenylethyl alcohol. (See also Yukawa, 1924.)

G. *candida* also performed this reaction:

l-Tryptophane   l-β-Indolelactic acid

Kotake *et al.* (1925) studied the intriguing question of change in optical rotation during transformation of amino acids by G. *candidum*, and, from work on tyrosine, concluded, in accordance with theoretical considerations, that the transformation proceeds via the optically inactive α-keto acid, which then is reduced by an enzyme which generates only the *l*-form. They were able to obtain quantitative yields of pure *d*-*p*-hydroxyphenyllactic acid from *l*-tyrosine and from *d,l*-tyrosine. Incrimination of optically inactive *p*-hydroxyphenyl pyruvic acid as an intermediate was achieved by isolating this compound when the organism was acting on *d*- and also *d, l*-tyrosine, yield from the latter being 5 per cent. A rather decisive experiment was that in which *p*-hydroxyphenylpyruvic acid in synthetic medium with urea as the N source was converted by the yeastlike fungus to *d*-*p*-hydroxyphenyllactic acid which was isolated and characterized chemically as conclusive evidence that the α-keto compound could function as an intermediate in the formation of the hydroxy compound. Yields in this experiment necessarily would be low owing to the fact that the keto compound was the only source of carbon; a portion had to be oxidized to provide hydrogen for the reduction of another portion. This type of dismutation is well-known in bacteriology where, for example, one molecule of pyruvic acid is oxidized (dehydrogenated) to furnish hydrogen for the reduction of a second molecule to lactic acid.

Another isomer specificity relates to the reverse reaction by G. *candidum*, where *l*-*p*-hydroxyphenyllactic acid as the sole carbon source is converted to *p*-hydroxyphenylpyruvic acid, but the *d*-form is not attacked.

Considering all the above evidence the formation of the hydroxy acid from amino acids, at least in the cases described above, comprises two steps; first, oxidative deamination by *l*- or by *d*-amino acid oxidase depending on the substrate, yielding the same optically inactive α-keto acid, regardless of the starting isomer; second, a reduction of the α-keto acid by a specific enzyme yielding the dextro-rotary form of hydroxy acid only.

Now the fact that quantitative yields of the *d*-hydroxy acid are obtained from the *l*-amino acid, with the assumption that the α-keto acid functions as an intermediate, calls for a modification of the reactions as given on p. 509 expressing the oxidative deamination, because there the α-keto acid is the *end product*, whereas in this case it is only an intermediate, the end product being a reduced compound (hydroxy acid). The present situation could be satisfied by the reasonable assumption that the α-keto acid functions as an hydrogen acceptor instead of oxygen in the dehydrogenation of amino acid to the imino acid, according to this scheme:

$$
\begin{array}{ccc}
\text{R—CH—COOH} & \xrightarrow{-2\text{H}} & \text{R—C—COOH} \\
| & & \| \\
\text{NH}_2 & & \text{NH} \\
\alpha\text{-Amino acid} & & \text{Imino acid} \\
& & \downarrow +\text{HOH} \\
\text{R—CHOHCOOH} & \xleftarrow{+2\text{H}} & \text{R—CO—COOH} \\
\alpha\text{-Hydroxy acid} & & \alpha\text{-Keto acid}
\end{array}
$$

This type reaction would account for quantitative yields of hydroxy acid where the single amino acid is the sole organic compound in the medium, and also conforms to the cyclic formation of oxidized product and subsequent reduction of it by the very hydrogen obtained in the oxidation (dehydrogenation) which is frequently encountered in various types of intermediary metabolism. It is evident that, when present, other oxidizable materials in the medium can supply the hydrogen for the reduction. In the final analysis, then, the formation of α-keto vs. α-hydroxy acid from amino acids depends on the nature of the hydrogen acceptor in the initial dehydrogenation reaction. When oxygen is the H-acceptor, α-keto acid results; when imino acid is the H-acceptor, α-hydroxy acid results.

With this mechanism of origin of α-hydroxy acid from amino acid established, one may inquire whether the conventionally assumed hydrolytic deamination actually exists. The theoretical reaction commonly employed in text books of bacteriology is R—CHNH$_2$—COOH + H$_2$O → R—CHOH—COOH + NH$_3$. According to Gale (1947) only one instance exists (Virtanen and Erkama, 1938) where this reaction is alleged to occur in bacteria and the evidence for that is not conclusive. It may well be that hydroxy acid formation arises exclusively by a reduction after initial oxidative deamination to the keto acid. This work of Kotane *et al.* has shown this does take place, and it may well be a generalized mechanism. Certainly hydrolytic deamination needs to be decisively demonstrated before it can be accepted unequivocally as a mode of amino acid breakdown in cases where it is claimed. Doubtless other forms of deamination exist in fungi, though not yet exposed, as they have been in bacteria. For example, one may visualize a reductive deamination in which a saturated acid results, or a desaturation whereby an unsaturated acid is formed.

2. DEAMINATION ACCOMPANIED BY DECARBOXYLATION

Theoretically four different types of compounds are possible by this route, to judge from events with bacteria: aldehydes, saturated acids, saturated alcohols, and hydrocarbons—all with one less carbon than the original amino acid molecule.   But one of these, saturated alcohol formation, has so far been identified in fungi.   This type reaction is well known in yeasts and in bacteria, and, indeed, is the mechanism whereby the higher alcohols (chiefly n-amyl alcohol and isoamyl alcohol) which make up fusel oil are formed in alcoholic fermentation by yeasts.   Ehrlich clarified these relationships by showing that these alcohols are derived from the corresponding amino acids isoleucine and leucine present in the medium naturally, or added artificially.   The keto acids generated by an initial oxidative deamination as described earlier are intermediates in the formation of the alcohols; and as a matter of fact, the situation here is entirely analogous to alcoholic fermentation of sugar where the alcohol is formed via an α-keto acid (pyruvic) followed by decarboxylation and reduction of the resultant aldehyde to the alcohol.   In addition to fusel oil components, tyrosol from tyrosine is the third principal alcohol derived from an amino acid in industrial alcohol and beer fermentations, and all three have been shown to be produced similarly by fungi.

Pringsheim (1908) recovered isoamyl alcohol from added synthetic leucine in fungus cultures in yields as follows: *Mucor racemosus,* 18.2 per cent; *Rhizopus tonkinensis,* 17.5; *Monilia candida,* 9.8; *Torula sp.,* 10.1. A yeast tested similarly for comparison yielded 30 per cent of the amyl alcohol. Yukawa (1924) obtained tyrosol from tyrosine by Monilia. The reactions doubtless are widespread among the fungi. All the above alcohols can also be obtained by simple deamination of the corresponding primary amines (see below).

3. DECARBOXYLATION YIELDING AMINES

Compared to the vast amount of work done on this subject in bacteria, information regarding the fungi is negligible. Putrescine and cadaverine were formed (Yamada and Ishida, 1926) by *Aspergillus oryzae* growing on soybean protein, and in another case tyramine from tyrosine (Yukawa, 1924), doubtless from the specific amino acids as follows:

$$H_2N(CH_2)_3CH(NH_2)COOH \xrightarrow{-CO_2} H_2N(CH_2)_4NH_2$$
$$\text{Ornithine} \qquad\qquad\qquad \text{Putrescine}$$

$$H_2N(CH_2)_4CH(NH_2)COOH \xrightarrow{-CO_2} H_2N(CH_2)_5NH_2$$
$$\text{Lysine} \qquad\qquad\qquad \text{Cadaverine}$$

$$HO-\langle\ \rangle-CH_2CHNH_2COOH \xrightarrow{-CO_2} HO-\langle\ \rangle-CH_2CH_2NH_2$$
$$\text{Tyrosine} \qquad\qquad\qquad\qquad \text{Tyramine]}$$

Autointoxication of *A. niger* through ammonia and amines it forms during growth on 5 per cent maltose-2 per cent urea medium has been reported (Boas, 1919b). The relatively aerobic nature of fungi and their ability to utilize carbohydrates as an energy source may be the reason why amino acid decarboxylase activity is less common in fungi than in bacteria. On the other hand, the subject has barely been studied in the fungi, and the reaction might be widespread in this group. It will be recalled that pyridoxal phosphate is the coenzyme for amino acid decarboxylase. The formation of tyramine in "Shoyu-Moromi," a Japanese seasoning sauce prepared mainly from soybeans, is said to account for the "spice" effect of this sauce through its property of contracting capillary blood vessels. Tyrosine may be oxidized to the dark-colored melanin type substances by an extract of the Basidiomycete *Lactarious vellereus.* This may be mechanism in lower fungi also (Robinson and McCance, 1925).

UTILIZATION OF AMINES

Many fungi can utilize various amines as sources of nitrogen (Lafar), and like many bacteria, probably decompose the simple amines completely. The stabilizing influence of ring structures holds true for *Oidium lactis* (*Geotrichum candidum*) and the yeast *Willia anomola* (Ehrlich and Pistschimuka, 1912). Here tyramine was converted in 83 per cent yield to tyrosol. Later Ehrlich (1916) tested *O. lactis* and *Penicillium glaucum* for their action on adrenaline and hordenine as representative secondary and tertiary amines. Mold growth on adrenaline was extremely slow and scanty, and no products were isolatable. *O. lactis* grew well on hordenine, culture filtrates of which gave quantitative yields of tyrosol.

$$\text{HO}-\langle\ \rangle-\text{CH}_2\text{CH}_2\text{N}(\text{CH}_3)_2 \xrightarrow{\text{HOH}} \text{HO}-\langle\ \rangle-\text{CH}_2\text{CH}_2\text{OH}$$

Hordenine   Tyrosol

The hydrolytic origin of alcohols from amino acids via amines is probably more typical of anaerobic putrefactive bacteria which possess strong amino acid decarboxylase activity as a means of generating the amines. Yeasts and fungi, not being strong in this regard, most likely form alcohols from amino acids via decarboxylation of the α-keto acid *after* deamination (see above). *P. glaucum* formed only traces of tyrosol from the tertiary amine, but considerable quantities of an unidentified oily acid giving the Millon reaction. This disappeared in older cultures, indicative of ring rupture. Where tyrosol is formed in 80 per cent yield from hordenine as the sole source of carbon and energy, it is evident that growth takes place at the expense of the dimethyl amine group which is split off. This is believed to undergo this reaction:

$$\text{NH}(\text{CH}_3)_2 + 2\text{H}_2\text{O} \rightarrow \text{NH}_3 + 2\text{CH}_3\text{OH}$$
Dimethyl amine   Methanol

The methanol would then be utilized as a carbon source. Ehrlich points out that the general biological transformation of mono-, di-, and triamino groups involves their replacement by OH groups. However, as in the case of amino acids, there is no evidence that the deamination of amines is hydrolytic, though the overall equation could be represented as such

$$\text{R·CH}_2\text{CHNH}_2 \xrightarrow{+\text{HOH}} \text{R·CH}_2\text{CH}_2\text{OH}$$

Information on monamine oxidase, an enzyme from animal tissues attacking primary, secondary, and tertiary amines, characterizes its action as an oxidative deamination yielding the corresponding aldehyde:

$$\text{R·CH}_2\text{CHNH}_2 + \text{O}_2 + \text{H}_2\text{O} \rightarrow \text{RCH}_2\text{CHO} + \text{NH}_3 + \text{H}_2\text{O}_2$$
$$\downarrow +2\text{H}$$
$$\text{RCH}_2\text{CH}_2\text{OH}$$

One may assume the same enzyme functions in microorganisms. The alcohol would of course be formed by reduction of the aldehyde by hydrogen from another substrate, or conceivably by the aldehyde functioning as H acceptor in the absence of oxygen, i.e., anaerobically. A situation analogous to amino acid oxidase is noted.

Werle (1941), who studied extensively histaminase in animal tissues, also found it in *A. oryzae, A. niger, Secale cornutum* and the ergot fungus *Claviceps purpurea*. Histaminase is a diamine oxidase attacking compounds with two free amino groups. Only amine N is split off, however, yielding the corresponding aldehyde exactly as the equation above for monamine oxidase. The fungus histaminase was destroyed in acetone-ether dried mycelium, but could be obtained in cell-free active preparations by grinding the mycelium with sand. Considerable purification was achieved by dialysis and evaporation of the residue to a dry state. The mold enzyme was inhibited by 0.001 M hydrazide of carboxymethyl-pyridinium chloride, 0.01 M semicarbazide or 0.001 M HCN. The entire subject of amine formation and oxidation is reviewed by Werle (1943).

Asparagine and Other Amides

Shibata (1904) apparently was the first to demonstrate amide-splitting powers in fungi, discovering, as a matter of fact, the enzyme urease. Acetone preparations of *A. niger* decomposed urea, acetamide and oxamide. An enzyme preparation from *A. flavus* deaminated acetamide, propionamide as well as asparagine (Thakur and Norris, 1928). Data cited below indicates the non-identity of asparagine and the other deamidases. Detailed examination of asparaginase, the endocellular enzyme splitting out the amide N from asparagine to form *l*-aspartic acid and ammonia has been made on *A. niger* by Bach (1928, 1929a) and by Schmalfuss and Mothes (1930). On the weak acid side, pH 4–6,

$$
\begin{array}{ll}
\text{CO·NH}_2 & \text{COOH} \\
| & | \\
\text{CH}_2 & \text{CH}_2 \\
| \quad\quad {\scriptstyle +\text{HOH}} & | \\
\text{CHNH}_2 \xrightarrow{\quad\quad} & \text{CHNH}_2 + \text{NH}_3 \\
| & | \\
\text{COOH} & \text{COOH} \\
\textit{l-}\beta\text{-Asparagine} & \textit{l-}\text{Aspartic acid}
\end{array}
$$

growth cultures utilized both the amide and amino N of asparagine equally, i.e., the asparagine was broken down completely. On the alkaline side, the amino N was utilized very little, the amide N being split off rapidly, and aspartic acid could be isolated from the medium. Despite the fact that the enzyme optimum pH is decidedly on the alkaline side (7.7–8.8) the optimum pH for growth on asparagine as a nitrogen source was 6.4. Obviously permeability or other factors are involved in asparagine utilization by the intact organism. Several different methods were tried in obtaining active cell-free preparations. Acetone-dried powdered mycelium was ineffective, and only fresh aqueous or glycerol extracts of ground mycelium were active. Though acetone-drying destroys asparaginase, urease in the same mycelium remains intact (Bach 1929b). Asparaginase (amidase) is apparently a constitutive enzyme in *A. niger* for it was formed when the fungus grew on inorganic N sources in the absence of asparagine. Optimum activity of the extracts was at pH 7.7 and 33°C., the temperature range being 7°–70°C. Asparaginase of the mold was specific for asparagine, as other simple amides, namely acetamide and oxamide were not split, nor was guanidine. Under Bach's conditions asparagine hydrolysis was only 80 per cent complete under optimum conditions. Velocity of enzyme action was reduced after about 24–36 hours due to inactivation of the enzyme and the addition of asparagine protected the enzyme from this autodestruction. When the initial asparagine content reached 1 per cent or more, the ammonia produced inhibited enzyme action.

UREA METABOLISM OF FUNGI

The enzyme urease is formed by a wide variety of different fungi. A simple demonstration of this fact may be had by testing various cultures in a glucose-salts medium with urea as the sole nitrogen source. Growth connotes the presence of urease which hydrolyzes urea to ammonia and CO_2, the ammonia being reassimilated as the immediate N source.

$$O=C\begin{smallmatrix} NH_2 \\ \\ NH_2 \end{smallmatrix} \xrightarrow[\text{Urease}]{+HOH} 2NH_3 + CO_2$$

On the other hand various fungi form and accumulate appreciable quantities of urea. This is true both of higher "fleshy" fungi and lower filamentous forms. In fact information pertaining to the latter is a direct consequence of the extensive pioneering work of the Russian microbiologist N. N. Iwanoff on higher fungi over the years 1923–1927. As this work rarely is even mentioned in treatises on bacteriology, and because fungi are involved, even if for the most part fleshy fungi, Iwanoff's work will be covered here.

During the ripening stage of the isolated fruiting body of several *Gasterales* and *Agaricaceae*, the N content becomes higher due mainly to respiratory loss of carbon, chiefly the trehalose in the tissue. The urea content is very low in the young stage, rises to a maximum at the beginning of fructification, then drops off virtually to zero at sporulation, though there is no urea in the spores. The sporogenic tissue of the higher fungi, the hymenium, is always richest in urea, the head, or pileus next, and the stalk or stipe lowest (Goris and Costy, 1922). The urea was believed to be in labile combination in the fungus tissue because it was extractable only with difficulty with alcohol, but easily with hot water. Amino nitrogen compounds were considered to be the precursors of the urea whose formation was viewed as a storage of nitrogen as the respirable carbon compounds disappear. The urea content of several higher fungi is given in Table 5.

TABLE 5

UREA CONTENT OF FRUITING BODIES OF SEVERAL FUNGI[1]

	Urea, per cent of dry weight
Lycoperdon saccatum	2.85
L. piriforme	4.62
L. gemmateum	10.70
L. molle	9.22
L. marginatum	5.84
L. echinatum	1.16
Bovista nigrescens	11.16
Psalliota campestris	6.18
P. protensis	1.61
Pholiota spectabilis	2.45
Cortinarius violaceus	0.51

[1] From Iwanoff.

The urea content of twenty-three other species of higher fungi is available elsewhere (Goris and Costy, 1922). If the fruiting body of pileated (mushroom type) fungi is allowed to stand in ammonia solution or NH_3 atmosphere during the ripening stage, ammonia is absorbed and an appreciable increase in urea content noted. In one case 11.3 mg. ammonia was absorbed with a concomitant increase of 4.43 mg. urea, i.e., 39 per cent conversion of the absorbed ammonia to urea. The head (pileus) of the fungus then contained 14.9 per cent urea. The urea increase was especially marked in the hymenium of the fruiting body where the spores are formed. Thiourea, a sulfur-containing analogue of urea, is also absorbed, but from a mixture of urea and thiourea only the former is taken up. One fungus, Bolbitius vitellinus, was shown to contain urease; this organism did not accumulate urea from a solution, but did accumulate thiourea since the latter is not attacked by urease.

Fruiting bodies of Lycoperdon, Psalliota and Tricholoma absorb sugar from aqueous solution, and this assimilation prevents the transformation of N compounds (autolytic processes) within the tissues, the latter process being the one associated with urea formation. In fact, placing a fungus of a given content of urea in a sugar solution leads to a rapid reduction in

urea content and to the formation of new fungus tissue, i.e., growth.
The glucose effect is obtained especially at time of fructification. This
situation is interpreted by Iwanoff to be analogous to that occurring in
green plants with respect to the nitrogen storage substances asparagine
and glutamine. The content of these substances increases in the plant
in the dark when no carbohydrate is available for growth, hence the
available N is stored. When carbohydrate is available, the nitrogen
reserves are utilized. According to Iwanoff, his experiments indicate
urea plays a similar function in higher fungi, i.e., a repository for N until
conditions are favorable for its utilization in growth processes. In an
overall sense the formation of urea depends on an excess of intermediary
nitrogen nutrition and the absence or deficiency of carbohydrates. The
association between high nitrogen nutrition and urea content is further
demonstrated by the urea content in relation to N level of *Lycoperdon
piriforme:*

Total N (high) = 7.8 per cent   Urea = 4.3 per cent of dry weight
Total N (low) = 4.2 per cent   Urea = 0

Growth of pure cultures of fungi in nitrogen-rich media such as malt
extract plus gelatin gives a high urea content in the fungus mycelial mat,
where growth in a nitrogen-poor medium, i.e., malt extract without
added gelatin, gave no trace of urea. In the liquid media the bulk of the
urea formed was excreted into the medium. In one case the urea formed
totaled 27.2 per cent of the fungus dry weight.

Iwanoff extended urea studies to several filamentous (lower) fungi
including *Aspergillus niger, Penicillium glaucum, Rhizopus nigricans,* and
Tieghamella orchidis, with special emphasis on the carbohydrate effect.
Cultivation of these fungi on a 3 per cent peptone-salts medium led to
appreciable urea formation. Analyses of a typical culture are given
in Table 6.

TABLE 6
UREA FORMATION FROM PEPTONE BY PENICILLIUM GLAUCUM[1,2]

Age	Dry wt., g.	Urea in medium, mg.	Urea as per cent of mycelial wt.	Total N in mycelium, mg.	Urea N in medium, mg.	Urea N as per cent of N in mycelium
10	.32	17.0	5.2	27.6	7.9	28.7
18	.33	28.4	8.7	27.7	13.3	47.8
25	.25	38.3	14.5	17.7	17.9	100

[1] From Iwanoff (1925) *Biochem. Z.* **157**, 231–242.
[2] 100 ml. medium.

It is evident that urea formation comprises a substantial portion of the metabolism of the organism, amounting as it does to 14.5 per cent of the mold weight and on a nitrogen basis being equivalent to the N content of the mycelium. In another experiment using *A. niger*, the mycelium contained 3.3 mg. urea whereas the medium containing 18.9 mg. In another case a 15-day old *A. niger* culture on 100 ml. of 2 per cent peptone-salts medium showed 74 mg. urea formed by 310 mg. dry mycelial weight (Chrzaszcz and Zakomorny, 1934a).

The presence of glucose in cultures of filamentous fungi leads to results exactly like those in higher fungi. Urea accumulation is eliminated so long as glucose is present and this was shown to be due to the presence of an active urease which at once decomposed any and all urea to ammonia and CO_2, the ammonia being assimilated for growth. This effect of glucose on inducing urease formation is rather clear cut: mycelium obtained from a glucose culture could be shown to possess urease when tested on urea solution in the presence of toluene, where the non-glucose control tested similarly showed complete absence of urease.

TABLE 7

GLUCOSE AND UREA FORMATION BY TIEGHAMELLA ORCHIDIS[1,2]

	Dry wt., g.	Urea, mg.	Urea as per cent of mycelial wt.	Total N of mycelium, mg.	Urea in culture liquid, mg.	Urea N as per cent of total N in mycelium
No sucrose........	0.20	9.4	4.7	24.1	4.39	21.8
5 Per cent sucrose..	.5	0	0	49.7	0	0

[1] From Iwanoff (1925).
[2] 10 ml. gelatine-malt extract medium.

Addition of glucose to a mature culture deficient in urease and which had accumulated urea, led to rapid formation of urease and rapid destruction of urea. Again urea formation is a matter of a relative abundant nitrogen nutrition vs. carbohydrate lack as demonstrated by the experiment in synthetic 1 per cent glucose-3 per cent NH_4NO_3-salts medium in which considerable urea was formed. The sugar effect is demonstrated in Table 7.

Thus, in keeping with what is known for a great many different enzymes in fungi, conditions of cultivation are most critical in the formation of urease.

Chrzaszcz and Zakomorny (1934a) have confirmed and extended Iwanoff's results on urea formation from peptone with sixteen different fungi of which the best urea formers were *Penicillium johannioli, Aspergillus niger* and *Rhizopus nigricans*. Glucose and other carbon sources, namely alcohol and acetate, inhibited urea formation, some organisms being more sensitive to the glucose than others. Iwanoff and Smirnova (1927) discovered that bacteria also (*Bacillus megatherium* and *B. tumescens*) could form urea from peptone, gelatine, or arginine, and arginine appeared indicated as the precursor of the urea, because none of the latter was formed where arginine was absent from the medium. Thus, urea generation here is by means of the enzyme arginase; along with the urea ornithine also results from this amino acid by *A. oryzae* (Tamiya and Usami, 1940). This subject was later studied intensively on *Corynebacter ureafaciens* where it was shown that any substance possessing the grouping :NCN:, especially creatine and creatinine, would generate urea in this bacterium (Krebs and Eggleston, 1939). However, from studies on urea formation from peptones by fungi, Iwanoff (1927) concluded that cleavage of arginine could account for only a small percentage of the total urea formed, indicative of some unknown mechanism. Obviously this exists since urea can be synthesized from inorganic nitrogen. Both mechanisms, one synthetic, the other degradative were shown to exist in the same organism (Iwanoff and Toschewikowa, 1927). The fruiting body of *Psalliota campestris* synthesized urea from ammonia and split off urea when furnished arginine. The press juice contained an active arginase.

$$\underset{\underset{NH_2}{\diagdown}}{\overset{\overset{NH}{\diagdown}}{}} CNH(CH_2)_3CHNH_2COOH \xrightarrow{+HOH} \underset{\underset{NH_2}{\diagdown}}{\overset{\overset{NH_2}{\diagdown}}{}} CO + NH_2(CH_2)_3CHNH_2COOH$$

           Arginine   Urea   Ornithine

Some modification of certain of Iwanoff's ideas have been proposed in view of the contribution of other workers. For example, it is possible for organisms, both higher fungi (Gotis and Costy, 1922) and lower filamentous forms (Fosse, 1914; Miwa and Yoshii, 1934) to contain, or produce, both urea and the urease simultaneously. Iwanoff gives the impression a qualitative cleavage holds. The Japanese workers proved that *A. niger* could excrete urea into the medium and yet possess in its mycelium an active urease. Naturally, there is an inverse relation between urease content and urea accumulation. As the enzyme is not only constitutive but endocellular in fungi (Bach, 1929a), the failure to destroy the urea in the medium was ascribed to inaccessability caused by slow rate of permeability of the urea into the cells. In view of the fact that the urea had already passed out of the cells, it would appear that permeability is not the entire explanation.

Miwa and Yoshii also showed that the carbohydrate effect on suppressing urea accumulation via urease formation is an indirect one, the effect being due not to carbohydrate *per se*, but to the reduced pH of the medium caused by organic acid formation from the sugar, and the same effects could be achieved merely by pH control of the medium with inorganic acids. This may explain why Chrzaszcz and Zakomorny got stimulation of urea formation by small (0.1 per cent) amount of glucose. Not enough would be present to produce acid. Thus, at pH values below approximately 6 and down to 1.6 there was no urea accumulation and the mycelium had high urease activity, the highest being at pH 1.6. Above pH 6–7 considerable urea formation took place and the urease content of the mycelium was always low, but never zero. The dependency of urease content of the mycelium on the pH of the external medium is illustrated in Fig. 1.

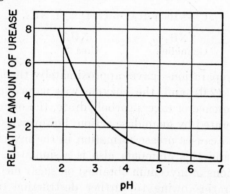

Fig. 1.—Dependency of urease content of *A. niger* mycelium on pH of external medium. (Constructed by Miwa and Yoshii (1934) from data of Bach (1929b). Curve based on 26 points.)

These workers interpret the relation between pH and urease activity in fungi as a regulatory mechanism. At high pH values high concentrations of ammonia, they believed, are toxic owing to the existence of the ammonia in the undissociated state, in which form it penetrates the mycelium easily and exerts a harmful effect. Hence, by suppressing urease formation at high pH values, urea splitting is prevented and the so-called toxic NH_3 is retained in the form of inocuous urea. On the other hand, they say that under conditions of low pH the organism acquires urease as a means of liberating NH_3 from urea in order to mollify the acidic state through neutralization. As a salt, ammonia is in ionized form and consequently not poisonous under these conditions. However attractive this line of teleological reasoning, it is unsound because (1) the amounts of ammonia the organisms contend with ordinarily and the conditions prevailing are rarely if ever toxic (2) the amount of urea in which the so-called toxic ammonia would be stored is so small that it hardly could be a helpful mechanism. Iwanoff's nitrogen storage concept appears to be the more attractive of the two theories interpreting the function of urea in fungus metabolism.

UREA FROM GUANIDINE

The ability of fungi (*A. niger*) to utilize guanidine as a nitrogen source has been known since 1914 (Kossowicz) but it was not until 1931 that Iwanoff and Awetissowa provided a more intimate understanding of the transformations of this substance. Fungus mycelium cultivated on N-rich media so that it is urease-free splits guanidine into urea and ammonia:

$$\underset{\text{Guanidine}}{\overset{\displaystyle NH_2}{\underset{\displaystyle NH_2}{\diagup C = NH}}} + H_2O \rightarrow \underset{\text{Urea}}{\overset{\displaystyle NH_2}{\underset{\displaystyle NH_2}{\diagup C = O}}} + NH_3$$

Dry mycelial preparations gave approximately theoretical ratios of urea-N:NH_3—N (2.0) and the enzyme was named guanidase. Cultivated in the presence of excess carbohydrate, the organism assimilates the ammonia liberated by guanidase action; however, as cited above, the carbohydrate also causes urease formation in the mycelium which then splits the urea, and this ammonia also is assimilated. Thus, dry cell powder preparations of mycelium obtained on sugar media give very low urea-N:NH_3-N ratios owing to further destruction of the urea. On the other hand, mycelium cultivated on peptone media without carbohydrate has no guanidase. Thus, to demonstrate its action apart from urease, the mycelium must first be grown on peptone-glucose medium whereby it contains both urease and guanidase. Now the urease in the mycelium is inactivated by replacing the culture medium with peptone solution, and the guanidine activity remains in dry powder preparations. To demonstrate guanidinase activity with living mycelium, an excess of carbohydrate must be present to suppress urease formation.

From studies on sixteen different species Chrzaszcz and Zakomorny (1934b) concluded that almost all fungi possess guanidinase. They tested the preformed mycelium on a solution of guanidine salts. Included were eight Penicillia, four Aspergilli, two Mucor, *Rhizopus nigricans* and *Dematium pullulans*, and all formed varying amounts, to a maximum (by *P. johannioli*) of 29.4 mg. urea per 100 ml. medium. The different amounts of urea formed was considered indicative of a differential rate of action between the two enzymes, guanidase generating urea, and urease decomposing it.   Urea also is produced from the proteins edestin, glutenin, and casein by *Verticillium albo-atrum, Botrytis cinerea* and *Pythium de baryanum* (Ovcharov, 1938).   The enzyme causing urea production from the proteins was called *deurease* and was found partly free in the medium and in the cells.   The existence of a single enzyme deurease is open to question until it is confirmed.   The Polish investigators expressed the belief that the urea formation observed on peptone and other complex nitrogenous substances, proceeds, as from the amino acid arginine, via guanidine.   Unfortunately no quantitative balances along this line are available, but the experiment of Chrzaszcz and Zakomorny (1934a) cited earlier, where *A. niger* produced 74 mg. urea in 100 ml. 2 per cent peptone solution indicates that neither arginine nor the guanidine moiety of the arginine in the medium could be the sole origin of urea.   On the assumption that the peptone was derived from casein which contains 5.2 per cent arginine, the maximum urea possible from this source was 35.5 mg.   However, it is known that urea can be synthesized from ammonia (Iwanoff, 1925) and so the presence of arginine is not a prerequisite of urea formation.   On the other hand, it may be that the urea is generated via a very active ornithine-citrulline-arginine intermediary cycle, these substances being synthesized rather than being assimilated preformed.   It will be recalled that an active arginine cycle has already been established for one fungus, *Neurospora crassa* (Chapter 6) and probably is common in fungi.   The synthesis of urea by fungi still needs considerable clarification.

THIOUREA

Ovcharov (1937) states that *Verticillium albo-atrum* and *Botrytis cinerea* produce this sulfur analogue of urea from synthetic media with

Thiourea

asparagine or ammonia as a nitrogen source and sulfate as the sulfur source.

ADENOSINE AND ITS DEAMINASE

This enzyme formed by *Aspergillus oryzae* (Mitchell and McElroy, 1946) and *Neurospora crassa* (McElroy and Mitchell, 1946) has been prepared in cell-free form.   It catalyzes the deamination of the riboside but not free adenine, and its reversibility could not be demonstrated under the conditions tested.

```
N=C—NH₂              ┌——O——┐                        N=C—OH
|    |               |       |              −NH₃      |    |
CH C—N              OH OH    |          ─────────→   CH C—N
||   ‖\              |   |    |          Adenosine    ||   ‖\
N—C—N  \CH ————————C—C—C—C—CH₂OH        deaminase    N—C—N  \CH
              |     H H H H                                     /
           Adenosine                           N—C—N—Ribose
                                                   Inosine
```

Adenosine deaminase was found to be present in considerable amounts in Takadiastase. This is a commercial crude diastatic enzyme preparation made by cultivating a selected strain of *A. oryzae* on wheat bran, drying the entire culture mass, extracting with water and precipitating the protein enzymes with alcohol. With this as a starting material adenosine deaminase was concentrated further by fractional alcohol precipitation, yielding a preparation eight times more active than the Takadiastase and 600 times more active than the original dry bran culture.

ALLANTOIN AND PRODUCTS

Higher fungi (sixty-five species) and *Aspergillus niger* and *A. phoenicis* contain allantoinase which splits allantoin to allantoic acid (Brunel, 1931, 1939).

```
NH₂                                    NH₂          NH₂
|                                       |            |
CO   CH—NH                             CO   COOH    CO
|    |     \CO        +H₂O             |    |        |
|    |     /      ─────────→          NH—CH ——NH
NH—CH—NH         Allantoinase
     Allantoin                            Allantoic acid
```

An interesting point is the inability of the fungi to attack uric acid of which allantoin is the oxidation product.

The allantoic acid is split further to urea and glyoxylic acid, the urea being further decomposed to ammonia and CO_2.

```
                                NH₂
                              /
                    H₂O      CO              + COOH
Allantoic acid   ────→                         |
                              \NH₂             CHO
                              Urea        Glyoxylic acid
                                |
                                ↓
                          4NH₃ + 2CO₂
```

Other oxidation products of uric acid and allantoic attacked by these *Aspergilli*, and for which presumably specific enzymes are present, were uroxanic acid, mesoxalic acid, oxaluric acid, and parabanic acid. Otani

(1935b) described a mold enzyme which decomposed benzoyl-*dl*-leucyl-glycine, hippuric acid, and benzoyldiglycine. It is not clear whether hippuricase, which splits hippuric acid into benzoic acid and glycine, is involved here. Neuberg and Rosenthal (1924) also mention a hippuric acid-splitting enzyme in Takadiastase, the crude commercial enzyme product from *A. oryzae*. This same Japanese author (Otani, 1935a) has shown that it is possible to obtain from numerous fungi cell-free enzymes (glycerol extracts) which split nucleic acids (nucleases).

Proteins and Peptones

Since the manner of breakdown of proteins, peptones and the products derived therefrom is a well-known subject and is not, in the fungi, different from other proteolytic systems including bacteria and plants and animals, it would be superfluous to treat this subject here. Protein utilization and ammonia accumulation therefrom is a property extremely common to fungi. The deamination mechanisms have been discussed above. Key papers for the reader interested in this subject and in the types of fungi involved are those of Waksman and Lomanitz (1925), Chrzaszcz and Pisula (1933), Chrzaszcz and Tiukow (1931), Chrzaszcz and Zakomorny (1933) and Butkewitsch (1922). (See Chapter 10 for oxalic acid formation from proteins and peptones.) A noteworthy point in the utilization of peptone by fungi is the fact that the ultimate products of proteolysis, namely, the amino acids, are not deaminated at the same rate, some in fact not being deaminated or further attacked at all, and they accumulate. Thus, leucine and tyrosine can easily be crystallized from peptone cultures of various fungi (Butkewitsch, 1902). This raises the interesting problem of preferential selection by the organism of amino acids in a mixture. It is doubtful if all are attacked at the same time, and it should be possible, by appropriate strain selection, to eliminate certain types of amino acids from a mixture, leaving other types behind.

The nature of mold proteolytic enzyme action is exemplified by the work of Berger *et al.* (1937–38) which also contains a summary of literature on the subject. Mycelium of *Aspergillus parasiticus* and *A. alliaceus* was ground in a mortar and extracted with water in the presence of toluene for 3–6 hours at pH 7. The extract was then dialyzed against running tap water to remove large amounts of amino-N substances from the enzyme solution. This proteolytic enzyme preparation hydrolyzed gelatine, lactalbumin, casein, egg albumin, and edestine to 82 to 100 per cent of completion, as judged by liberation of amino nitrogen.

Synthetic di- and tripeptides are also split by fungi (*A. niger*), oxalic acid accumulating in the medium: glycylglycine, diglycylglycine, alanyl-alanine, glycine anhydride, alanine anhydride, leucyl glycine, glycylalanine, leucylglycylglycine, leucylasparagine (Abderhalden and Teruuchi, 1906). A. oryzae also utilizes polypeptides (Tazawa and Yamagoto, 1937). This organism could utilize only two of fourteen diketopiperazines tested as a source of N, namely aspartan and diamino-propionic anhydride.

Sulfopeptidase is an enzyme which splits peptide derivatives of β-naphthalenesulfonic acid. The enzyme can be obtained in cell-free form as a glycerol extract of A. niger mycelium, and has been studied extensively by Otani (1934). It can be further purified by absorbtion procedures. It hydrolyzes β-naphthalenesulfoglycylglycine to β-naphthalenesulfoglycine and glycine, the former not being further decomposed, and is isolatable. The enzyme was present in all of nine other fungi tested including Phycomycetes and Fungi Imperfecti. Glycine markedly inhibits the enzyme. o-Toluenesulfo- and benzenesulfoglycylglycine are also attacked.

REFERENCES

Aberhalden, E., and Teruuchi, Y. 1906. Z. physiol. Chem. 47, 394–396.
Allison, F. E., Hoover, S. R., and Morris, H. J. 1934. J. Agr. Research 49, 1115–1123.
Bach, D. 1928. Compt. rend. 187, 955–956.
Bach, D. 1929a. Bull. soc. chim. biol. 11, 119–145, 995–1006, 1007–15.
Bach, D. 1929b. Compt. rend. soc. biol. 100, 831–833.
Bach, D., and Desbordes, D. 1933. Compt. rend. 197, 1772–1774.
Berger, J., Johnson, M., and Peterson, W. H. 1937–38. Enzymologia 4, 31–35; J. Biol. Chem. 124, 395–408; J. Bact. 36, 521–545.
Boas, F. 1919a. Ber. deut. botan. Ges. 37, 57–62.
Boas, F. 1919b. Ber. deut. botan. Ges. 37, 63–65.
Boas, F., and Leberle, H. 1919. Biochem. Z. 95, 170–178.
de Boers, S. 1940. Proc. Acad. Sci. Amsterdam 73, 715–720.
Brunel, A. 1931. Compt. rend. 192, 442–444.
Brunel, A. 1939. Bull. soc. chim. biol. 21, 380–387, 388–406.
Bünning, E. 1936. Flora 131, 81–112.
Burkholder, P. R., and McVeigh, I. 1940. Am. J. Botany 27, 634–640.
Burris, R. H., and Wilson, P. W. 1947. Ann. Rev. Biochem. 14, 685–708.
Butkewitsch, W. 1902. Jahrb. wiss. Botan. 38, 147–240.
Butkewitsch, W. 1922. Biochem. Z. 129, 145–154, 455–463.
Cantino, E. C. 1948. Am. J. Botany 35, 238–243.
Chrzaszcz, T., and Pisula, F. 1933. Biochem. Z. 266, 29–45.
Chrzaszcz, T., and Tiukow, D. 1931. Biochem. Z. 242, 137–148.
Chrzaszcz, T., and Zakomorny, M. 1933. Biochem. Z. 263, 105–118.
Chrzaszcz, T., and Zakomorny, M. 1934a. Biochem. Z. 273, 31–42.
Chrzaszcz, T., and Zakomorny, M. 1934b. Biochem. Z. 275, 97–105.
Clifton, C. E. 1946. Advances in Enzymol. 6, 269–308.
Currie, J. N. 1917. J. Biol. Chem. 31, 15–37.
Demmler, F. P. 1933. Phytopath. Z. 5, 275–313.

Desbordes, J. 1936. Assimilation de la molecule nitrique par "l'Aspergillus repens de Bary." Paris, Les Presses Modernes, 183 pp.

Dimond, A. E., and Peltier, G. L. 1945. *Am. J. Botany* **32,** 46–50.

Duggar, B. M., and Davis, A. L. 1916. *Ann. Missouri Botan. Garden* **3,** 413–437.

Ehrlich, F. 1906. *Biochem. Z.* **1,** 8–31.

Ehrlich, F. 1916. *Biochem. Z.* **75,** 417–430.

Ehrlich, F., and Jacobsen, K. A. 1911. *Ber.* **44,** 888–897.

Ehrlich, F., and Pistschimuka, P. 1912. *Ber.* **45,** 1006–1002.

Emerson, R. L., Knight, S. G., and Puziss, M. 1949 *Soc. Am. Pact.*, Abstracts 49th Gen. Meeting pp. 40–41.

Fellows, H. 1936. *J. Agr. Research* **53,** 765–769.

Fosse, R. 1914. *Compt. rend.* **158,** 1374–1376.

Foster, J. W., and Allen, R. R. 1948. Unpublished.

Gale, E. E. 1947. Chemical Activities of Bacteria. Univ. Tutorial Press, London.

Giesberger, G. 1936. Beitrag zur Kenntnis der Gattung Spirillum Ehbg. Dissertation, Delft.

Goris, A., and Costy, P. 1922. *Compt. rend.* **175,** 539–540; 998–999.

Hagem, O. 1910. *Videnskappelseapets-Skrifter I. Mat. naturv. Klasse, Koistiania* **4,** 1–152; *Ann. Mycol. Notitiam Sci. Mycol. Univ.* **8,** 265–286.

Halpern, P. E., Siminovitch, D., and McFarlane, W. D. 1945. *Science* **102,** 230.

Hockenhull, D. 1948. *Nature* **161,** 100.

Horowitz, N. H. 1944. *J. Biol. Chem.* **154,** 141–149.

Hayasida, A. 1938. *Biochem. Z.* **298,** 169–178.

Itzerott, D. 1936. *Flora* **131,** 60–81.

Iwanoff, N. N. 1923. *Biochem. Z.* **135,** 1–20; **136,** 1–8, 9–19; 1924. *ibid.* **150,** 115–22; **154,** 376–390, 391–398; 1925, *ibid.* **157,** 231–242; 1926, *ibid.* **175,** 181–84; 1927, *ibid.* **181,** 8–16; *Z. physiol. Chem.* **170,** 274–288.

Iwanoff, N. N., and Awetissowa, A. N. 1931. *Biochem. Z.* **231,** 67–78.

Iwanoff, N. N., and Smirnova, M. I. 1927. *Biochem. Z.* **181,** 8–16.

Iwanoff, N. N., and Toschewikowa, A. 1927. *Biochem. Z.* **181,** 1–7.

Jones, W. N., and Smith, M. L. 1928. *Brit. J. Exptl. Biol.* **6,** 167–189.

Kasselbach, E. 1931. *Jahrb. wiss. Botan.* **75,** 377–397.

Klein, G., Eigner, A., and Müller, H. 1926. *Z. physiol. Chem.* **159,** 201–234.

Klotz, L. J. 1923. *Ann. Missouri Botan. Garden* **10,** 299–368.

Knight, S. G. 1948. *J. Bact.* **55,** 401–408.

Koser, S. A., Wright, M. H., and Dorfman, A. 1942. *Proc. Soc. Exptl. Biol. Med.* **51,** 204–205.

Kossowicz, A. 1912. *Garungsphysiol.* **1,** 60–62; **2,** 51–54.

Kossowicz, A. 1914. *Biochem. Z.* **67,** 400–419.

Kostytschew, S., and Tswetkowa, E. 1930. *Z. physiol. Chem.* **111,** 171–2001.

Kotake, Y., Chikano, M., and Ichihara, K. 1925. *Z. physiol. Chem.* **143,** 218–228.

Krebs, H. A., and Eggleston, L. V. 1939. *Enzymologia* **7,** 310–320.

Labrouse, F. 1931. *Compt. rend.* **192,** 981–983.

Laurent, E. 1889. *Ann. inst. Pasteur* **3,** 362–374.

Lemoigne, M., and Desveaux, R. 1935. *Compt. rend.* **201,** 239–241.

Lemoigne, M., Monguillon, M., and Desveaux, R. 1936a. *Bull. soc. chim. biol.* **18,** 1291–1296.

Lemoigne, M., Monguillon, M., and Desveaux, R. 1936b. *Bull soc. chim. biol.* **18,** 1297–1303.

Lemoigne, M., Monguillon, M., and Desveaux, R. 1937. *Compt. rend.* **204,** 1841–1843.

Lemoigne, M., Monguillon, M., and Desveaux, R. 1938. *Compt. rend. soc. biol.* **127,** 1403–1405.

Leonian, L. H., and Lilly, V. G. 1938. *Phytopathology* **28,** 531–548.

Leonian, L. H., and Lilly, V. G. 1940. *Am. J. Botany* **27,** 18–26.

McElroy, W. D., and Mitchell, H. K. 1946. *Federation Proc.* **5,** 376–379.

Mahdihassan, S. 1930. *Biochem. Z.* **226,** 203–208.

Mitchell, H. K., and McElroy, W. D. 1946. *Arch. Biochem.* **10,** 351–358.

Miwa, T., and Yoshii, S. 1934. *Sci. Repts. Tokyo Bunrika Daigaku* **B1,** 243–270.

Mosher, W. A., Saunders, D. A., Kingery, L. B., and Williams, R. J. 1936. *Plant Physiol.* **11,** 795–806.

Neuberg, C., and Rosenthal, O. 1924. *Biochem. Z.* **105,** 186–188.

Otani, H. 1934. *Acta Schol. Med. Univ. Imp. Kioto* **17,** 242–248, 249–259, 260–268, 269–287. (*Chem. Abstracts* **29,** 2205, 1935.)

Otani, H. 1935a. *Acta Schol. Med. Univ. Imp. Kioto* **17,** 323–329.

Otani, H. 1935b. *Acta Schol. Med Univ. Imp. Kioto* **17,** 330–333.

Otani, H., and Ichihara, K. 1925. *Folia Jap. Pharmacol.* **1,** 397–405 (cited in Janke, A. 1930. *Arch. Mikrobiol.* **1,** 304–332).

Ovcharov, K. E. 1937. *Compt. rend. acad. sci. URSS* **16,** 461–464.

Ovcharov, K. E. 1938. *Compt. rend. acad. sci. URSS* **20,** 377–380 (in English).

Padwick, G. W. 1936. *Sci. Agr.* **16,** 365–372.

Plattner, P. A., and Clausson-Kaas, N. 1945a. *Helv. Chim. Acta* **28,** 188–195.

Plattner, P. A., and Clausson-Kass, N. 1945b. *Experientia* **1,** 195–196.

Pringsheim, H. 1908. *Biochem. Z.* **8,** 128–131.

Quastel, J. H. 1947. *Endeavor* **6,** No. 23, 129–134.

Raynor, M. C. 1922. *Botan. Gaz.* **73,** 226–235.

Regnier, J., Lambin, S., and Dubost, M. 1946. *Ann. pharm. franc.* **4,** 149–153.

Rippel, K. 1931. *Arch. Mikrobiol.* **2,** 72–135.

Ritter, G. 1916. Material on the Physiology of Fungi. p. 1–17 (in Russian). (Cited in Kostytschew and Tswetkowa, 1930.)

Robbins, W. J. 1924. *J. Gen. Physiol.* **6,** 259–271.

Robbins, W. J. 1937. *Am. J. Botany* **24,** 243–250.

Robbins, W. J., and Ma, R. 1945. *Am. J. Botany* **32,** 509–523.

Robbins, W. J., and McVeigh, I. 1946. *Am. J. Botany* **33,** 638–647.

Roberg, M. 1932. *Zentr. Bakt. Parasitenk. Abt II* **86,** 466–479.

Robinson, M. E., and McCance, R. A. 1925. *Biochem. J.* **19,** 251–256.

Saida, K. 1901. *Ber. deut. botan. Ges.* **19,** 107–115.

Sakaguchi, K., and Chang, W. Y. 1934. *J. Agr. Chem. Soc. Japan* **10,** 459–476.

Sakamura, T. 1930. *Planta* **11,** 765–814.

Sakamura, T. 1934. *J. Faculty Sci. Hokkaido Imp. Univ.* **3,** Series V, 121–138.

Sakamura, T. 1935. *J. Faculty Sci. Hokkaido Imp. Univ.* **4,** Series V, 2.

Schade, A. L. 1940. *Am. J. Botany* **27,** 376–384.

Schade, A. L., and Thimann, K. V. 1940. *Am. J. Botany* **27,** 659–670.

Schmalfuss, K., and Mothes, K. 1930. *Biochem. Z.* **221,** 134–153.

Schober, R. 1930. *Jahrb. wiss. Botan.* **72,** 1–105.

Schopfer, W. H. 1935. *Z. Vitaminforsch.* **4,** 187–206.

Schopfer, W. H., and Blumer, S. 1942. Cited in Schopfer, W. H., and Guilloud, M. 1945. *Z. Vitaminforsch.* **16,** 181–296.

Schroder, M. 1931. *Jahrb. wiss. Botan.* **75,** 377–398.

Segal, W., and Wilson, P. W. 1948. *Proc. Soc. Am. Bact. 48th Gen. meeting* p. 6.

Senn, G. 1928. *Biol. Revs. Biol. Proc. Cambridge Phil. Soc.* **3,** 77–91.

Shibata, K.   1904.   *Hofmeister's Beitr. g. chem. Physiol. u. Path.* **5** (cited in Schmal-
    fuss, K., and Mothes, K. 1930).
Skinner, C. E., Emmons, C. W., and Tsuchiya, H. M.   1947.   In Henrici's Molds,
    Yeasts, Actinomycetes.   Wiley, New York.
Sprince, H., and Wooley, D. W.   1944.   *J. Exptl. Med.* **80**, 213–217.
Stanier, R. Y.   1942.   *J. Bact.* **43**, 499–520.
Steinberg, R. A.   1937.   *J. Agr. Research* **55**, 891–902.
Steinberg, R. A.   1939a.   *Botan. Rev.* **5**, 327–350.
Steinberg, R. A.   1939b.   *J. Agr. Research* **59**, 749–763.
Steinberg, R. A.   1939c.   *J. Agr. Research* **59**, 731–748.
Steinberg, R. A.   1942.   *J. Agr. Research* **64**, 455–475.
Tamiya, H.   1932.   *Acta Phytochim. Japan* **6**, 1–129 (in German).
Tamiya, H., and Usami, S.   1940.   *Acta Phytochim. Japan* **11**, 261–298 (in German).
Tazawa, Y., and Yamagoto, S.   1937.   *Acta Phytochim. Japan* **9**, 299–310 (in
    German).
Ternetz, C.   1907.   *Jahrb. wiss. Botan.* **44**, 353–408.
Thakur, A. K., and Norris, R. V.   1928.   *J. India Inst. Science Series A*, **11**, 141–160.
Tove, S. R., Niss, H. F., and Wilson, P. W.   1949.   Abstracts of papers, 49th Gen-
    eral Meeting, Soc Am. Bact., p. 59.
Uemura, T.   1937.   *J. Agr. Chem. Soc. Japan* **13**, 1146–1152, 1153–1158.
Uemura, T.   1939.   *J. Agr. Chem. Soc. Japan* **15**, 353–358.
Van Niel, C. B.   1940.   Occasional Publ. 14, *Am. Assoc. Advancement Sci.*, p. 106.
Virtanen, A. I., and Erkama, J.   1938.   *Nature* **142**, 954.
Virtanen, A. I., and Csáky, T. Z.   1948.   *Nature* **161**, 814–815.
Vita, N.   1937.   *Ergeb. Enzymforsch.* **7**, 209–233.
Waksman, S. A., and Lomanitz, S.   1925.   *J. Agr. Research* **30**, 263–281.
Werle, E.   1941.   *Biochem. Z.* **309**, 61–76.
Werle, E.   1943.   *Chemie* **56**, 141–148.
White, N. H.   1941.   *J. Council Sci. Ind. Research* **14**, 137–146.
Wilson, P. W., and Burris, R.   1947.   *Bact. Revs.* **11**, 41–73.
Wirth, J. C., and Nord, F. F.   1943.   *Arch. Biochem.* **2**, 463–68.
Wolf, F. F.   1948.   *Arch. Biochem.* **16**, 103–149.
Wolf, F. F., and Shoup, C. S.   1943.   *Mycologia* **35**, 192–200.
Wolff, H.   1926.   *Jahrb. wiss. Botan.* **66**, 1–34.
Woolley, D. W.   1946.   *J. Biol. Chem.* **166**, 783–784.
Woolley, D. W.   1948.   *J. Biol. Chem.* **176**, 1291–1298, 1299–1308.
Woods, D. D.   1938.   *Biochem. J.* **32**, 2000–2012.
Yamada, M., and Ishida, S.   1926.   *J. Agr. Chem. Soc. Japan* **2**, No. 7, 1 p.
Yukawa, M.   1924.   *J. Coll. Agr. Tokyo Imp. Univ.* **5**, 291–299.
Zaleski, W., and Pjukow, D.   1914.   *Ber. deut. botan. Ges.* **32**, 479–483.

CHAPTER 18

OTHER TRANSFORMATIONS IN FUNGI

Sulfur Metabolism

Compared to details known about transformation of sulfur-containing compounds in bacterial and animal tissues, information on this phase of metabolism in fungi is limited and largely empirical. It goes without saying that fungus cell material contains sulfur compounds common to all biological systems: cystine, methionine (and its precursor cystathionine), biotin, and thiamine. In addition, certain sulfur compounds not known generally, if at all, in other systems are present in fungi or formed by fungi: penicillin(s), cyclic choline sulfate, gliotoxin. Also known in fungi are thiourea and methyl mercaptan. These individual compounds will be discussed later.

1. Utilization of Different Forms of Sulfur

Almost invariably sulfate serves as a satisfactory source of sulfur for fungi, the organisms utilizing it for synthesis of various cellular constituents. Obviously sulfate utilization connotes sulfate reduction because the sulfur in most biochemical molecules is in more or less a state of reduction. Nevertheless, there are some instances in which fungi lack the ability to perform the reduction processes essential for the utilization of sulfate and require the sulfur in some reduced form such as cysteine, cystine, sulfide, hyposulfite, thioacetate, thioglycolate, or thiourea. Thiosulfuric ($S_2O_3H_2$) and thiocarbonic (CSO_2H_2) acids also are utilizable. This feature seems to be a property characteristic of many species of Saprolegniaceae (Volkonsky, 1932; 1933a and b; 1934). Not only is sulfate non-utilizable, but other oxidized forms of sulfur also: sulfite, bisulfite, persulfate and dithionate. Nevertheless, strain differences do exist within the Saprolegniaceae, for one species, *Brevilignia gracilis*, uses sulfur in all the above forms except dithionate (Bhargava, 1945). Volkonsky (1933) coined the terms *parathiotroph* for organisms utilizing only reduced forms of sulfur, and *euthiotroph* for those utilizing sulfate and other oxidized sulfur. This author also ascribes this physiological peculiarity of the Saprolegniaceae to their ecological background. In nature these organisms grow on living animals and dead organic matter where reduced sulfur (cysteine) ostensibly is always available, and also in putrefying organic matter generally immersed in water where the anaerobic conditions are conducive to the formation of H_2S and other reduced sulfur compounds through bacterial action. This line of reasoning may be somewhat teleological in view of the fact that other sulfate-utilizing fungi also are present under the same conditions, and that sulfate probably is present even though in minute amounts.

Steinberg (1941) has made the most extensive tests in utilizability of sulfur in different inorganic and organic combinations. *Aspergillus niger* was the test organism for some forty-odd compounds of sulfur. Sulfate, hyposulfite and sulfoxylate were all used, the last-named being the lowest state of oxidation in which inorganic S can be used efficiently. Thiosulfate, sulfanic acid and persulfate all were good S sources. A great variety of different organic S compounds could serve as a source of sulfur for growth. Cystine and methionine were excellent, but sulfur in the form of thiamine could not be utilized for synthesis of other cell constituents. Presumably the thiazole ring cannot be ruptured by *A. niger*. Other examples of good sulfur sources were thioacetamide, thiooxalate, and hydroxymethane sulfinate, and some alkyl sulfonates. According to Steinberg utilization of S in alkyl sulfonates and alkyl sulfinates involves removal of the sulfur as free sulfinic acid, HSOH, probably enzymatically by a "desulfinase." In general, assimilability of organic sulfur varied with the molecular configuration of the compounds and was correlated with the presence of adjacent oxygen in the molecule. Steinberg concluded that reduction is a normal preliminary process in the utilization of S compounds. However, the reduction may not be too far, for compounds like sulfoxylate and sulfinate are too reduced and are poor S sources, and sulfide, disulfide, and mercaptan S are non-assimilable. Oxidized sulfur compounds are believed to be converted to organic S compounds in the cell via reduction to sulfoxylic acid (HSOOH).

2. REDUCTION OF SULFUR COMPOUNDS

Under the proper conditions the reduction of a variety of different sulfur compounds to hydrogen sulfide can be demonstrated. This action is favored by a suitable organic hydrogen donor (carbohydrate), amounts of sulfur compound in excess of the sulfur requirements of the organism and more or less anaerobic conditions. In essence, the action can be interpreted as the oxidized form of sulfur functioning as a hydrogen acceptor in the dissimilation of the carbohydrate. Armstrong (1921) found that $MgSO_4$, $Na_2S_2O_3$, KSH, $KHSO_3$, $K_2S_2O_8$, KCNS, and NH_4CNS all were good sources of sulfur for *Aspergillus niger*, *Penicillium glaucum*, and *Botrytis cinerea*. H_2S was produced from all the compounds except $SO_4^=$ and $S_2O_8^=$. From thiosulfate ($S_2O_3^=$), in addition to H_2S, tetrathionate and molecular sulfur was formed, which appear as globules in the hyphae, and in old, somewhat dried-out cultures, as crystals. These observations in the main confirmed earlier work (Kossowicz and Leow, 1912). Tanner (1918) demonstrated reduction of sulfate to H_2S by the yeastlike forms *Torula monosa* and *T. dattila;* similar action was obtained with peptone, cystine, thiourea and molecular sulfur.

The reduction of free sulfur to H_2S by living systems is well-known as phytochemical reductions, that is, reduction of substances not normally a part of the particular system. It is simply a matter of another hydrogen acceptor competing for hydrogen made available by cellular dehydrogenases and hydrogen carriers, and it may be predicted with reasonable certainty that all organisms can form some H_2S from S. Addition of elementary sulfur stimulates the growth of *Fusarium lini* with isopropanol and glycerol as substrates (Sciarini and Nord, 1943). The sulfur was interpreted as functioning as an accessory H acceptor. In the case of isopropanol the reaction was represented as:

$$CH_3CHOHCH_3 \xrightarrow[\text{Dehydrogenase}]{-2H} + S = CH_3COCH_3 + H_2S$$

Isopropanol   Acetone

though the stoichiometric balance was not established. A positive lead acetate test for H_2S was obtained in less than 15 minutes after addition of sulfur to Fusarium cultures on isopropanol. In glucose cultures, elementary sulfur reduced the amount of pyruvic acid which typically accumulates in sugar fermentation by this organism (Chapter 9), and increased the mycelium weight and also the amount of alcohol produced. Ordinarily the pyruvate accumulation is increased owing to nitrite inhibition of carboxylase, the nitrite arising via reduction of nitrate as the nitrogen source in the medium. Here the sulfur is believed to compete with nitrate for available hydrogen, less inhibition of carboxylase then occurring owing to lesser amounts of nitrite, and pyruvate decarboxylation proceeds to give enhanced alcohol yields.

In some cases reduction of sulfate is not accompanied by the usual inorganic products, but rather by "neutral" sulfur compounds, i.e., organic-combined sulfur. This accumulates in the mycelium of *A. niger* and to some extent in the medium, the latter rising sharply in old cultures due to autolytic release of cellular sulfur-containing substances (Mothes, 1938; Rippel and Behr, 1937). The S content of *A. niger* protein was determined as 3.4 per cent. Glutathione was detected as one of the sulfur-containing compounds released during autolysis.

3. OXIDATION OF SULFUR

This is not in the sense that sulfur oxidation can be utilized as the sole energy source as it can in the case of autotrophic bacteria. Oxidation of reduced sulfur compounds to SO₄ is an incidental side reaction observed to take place weakly in fungus cultures. Elementary S can be oxidized to sulfate (Sciarini and Nord, 1943) as can sulfur in organic combination. Thus Garreau (1941) found that 16.4 per cent of the sulfur in methionine was converted to sulfate, the figures for cysteine and taurine being 40–50 and 25–30 per cent respectively. Compounds yielding no sulfate were cysteic acid, ethylene sulfonate, isothionate, sulfoacetate and ethanesulfonate. Sulfate is the chief product of conversion of sodium thiosulfate by certain fungi (Armstrong, 1921). In some cases sulfate formation accounts for the major portion of the sulfur transformation. Thus with amounts of sulfur as cystine ranging from 41 to 124 mg., sulfate equivalent to 80–90 per cent of the initially-present sulfur was formed, only a small amount of S being assimilated into the mycelium (Mothes, 1938). The oxidation proceeds best at more alkaline pH values; oxygen was necessary, and most sulfate was formed in the absence of sugar. The presence of nitrate favored the oxidation process. One may assume that the presence of carbohydrate would tend to favor maintenance of the sulfur in the reduced state.

4. SULFATASE

This enzyme hydrolyzes sulfuric acid esters according to this equation:

$$R \cdot OSO_3K + H_2O \rightarrow ROH + KHSO_4$$

The enzyme can be obtained in a water extract of dry *Aspergillus oryzae* mycelium and it splits ethereal sulfates of simple phenols, naphthols, dihydroxybenzene, substituted phenols, phenolic aldehydes and acids, quinoline and indole (Neuberg and Wagner, 1925–26).

5. INTERMEDIARY METABOLISM OF SULFUR COMPOUNDS IN FUNGI

The bulk of available information on this subject and dealing with cystine, methionine, thiamine and biotin is described in Chapter 6. For bromine-oxidizable S compounds see Plumlee and Pollard (1949).

6. OTHER SULFUR-CONTAINING SUBSTANCES SYNTHESIZED BY FUNGI

(a) *Gliotoxin*. This is an antibiotic substance produced by various species of *Trichoderma*, *Gliocladium fimbriatum*, *Aspergillus fumigatus*, and *Penicillium* sp., having the following composition: $C_{13}H_{14}O_4N_2S_2$. Boiling with caustic potash results in rapid loss of sulfur as sulfide. The ultraviolet absorption spectrum indicates the presence of an indole nucleus.   Tentative structure:

$$CHOH$$
$$CH \cdot CO$$
$$S \cdot (HO)C \longrightarrow C(OH) \cdot N \cdot CH_3$$
$$S \longrightarrow CH_2 \qquad \text{(Dutcher } et\ al., 1945)$$

(b) *Penicillin.*   (See Chapter 19 for chemistry.)   Sulfur is in the ring structure of all penicillins.   Upon acid hydrolysis a sulfur-containing amino acid (penicillamine) is liberated.   It is d-β, β-dimethylcysteine.

$$CH_3$$
$$HSC \longrightarrow CH \longrightarrow COOH$$
$$CH_3 \quad NH_2$$

(c) *Cyclic Choline Sulfate.*

$$(CH_3)_3NCH_2CH_2OSO_2$$
$$\lfloor O \rfloor$$

This betaine type substance was isolated from the mycelium of *Aspergillus sydowi;* it is the anhydride of a sulfuric acid ester of choline (Woolley and Peterson, 1937).

(d) *Methyl Mercaptan, CH_3SH.*   This compound is formed with H_2S from sulfate by the wood-rotting fungus *Schizophyllum commune* (Birkinshaw et al., 1942).   This was considered to be the first instance of reduction of sulfate to sulfide by fungi.   The formation of methyl mercaptan obviously involves a reduction and a methylation of inorganic sulfur, which is different from the methylation of organically-linked sulfur carried out by *Penicillium brevicaule* (Challenger and Rawlings, 1937).   See next section.   (See urea section in Chapter 17 *re thiourea.*)

(e) *Alkyl Thiols and Methylated Alykl Sulfides.*   Challenger and coworkers have studied certain transformations of organic sulfides by *Scopulariopsis brevicaulis* (*Penicillium brevicaule*) in connection with the comparative biochemistry of organo-metalloidal compounds in fungi (see arsenic section).   The failure to methylate inorganic S compounds by this organism is in contrast to the methylation of inorganic sulfate yielding methyl mercaptan reported above for *Schizophyllum commune.* Unlike what happens when selenium or tellurium is added to cultures of *S. brevicaulis*, the corresponding dimethyl sulfide is not obtained (Challenger, 1945).   However, this organism is able to split the disulfide linkage in diethyl sulfide (CH_3CH_2S—SCH_2CH_3) forming ethylthiol, CH_3CH_2SH. Dialkyl disulfides, RSSR, always yield the alkyl thiol, RSH, and in addition the methyl alkyl sulfide, $RSCH_3$. Thus two distinct actions take place: fission of the disulfide linkage and methylation. The former may be interpreted as a reduction, and *S. brevicaulis* cultures have strong-reducing properties (Challenger and Ellis, 1935; Challenger and Higginbottom, 1935). The disulfide fission holds for all simple aliphatic disulfides:

$$RSSR \rightarrow RSH + RSCH_3$$
Disulfide   Thiol   Methyl alkyl
sulfide

Disulfide	Products
Diethyl	Ethyl thiol and ethyl methyl sulfide
Di-*n*-propyl	Propyl thiol and propyl methyl sulfide
Di-*n*-butyl	Butyl thiol and butyl methyl sulfide
Di-*n*-amyl	Amyl thiol and amyl methyl sulfide

(Challenger and Blackburn, 1938.) The wood-rotting fungus *Schizophyllum commune* also does this (Challenger and Charleton, 1947).

The methylation reaction apparently is the result of a secondary action on the thiol compound, for addition of ethyl thiol and propyl thiol to *S. brevicaulis* cultures in the absence of the disulfide gives rise to the corresponding methylated compound. This methylation process is believed to occur via ionization of the thiol and transfer of a methyl group from some methyl donor such as betaine or choline

$$RSH \longrightarrow RS^- + H^+$$
$$RS^- + CH_3^+ \longrightarrow RSCH_3$$

(Challenger and Blackburn, 1938; Challenger and Rawlings, 1936; Challenger, 1945.)

The strong reducing powers of *Scopulariopsis brevicaulis* leads to a direct reduction of added diethyl sulfoxide, $(C_2H_5)_2SO$, to diethyl sulfide, $(C_2H_5)_2S$ (Challenger and North, 1934). *S. brevicaulis* also attacks S-containing amino acids and derivatives (Challenger and Charleton, 1947). From methionine are produced methyl mecaptan and dimethyl sulfide and from S-methyl-, S-ethyl-, and S-propylcysteines the corresponding alkyl methyl sulfides are produced. The authors consider the fission of these alkyl-S-C linkages to be a new type of biological action analogous to the fission of cystathionine in animals and in Neurospora.

CHLORINE METABOLISM OF FUNGI

Through the years the presence of chlorine in a medium for cultivation of fungi was purely fortuitous, its presence being due to the fact that certain cations required for growth are furnished as the chlorides. The outstanding example of this is the use of KCl in Czapek's solution and of NaCl, CaCl₂, FeCl₃, etc. in other common media. Though it is possible that KCl or NaCl play some role in ionic equilibria in the protoplasm of the cell, this effect would be non-specific, at least insofar as chloride ion goes. At least it may be said that no absolute requirement for chlorine is known in fungi, for excellent growth is made in its absence.

This point in itself created the idea that when chloride was present it was inert with respect to the organic nutrition of the organism. As a matter of fact, Raistrick and Smith's discovery in 1936 of two chlorine-containing organic compounds synthesized by *Aspergillus terreus*, namely, geodin and erdin, has proved that chlorine is metabolized by fungi. Later work has led to the identification of three more different chlorine-containing metabolic products of fungi, and to proof that chloride utilization in varying degrees is a general property of fungi.

In a survey of 139 species and strains tested with regard to the percentage of the available chloride assimilated, ten groups were differentiated (Clutterbuck, *et al.*, 1940). The medium was Czapek-Dox containing 0.5 g./liter KCl as the sole source of chloride.

Group	species metabolized	of total chloride originally present
Group I— 7	species metabolized 0–1%	of total chloride originally present
II—14	" " 1–2%	" " " " "
III—21	" " 2–3%	" " " " "
IV—15	" " 3–5%	" " " " "
V—16	" " 5–6%	" " " " "
VI—14	" " 6–7%	" " " " "
VII—11	" " 7–10%	" " " " "
VIII—23	" " 10–15%	" " " " "
IX—13	" " 15–25%	" " " " "
X— 5	" " over 25%	" " " " "

The organisms in the last two groups are listed to show the variety of types found to metabolize chloride: Group IX—*Aspergillus itaconicus*, *A. niger*, *A. terreus* (two strains), *A. versicolor*, *Penicillium candido-fulvum*, *P. chloro-leucon*, *P. commune*, *P. griseo-roseum*, *P. westlingi*, *Alternaria tenuis*, *Syncephalastrum racemosum*, *Trichoderma viride*. Group X—*Absidia spinosa*, 26.6 per cent of Cl metabolized; *Aspergillus terreus*, 33.5 per cent; *A. terreus* strain 45, 96.8 per cent; *Caldariomyces fumago*, 71.5 per cent; *C. fumago* strain Ag 92, 95.7 per cent.

These data show that extensive utilization of chloride by fungi is relatively rare, only five of 139 utilizing more than a quarter of the 238 mg. chloride available per liter and 118 organisms utilizing less than 10 per cent of this amount of chloride. Strain specificity with respect to Cl utilization is also apparent.

Table 1 shows a chlorine balance for the strongest chlorine metabolizer, *A. terreus* strain 45.

TABLE 1

CHLORINE BALANCE OF A. TERREUS[1]

	Cl as KCl, g.	Cl as per cent of KCl originally present
Original metabolism soln.....	15.575	100.0
(I) Residual inorganic Cl........	0.460	2.95
(II) Total Cl in soln.............	13.809	88.65
(III) Organic Cl in soln...........	13.349	85.70
(IV) Cl in H₂SO₄ ppt.............	9.672	62.10
(V) Total Cl in acid filtrate......	4.019	25.80
(VI) Cl in mycelium.............	1.835	11.78

Sum of (II) and (VI) equals 100.43%

[1] From Clutterbuck *et al.*, 1940. Total culture liquid initially = 311.5 liters.

Fraction IV contains the chlorine-containing geodin and erdin and these are extractable into ether, which removes all the Cl from the acid precipitate. No other Cl-containing compounds were present in this fraction. Some erdin and geodin were present in the acid filtrate fraction. The mycelium contained 11.78 per cent of the Cl present originally in the medium, but it was not in the form of geodin or erdin. Evidently chlorine compounds of unknown nature can be fixed into cell material.

The metabolism of fungi apparently is specific for chloride, because substitution of KI or KBr for KCl does not lead to formation of corresponding metabolic products containing either of these elements (Raistrick and Smith, 1936; Reilly and Curtin, 1943) though organic Br compounds were formed by *Caldariomyces fumago* (Clutterbuck *et al.*, 1940).

1. GEODIN, $C_{17}H_{12}O_7CL_2$ AND ERDIN, $C_{16}H_{10}O_7CL_2$

Isolation from *Aspergillus terreus* cultures and chemical properties may be found in Raistrick and Smith (1936), Calam *et al.* (1939) and Clutterbuck *et al.* (1937). These two substances are closely related in structure, geodin being the dextro-rotary isomeride of a monomethyl ether of the optically inactive erdin. Their close relation is indicated by the fact that each gives rise to a dihydro-derivative on catalytic reduction, dihydrogeodin being the methyl ester of dihydroerdin. Both are benzophenone derivatives.

2. GRISEOFULVIN, $C_{17}H_{17}O_6CL$ (Oxford *et al.*, 1939; Grove and McGowan, 1947)

Griseofulvin

This was first obtained in 1.65 per cent yield from the mycelium of *Penicillium griseo-fulvum* grown on Czapek-Dox medium. No griseofulvin was formed when ammonium tartrate was used as a source of N instead of nitrate. The "curling factor" present in culture filtrates of *Penicillium janczewskii* which causes stunting, excessive branching and characteristic distortions in germ tubes of *Botrytis allii* and other fungi (Brian *et al.* 1945, 1946) was isolated and found to be identical with griseofulvin (Grove and McGowan, 1947). Thus a chlorine-containing metabolic product of a mold is found to possess physiological activity. One is reminded of the antibacterial and antirickettsial properties of chloromycetin, a chlorine-containing substance isolated from culture filtrates of an unidentified actinomcyete belonging to the genus *Streptomyces* (Smith *et al.*, 1948).

3. CALDARIOMYCIN ($C_5H_8O_2CL_2$)

This ether-soluble substance has been isolated from culture filtrates of *Caldariomyces fumago* (Clutterbuck *et al.*, 1940), in yields up to 6.3 g. pure material per 35 liters of broth. Here again a large fraction (21 per cent) of the Cl utilized was fixed in the mycelium as unidentified substances. Other organic Cl-containing substances besides caldariomycin were present in the filtrates. Caldariomycin was shown to be probably 2:2-dichloro-cyclopentane-1:3-diol.

4. SCLEROTIORINE ($C_{20}H_{20}O_5CL$)

Isolated in 2% yield from the dry mycelium of *Penicillium sclerotiorum* (Curtin and Reilly, 1940; Reilly and Curtin, 1943). Sclerotiorine is a pH indicator being wine red in NH_4OH solution and yellow in acid solution. Like all the other Cl substances isolated from fungi it is soluble in fat solvents. This organism also produces other unknown Cl-containing organic substances.

Though few halide-containing substances are known at this time to be produced by fungi, enough evidence is available to indicate that halides participate in the organic metabolism of numerous fungi and it may well be a generalized property. Fungi whose natural habitat is a saline environment should be of particular interest in this connection. It is of special interest that chloride is not essential for the growth of fungi. In addition to the chlorine-containing products of actinomycete and fungus metabolism described above, one may mention two organic-Cl compounds isolated from lichens: gangaleoidin, $C_{18}H_{14}O_7Cl_2$ from *Lecanora gangaleoides* and diploicin, $C_{16}H_{10}O_5Cl_4$ from *Buellia canescens* (Nolan, 1934; Hardiman *et al.*, 1935). This calls to mind that lichens represent a symbiotic relationship between a fungus and an alga. Raistrick in his review (1940) points out the chemical relationship between erdin and geodin and sulochrin ($C_{17}H_{16}O_7$) a substance isolated from *Oospora sulphurea-ochracea* by Nishikawa (1939). All three substances are substituted benzophenones.

Since chlorine- and bromine-containing organic metabolic products of fungi have been established, one may expect eventually that iodine and fluorine compounds also will be discovered. The function of iodine in iodogorgic acid, the precursor of the hormone thyroxine in animals, is evidence for a biological function of that element.

As a matter of fact, almost a half a century ago it was claimed that *Aspergillus niger* produced an enzyme specifically acting on iodides, oxidizing them to free iodine (Raciborski, 1905). This action of the culture filtrates of *A. niger* has been confirmed several times and the so-called enzyme even named "iodide oxidase." The situation was clarified decisively by Pearce (1940) who showed that the oxidation is not catalyzed by a specific iodide oxidase or oxygenase as previously believed, but by hydrogen peroxide in the medium. The H_2O_2 is produced as a result of glucose oxidase or any other H_2O_2-producing system (e.g., xanthin oxidase) (see Chapter 15). The reaction is: $H_2O_2 + 2HI \rightarrow 2H_2O + I_2$. Naturally, the presence of catalase destroys the "iodide oxidase" activity of the culture solution.

ORGANO-METALLOIDAL COMPOUNDS OF ARSENIC, SELENIUM, AND TELLURIUM

1. ARSENIC

Most of our knowledge of this subject in relation to fungi we owe to F. Challenger (see review 1945), University of Leeds, England. This subject became established as a result of numerous cases of arsenic poisoning in Europe which were traced to inhalation of volatile arsenic compounds which originated from arsenic-containing pigments used as designs on the wallpaper. Rooms in which the poisonings recurred usually had a garlic odor typical of volatile arsenic compounds. While much attention had been devoted to the subject previously a systematic study of this situation was done first by the Italian Gosio in 1891. It is now known that the gas is formed by molds growing on the wallpaper when moisture conditions are suitable. Gosio (1897) showed that many pure cultures of fungi isolated from nature, including *Aspergillus glaucus*, *A. virens*, *Mucor mucedo* and *Penicillium brevicaule*, produce the garlic odor of volatile arsenic compounds from ordinary media to which a small amount of arsenious oxide was added. *Penicillium notatum* and *P. chrysogenum* also carry out these reactions (see Challenger, 1945). Bacteria were inactive in this respect. *Penicillium brevicaule* was especially active and this organism has been used as experimental object matter through to the present day. Modern nomenclature for this organism is *Scopulariopsis brevicaulis* and sometimes it is referred to as the arsenic fungus. Numerous other fungi including *Aspergillus fischeri*, *A. sydowi*, *A. fumigatus*, *A. glaucus* and *A. ochraceus* have been found positive, but the majority are negative (Thom and Raper, 1932). Here fifteen species of Penicillium and seventeen of twenty-two species of Aspergillus were negative. Ten strains of *P. brevicaule* and fourteen of *A. sydowi* have also been shown to liberate Gosio gas, as the volatile arsenic substance is often called (Thom and Raper, 1932).

The garlic odor is so distinctive and the human nose so sensitive to it that this biological process is perhaps the most sensitive qualitative test for arsenic known. Gosio formulated the procedure whereby the arsenic is extracted from the test material with water or dilute acid, evaporated to a small volume or to dryness, and a portion of the residue added to a slice of sterile potato previously inoculated with the mold. After 2 hours incubation, any inorganic arsenic originally added can be detected by the characteristic garlic odor. This technique permits recognition of less than 1 μg. As_2O_3 per gram (0.76 ppm As) of original test material (Smith and Cameron, 1933). This method involves addition of the As sample directly onto the mold surface on synthetic agar media.

On the basis of combustion analysis for carbon and hydrogen in the gas, Gosio believed it was diethyl arsine, $(C_2H_5)_2AsH$, a compound previously unsynthesized chemically. However, the true identity of Gosio gas was revealed as trimethyl arsine $(CH_3)_3As$ by Challenger *et al.*, in 1933. The volatile arsenic compound was isolated by absorbing it in a solution of mercuric chloride in dilute HCl. Trimethyl arsine forms an insoluble dimercurichloride of trimethyl arsine $(CH_3)_3As\cdot2HgCl$, which then may be identified chemically. In addition, arsenious oxide, sodium methylarsonate $(CH_3As(ONa)_2)$, and sodium cacodylate $(CH_3AsOONa)$ added to *S. brevicaulis* cultures also generated trimethyl arsine.

The gaseous substances obtained when sodium ethyl arsonate, $C_2H_5As(ONa)_2$, was added to the mold culture was not identical with that produced from sodium methyl arsonate, i.e., instead of trimethyl arsine there was produced ethyl dimethyl arsine, $(CH_3)_2AsC_2H_5$. Similar results were obtained with homologous alkyl arsonates (Challenger and Ellis, 1935; Challenger and Rawlings, 1936):

Alkyl arsonic acid added	Formula	Gas formed	Formula
Diethyl..............	$(C_2H_5)_2AsOOH$	Methyldiethylarsine	$(C_2H_5)_2AsCH_3$
n-Propyl.............	$(C_3H_7)AsO(OH)_2$	Dimethylpropylarsine	$(C_3H_7)As(CH_3)_2$
Methyl-n-propyl......	$(C_3H_7)(CH_3)AsOOH$	Dimethylpropylarsine	$C_3H_7As(CH_3)_2$
Ethyl-n-propyl.......	$(C_3H_7)(C_2H_5)AsOOH$	Methylethylpropylarsine	$(C_3H_7)(C_2H_5)AsCH_3$
Allyl................	$CH_2{=}CHCH_2AsO(OH)_2$	Dimethylallylarsine	$CH_2{=}CHCH_2As(CH_3)_2$

In essence, the fungus completes the alkylation of arsenic compounds by methylating non-alkylated bonds. It is evident that besides methylation, *S. brevicaulis* must effect reductions in order to convert substances such as sodium arsenate and the mono- and di-alkyl arsonic acids to methylated tertiary arsines. The prominent reducing powers of this organism also are manifested by its reduction of diethylsulfoxide $(C_2H_5)_2SO$, and hydroxydimethylselenonium nitrate (the nitrate of the selenoxide, $(CH_3)_2Se(OH)NO_3$) respectively to diethyl sulfide, $(C_2H_5)_2S$, and dimethyl selenide $(CH_3)_2Se$ (Challenger and North, 1934). Also direct reducing actions are the conversion of hydroxytrimethylarsonium nitrate (the nitrate of trimethylarsine oxide, $(CH_3)_3AsONO_3$), to trimethyl arsine, $(CH_3)_3As$, and of tripropylarsine oxide $(C_3H_7)_3AsO$, to tripropylarsine, $(C_3H_7)_3As$ (Challenger and Higginbottom, 1935).

These reducing powers evidently are enzymatically specific to judge from the fact that an organism effecting such unquestioned reductions, does not reduce the allyl side chain to propyl during the conversion of allylarsonic acid to allyldimethyl arsine (see above).

2. ARSENIC TOLERANCE

Certain fungi can grow in the presence of concentrations of arsenic that are strongly inhibitory to other fungi. *Cladosporium herbarum*, for example, tolerates 2 per cent arsenic. However, it has been shown that fungi tolerant to high arsenic concentrations do not metabolize the arsenic in the manner described above (Challenger, 1945). Soils heavily infested with arsenic residues from arsenical sprays have yielded fungi volatilizing arsenic: two Fusaria, one Paecilomyces, and one sterile brown fungus (Thom and Raper, 1932).

3. SELENIUM

Arsenic, selenium, and tellurium are similar in numerous chemical (as well as toxological) properties and it is not unexpected to find they are metabolized by biological systems in similar fashion. It has been long known that the ingestion of soluble selenium or tellurium compounds by animals or humans leads to development of extremely unpleasant odors in the breath. These odorous substances are dimethyl selenide and dimethyl telluride. Similar odoriferous substances have been known to be formed from inorganic compounds of selenium and tellurium by *S. brevicaulis* in a work modeled after Gosio's experiments with arsenic (Rosenheim, 1902). The tellurium smell was garliclike, resembling Gosio gas, whereas the selenium smell has a putrefactive pungency. Challenger and North (1934) have identified by adequate chemical criteria the gases generated by *S. brevicaulis* from selenium compounds as dimethylselenide, $(CH_3)_2Se$.

Similar to events with arsenic analogues, methyl-, ethyl-, and propyl-selenic acids give rise to the corresponding methylated compounds: dimethyl selenide $(CH_3)_2$ Se, methylethyl selenide, $(CH_3)(C_2H_5)Se$, and methylpropyl selenide, $(CH_3)(C_3H_7)Se$. The corresponding alkylated selonic acids, $RSeO_2OH$, yield only dimethyl selenide regardless of the nature of R. This is due to the fact that the alkylated selonic acids undergo spontaneous hydrolysis to the corresponding alcohol, ROH, and potassium acid selenite, $KHSeO_3$, the latter in each case being converted to the dimethylselenide (Bird and Challenger, 1942).

4. TELLURIUM

The gaseous product formed by *S. brevicaulis* in this case is dimethyltelluride, $(CH_3)_2Te$ (Bird and Challenger, 1939). Soluble tellurites also are reduced to black amorphous tellurium by the fungus. *Penicillium notatum* and *P. chrysogenum* also produce dimethyl telluride from tellurium salts, dimethyl selenide from selenium salts (Bird and Challenger, 1939) and trimethylarsine from methylarsonate and cacodylate, and allyldimethyl arsine from allylarsonate (see Challenger, 1945). These organisms convert arsenious oxide to trimethylarsine.

It is evident that all three metallic substances are reduced and methylated by these fungi, and it is probable that the methylating mechanisms are identical in all cases. Differences between organisms (strain specificity) most likely is a function of the reducing power towards specific substances, e.g., weak action of Penicillia on arsenine oxide. Inorganic antimony compounds are not converted to the corresponding alkyl stibines.

5. MECHANISM OF METHYLATION

Challenger (1945) considers several theories and favors that generally accepted to occur in animal tissue, namely, the transfer of a methyl group from some already methylated compound such as choline or betaine.

Both these substances are virtually universal in biological systems. This is the mechanism whereby methionine synthesis occurs: the methyl of a donor such as choline or betaine is transferred to the sulfur of homocysteine to give methionine. The reverse reaction also is true. These methyl donors have not yet been incriminated experimentally in methylation of the metallic substances by fungi, but on the basis of comparative biochemistry it is the likely explanation. Apart from the source of the methyl group, there is the problem of the reduction. Again details are not available and the Leeds school (Challenger, 1945) visualizes the following sequence in the methylation of arsenious acid. All the compounds which undergo methylation either by molds or the animal body, are capable of furnishing negative ions. They also are distinguished by their content of unshared electrons, so that coordination of a positive methyl group by the ion forms a neutral molecule, which could then be reduced, undergo ionization again as above, and form another neutral molecule by coordination of a second methyl radical. The CH_3^+ presumably comes from betaine, choline or methionine. Demethylation leaves a negative ion which binds the hydrogen ion of the compound RH undergoing methylation. This last is pictured as follows (Challenger *et al.*, 1942).

$$(CH_3)_3{}^+NCH_2COO^- + RH \rightarrow (CH_3)_2NCH_2COOH + RCH_3$$

Transformations suggested by the Leeds school to take place in arsenious acid are as follows:

$$As(OH)_3 \rightarrow H^+ + (HO)_2AsO^- \xrightarrow{CH_3{}^+} CH_3\,As\underset{\overset{|}{OH}}{\overset{\displaystyle O}{\diagdown\!\!\parallel}}OH \rightarrow$$

Methylarsonic acid

$$H^+ + CH_3As\underset{O^-}{\overset{O}{\diagup\diagdown}}OH \xrightarrow{\text{Reduction}} CH_3 : As\underset{O^-}{\overset{OH}{\diagup\diagdown}} \xrightarrow{CH_3{}^+}$$

(Ion)

$$CH_3 : As\underset{CH_3\,O}{\overset{OH}{\diagup\diagdown}} \xrightarrow[\text{and reduction}]{\text{Ionization}} H^+ + CH_3 : As\underset{CH_3}{\overset{}{\diagdown}}O^- \xrightarrow{+CH_3{}^+}$$

Cacodylic acid

$$CH_3 : As\underset{CH_3}{\overset{CH_3}{}}\!\!\!-O^- \xrightarrow{\text{Reduction}} (CH_3)_3As$$

Trimethylarsine oxide   Trimethyl arsine

Thus a series of successive methylation reactions take place as the arsenic is sequentially prepared by ionization and reduction leading to sharing of electrons in the stable methylated compound. In the case of selenious acid:

$$H_2SeO_3 \rightarrow H^+ + \; : Se \overset{O^-}{\underset{O}{\diagup\diagdown}} OH \xrightarrow{CH_3^+} CH_3Se \overset{O}{\underset{O}{\diagup\diagdown}} OH \rightarrow$$

Methaneselenonic acid

$$\xrightarrow[\text{and reduction}]{\text{Ionization}} CH_3Se \overset{O^-}{\underset{O}{\diagup\diagdown}} : \xrightarrow{CH_3^+} (CH_3)_2Se \overset{O}{\underset{O}{\diagup\diagdown}} \xrightarrow{\text{Reduction}} (CH_3)_2Se \;\; :$$

Ion of methane-   Dimethyl-   Dimethyl
seleninic acid   selinone   selenide

None of the intermediates represented in these schemes has been detected or identified in the process as it occurs in fungi, but their addition artificially leads to their further conversion to trimethyl arsine. This holds for methylarsonic acid, cacodylic acid and trimethylarsine oxide (as the nitrate) (Challenger, Higginbottom and Ellis, 1933).

Cell-free enzyme preparations obtained by grinding the mold mycelium and obtaining the press juice do not form trimethylarsine from arsenious acid; nor do acetone-dry preparations nor the sterile culture filtrates. Evidently the enzymes involved are very delicate (Challenger and Higginbottom, 1935).

Pectin Enzyme Complex

Pectin is a polyuronide of plant origin and is of somewhat variable composition depending on the source. Complete acid hydrolysis of pectin yields D-galacturonic acid amounting to about two-thirds of the total, galactose, arabinose, acetic acid and methyl alcohol. Pectin occurs chiefly in the middle lamella (intracellular layer) of plant tissue and may be looked on as the cementing material lending rigidity to the tissue. Many fungi, including well-known plant pathogens, secrete enzymes which destroy (solubilize by hydrolysis) the pectin *in situ* causing the softening characteristic of rotting. The tissues are thereby transformed into a mass of more or less isolated cells surrounded by a large amount of clear light-colored liquid. This process is known as "maceration." Plant pathologists believe that the ability of fungi to secrete extracellular pectin-decomposing enzymes which soften the tissues considerably in advance of the hyphal tips, is one of the key biochemical features making for pathogenicity of these organisms. The dissolution action on the plant cell wall was first shown by DeBary for *Sclerotinia libertiana* in 1886.

The secretion of the pectin enzymes is not the means of access of the fungus to the tissue. This takes place only after the protective layer of the plant material has been penetrated by other organisms or by mechanical injury.

In the plant tissue pectin does not exist free, but in the form of a labile combination with cellulose and possibly other materials such as hemicellulose, of which araban is an example. The pectin material in this state is known as protopectin. Pectin is obtained from protopectin by treatment with hot water, acids and enzymes. The enzyme which liberates pectin is protopectinase. It is actually the splitting of proto- pectin by protopectinase which is responsible for the maceration process described above, and also for the liberation of cellulose fibers in retting of flax. The liberation of pectin from protopectin by protopectinase apparently is a hydrolysis. Davison and Willaman (1927) made a detailed study of the occurrence in fungi of protopectinase. The enzyme is produced by *Botrytis cinerea*, and species of Rhizopus which are parasitic on sweet potatoes, especially *R. tritici*. No protopectinase was found in *Sclerotinia libertiana* and related forms. The enzyme occurs in the culture filtrates and in the mycelium. On the other hand, *Sclerotinia cinerea*, the plum-rotting fungus, and *Fusarium chronyophthoron* form this enzyme (Sideris, 1924), as do *Botrytis cinerea* (Brown, 1915), numerous species of *Rhizopus* (Harter and Weimer, 1921) and various Penicillia including *P. erhlichii* (Ehrlich, 1932b). Sideris showed that extracellular protopectinase of *Sclerotinia cinerea* is formed only in older cultures where it exists also intracellularly in the fungus. In young cultures the enzyme is not liberated and is intracellular only. The best measure of the presence and activity of protopectinase is the maceration action on thin slices of plant tissue, such as potato, carrot or turnip. Active dry preparations can be made by precipitation of the culture filtrate or of mycelial extracts with 80 per cent ethanol. Other enzymes attacking the liberated pectin also were formed by these organisms.

The fact that an enzyme complex consisting of several individual enzymes is involved in the complete hydrolysis of pectin has long been known, mainly through the work of F. Ehrlich.

In fact, Kertesz (1936) postulates six enzymes in the complex, differing according to the groups split. However, in addition to protopectinase, the other two generally accepted enzymes attacking pectin are pectase and pectinase. Pectase is an esterase, (sometimes called pectinesterase) which hydrolyzes the methoxy groups off from the esterified carboxyl- groups of the galacturonic acid residues in the soluble pectin molecule. Methyl alcohol results and in the presence of calcium ion, the soluble pectin is converted into a gel. For this reason calcium chloride added to commercial can packs, such as tomatoes, gives a firm product.

Pectase action is a necessary prerequisite for pectinase action, for only deesterified (demethoxylated) pectin is attacked by the latter enzyme (Jansen and MacDonnell, 1945). Though these two enzymes are distinct and separable, in virtually every case they are produced together by fungi attacking pectin (Gäumann and Böhni, 1947; Ehrlich, 1937). The following tabulation from Davison and Willaman summarizes the principal differences between pectin enzymes:

	Protopectinase	Pectase	Pectinase
Substrate..................	Protopectin	Pectin	Pectic acid
Gross effect of action.........	Maceration of plant tissue	Coagulation (gel formation in presence of Ca^{++})	Hydrolysis
Type of linkage attacked......	Unknown	Ester	Ether (glucosidic)
Thermal inactivation.........	48°C.	68–70°	60°
Optimum pH...............	5	Above 7	3.0–3.5

The action of pectase may be represented as follows:

$$[\text{R—COOCH}_3]n + n\ \text{H}_2\text{O} \rightarrow n\ \text{R·COOH} + n\ \text{CH}_3\text{OH}$$

Pectase is not specific for pectin, hydrolyzing various esters, and various esterases possess pectase activity (Kertesz, 1936). Pectase is activated by various mono- and divalent cations (Lineweaver and Ballou, 1945).

By far the greatest amount of work has been devoted to pectinase, the enzyme responsible for complete rupture of the polymerized pectin molecule into its structural components. This enzyme is extremely widespread in fungi, both parasites and saprophytes. From a study of *Aspergillus niger, Penicillium* sp. and *Fusarium* sp. Waksman and Allen (1933) concluded that different fungi vary in the rate and nature of the decomposition of the pectin uronic acid complex. Strain specificity is involved here: one strain of *Aspergillus oryzae* is four times more active than another (Proskuriakov and Ossipov, 1939). All of the organisms already mentioned in this section on pectin produce pectinase; the following parasites also (Menon, 1934): *Monilia fructigena, Pythium de baryanum, Phytophthora erythroseptica, Fusarium fructigenum* and *Glocosporium fructigenum*. Pectin decomposition evidently is not the sole factor governing parasitism. For example, *Rhizopus nigricans* and *R. artocarpi*, severe potato parasites, were low in enzyme production whereas two non-parasitic forms, *Rhizopus chinensis*, and *R. microsporus*, produced the pectin enzymes abundantly in solution, though the mycelium itself was not rich in the enzyme (Harter and Wiemer, 1921–23).

Aspergillus oryzae, A. niger and *Mucor* sp. are other pectinase-producing fungi (Proskuriakov and Ossipov, 1939).

Numerous investigators have shown that the pectinase enzyme complex is formed only when the organism grows on vegetable extracts (contain pectin) or in synthetic medium to which pectin is added. In synthetic or in nitrogenous media in which pectin is absent these enzymes are not formed. It is clear then that these are adaptive enzymes, i.e., formed only when the organism grows in the presence of the specific substrate or greatly increased by addition of pectin (Harter and Wiemer, 1922; Proskuriakov and Ossipov, 1939; Gäumann and Böhni, 1947; Pfaff, 1947). This situation is not entirely clear, however, and the situation may be different in different fungi. Gäumann and Böhni (1947) working with *Botrytis cinerea* found that pectinase was a constitutive enzyme and pectase strongly adaptive. Extracellular enzyme formation was studied in each case. In synthetic medium with glucose as the sole carbon source pectinase was strong but there was practically no pectase formed. When pectin was present either in the presence or absence of glucose, abundant pectinase formation was observed, reaching a maximum in 4 days. Pectase was not detected until the 5th day and reached its maximum in 21 days. On the other hand, Pfaff's (1947) studies with *Penicillium chrysogenum* indicate that extracellular pectinase formation takes place only in response to the presence of certain specific substances in the medium: pectin, gum tragacanth, mucic acid, L-galactonic acid (γ-lactone) and D-galacturonic acid. The optical antipodes of the last two were inactive.

Appreciation of Pfaff's results depends on understanding of the chemical constitution of pectin (Ehrlich, 1932a and b). The pectin molecule is considered by Ehrlich to have as its basic structural component a tetragalacturonic acid complex. This accounts for 68 per cent of the pectin molecule. In combination with other substances this galacturonic acid complex is known as pectic acid: triacetylarabinogalacto-dimethoxytetragalacturonic acid. This complex is said to make up 94 per cent of pectic acid. The structural base of pectic acid is an anhydro ring configuration of the four galacturonic acid residues. This is called pectolic acid ($C_{24}H_{34}O_{25}$) (see p. 93 of *Biochem. Z.* **281**, 1935).

The ring structure is split by enzymatic hydrolysis at one point yielding pectolactonic acid which then is split further into four molecules of D-galacturonic acid. Ehrlich claims individual enzymes carry out these various steps, but, as little is known of these, we may for our purpose consider pectinase action to consist of acting on pectin and proceeding through the hydrolysis of linkages between the uronic acid residues in the polygalacturonic acid complex with liberation of free D-galacturonic acid.   One will observe that the reducing power of the solution increases owing to fission of the glucosidic linkage liberating aldehydic reducing groups.

This hydrolysis dissolves pectin gels and eliminates their viscosity forming the basis of the use of pectic enzymes in the clarification of fruit juices and other products containing pectin in the gel colloidal state. An enzyme (pectolase) polygalacturonidase obtained from *Penicillium erhlichii* acting on the polygalacturonide pectolic acid led to 85% recovery of D-galacturonic acid in crystalline form (Ehrlich *et al.*, 1935).

Returning to Pfaff's work, each of the five substances provoking polygalacturonidase formation by *P. chrysogenum*, namely, L-galactonic acid, D-galacturonic acid, mucic acid, pectin, and gum tragacanth all have in the molecule this basic structure

$$
\begin{array}{c}
| \\
-\mathrm{C}- \\
| \\
\mathrm{HCOH} \\
| \\
\mathrm{HOCH} \\
| \\
\mathrm{HOCH} \\
| \\
\mathrm{HCOH} \\
| \\
\mathrm{COOH}
\end{array}
$$

D-Galacturonic acid is present in mucic acid and in gum tragacanth. This structure is, therefore, essential for enzyme formation in *P. chrysogenum*.   In other words, not only does the substrate stimulate enzyme formation, but the product obtained from the substrate acts similarly. In the case of mucic acid and gum tragacanth, other enzymes are believed to split them, liberating the essential residue which then stimulated polygalacturonidase enzyme formation.   Pectinase itself does not attack these substances.   A similar situation is known for yeast invertase: the products of the reaction as well as the substrate stimulate invertase action (von Euler and Cramer, 1913) and it was found to hold true for gallic acid, the product of tannin hydrolysis by tannase in *A. niger* (Pottevin, 1900; Knudson, 1913b).

Pfaff found that pectase (pectinesterase) was absent whenever polygalacturonidase was absent, i.e. is adaptive, as found for *Botrytis cinerea* (Gäumann and Böhni, 1947).   Both enzymes require for their formation the same configurational grouping.   Interestingly enough, the product of the enzyme action (galacturonic acid) has much greater stimulating powers for enzyme formation than does the substrate itself.   Pfaff interprets his results on Yudkin's (1938) mass action theory of enzyme action which postulates a steady state equilibrium in the absence of substrate between enzyme and the enzyme precursor. The enzyme combines with the substrate or the product, thereby disturbing the equilibrium by removing enzyme, thereby favoring this reaction: precursor → more enzyme.

As a result of pectin decomposition, the pH of the solution drops. This is due to pectinesterase liberation of carboxyl groups and also to polygalacturonidase liberating monogalacturonic acid which is a stronger acid than the poly-compound.

The pectin enzymes of *P. chrysogenum* are almost entirely extracellular, only a very small amount being retained in the mycelium. A given mold surface pad produces undiminished amounts of pectinase through three successive changes of pectin-containing medium. Ammonia nitrogen was the best nitrogen source for enzyme production. Pectin-decomposing enzymes are as a class quite stable. Active preparations result not only from alcohol precipitation of aqueous enzyme solutions, but by ether-acetone dried mycelium and also by desiccation of active mycelium *in vacuo* over a drying agent.

Gallic Acid Formation from Tannins

Tannins (tannic acid) make up a heterogeneous group of substances which in general are esters of polyhydroxy phenols with an aromatic acid. They are sometimes called depsides. Many of the tannins have glucose attached via glucosidic linkage. Others contain phloroglucinol instead of glucose and protocatechuic acid instead of gallic. They occur only in plants and are especially rich in gall nuts formed in certain trees in response to insect injury. They occur especially rich in sumac leaves, in the bark of the hemlock and the oak, and in the wood of chestnut and quebracho trees. These latter all are utilized as commercial sources of tannins for use in tanning of hides to produce leather and they have certain pharmaceutical uses. Common to the majority of tannins is gallic acid (trihydroxy benzoic acid), $HO\left\langle\begin{array}{c}HO\\ \\HO\end{array}\right\rangle COOH$, which is in ester form and which is hydrolyzed by the enzyme tannase according to the general equation:

$$\text{Tannin} + n\ H_2O \rightarrow \text{Gallic acid} + \text{Other substances}$$

Gallotannin is the regular article of commerce. The splitting of digallic acid by tannase is as follows:

$$\text{HO–}\bigodot\text{–CO·O–}\bigodot\text{–COOH} \xrightarrow{+\,H_2O} 2\ \text{HO–}\bigodot\text{–COOH}$$

Digallic acid   Gallic acid

Tannase in gall nuts was discovered by Scheele in 1786 and discovered in fungi by Raulin in the early 1860's (Thom and Raper, 1945). The active fungus in gall nut fermentations was named and described for the first time as *Aspergillus niger* by van Tiegham in 1867. The significance of tannase for the microbiologist lies in the fact that a product of tannase action on tannins, namely gallic acid, has commercial value, and that certain fungi are the most potent sources of the enzyme and are utilized in commercial "fermentations" to produce gallic acid. Gallic acid is utilized in the manufacture of gallocyanin, a dye, and alizarin brown. It is also utilized in the manufacture of inks, hexahydroxyanthraquinone, and pharmaceutical skin preparations.

Though other fungi, notably of the *Penicillium glaucum* group, have been found to produce tannase since van Tiegham's studies, *A. niger* is generally more potent and is universally employed in this practice. Nowadays the fermentation is done on clear aqueous tannin-containing extracts of the plant material under submerged conditions, i.e., aeration and agitation after inoculation with the selected fungus strain. Formerly the hydrolysis was done in moist heaps of gall nuts, and the gallic acid recovered from the mass by leaching.

When the tannin content of the substrate is high (10 per cent solution) the gallic acid liberated crystallizes out in the medium. van Tiegham (1867) showed that air was essential for the mold growth but if the mycelium was submersed below the surface of the medium, the glucose resulting from the hydrolysis would accumulate at first and disappear later. Gallic acid itself was also believed to be consumed further. Calmette in 1902 patented a submerged process for the production of tannins, the first such application of this technique (German Patent 129,164). Fernbach (1900) and Pottevin (1900) independently discovered the enzymatic nature of the process and prepared cell-free preparations. Desiccated mycelium and alcohol precipitates of macerated mycelium yielded very active tannase preparations. Pottevin (1900) clearly described the adaptive nature of the enzyme: it was not formed in the usual Raulin carbohydrate synthetic medium, but only when the substrate tannin or the product of the enzyme action, gallic acid, was present was tannase formation by the mold induced (Knudson, 1913b confirmed this; see also Rippel and Keseling, 1931). (See also section on pectin.) The *A. niger* tannase also attacked tannates, i.e., precipitates of tannic acid with substances such as gelatine. Analogues also hydrolyzed were phenyl- and methylsalicylate, though probably this action was due to esterase impurities in the tannase preparation (see later).

Knudson's studies (1913a and b) are the most comprehensive on the microbiological aspects of tannins and tannase. Of 23 different fungus species tested in various concentrates of tannic acid in synthetic medium only one-third grew, the tannic acid being toxic for the others. Only *A. oryzae*, *A. flavus*, *A. niger*, and *Penicillium glaucum* survived 10 per cent. Only the last two were extremely tolerant to high concentrations of tannins and these alone were found to grow on tannin as the sole carbon source. In general one may conclude that saprophytic fungi are more tolerant to tannin toxicity, as large numbers of parasitic fungi were found to be inhibited by 0.1–0.8 per cent tannin (Cook and Taubenhaus, 1911). As van Tiegham and Pottevin had shown some 40 years earlier, Knudson found that gallic acid formed initially during growth of *A. niger* on tannin medium was further attacked and destroyed, this coinciding with the exhaustion of other utilizable organic materials generated from the tannin. In fact, one strain of Penicillium utilized the gallic acid faster than it was formed, hence it did not accumulate. Addition to the medium of 10 per cent sugar protected the gallic acid completely and permitted its accumulation, presumably a matter of preferential utilization of energy (see Chapter 4). Five per cent sugar was ineffective, possibly because it was rapidly consumed. The selective nature of this process in tannin solution is indicated by the fact that in a pure solution of gallic acid and glucose, only the latter was used. The mechanism of gallic acid utilization was clarified by Nicholson *et al.* (1931) who showed that *A. niger* produced not only tannase but a specific enzyme attacking gallic acid, named pyrogallase, which was obtained in cell-free form. The existence of this enzyme at once explains why theoretical yields of gallic acid from tannins are rarely obtained. The enzyme is produced also on a medium containing pyrogallol or gallic acid as sole carbon sources. Decomposition products were not isolatable, but a profound change takes place as indicated by loss of color properties with iron salts.

Excessive aeration, while favoring growth of the fungus, is unfavorable to gallic acid accumulation, presumably because the latter is utilized for cell synthesis and energy. Highest gallic acid yields were obtained under conditions of limited anaerobiosis, similar to van Tiegham's findings. Here the organism can hydrolyze the tannin, but lacks sufficient oxygen for further oxidation of the product. Under these conditions 1 mg. mycelium (dry weight) transformed 2.7 g. tannin in 10 days. Passage of *A. niger* 6 successive times through gallotannin medium enhanced considerably the tannase-producing ability of three strains; in one case the activity was almost doubled (Nicholson *et al.*, 1931).

All Knudson's studies dealt with stationary surface growth and, in summary, the economic method for gallic acid production centers around two features; (1) growth in tannin under aerobic conditions in the presence of 10 per cent sugar, (2) growth in tannin as the sole carbon source, under limited oxygen tension. Tannase is excreted abundantly into the medium when tannins or gallic acid are present. Knudson (1913b) has shown that enzyme production is proportional to the concentration of tannin in 10 per cent sugar medium, but with lower sugar concentration tannase production is actually decreased.

Tannase Preparation and Characteristics of Tannase Action

These have been studied by several authors. *A. niger* is generally used as starting material though *A. luchuensis* has also been used. Enzyme activity can be followed by NaOH titration of the carboxyl groups liberated during the hydrolysis (Freundenberg and Vollbrecht, 1921) of gallic acid methyl ester. Utilization of tannin may be followed by precipitation of unchanged material (gallotannin) with casein, and weighing the product (Nicholson *et al.*, 1931). The transformation can also be followed polarimetrically, tannin having a positive rotation, the products having zero rotation (Fernbach, 1900; Pottevin, 1900).

The most detailed studies of the properties of fungus tannase are by Dyckerhoff and Armbruster (1933). Extraction of the mycelium of *A. niger* was made with dilute HCl to destroy oxidases which would otherwise be present in the tannase preparations. The crude preparation would attack a great variety of tannin substances and esters, and the true specificity of the tannase distinct from the always-associated esterases was established by selectively destroying the latter by heating 10 minutes at 40°C. at pH 8.9. It is to be recalled that esterases also attack certain tannin esters; that is, two enzymes, tannase and esterase, have this property. Separation of these enzymes has also been accomplished by chromatography (Toth and Barsony, 1943). The esterase is retained on the aluminum oxide column, the tannase passing through. These authors find another tannin, glucotannin, is also split by two distinct enzymes, β-glucosidase and tannase. That different enzymes attacking the same substrates are present in *A. niger* extracts is shown by the fact that the hydrolyzing action of the extracts on methyl gallate, tannic acid and *m*-digallic acid is very much changed by Al_2O_3 absorption.

Tannase preparations freed from oxidases and esterases by heating as above, attack only those tannin compounds which contain at least two phenolic hydroxy groups in the acid component. The esterified carboxyl must be on the oxidized benzene ring and must not be σ- to one of the OH groups. Thus, tannic acid, chebulinic acid, *m*-digallic acid, methyl gallate and methyl protocatechuate are all attacked. If only 1 hydroxy is present, tannase is inert toward the compound.

As stated before, fungus esterase can also attack such substances in varying degrees. It is evident that mycelial extracts or culture filtrate preparations acting on tannins and called tannase, actually contain a mixture of enzymes capable of attacking tannin substances, and only one is a true tannase. The other enzyme impurities, as seen above, are esterases and glucosidases, if not others. As a matter of fact, Toth (1944) has shown that glucogallin and m-digallic acid are attacked by two distinct enzymes in *A. niger* extracts; the first he calls gallic acid esterase, the latter a depsidase.

Theotannin in extracts from tea is split by *A. niger* tannase (Deys and Dijkman, 1937).

OXIDATION OF LONG CHAIN SATURATED FATTY ACIDS

Utilization and metabolism in fungi of the lowest members of the fatty acid series, formic and acetic acids, has been covered in detail elsewhere in this book.

1. PROPIONIC ACID

This fat acid is highly toxic for fungi and its salts are utilized as commercial inhibitors of mold growth, finding especial application in the preservation of bread ("Mycoban"). Generally 2 to 3 ounces are added to each 100 lbs. of flour. Nevertheless, *Aspergillus niger* has been found to metabolize calcium propionate, lactic acid and pyruvic acid being identified as products (Walker and Coppock, 1928). Because the lactic acid accumulated earlier and more abundantly, the oxidation of propionate was considered as: fat acid → α-hydroxy acid (lactic) → α-keto acid (pyruvic).

2. HIGHER FATTY ACIDS

Most of our information on this subject comes from studies on the nature of rancidity of plant fats such as coconut and palm oils. The rancidity is due chiefly to the oxidative breakdown by fungi of fatty acids liberated by prior lipolytic action, yielding a series of methyl ketones containing one carbon less than the fatty acid of origin. Methyl amyl-, methyl heptyl-, and methyl nonyl ketones are those present usually, the methyl amyl ketone being responsible for the perfume-like quality of the odor of rancid oil. Also formed by fungi and contributing to rancidity are secondary alcohols corresponding to the ketones, esters of the secondary alcohols and of fatty acids, and free fatty acids.

Discovery and the role of fungi as causative agents of the rancidity process was made by Stärkle (1924). *Penicillium glaucum* was isolated from rancid oil, and it, and *A. niger* and *A. fumigatus* were shown to form methyl ketones when grown in pure culture on individual fatty acids as the carbon source.

According to Stärkle (1924), rancidity in butter is not due, as previously thought, to butyric acid esters, but to methyl propyl ketone and methyl nonyl ketone from the caproic and lauric acids present in the butter fat. Similarly, the strong ester-like distinctive odors of cheeses (Roquefort, Gorganzola, Stracchina, Parmesan, Stilton) whose curing is accomplished characteristically by molds, mainly *Penicillium*, though others such as *Cladosporium*, etc. are also active, are ascribed to volatile ketones formed from the fat originally present. Methyl amyl ketone and methyl heptyl ketone have been isolated from Roquefort cheese (Stärkle, 1924).

Conversion of individual fatty acids to the corresponding methyl ketones by pure cultures of *Penicillium glaucum* has been confirmed and extended by others (Acklin, 1929; Stokoe, 1928; Thaler and Geist, 1939a; Coppock *et al.*, 1928). The following represents a composite of fat acid $\rightarrow$ ketone conversions recorded by these authors:

	Fat acid	Corresponding ketone
C_4	Butyric	Acetone
C_5	Isovaleric	Acetone
C_5	Valeric	Methyl ethyl ketone
C_6	Caproic	Methyl propyl ketone
C_7	Enanthic (heptylic)	Methyl butyl ketone
C_8	Caprylic	Methyl amyl ketone
C_9	Pelargonic	Methyl hexyl ketone
C_{10}	Capric	Methyl heptyl ketone
C_{11}	Undecylic	Methyl octyl ketone
C_{12}	Lauric	Methyl nonyl ketone
C_{13}	Tridecylic	Methyl decyl ketone
C_{14}	Myristic	Methyl undecyl ketone

In some cases the expected ketones were obtained when the pure triglycerides were provided. From tricaproin, yields of methyl propyl ketones up to 48 per cent of theory were obtained (Acklin, 1929). With free fatty acids the yields were smaller and inversely proportional to the concentration:

Caproic Acid, Per Cent	Yield, Methyl Propyl Ketone Per Cent
0.25	10
0.5	7
1.0	3

3. MECHANISM OF KETONE FORMATION

The immediate precursor of the ketone is believed by the above investigators and other authorities (Breusch, 1948) to be the corresponding

β-keto acid, which by decarboxylation yields the ketone: $R \cdot CO \cdot CH_2 \cdot$ COOH $\xrightarrow{-CO_2}$ RCOCH$_3$. This decarboxylation has been established conclusively for acetone formation from acetoacetic acid in other systems, animal and bacterial, and by analogy and deduction one may conclude this is the reaction occurring in the fungi, though the decarboxylation of β-keto acids *per se* has not been studied nor have stoichimetric balances been established. However, there is no reason to doubt the occurrence of this reaction.

A point of special interest is that methyl ketones are not invariable products of saturated fatty acid breakdown by fungi. The latter are utilized readily by many fungi without any trace of ketone formation, and furthermore where ketone is formed the yields are not quantitative, indicating alternative methods of breakdown. Present day knowledge of fatty acid catabolism places Knoop's β-oxidation theory in a key position in this process (for up-to-date status see Breusch, 1948). This theory is epitomized as follows:

$$R \cdot CH_2 \cdot CH_2 \cdot COOH \rightarrow RCOCH_2COOH \rightarrow RCOOH + 2CO_2$$

Fatty acid $\qquad$ β-Keto acid $\qquad$ Fatty acid 2
carbons shorter

Thus, the fat acid is shortened by oxidizing off the end two carbons. The shortened fat acid is now further shortened in the same manner until the chain length is 4 or 2 carbons, i.e., acetoacetic acid or acetic acid. This then is metabolized via the citric cycle as described in previous chapters. Sometimes the successively-split-off two carbon atoms are pictured as being acetate, which also is metabolized to CO_2 and water via the citric cycle. As a matter of fact, the C_2 fragment probably is never liberated as such but is at once introduced into the C_6 tricarboxylic (citric) acid respiratory cycle via a coupled oxidation of the β-keto acid with oxalacetic acid. This is represented as follows (Breusch, 1948).

The β-ketoacid represented above usually is the end β-oxidation product, acetoacetic acid, though the higher analogues are involved in the reactions generating the acetoacetate.

Thus, two mechanisms compete for the β-keto acid in fat acid oxidation: decarboxylation to ketone formation and β-oxidation to CO_2 and H_2O. The explanation of Stokoe (1928) accounting for ketone formation is credible. He holds that Knoop's decomposition mechanism is the normal scheme, and prevails ordinarily, but that in ketone-forming fungi such as *Penicillium glaucum*, the long chain fatty acids are poisonous to an extent sufficient to inhibit the respiration and oxidative processes of the organism, and an abnormal decomposition of the β-keto acid now results, i.e., decarboxylation to the ketone. Stokoe showed that the fatty acids are poisonous to *P. glaucum*, increasing with chain length to a maximum with caprylic acid, then decreasing, possibly due to insolubility.

The secondary alcohols (carbinols) usually accompanying the ketones may be looked upon as a reduction product of the ketone, although Stokoe postulates that they are actually precursors of the ketone. This idea is based on the supposition that decarboxylation of either the β-keto acid or the β-hydroxy acid can yield ketone, represented as:

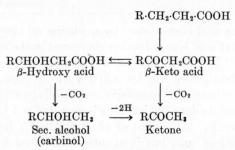

$$R \cdot CH_2 \cdot CH_2 \cdot COOH$$

$$\downarrow$$

RCHOHCH₂COOH ⇌ RCOCH₂COOH
β-Hydroxy acid   β-Keto acid

$$\downarrow -CO_2 \qquad \qquad \downarrow -CO_2$$

RCHOHCH₃ $\xrightarrow{-2H}$ RCOCH₃
Sec. alcohol   Ketone
(carbinol)

However, there is no support of this theory and in view of the rather widespread formation of secondary alcohols in biological systems via reduction of intermediary ketones, it seems likely the ketone is an intermediate in the carbinol formation rather than vice-versa. For example, in butyric acid fermentations by bacteria isopropanol formation results via reduction of acetone:

$$CH_3COCH_3 \xrightarrow{+2H} CH_3CHOHCH_3$$

Similarly, addition of ketones to yeast fermentation results in reduction to the secondary alcohol by phytochemical reduction. Furthermore, the common product of bacterial fermentations 2, 3: butylene glycol, originates via reduction of the corresponding ketone, acetyl methyl carbinol (acetoin).

$$CH_3 \cdot CHOH \cdot CO \cdot CH_3 \xrightarrow{+2H} CH_2CHOH \cdot CHOH \cdot CH_3$$

Acetoin   2,3:Butylene glycol

Carbinol formation by the fungi is therefore very likely as follows:

$$R \cdot CO \cdot CH_3 \xrightarrow{+2H} R \cdot CHOH \cdot CH_3$$

Methyl ketone   Secondary alcohol
(carbinol)

4. FORMATION OF β-KETO ACID FROM FATTY ACID

Granting that a β-keto acid is the key intermediate in fat metabolism irrespective of which further dissimilation takes place, the question now arises as to the origin of this compound from the original saturated fatty acid. Various theories have been proposed to explain this (Acklin, 1929), and absolute proof is still lacking, but the evidence favors the occurrence of this sequence:

$$R—CH_2—CH_2—COOH \xrightarrow{-2H} R—CH{=}CH—COOH \xrightarrow{+HOH}$$

β   α   α,β-Unsaturated acid

$$R—CHOH—CH_2—COOH \xrightarrow{-2H} R—CO—CH_2—COOH$$

β-Hydroxy fatty acid   β-Keto fatty acid

$$\nearrow^{-CO_2} \text{Ketone}$$
$$\searrow_{-2C} \text{Knoop oxidation}$$

These reactions have been demonstrated in other systems, and on the basis of comparative biochemistry is analogous to the ubiquitous Thunberg-Wieland mechanism of oxidation of the saturated dicarboxylic acid, namely succinic acid, yielding the β-keto acid, oxalacetic acid (see Thaler and Eisenlohr, 1941).

$$HOOC—CH_2—CH_2—COOH \xrightarrow{-2H} HOOC—C{=}C—COOH \xrightarrow{+HOH}$$

Succinic acid   Fumaric acid

$$HOOC—CHOH—CH_2—COOH \xrightarrow{-2H} HOOC—CO—CH_2—COOH \rightarrow \text{further metabolism}$$

Malic acid   Oxalacetic acid

Furthermore, as seen in Chapter 17 the first step carried out by amino acid oxidase is in essence an α,β-dehydrogenation. Finally there is the more direct evidence indicating that the α,β-unsaturated acid and the β-hydroxy fatty acids are intermediates in conversion of saturated fat acids to β-keto acids and hence the ketone, in experiments where these intermediates added individually as the sole carbon sources to *P. glaucum* cultures are converted to the corresponding ketones. Thus these β-hydroxy acids were partially converted as follows (Thaler and Geist, 1939b):

    (C_{10}) β-Hydroxycapric acid $\rightarrow$ Methyl heptyl ketone
    (C_6) β-Hydroxycaproic acid $\rightarrow$ Methyl propyl ketone
    (C_{14}) β-Hydroxymyristic acid $\rightarrow$ Methyl undecyl ketone
    (C_4) β-Hydroxybutyric acid $\rightarrow$ Acetone

In each case the ketone was isolated and identified as the p-nitrophenylhydrazone.

The following α,β-unsaturated homologues supplied as sole carbon sources also yielded the corresponding methyl ketones (Thaler and Eisenlohr, 1941):

α,β-Unsaturated acid		Corresponding to	Ketone isolated
Name	Formula		
Crotonic acid...............	$CH_3CH{=}CHCOOH$	Butyric acid	Acetone
2-Hexenoic acid............	$CH_3(CH_2)_2CH{=}CHCOOH$	Caproic acid	Methyl propyl ketone
2-Decenoic acid.............	$CH_3(CH_2)_6CH{=}CHCOOH$	Capric acid	Methyl heptyl ketone
2-Tetradecenoic acid........	$CH_3(CH_2)_{10}CH{=}CHCOOH$	Myristic acid	Methyl undecyl ketone

Further supporting the occurrence of the β-hydroxy acids as intermediates is the instance where β-hydroxy valeric acid is formed along with methyl ethyl ketone from valerate by *A. niger*, and β-hydroxybutyric and acetocetic acids along with acetone from butyrate (Coppock, *et al.*, 1928).

Formation of acetone has also been discussed as a product of citric acid breakdown by *A. niger* (see citric acid chapter).

5. UNSATURATED FATTY ACIDS

The common acids in this group, oleic, linoleic and linolenic acids, have not been studied with respect to mechanism of utilization by fungi, and one may assume the process is similar to that in other biological systems.

REFERENCES

Acklin, O. 1929. *Biochem. Z.* **204**, 253–274.
Armstrong, G. M. 1921. *Ann. Missouri Botan. Garden* **8**, 237–281.
Bhargava, K. S. 1945. *Proc. Indian Acad. Sci.* **21B**, 344–349.
Bird, M. L., and Challenger, F. **1939**. *J. Chem. Soc.* 163–168.
Bird, M. L., and Challenger, F. **1942**. *J. Chem. Soc.* 574–577.
Birkenshaw, J. H., Findlay, W. P. K., and Webb, R. A. 1942. *Biochem. J.* **36**. 526–529.
Breusch, F. L. 1948. *Advances in Enzymol.* **8**, 343–423.

Brian, P. W., Curtis, P. J., and Hemming, H. G. 1946. *Trans. Brit. Mycol. Soc.* **29**, 173–187.

Brian, P. W., Hemming, H. G., and McGowan, J. C. 1945. *Nature* **155**, 637.

Brown, W. 1915. *Ann. Botany* **29**, 319–348.

Calam, C. T., Clutterbuck, P. W., Oxford, A. E., and Raistrick, H. 1939. *Biochem. J.* **33**, 579–588.

Challenger, F. 1945. *Chem. Rev.* **36**, 315–361.

Challenger, F., and Blackburn, S. **1938**. *J. Chem. Soc.* 1872–1878.

Challenger, F., and Charleton, P. T. **1947**. *J. Chem. Soc.* 424–429.

Challenger, F., and Ellis, L. **1935**. *J. Chem. Soc.* 396–400.

Challenger, F., and Higginbottom, C. 1935. *Biochem. J.* **29**, 1757–1778.

Challenger, F., Higginbottom, C., and Ellis, L. **1933**. *J. Chem. Soc.* 95–101.

Challenger, F., and North, H. E. **1934**. *J. Chem. Soc.* 68–71.

Challenger, F., and Rawlings, A. A. **1936**. *J. Chem. Soc.* 264–267.

Challenger, F., and Rawlings, A. A. **1937**. *J. Chem. Soc.* 868–875.

Challenger, F., Taylor, P., and Taylor, B. **1942**. *J. Soc. Chem.* 48–55.

Clutterback, P. W., Koerber, W., and Raistrick, H. 1937. *Biochem. J.* **31**, 1089–1092.

Clutterbuck, P. W., Mukhopadhyay, S. L., Oxford, A. E., and Raistrick, H. 1940. *Biochem. J.* **34**, 664–677.

Cook, M. T., and Taubenhaus, J. J. 1911. *Delaware Agr. Exptl. Sta. Bull.* **91**, 77 pp.

Coppock, P. D., Subramaniam, V., and Walker, T. K. **1928**. *J. Chem. Soc. London* 1422–1427.

Curtin, T. P., and Reilly, D. 1940. *Biochem. J.* **34**, 1419–1421.

Davison, F. R., and Willaman, J. J. 1927. *Botan. Gaz.* **83**, 329–361.

Deys, W. B., and Dijkmann, M. J. 1937. *Proc. Acad. Sci. Amsterdam* **40**, 518–525.

Dutcher, J. D., Johnson, J. R., and Bruce, W. F. 1945. *J. Am. Chem. Soc.* **67**, 1735–1745.

Dyckerhoff, H., and Armbruster, R. 1933. *Z. physiol. Chem.* **219**, 38–56.

Ehrlich, F. 1932a. *Biochem. Z.* **250**, 525–534.

Ehrlich, F. 1932b. *Biochem. Z.* **251**, 204–222.

Ehrlich, F. 1937. *Enzymologia* **3**, 185–199.

Ehrlich, F., Guttman, R., and Haensel, R. 1935. *Biochem. Z.* **281**, 93–102.

von Euler, H., and Cramér, H. 1913. *Biochem Z.* **58**, 467–469.

Fernbach, A. 1900. *Compt. rend.* **65**, 1091–1094.

Freundenberg, K., and Vollbrecht, E. 1921. *Z. physiol. Chem.* **219**, 38–56.

Gäumann, E., and Böhni, E. 1947. *Helv. Chim. Acta.* **30**, 24–38.

Garreau, Y. 1941. *Compt. rend. soc. biol.* **135**, 508–510.

Gosio, B. 1897. *Ber.* **30**, 1024–1026.

Grove, S. F., and McGowan, S. C. 1947. *Nature* **160**, 572.

Hardiman, J., Keane, J., and Nolan, T. J. 1935. *Sci. Proc. Roy. Dublin Soc.* **21**, 141–145.

Harter, L. L., and Weimer, J. L. 1921–23. *J. Agr. Research* **21**, 609–625; **22**, 371–377; **24**, 861–878 (1922); **25**, 155–164.

Jansen, E. F., and MacDonnell, L. R. 1945. *Arch. Biochem.* **8**, 97–112.

Kertesz, Z. I. 1936. *Ergeb. Enzymforsch.* **5**, 233–258.

Knudson, L. 1913a. *J. Biol. Chem.* **14**, 159–184.

Knudson, L. 1913b. *J. Biol. Chem.* **14**, 185–202.

Kossowicz, A., and Leow, W. 1912. *Z. Gärungsphysiol.* **2**, 87–103.

Lineweaver, H., and Ballou, G. A. 1945. *Arch. Biochem.* **6**, 373–387.
Menon, K. P. V. 1934. *Ann. Botany* **48**, 187–210.
Mothes, K. 1938. *Planta* **29**, 67–109.
Neuberg, C., and Wagner, J. 1925. *Biochem. Z.* **161**, 492–505; 1926, **174**, 457–463.
Nicholson, W. N., Nierenstein, M., Pool, J. C., and Price, N. V. 1931. *Biochem. J.* **25**, 752–755.
Nishikawa, H. 1939. *Acta Phytochim. Japan* **11**, 167–185.
Nolan, T. J. 1934. *Sci. Proc. Roy. Dublin Soc.* **21**, 67–71.
Oxford, A. E., Raistrick, H., and Simonart, P. 1939. *Biochem. J.* **33**, 240–248.
Pearce, A. A. 1940. *Biochem. J.* **34**, 1493–1500.
Pfaff, H. 1947. *Arch. Biochem.* **13**, 67–81.
Plumlee, C. H. and Pollard, A. H. 1949. *J. Boct.* **57**, 405–407.
Pottevin, H. 1900. *Compt. rend.* **131**, 1215–1217.
Proskuriakov, N. J., and Ossipov, F. M. 1939. *Biokhimiya* **4**, 50–59.
Raciborski, . 1905. *Bull. Acad. Sci. Cracowie* p. 693. (Cited in Pearce, 1940.)
Raistrick, H. 1940. *Ann. Rev. Biochem.* **9**, 571–592.
Raistrick, H., and Smith, G. 1936. *Biochem. J.* **30**, 1315–1322.
Reilly, D., and Curtin, T. P. 1943. *Biochem. J.* **37**, 36–39.
Rippel, A., and Keseling, J. 1931. *Arch. Mikrobiol.* **1**, 60–77.
Rippel, A., and Behr, G. 1937. *Arch. Mikrobiol.* **7**, 584–589.
Rosenheim, O. 1902. *Proc. Chem. Soc.* p. 138.
Sciarini, L. J., and Nord, F. F. 1943. *Arch. Biochem.* **3**, 261–267.
Sideris, C. P. 1924. *Phytopathology* **14**, 481–489.
Smith, H. R., and Cameron, E. J. 1933. *Ind. Eng. Chem. Anal. Ed.* **5**, 400–401.
Smith, R. M., Joslyn, D. A., Gruhzit, O. M., McLean, I. W., Penner, M. A., and Ehrlich, J. 1948. *J. Bact.* **55**, 425–447.
Stärkle, M. 1924. *Biochem. Z.* **151**, 371–415.
Steinberg, R. A. 1941. *J. Agr. Research* **63**, 109–137.
Stokoe, W. N. 1928. *Biochem. J.* **22**, 80–93.
Tanner, F. W. 1918. *J. Am. Chem. Soc.* **40**, 663–669.
Thaler, H., and Eisenlohr, W. 1941. *Biochem. Z.* **308**, 88–102.
Thaler, H., and Geist, G. 1939a. *Biochem. Z.* **302**, 121–136.
Thaler, H., and Geist, G. 1939b. *Biochem. Z.* **302**, 369–383.
Thom, C., and Raper, K. B. 1932. *Science* **76**, 548–550.
Thom, C. and Raper, K. B. 1945. A Manual of the Aspergilli. Williams and Wilkins, Baltimore p. 237.
Toth, G. 1944. *Magyar Timar.* **5**, 1.
Toth, G., and Barsony, G. 1943. *Enzymologia* **11**, 19–23.
Van Tiegham, M. P. 1867. *Compt. rend.* **65**, 1091–1094.
Volkonsky, M. 1932. *Compt. rend. soc. biol.* **109**, 614–616.
Volkonsky, M. 1933a. *Compt. rend.* **197**, 712–714.
Volkonsky, M. 1933b. *Ann. Inst. Pasteur* **50**, 703–730.
Volkonsky, M. 1934. *Ann. Inst. Pasteur* **52**, 76–101.
Waksman, S. A., and Allen, M. C. 1933. *J. Am. Chem. Soc.* **55**, 3408–3418.
Walker, T. K., and Coppock, P. D. **1928**. *J. Chem. Soc.* 803–809.
Woolley, D. W., and Peterson, W. H. 1937. *J. Biol. Chem.* **122**, 213–218.
Yudkin, J. 1938. *Biol. Rev. Cambridge Phil. Soc.* **13**, 93–106.

CHAPTER 19

MICROBIOLOGICAL ASPECTS OF PENICILLIN

The development of penicillin is one of the most fabulous stories in the history of microbiology, if not medicine itself. Discovered in England in 1929, it has been ranked as second only to Harvey's discovery of the circulation of blood in the list of great contributions of the English in the field of medicine and has inspired one authority to characterize it as "Science's Cinderella" (Coghill, 1944). The significance of penicillin transcends the obvious immediate fact of its life-saving properties in certain virulent infections. At once it spawned enormous developments in microbiology and chemistry, henceforth to be known as the field of antibiotics, and which already has brought forth streptomycin, chloromycetin, bacitracin, and many other antibiotics of promise in one way or other. It has mushroomed in the space of only five years into a giant industry in the United States and already has spread to many foreign countries. It was directly responsible, because of many hitherto unrecognized and distinctive requirements of the process, for the development of the science of microbiological or fermentation design and engineering, as we know it today—a highly specialized and technical field. It is only because of the lessons from and triumphs of penicillin that the spectacular engineering development of streptomycin to full industrial scale only three years after its discovery has been possible.

Because the history of penicillin is virtually current, and because the principles and practices acquired from penicillin have proved basic and applicable in one way or other to the entire field of antibiotics, and indeed, to the subject of general microbiology itself, it behooves the student to be cognizant of the historical aspects, and this will be briefly discussed here.

In a general way the advances in penicillin from a microbiological point of view may be said to fall into several well-defined phases, though they are not strictly independent.

    (a) Surface process
    (b) Development of fungus strains
    (c) Submerged process
    (d) Culture medium
    (e) Chemical extraction
    (f) Engineering design of pilot and plant equipment

HISTORICAL ASPECTS

In 1929 Alexander Fleming in St. Mary's Hospital, London, observed that an air-borne mold contamination became established in a culture plate in which staphylococcus colonies had been examined and which had been set aside for several days. Around the mold colony, to quote Fleming, " . . . the staphylococcus colonies became transparent and were obviously undergoing lysis." Preparation of liquid cultures with the isolated fungus confirmed that the fungus excretes into the medium a substance which inhibited growth of certain bacteria and not of others. In the former group were pyogenic cocci and diphtheria organisms; the resistant group consisted of the coli-typhoid and influenza bacilli and the enterococci.

Fleming characterized a number of properties of the inhibitory substance, such as its lability to heat, acidity and alkalinity, and solubility in alcohol, but not fat solvents. Fleming did not succeed in purifying the active principle, and he called the entire bacteriostatic mold culture filtrate "penicillin." Of course, today penicillin is the specific chemical substance isolated from these broths. He made the extremely important observation that large doses of the active filtrates were non-toxic to animals, supplied intravenously or intraperitoneally, and that constant irrigation of large infected surfaces in man, was non-toxic and non-irritating. Though no clinical trials were actually made, Fleming visualized the implications of his work, stating "penicillin may be an effective antiseptic for application to, or injection into, areas infected with penicillin-sensitive microbes."

Fleming utilized penicillin as an adjunct to differential media used for isolation of *Bacillus influenzae* from human throats. The penicillin inhibited the great majority of organisms present, they being gram positive, allowing growth and detection of the causative *B. influenzae* even in small numbers (see also Fleming and MacLean, 1930).

Recognizing as he did the potentialities of penicillin, it has been something of a mystery why Fleming did not promote its development for human chemotherapy. Subsequent workers who examined some of the properties of penicillin in broth filtrates, found the active material so elusive that testing was not attempted (Reid, 1935; Clutterbuck *et al.*, 1932). Fleming had called the fungus strain he isolated *Penicillium rubrum* but later (1944, 1945) Charles Thom, the distinguished American authority on the Penicillia, identified the organism as being closely related to *P. notatum* in the *P. chrysogenum* series.

True exploitation of the medical potentialities of penicillin began 10 years after its discovery when a team of workers under the leadership of Florey at Oxford University announced the dramatic results obtained in animals (Chain *et al.*, 1940) and in humans (Abraham *et al.*, 1941) with purified preparations of penicillin. Details of laboratory scale production, pharmacological effects, clinical trials on humans, and the now universally employed cylinder or cup method of assay were presented in the celebrated 1941 paper. The key to chemical concentration and purification was furnished by the discovery that penicillin can be extracted by immiscible fat solvents, notably amyl acetate and ether, from the culture filtrates adjusted to pH 2–2.5 and that the penicillin is re-extractable by neutral aqueous solutions. Penicillin is therefore an organic acid whose dissociation constant is such that it exists virtually entirely in the undissociated acid state at pH 2 and is soluble in fat solvents in that condition.

During the first few years, the best penicillin preparations were far from pure, and contained from 3 to 25 per cent active material, according to the potency of pure penicillin obtained some time later.

These pioneering studies were done while England was already at war with Germany and the potentialities for penicillin in connection with war wounds, epidemics, venereal disease, etc., were so obvious that its large scale manufacture was at once desired. Because of the extremely small concentrations of penicillin then obtainable in the mold culture filtrates, and because of the relatively low extraction yields owing to the lability of penicillin, and also because of the overall complexity of the entire process, it was evident that the facilities and skilled man-power in England could not be spared from other military activities. Through the auspices of the Rockefeller Foundation, Professor Florey and his associate, N. G. Heatley, came to the United States with the objective of stimulating the interest of American pharmaceutical manufacturers and other organizations in penicillin research and production, the idea being that American-made penicillin would be available to the British for use in connection with the military.

Several industrial laboratories were already studying penicillin, and Florey and Heatley aided in its development by giving first-hand advice and instructions based on their own experience. N. G. Heatley remained in this country several months for this purpose. Production for the better part of two years was confined almost exclusively to the only process available, i.e., surface production in bottles or trays. Production even on a pilot plant scale involved so many problems that almost two years elapsed before sufficient penicillin had been produced for the extensive clinical evaluations deemed essential before full-scale factory production could be justified. By this time the United States was also at war and it became a matter of supplying penicillin for the American military.

The complexity of the process and the effort and scale of production required, necessitated an organized program and government aid in the matter of draft deferment of technical men and in priorities for securing the huge amounts of materials and equipment, all critical during the war. The Government coordinating agency was the Committee on Medical Research in the Office of Scientific Research and Development. This committee set up a panel of medical experts in various aspects of bacterial infections known as the Committee on Chemotherapeutic and Other Agents under the auspices of the National Research Council, with the understanding that all of the extremely limited supply of penicillin being produced should be at their disposal for a comprehensive scientific evaluation of penicillin in the control of bacterial infections in human beings, dosages, and in pharmacological side reactions. The conclusions of this clinical research was later made public (Richards, 1943; Keefer et al., 1943). Similar groups were functioning in England.

When, as a result of these reports, it became known that penicillin was well-nigh the perfect chemotherapeutic agent for susceptible infections, concerted effort was directed to full scale production. Research on both microbiological and chemical aspects had meanwhile led to impressive improvements in yields, and full exchange of information was performed between scientists in the United States and England. In this country, under the auspices of the Government War Production Board and Office of Production Research and Development, several projects were established at different non-commercial research institutions to study detailed phases of the penicillin picture: laboratory production at the Northern Regional Research Laboratories (NRRL) of the United States Department of Agriculture at Peoria, Ill., pilot plant production at University of Wisconsin, chemical extraction and synthetic media development at Pennsylvania State College, mutation program for strain improvement at Stanford University, University of Minnesota, University of Wisconsin and Carnegie Institute at Cold Spring Harbor. Also sponsored were studies on the chemical constitution of penicillin, with the ultimate objective of possible commercial synthesis. At the same time, a great deal of work on all these various lines was being done in a score or more of industrial research laboratories. The contributions of the workers at the NRRL are especially acclaimed as having played a major role in the establishment of the penicillin process on a firm foundation.

Few people even today are fully aware of the emphasis the United States Government placed on penicillin research and development during the war. An authoritative expression may be quoted from the *Bulletin of the U. S. Army Medical Department* (1946): "This (penicillin) program was granted the highest priorities accorded to any military item, except the atomic bomb."

Total production of pure penicillin monthly in the United States is currently about 7 trillion units (7×10^{12}) or approximately 4,400 kilos (Stevenson, 1948).

PRODUCTION OF PENICILLIN IN SURFACE CULTURE

This subject is largely of historical interest. All commercial production and virtually all research on penicillin nowadays deal with the submerged process. The surface process itself, despite its transitory role in the development of penicillin, underwent a substantial evolution during the approximately three years it was utilized. This may be judged from the fact that broth potencies obtained in the early days of penicillin were 1 to 4 units per ml. whereas at the time the surface process was abandoned yields of 200 units per ml. were not unusual. Three main features were responsible for this increase: (1) improved strain of fungus with respect to penicillin-producing capacity, (2) improved media, and (3) certain physical factors. The incubation time required to achieve these yields was also reduced appreciably, resulting in higher production rate than previously. The first two of these topics are discussed in the appropriate sections below.

Production in bottles on a manufacturing scale involves a great deal of mechanical handling of the tens of thousands of bottles that must be cleaned, filled, plugged, sterilized, inoculated, incubated, and harvested each day. The several plants which reached large or semi-large scale production by the surface or "bottle" process adapted the conveyor belt system and much other machinery employed in food and beverage bottling and canning industries. An appreciation of the factors involved in a surface bottle process for microbiological production on a factory scale may be obtained by consulting Ainsworth et al. (1948). A few examples of the microbiological problems involved in a large scale surface process may be instructive. The problem of inoculating thousands of bottles itself involves a specialized approach. Two methods were tried. One involved the sterilization of the medium as one batch in a closed steam kettle, cooling and seeding the entire batch with a spore suspension. Distribution was maintained by an agitator. The already inoculated medium was then filled into sterilized plugged empty bottles, which then were stacked on their sides in the incubator. This method has the failing that the spores tend to sink to the bottom of the liquid and the essential entire surface pad of fungus is very slow in developing.

The favored procedure was to sterilize the medium in the bottles and inoculate each individually. This was developed to a state of traditional production line efficiency. The cooled sterilized bottles passed on a conveyor belt through a wall slot into a small chamber flooded with ultraviolet light to minimize airborne contamination. Inoculation was done by technicians using air-pressure atomizers to blow the inoculum into the bottles in a momentary blast. A great deal depends on this step, for the efficiency of the entire process is dependent on two points here: (a) amount of inoculum and (b) keeping the spores floating on the surface. If the spores drop to the bottom, their germination and growth is retarded so that surface pellicle formation is retarded. Fortunately, spores of Penicillia harvested from surface cultures are difficult to wet, and surface tension forces tend to keep them floating. Up to a certain point, the time required for appearance of an entire surface growth is inversely proportional to the amount of inoculum. Because of surface tension, great numbers of spores tend to migrate to the edge of the liquid. Enough spores must be introduced and spread uniformly over the surface so that soon after germination each young mycelium contacts neighboring ones, quickly forming a surface mat. Rapid and abundant penicillin production never takes place in the absence of such a mat. Frequently encountered is the problem of a ring of fungus growth around the periphery of the liquid, with very slow or no fill-in across the center.

Massive numbers of spores for inoculum purposes can be obtained as a surface pad on liquid medium (Moyer and Coghill, 1946a) containing glycerol, molasses, cornsteep liquor, and peptone. The peptone in this medium assures rapid and abundant mycelium development and experiments show that the concentration of NaCl is important for sporulation at 30°C. but not at 23°C. That is, 0.4 per cent NaCl stimulated spore formation at the lower temperature, but, with the exception of a few strains, not at the higher temperatures. Four per cent NaCl stimulated spores at both temperatures (Gailey et al., 1946). The most systematic study of spore formation in P. chrysogenum surface cultures with emphasis on quantitative counts of spores is that by Frank et al. (1948). Using strain NRRL 1249B21, a synthetic medium was developed which gave spore yields as good as the molasses organic medium—about 300–500 million per milliliter of culture liquid. The presence of citric acid (0.75 per cent) was especially good for spore formation. The curious fact was revealed that in any given vessel the total spore yield was a direct function of the depth of the medium rather than the surface area. Hitherto it was supposed that surface area was the important issue; it is evident that the total available nutrients, such as depends on the volume of medium, is a crucial factor in numbers of spores formed per unit surface area of mold mycelium.

A superior method from the practical standpoint is to cultivate the organism on particulate organic material which, per unit of weight and volume, has a very large surface area, for spores are borne aerially on surfaces. Moistened rice or wheat bran, or whole grains such as rice, or even sliced bread or potatoes are useful for this purpose.   In shallow layers in flasks or bottles, the fungus sporulates profusely and the substrate dries out at the same time, leaving a dry crumbly mass, which, upon shaking, releases literally clouds of spores, all dry and ideal for floating on the surface of liquid. A practice commonly employed was to incorporate a large bulk of a light, fluffy material such as ground oat hulls as a carrier. The spores adhere to this material, which, when blown from the atomizer, uniformly covers the surface of the liquid and floats, ensuring rapid development of a surface pad.

Stacking of hundreds or thousands of bottles in incubator rooms leads to the observation that bottles in the middle of the stacks produce much less penicillin than bottles in the outer regions. This is due to self-heating. As the fungus grows, it consumes carbohydrate via respiratory processes and these are strongly exothermic. The heat evolved is not conducted away fast enough through the glass and through the dead air spaces in the contiguous bottles, hence the temperature may easily rise to a stage where not only penicillin is destroyed, but its formation is markedly inhibited, and growth of the fungus itself may suffer. Suitable ventilation and narrow piles with recurrent openings are necessary to remove accumulated heat by air circulation.

An especially formidable problem in surface culture is the fact that the penicillin assay on a batch representing the pooling of hundreds of bottle cultures frequently is substantially lower than samples taken from a few individual bottles would indicate. This proved to be due to the fact that despite rigorous inspection, an occasional fungus culture contaminated with bacteria would escape detection and be pooled with bacteria-free cultures. Unfortunately, numerous airborne contaminants produce an extracellular enzyme destroying penicillin, penicillinase (Abraham and Chain, 1940; Foster, 1945; Woodruff and Foster, 1945; Benedict et al., 1945; Duthie, 1944; McQuarrie et al., 1944; Housewright and Henry, 1947; Henry and Housewright, 1947; Morgan and Campbell, 1947). Aerobic sporeforming bacteria (Bacillus subtilis) and coliform bacteria (Escherichia coli) are most active in this respect.

In media favoring rapid growth one may find that the rate of consumption of oxygen in the container exceeds the rate at which oxygen diffuses through ordinary cotton plugs, unless particular attention is given to avoid dense and tight plugs. This applies also to shake flask cultures. Thin cotton plugs or metal cap substitutes prevent this.

With the strains of Penicillium utilized during the early days of penicillin when synthetic media appeared to have advantages, the trend of pH changes in the culture was markedly indicative of radically different events occurring in the cultures. The English workers first used a synthetic medium (Czapek's) to which small amounts of yeast extract sometimes were added. They noted that the usual course of events was a rapid fall in the pH of the culture solution to 3.0–4.5 for the first 3 to 5 days, followed by a rapid rise so that in the later stages (10–15 days), the pH exceeded neutrality. Penicillin formation was associated with the rise in pH. Depending on the nutritional status of the medium, the pH sometimes fails to rise, and the penicillin is not formed, but another antibiotic substance is—notatin (glucose oxidase; see Chapter 15). To a large extent this course of events is controlled by the zinc content of the medium (Foster *et al.*, 1943). If zinc is deficient, growth is greatly retarded, the surface pad being thin and abnormal, and the pH drops owing to gluconic acid formation by the fungus. These are the conditions favorable for notatin formation and unfavorable for penicillin formation. Zinc probably exerts its effects by acting as a catalyst in the oxidation and assimilation of glucose by the mold, preventing the accumulation of gluconic acid as a metabolic byproduct (see Chapter 7), this being responsible for the fall in pH. At the higher pH prevailing, penicillin formation is promoted. Proper levels of zinc also enhance the formation of the characteristic golden yellow pigments accompanying the growth of virtually all penicillin-producing fungi. In media containing substantial quantities of complex organic nitrogenous materials, the pH fall is prevented owing to the ammonia liberation from nitrogenous constituents.

The medium constituents of the surface process are discussed in a later section. A great many details relating to the surface process, including physiological changes taking place during growth of the organism may be found in the comprehensive report of Moyer and Coghill (1946a). The process as reported there represents the highest stage of development of the surface methods used industrially.

Development of Potent Fungus Strains

This clearly was the greatest single factor contributing to large scale penicillin production. It early became recognized that strain specificity in regard to penicillin production is fully as crucial as in citric acid formation or any other of the numerous physiological properties of fungi previously discussed.

The production of penicillin by fungi is not by any means limited to a few strains of a single species, but is widely distributed among fungi. In general, however, one may say that this property is rather characteristic of the *Penicillium notatum-chrysogenum* group as a whole, whereas in the case of other species, only an occasional strain produces penicillin. In one test of thirty-five different stock culture strains of this group, almost all produced penicillin (Moyer and Coghill, 1946a), but the most extensive of tests on this line were those of Raper *et al.* (1944). From soils and food material samples collected from all over the world by the United States Air Transport Command, 241 different members of the *P. notatum-chrysogenum* group were tested for penicillin and all but twenty-four produced measurable quantities. Great variation prevailed among these organisms. Some were superior in surface culture, others in submerged culture. As a guide to the natural frequency of penicillin potency among strains of this group the following data from Raper *et al.* (1944) are instructive:

	Penicillin, units per ml.[1]												
	0	1–10	11–20	21–30	31–40	41–50	51–60	61–70	71–80	81–90	91–100	Over 100	Total
No. strains.......	24	31	23	45	29	13	18	32	16	4	4	2	241
Per cent of total..	10	13	10	19	12	5	7	13	7	2	2	1	100

[1] On cornsteep liquor medium; surface culture.

Mycological aspects of penicillin-producing fungi are covered comprehensively in Raper *et al.* (1944) and Raper and Alexander (1945). Especially emphasized in the latter is natural variation among the early used penicillin strains, including the ancestral strain from which the culture utilized industrially today is derived. An attempt was made to associate high penicillin yields with the degree of sporulation of the fungus strains. While such a correlation may hold in a general way, it is not strictly true. Raper's work excellently treats the subject of cultural, morphological, and penicillin variations among subculture progeny of many strains. (See also Chapter 5.)

As new superior strains were developed, they were rapidly distributed to all production and research laboratories working on penicillin and previous strains were abandoned in favor of the new ones virtually at once. The following chart summarizes the evolution of surface culture strains.

Fleming strain

↓ Subculture

Squibb 1249

↓ Colony isolate

*NRRL 1249.B21

* Northern Regional Research Laboratory, Peoria, Illinois.

Strain NRRL 1249.B21 was utilized for the bulk of industrial surface culture. Thereafter submerged production came into vogue. Maximum yields of 160–200 units per ml. were obtainable with it. Soon after submerged production definitely rendered the surface process obsolete, Raper and Alexander (1945) described NRRL 1978.B2, which gave yields 40 per cent higher in surface culture than 1249.B21. However, its advent was too late to be utilized commercially.

Geneology of submerged culture strains (see Raper and Alexander, 1945 and Raper, 1946):

> NRRL 832   40–80 units per ml.
> NRRL 1951.B25   100–200 units per ml.
>   ↓ X-ray mutation
> X-1612   300–500 units per ml.
>   ↓ Ultraviolet mutation
> Q-176   1000 or more units per ml.

NRRL 1951.B25 is a single spore progeny of a *P. chrysogenum* strain isolated from a rotten cantalope. By irradiating conidia with x-rays, a mutant, X-1612, giving up to 500 units per ml., was obtained. This was truly a collaborative effort: the stock was supplied by NRRL, the irradiation was done at Carnegie Institute at Cold Spring Harbor, Long Island, N. Y., preliminary potency testing was done at the University of Minnesota, and pilot plant tests at the University of Wisconsin. Curiously enough, the superiority of X-1612 over its parent proved to be much greater when tested in pilot plant fermenters than in laboratory experiments. Generally the reverse is true: organisms prove less superior in fermenters than preliminary laboratory tests indicate.

In a similar way, Q176 was obtained by ultraviolet irradiation of X-1612 by Bachus *et al.* (1946) at the Botany Department of the University of Wisconsin. The distribution of Q176 to all manufacturers was the last organism covered under the collaborative program between the government and industrial laboratories, as the war was now over. It is not unreasonable to assume that industrial laboratories have succeeded in obtaining even higher yielding mutants from Q176 (see plant patent issued to Foster, 1949). Q176 has proved to be considerably superior to NRRL 1249.B21 or 1978.B2 in extensive commercial surface production in Japan. In the synthetic medium of Stone and Farrell (1946) yields in excess of 500 units per ml. have been attained (Umezawa *et al.*, 1948).

As discussed later, several different penicillins are known, and different strains of fungi produce different kinds and in various ratios. Because of the fact that penicillin X was shown to be more effective than penicillin G, the common form, against gonococci and other bacteria under therapeutic conditions, commercial production of penicillin X appeared to be a distinct possibility. At NRRL Raper and Fennell (1946), by ultraviolet irradiation, developed a strain in which penicillin X represented 50 to 70 per cent of the penicillin yield on a weight basis, and about 50 per cent on an assay basis. This discrepancy is due to the fact that mole for mole penicillin X is less active than penicillin G against *Staphylococcus aureus*, the standard assay organism. Under the same conditions the proportion of penicillin X in strain X-1612 was less than 20 per cent. This high X-yielding strain is a submerged culture and is known as NRRL 1984.N22.

As it happened, though the proportion of penicillin X was high, the total X unitage was much less than that obtainable with X-1612 (and Q176 later), and the fact that higher dosages and procedures to prolong blood levels were adopted successfully in clinical cases where penicillin X might have been useful, all militated against commercial exploitation of penicillin X.

As mentioned above, penicillin formation is not confined to the *P. notatum-chrysogenum* group. Numerous other fungi produce penicillin or penicillin-like substances. In the Penicilli are: *P. avellaneum*, *P. rubens*, *P. turbatum* and two members of the *P. notatum-chrysogenum* group, *P. baculatum* and *P. fluorescens;* also *P. lanosum*, *P. roseo-citreum*, *P. griseofulvum*, *P. griseo-roseum*, *P. citreo-roseum*, *P. cyaneofulvum*, *P. brunneorubrum*, and *P. crustosum*. Among the Aspergilli are: *A. flavus*, *A. parasiticus*, *A. oryzae*, *A. giganteus*, *A. flavipes*, *A. nidulans*, *A. caespitosus*, *A. niger*, and *A. sydowi*. (Bush and Goth, 1943; McKee, *et al.*, 1944; Waksman and Bugie, 1943; Cook and Lacey, 1944; Benedict, 1946; Robbins, 1946; Florey *et al.*, 1944; Wickerham, 1946; Raper *et al.*, 1944; Yermolieva *et al.*, 1945; Foster and Karow, 1945; Fried *et al.*, 1946.)

Other totally unrelated genera are *Trichophyton mentagrophytes*, the dermatophyte (Peck and Hewitt, 1945) and *Malbranchea pulchella* (Rode *et al.*, 1947). The last named organism is a thermophilic fungus producing penicillin at 52°C., a point of interest because of the thermolability of penicillin in solution.

Naturally, the penicillin yields obtained with all these strains are low. However, it should be mentioned that almost certainly any one of these organisms could be subjected to a mutation program which would yield high potency strains in the same manner as *P. chrysogenum* X-1612 and Q176. For example, limited attempts toward simple substrain selection with *Aspergillus oryzae* effected a six to ten-fold increase in penicillin producing powers (Foster and Karow, 1944).

Submerged Process and Culture Medium

The respective features, principles, and practical aspects of the submerged vs. surface processes are detailed in Chapter 2. In connection with penicillin, a crucial fact is that a fungus strain potent in surface culture is very apt to be inferior in submerged culture, whereas a superior submerged strain is apt to hold that relative position in surface culture. Nevertheless it is true that in many cases there is not much difference between surface and submerged tests with any one culture. These behaviors are of course a function of the particular organism—strain specificity. Raper *et al.* (1944) compare forty-three strains in this regard (see also Foster *et al.*, 1946a). The two strains widely used in the early days of production behaved thusly:

Culture	Maximum penicillin yields in	
	Surface culture	Submerged culture
(Submerged) NRRL832........	64	51
(Surface) 1249 B21............	122	26

It is clear that 832 is twice as good as 1249.B21 in submerged culture, but the reverse holds true in surface tests. The exceptionally potent submerged strains X-1612 and Q176 are superior to 1249.B21 in surface culture, and Q176 has been used the last few years for commercial surface production in Japan.

Though the discussion here will describe the process as done with Q176, published information on this organism is relatively scanty, and principles exemplified by use of earlier less potent strains are discussed. Though quantitative aspects may differ, it is a reasonable assumption that the qualitative aspects of this process are similar, especially between directly related strains. The bulk of the published information on the metabolism of penicillin producing fungi has been furnished by workers at the University of Wisconsin.

Pilot plant and factory aspects of submerged penicillin production are discussed in a later section, but preparation of inoculum for large scale production and laboratory experimentation have much in common. Cultivation in the laboratory customarily is done on rotary or reciprocal shaking machines (Chapter 2). The system of handling stock cultures is described in Chapter 5. On an industrial scale, the inoculum for production tanks, which may be between 5 to 15 thousand gallons capacity, is prepared in a series of tanks of ascending size, each one of which is about 5 to 10 per cent of the capacity of the subsequent one. These are called seed tanks. Thus, the inoculum for a tank holding 10,000 gallons of penicillin medium consists of about 500 to 1,000 gallons of submerged culture in the logarithmic phase of growth, which is transferred as inoculum to the larger tank. In the same fashion, inoculum for the 1,000 gallon seed tank is obtained in a tank about one tenth that size, and the submerged culture transferred in the logarithmic phase. This 50 to 100 gallon seed tank may be inoculated with the culture contents of a laboratory bottle or flask or with the contents of a 5 to 10 gallon fermenter. In either case, the primary inoculum consists of spores to obtain the first submerged inoculum for propagation on a successively larger scale, as the buildup occurs through the successive tanks for the objective of furnishing inoculum for the largest production vessel.

The primary spore inoculum may consist of spores obtained from surface cultures, either liquid or solid, of spores obtained in submerged cultures, or of surface pellicles fragmented into a suspension of mycelial pieces and spores.

Evidently the formation of spores in submerged cultures of fungi is rare, the cultures consisting exclusively of vegetative mycelium. Formation of typical conidiospores together with the characteristic penicillus structure was reported for the first time in *P. notatum-P. chrysogenum* cultures (Foster *et al.*, 1945). Spore counts of 400 million per ml. of culture were obtained. Submerged conidiospore production in the simple synthetic medium used depended on the presence of 0.5 to 5.0 per cent $CaCl_2$ in the medium, and, to a certain extent, on the heavy metal nutrition. Abundant sporulation was associated with sparse vegetative growth.

Gilbert and Hickey (1946) found that, of the heavy metals, iron in amounts of 0.5 to 1.0 mg. per ml. definitely favored sporulation in media with complex nitrogen sources. Fragmentation of surface or submerged fungus mycelium by means of a Waring blendor does not impair the potency or viability of the inoculum, and, as a matter of fact enormously increases the efficiency of any given inoculum over the conventional methods (Savage and Vander Brook, 1946; Dorrell and Page, 1947). Thus, *P. notatum* submerged mycelium so treated ("blended"), when diluted 1:40,000 times, adequately substitutes for unblended culture inoculum used at a 10 per cent rate. The point of this approach depends of course on the total number of viable particles, growth being much faster with larger numbers of inoculum particles. It is obvious that a spore and a mycelial particle are equivalent insofar as inoculum is concerned. However, theoretically the mycelial particle proliferates immediately, the spore requiring many hours to germinate. Hence the value of pregerminated spores as a time-saving factor. According to Grenfell *et al.* (1947) only about less than half the surface spores of X-1612 and Q176 are viable, a factor to be considered in judging the amount of inoculum to be used from the total spore numbers.

CULTURE MEDIUM

Second in importance only to the development of more potent fungus strains was the discovery that corn steep liquor has a remarkable stimulating effect on penicillin production by all penicillin-producing fungi. This discovery was made by A. J. Moyer of the NRRL and has since been utilized universally in commercial penicillin production both in surface culture and submerged.

Corn steep liquor is a cheap bulk material obtained as a byproduct in the manufacture of corn starch. Its previous use has been as a nutrient in yeast and other fermentations, and as a feed for livestock. It is essentially a concentrate of the water soluble extractives in the corn grain, which are principally nitrogenous. Other information as to its manufacture: (Moyer and Coghill, 1946a) "Before the corn is ground, it is steeped for approximately 30 hours in water originally containing 0.1 to 0.3 per cent of sulfur dioxide. The water has previously washed the starch and passed through the gluten settling tank. The addition of sulfur dioxide, at the time steeping begins, inhibits fermentation. Prior to concentration, a lactic acid fermentation occurs to a variable extent. There is considerable variation in sugar and lactic acid contents. Steep liquor is sold on a basis of approximately 55 per cent solids, although different batches may vary rather widely from this value. . . . A typical analysis is as follows: total solids, 52 per cent; total N, 4.3 per cent; ash, 7.9 per cent; free reducing sugar, 5.6 per cent; total reducing sugar calculated as glucose after acid hydrolysis, 6.8 per cent; specific gravity, 1.25; and pH 4.0." Lactic acid is present in amounts ranging from 5 to 15 per cent. According to Bowden and Petersen (1946) the most potent steep prepared in the laboratory was from sprouted corn extracted at 65°C. at pH 6 in the presence of 0.24 per cent Na_2SO_2. See Liggett and Koffler (1948) for further description of corn steep liquor.

Much of our basic information relative to medium ingredients insofar as commercial production goes was contributed by Moyer and Coghill (1946a and b). As a carbon source, lactose is definitely superior; and, together with corn steep liquor and the addition of $CaCO_3$ to control the pH, provides the basis of penicillin media. For surface production and for submerged production with NRRL 832 the inclusion of the Czapek's minerals was recommended but in the commercial process today these are not used. A typical commercial production medium has this composition:

	Per Cent
Corn steep liquor solids	2 to 4
Lactose	2 to 4
$CaCO_3$	0.5 to 1
Precursor	0.1 to 0.5

With two exceptions, the stimulating power of corn steep liquor is not found in any other natural nitrogenous material. The exceptions are cottonseed meal (Foster *et al.*, 1946b) and an extract of ground peas (Cook *et al.*, 1945). The distinctive effect of these materials is specifically on penicillin formation, for many other complex natural materials accelerate growth as well as corn steep liquor does, but have little effect on penicillin synthesis (Bowden and Peterson, 1946). As a matter of fact, at optimum concentrations (4 and 2 per cent solids, respectively), cottonseed meal is definitely superior to corn steep liquor with strains X-1612 and Q176, but this superiority levels off in the presence of the commercially employed precursors (phenylacetyl compounds).

The special stimulating properties of corn steep liquor have been the subject of much investigation, and it is probable that a combination of factors are responsible as apparent from the following.

1. MINERALS

Minerals in the corn steep liquor evidently play some role in penicillin production, because the ash of corn steep liquor added to a basal synthetic medium which supported good growth but small penicillin yields, markedly increased penicillin yields by X-1612 in submerged culture (Knight and Frazier, 1945a). Spectrographic analysis of corn steep ash showed the presence of Al, As, B, Ca, Cr, Co, Cu, Fe, Pb, Li, Mg, Mn, Ni, P, K, Si, Ag, Sn, W, Zn (Koffler *et al.*, 1947).

The penicillin-promoting properties of the ash resided in the acetic acid-insoluble fraction. Addition of iron and soluble phosphate supported penicillin production as well as corn steep ash, and presumably were the active fractions in the ash. Iron by itself was highly stimulating, but phosphate by itself had little effect (Koffer *et al.*, 1947). Copper (> 2 p.p.m.) completely inhibits penicillin production without affecting growth of the fungus. This effect was entirely neutralized by the addition of iron (1 p.p.m.). The relation between these two elements was considered to be a case of ion antagonism, and was shown not to result from a destruction of penicillin but from an affect on the biosynthesis of penicillin.

Of the other trace elements in the ash, chromium also appeared stimulatory. Iron and chromium were almost as good as iron and phosphorous. Zinc also play a role in penicillin production (Foster *et al.*

1946a). Ash of brown sugar also was found to stimulate penicillin. Other studies on mineral aspects of the penicillin process are given by Pratt and Hok (1946) and Moyer and Coghill (1946b).

Worth emphasizing is the point that the optimum salt concentration for one strain of fungus are not apt to be so for other strains. As mentioned above, corn steep liquor contains sufficient ash that when the organic medium is used the addition of other minerals is unnecessary, especially when tap water is employed.

2. AMINO ACIDS

The fact that corn steep liquor is largely a nitrogenous substance has led to some limited attempts to substitute pure amino acids for the gross melange which corn steep liquor is. The medium resulting from such efforts becomes thereby a synthetic one, and details of synthetic media are discussed below. According to White et al. (1945), a substantial portion of the stimulating action of corn steep liquor in surface culture can be duplicated by a mixture of three pure amino acids in the medium, arginine, histidine, and glutamic acid at the rate of 0.03, 0.03, and 0.04 per cent, respectively. (See also Cook and Brown, 1947.) Stone et al. (1946) working with X-1612 in submerged culture, found, out of all the amino acids, that only l-leucine had a stimulating role in penicillin formation. The sulfur containing amino acids appeared to stimulate, but inconsistently. The butyl alcohol fraction of wheat extracts and protein hydrolysates contained a stimulatory factor, though the yields were much lower than those possible (Halpern et al., 1945). The major portion of the activity of aqueous extracts of peas resides in the 80 per cent alcohol-insoluble fraction (Cook and Tullock, 1944; Cook et al., 1945).

3. PENICILLIN PRECURSORS

a. Precursors of Benzylpenicillin

The term precursors, as used here, denotes an organic compound which is assimilated from the medium by the fungus and incorporated directly into the penicillin molecule. Unlike other organic carbon and nitrogen sources, a precursor is not broken down into smaller fragments which then are resynthesized into cellular constituents and metabolic products; it is incorporated in the preformed state with at most only relatively minor alterations so that the compound still retains its virtual identity with that originally furnished in the medium. The discovery of penicillin precursors and their utilization in the industrial manufacture of penicillin has made it possible for the industrial output to be perhaps 100 per cent greater than it would be otherwise.

Behrens (1948) gives a comprehensive review of this subject of penicillin precursors. Even before the entire structural formula for penicillin was worked out, phenylacetic acid was known to be a product obtained from it by hydrolytic fission. The following structure of penicillin G (benzylpenicillin, the penicillin of commerce) and the points of fission indicate the origin of phenylacetic acid, together with the aminomalonsemialdehyde and penicillamine, the remaining two fragments.

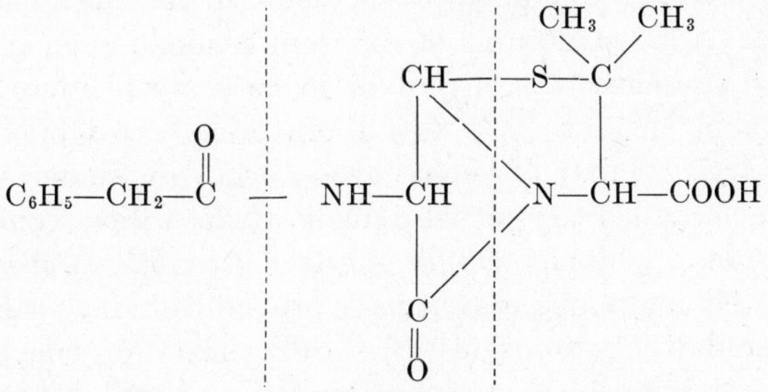

$$\begin{array}{c}
\text{CH}_3 \quad \text{CH}_3 \\
\text{CH}\!-\!\text{S}\!-\!\text{C} \\
C_6H_5\!-\!CH_2\!-\!\overset{O}{\overset{\|}{C}} \;\big|\; NH\!-\!CH \quad N\!-\!CH\!-\!COOH \\
\overset{C}{\underset{O}{\|}}
\end{array}$$

Phenylacetic acid   Amino-malon-   Penicillamine
semialdehyde

That portion of the molecule exclusive of the phenylacetic acid side chain (R) is known as an oxazolone-thiazolidine nucleus or β-lactam ring. Penicillin G has been synthesized (du Vigneaud *et al.*, 1946), but on an economic basis it is most unlikely that chemical synthesis will displace microbiological synthesis for commercial production.

Moyer and Coghill in 1943 discovered that addition of phenylacetic to the culture medium increased the penicillin yield, though for war-time security reasons this work was published only in 1947. The increase amounted to approximately 30 to 50 per cent and was obtained both with the surface and submerged cultures available at that time. The phenylacetic acid was toxic if the pH of the medium was below 5.0. With surface culture 1249.B21, Moyer and Coghill estimated that for the addition of every 5 mg. of phenylacetic acid there was a 1 mg. increase in penicillin yield. Optimum concentration of phenylacetic acid was 0.3–0.4 g. per liter. These workers reported, however, that the phenylacetic acid did not affect the type of penicillin produced by the fungus 1249.B21 as tested by differential bacterial assays which permit estimation of the types of penicillin present. Thus it was not proved that phenylacetic acid was a precursor, but only that it stimulated penicillin production, and the belief developed that phenylacetic acid functioned like the plant hormones, e.g., indolacetic acid, etc. It is now known, however, that phenylacetic acid is, indeed, a penicillin precursor and that the Peoria workers' failure to detect this in their early work was due to the fact that their organisms, principally 1249.B21, produced mainly benzylpenicillin to begin with. Hence the only effect of the precursor was to increase the amount of penicillin, not the type.

The stimulus which opened up the true significance of precursors of penicillin was provided by a report from Imperial Chemical Industries in England that two different strains of *Penicillium notatum* produced benyzlpenicillin when grown on corn steep liquor medium, and 2-pentenyl-penicillin (Penicillin F) on a synthetic medium, i.e., the type of penicillin was changed. (See structures of different penicillins on p. 584.) This indicated the presence of a precursor in corn steep liquor; and Smith, Bide and Robinson of the Glaxo Laboratories tested phenylalanine as the possible active source of benzyl group occurring in corn steep liquor. This amino acid added to synthetic media (0.25–1.0 per cent) stimulated increased yields of benzylpenicillin over the control. A great number of different related compounds eventually proved to induce the same effect; these are listed by Behrens (1948). Some sixty of one hundred and thirty-odd compounds tested, containing the phenyl group, stimulated yields of benzylpenicillin.

Meanwhile Mead, Stack, Steward and Bradley (British Drug Houses, Inc.) isolated β-phenylethylamine from corn steep liquor (0.017 per cent), a precursor of benzylpenicillin, and tyramine (0.018 per cent), a precursor of p-hydroxybenzylpenicillin (penicillin X). These substances probably arise from phenylalanine and tyrosine, respectively, by decarboxylation during the active fermentation of corn steep liquor. They are believed to account for the formation of benzylpenicillin and occasionally penicillin X in corn steep liquor medium. Using the labelled precursor deuterophenylacetyl-N[15]-valine, a group of American workers (at Lilly, Abbott, Upjohn, and at Columbia University) jointly established that the phenylacetyl moiety of the precursor appeared unbroken in penicillin formed from it. The remainder of the precursor molecule, as doubtless with all other precursors, was metabolized in unknown ways. One exception to this rule is the interesting case studied at the Lilly and the Heyden Laboratories in which compounds that did not contain the phenylacetyl group were active benzylpenicillin precursors. These were phenylbutyryl compounds from which the phenylacetyl group is generated by the mold by degrading the 4-carbon chain to the 2-carbon chain.

b. *Precursors of Other Natural Penicillins*

Of the five other natural penicillins known (listed on p. 584) precursors have been established only for one, p-hydroxybenzylpenicillin (penicillin X). The active precursors here are p-hydroxyphenylacetic acid and tyramine. Addition of derivatives of the R groups of the aliphatic penicillins is fruitless.

c. Precursors of Other Portions of Penicillin Molecule

Despite extensive search, precursors for the other portion of the penicillin molecule have not been found. Of the sulfur compounds, only sulfate, cystine and methionine are useful for growth and penicillin formation, these not being precursors of the penicillamine moiety. DL-Penicillamine is inactive as a precursor of penicillin, though recently a biological function for L-penicillamine was demonstrated (Wilson and du Vigneaud, 1948) by the fact that when fed to rats it inhibited their growth; and choline and its precursors, di-, mono-, and aminoethanol reverses the inhibition. Leucine is the only other substance stimulating penicillin formation. The stimulation here is observed both with and without precursors of benzylpenicillin, and occurs in synthetic media with strain X-1612, but not in corn steep liquor. The latter contains, of course, leucine. The mechanism of this stimulation is unknown.

It is important to keep in mind that not all strains of fungi react alike to any given precursor; certain submerged cultures respond poorly to the addition of phenylacetic acid, whereas others respond well to it.

This obviously is a point of strain specificity relating to the moiety of the penicillin molecule whose synthesis is the limiting factor in penicillin formation by the organism. This would be expected to vary from organism to organism. Furthermore, evidently the synthesis of the phenylacetyl moiety is limiting for the corresponding penicillins, but in the case of the other natural penicillins, whose synthesis does not respond to the addition of the corresponding side chain moiety, one can only conclude that the limiting factor in penicillin synthesis is not the side chain, or that the side chain cannot be utilized directly.

Apart from chemical isolation, there are two superior methods of distinguishing the presence and amounts of different penicillins in one culture, (1) differential bacteriological assay and (2) partition chromatogram. The importance of these tools* is paramount because different strains of Penicillia produce different kinds of penicillin, and any one may produce mixtures of penicillin of varying composition depending on the cultural conditions. Penicillin F was of great significance when the early strains of fungi were being utilized, but in commercial penicillin production today it is of little or no significance, as strain Q176 does not produce it in significant amounts. On the other hand, penicillin K is

---

* All methods for estimation of total and individual penicillins, biological, chemical, and physical, are discussed excellently in symposia of several different authors in *Analyst* **73**, 197–216; 244–257 (1948).

formed by Q176, some small amounts being present even though the use of precursors make it possible for the bulk of the output of this organism to be penicillin G.

The differential bacteriological assays are based on the fact that it takes different amounts of the pure penicillins to inhibit two or more different standard bacteria. The percentage composition of the penicillin mixture can then be computed from the ratios of the activities of the different penicillins against the different bacteria. Thus, penicillin G by definition has 1,667 units per mg. against *Staphylococcus aureus* and *Bacillus subtilis*, whereas for penicillin F the values are 1,490 and 970 units per mg. respectively, and for penicillin X, 845 and 1,200–1,700 units per mg. respectively (Schmidt *et al.*, 1945). Because of the ease of separation of penicillin X from the others by virtue of its insolubility in chloroform, the content of this penicillin can easily be made separately. The method of Higuchi and Peterson (1947) utilizes *S. aureus*, *Bacillus brevis* and *Bacillus* sp. to measure penicillins G, X and K in a mixture. It requires setting up simultaneous equations based on the potencies of the pure penicillins against individual organisms and is particularly applicable at present to commercial penicillin broths which consist primarily of Penicillins G, X and K. Table 1 exemplifies the type of information obtainable with this method of assay, and at the same time illustrates the effect of added precursors on the nature of the penicillins produced (Higuchi *et al.*, 1946) by strain Q176 in corn steep liquor medium under tank conditions:

TABLE 1

PRECURSORS AND PRODUCTION OF PENICILLIN[1]

Precursor added	Age of culture, hours	Total penicillin, units per ml.	Composition of penicillin, per cent		
			G	X	K
None	60	161	44	3	53
	108	569	22	1	70
β-Phenylethylamine	60	267	93	2	5
	108	726	78	5	17
Phenylacetamide	60	335	103	1	− 4
	108	616	78	2	20
Phenylacetic acid	60	448	109	3	−12
	108	673	76	−1	25
p-hydroxyphenylacetic acid	60	209	39	26	35
	108	462	34	10	56

[1] From Higuchi *et al.* 1946.

Important conclusions obtainable from these data are: (1) *Penicillium chrysogenum* Q176 normally produces about a half and half mixture of penicillins G and K in corn steep medium; (2) the composition of the penicillin mixture changes with age of the culture; (3) phenylacetic acid derivatives all increase the total amount of penicillin produced; (4) they cause a marked shift in the kind of penicillin in favor of penicillin G at the expense of K, so that the penicillin produced is preponderantly G; (5) *p*-hydroxyphenylacetic does not increase the total amount of penicillin nor the amount of penicillin G, but does increase clearly the penicillin X content of the medium. The response to *p*-hydroxyphenylacetic acid via synthesis of penicillin X is always much smaller than the response to phenylacetic acid for the synthesis of penicillin G. In a synthetic medium Q176 produced 12 per cent G and 88 per cent K. The presence of corn steep liquor, known to contain phenylacetic acid derivatives, increased the G content to 44 per cent. Addition of phenylacetic acid to synthetic media raised the G content to 74 per cent.

Paper chromatography, a tool which has undergone very extensive development since its resurrection only a few years ago, has found profitable application to penicillin (Goodall and Levi, 1946, 1947). The method involves placing a drop of penicillin culture filtrate near the margin of a strip of filter paper. That edge of the paper is now placed in a suitable solvent which rises via capillary action and absorbtion carrying the various penicillins, which, however, are absorbed by the paper selectively at separate spots, so that a separation of the components of the mixture has been achieved. After elimination of the solvent, the strip of paper is placed on the surface of a seeded agar plate. Inhibition occurs whenever penicillin was absorbed on the paper, and by a different penicillin for each spot. By comparing the points of absorbtion of pure known penicillins, the presence of known penicillins in the mixture can be ascertained as well as any new penicillins. The various penicillins can even be estimated quantitatively by this technique. Evidence has already been obtained that nine different penicillins are produced by *P. chrysogenum* Q176 in corn steep medium, including some which appear to be ones not previously described.

THE NATURAL PENICILLINS

This term refers to any penicillin which is formed normally by growth of a fungus on a synthetic or complex medium. This is constrasted to the method of obtaining new biosynthetic penicillins described in the next paragraph. All penicillins are members of one chemical family and differ in the nature of the substituents R. The empirical formula is $C_9H_{11}O_4SN_2 \cdot R$. The structures of the various known natural penicillins are tabulated as follows (Medical Research Committee, 1945):

Type	R	Name

G — Benzylpenicillin

F $CH_3CH_2CH{=}CH{-}CH_2{-}\overset{O}{\underset{\|}{C}}{-}$ Δ^2-Pentenyl-penicillin

X $HO{-}\langle\ \rangle{-}CH_2{-}\overset{O}{\underset{\|}{C}}{-}$ p-Hydroxybenzyl-penicillin

K $CH_3(CH_2)_6{-}\overset{O}{\underset{\|}{C}}{-}$ n-Heptylpeni-cillin

Flavicin $CH_3CH{=}CHCH_2CH_2{-}\overset{O}{\underset{\|}{C}}{-}$ Δ^3-Pentenylpeni-cillin

Dihydro-F penicillin $CH_3CH_2CH_2CH_2CH_2\overset{O}{\underset{\|}{C}}{-}$ Amylpenicillin

Flavicin and dihydro F penicillin are produced by Aspergilli; of the remaining four, only penicillins G and K are of practical significance nowadays because the metabolism of the commercial strain Q176 centers around these two predominantly. Penicillins X and G are the most stable of the penicillins from a chemical point of view. Just as each penicillin shows differences in activities against various susceptible bacteria, they also show differences in chemical and in pharmacological properties. These last two are of major significance for they have direct and all-important implications for industrial production and chemotherapeutic use of penicillin.

The chemical stability of penicillin G as well as its partition coefficients in organic solvents are such that it is possible to secure maximum recovery yields of this penicillin during the extraction procedure. Considerably more of K and F penicillins are lost during the recovery process. Furthermore, the latter two crystallize with difficulty, giving yields of crystalline sodium penicillin substantially less than penicillin G which crystallizes cleanly in high yields. Finally, the recovery of crystalline G penicillin is appreciably greater when penicillin G is the predominant or the sole penicillin present.   Recoveries are much lower when done on a mixture of penicillins.

From the pharmacological standpoint the features of penicillin X have already been mentioned; despite its indicated superiority over the other penicillins as a drug, it is not economical to manufacture it because of the low total yield.   Penicillin G is the penicillin of choice from all the others.   It is excreted from the body at a much slower rate than penicillin K, for example, and is considerably more stable in the body, thus prolonging the effective blood level of penicillin—a highly desirable feature (Ungar, 1948).   Penicillin G is also more potent in inhibiting bacteria than is penicillin K.   Table 1 shows conclusively that it is possible to divert the production of unwanted K by the high yielding strain Q176 to the therapeutically desired penicillin G.

During the first six months or so that Q176 was utilized for commercial production, a decided lessening in the clinical efficacy of penicillin against all kinds of infections was noted throughout this country and the belief became current that the infectious organisms were acquiring a resistance to penicillin and that the resistant forms were now building up to comprise the majority of infections.   Actually what happened is that several manufacturers failed to recognize that Q176 produced penicillin K in abundance and were not including penicillin G precursor in the medium. The penicillin being utilized clinically during that time contained a substantial proportion of the less effective K, which gave the poor results described.

New Biosynthetic Penicillins

The success with the incorporation of precursors of two of the natural penicillins led quite naturally to the idea that new penicillins, not known naturally, might be produced if the fungus were to utilize unnatural compounds as precursors of penicillin, in a manner analogous to the natural ones.   As Behrens (1948) stresses, detection of a new biosynthetic penicillin is not always easy nor certain.   The easiest criterion is the enhanced production of penicillin as indicated by the usual potency assay.   However, a new penicillin may be synthesized which, on a mole for mole basis, is less active than the natural penicillin being formed in the control flasks, and which, therefore, may not only fail to give a higher assay but may even register as a less potent solution.   The best screening criterion is to employ the differential assay utilizing several test bacteria. If the ratios of activities against the various test bacteria are different, one may assume the presence of a new penicillin.   Of course, the ultimate proof is chemical isolation and characterization of the R— group. Investigators at the Lilly laboratories and also British workers have succeeded in this way in isolating and characterizing eleven new penicillins (Table 2).

TABLE 2

New Crystalline Biosynthetic Penicillins[1]

Penicillin formed	Precursor used	Activity, units/mg.	Differential assay ratio
Sodium-p-methoxybenzyl-penicillin	N-(2-hydroxyethyl)-p-methoxyphenylacetamide	1510	0.82
Sodium-p-nitrobenzyl-penicillin	N-p-nitrophenylacetyl-dl-valine	1700(?)	0.86
Sodium-p-fluorobenzyl-penicillin	N-(-2-hydroxyethyl)-p-fluorophenylacetamide	1650	0.89
Sodium-m-fluorobenzyl-penicillin	N-(2-hydroxyethyl)-m-fluorophenylacetamide	2340	0.76
Sodium-o-fluorobenzyl-penicillin	N-(2-hydroxyethyl)-o-fluorophenylacetamide	1340	1.08
Sodium-p-chlorobenzyl-penicillin	N-p-chlorophenylacetyl-dl-valine	2460	0.73
Sodium-p-bromobenzyl-penicillin	N-(γ-p-bromophenyl-butyryl-dl-valine	2270	0.65
Sodium-p-iodobenzyl-penicillin	N-(2-hydroxyethyl)-p-iodophenylacetamide	2800(?)	0.67
Sodium-2-thiophenemethyl-penicillin	N-(2-hydroxyethyl-2-thiophenacetamide	1685	1.13
Sodium-phenoxymethyl-penicillin	N-(2-hydroxyethyl)-phenoxyacetamide	1670	0.87
Sodium-p-tolylmercapto-methyl-penicillin	p-Tolylmercaptoacetyl-dl-valine	1285(?)	0.83

[1] From Behrens (1948).

Of special significance is the fact that many of these penicillins contain "biologically-foreign substances," i.e., especially the halogen substituted acyl group. In addition to those crystallized, some thirty other precursors were found to stimulate penicillin formation over the controls—presumptive evidence of their role as precursors. These have yet to be confirmed by isolation. In any case, it is evident that great numbers of different new penicillins can be obtained in this way. It is to be expected that some may exhibit special potency against certain organisms and may therefore be utilized for the control of a specific type of infection.

In general a substituted benzene ring is essential for a precursor function. The phenyl group may be replaced by certain acyclic rings or by certain heterocyclic or polycyclic rings, but ring systems containing nitrogen give no marked stimulation. Only monosubstituted acetic acids are effective, indicating that the α-methylene grouping is essential for precursor activity.

Partially Synthesized Penicillins

It is possible to isolate a biologically-produced penicillin, and then prepare a great variety of derivatives by the usual methods of synthetic organic chemistry. A number of such compounds have been prepared and they retain antibacterial activity. See Chemistry of Penicillin, 1948, Princeton Univ. Press. It is evident that far-reaching possibilities exist for creation of still new penicillins with different properties. Penicillins X and G are the preferred starting materials because of their crystallizability, stability in chemical reactions, and possibilities for additions of substituents in and diazotization of the phenyl groups.

Carbon Sources in the Penicillin Production Medium

Among the simple sugars, lactose is decidedly superior for penicillin formation, both in surface and submerged culture. Various carbon sources are evaluated for both processes by Moyer and Coghill (1946a and b). In the surface process with 1249.B21 certain crude carbohydrate sources such as ground whole corn and wheat, and cornstarch itself were as good as lactose; presumably, some stimulating materials are present in the substances. In the submerged process no other carbohydrate is as satisfactory as lactose. The superiority of lactose is associated with its slow rate of utilization as compared with other carbohydrates. The exact manner in which this influences penicillin synthesis is not known.

Other Stimulating Substances

Substances other than the components of corn steep liquor or the medium can stimulate penicillin formation, evidently in an indirect fashion, at least different from precursors. Of forty-nine different chemicals tested, only boric acid (borax) and sodium citrate increased penicillin yields, using NRRL 1951. B25 and 832 in submerged corn steep culture (Koffler et al., 1945b) and in synthetic medium with X-1612 (Koffler et al., 1946). The stimulation varied with the strain, and in some cases amounted to over 100 per cent. The boron-fed fungus utilized lactose more rapidly, had a higher rate of respiration and nitrogen utilization, had a less abundant mycelium which contained less nitrogen, and had an internal balance which was reflected outside the organism in lower ammonia levels and higher penicillin yields.

Synthetic Media for Penicillin Production

In the initial stages of development of penicillin, the difficulties experienced in extracting the penicillin from low potency broth, and the low yields of purified penicillin eventually obtained, placed a premium on a synthetic medium as compared to a complex organic one from the standpoint that fewer impurities would accompany the penicillin extracted from synthetic media and thus yield purer penicillin. Invariably higher total yields were also obtained. In the organic media impurities would arise from unassimilated substances, from breakdown products of medium components, and from substances synthesized from medium components. Though considerable attention has been given to development of synthetic media for penicillin production (Pratt and Dufrenoy, 1945; White et al., 1945; Foster et al., 1943, 1946a; Koffler et al., 1946; Stone and Farrell, 1946), these media have lost their former significance for penicillin production, and evidently have been abandoned since about 1945.

The steady successive advances in improving fungus strains have eclipsed such advantages of synthetic media as existed as long as broth potencies were low, for high potency broths together with highly efficient extraction procedures which eliminate impurities are the rule today. Furthermore, penicillin production in the organic corn steep liquor media occurs at a considerably faster rate than in synthetic media, a factor of critical industrial significance. Another fundamental obstacle to synthetic media is the evidence that virtually every different strain would have to have its own optimum medium worked out. Cost of pure chemicals in synthetic media would be prohibitive on a production basis as compared to corn steep media.

At the highest stage of development, synthetic media would produce only about one-half the yield of penicillin that would corn steep liquor. Using Q176, the following synthetic medium gave a maximum yield of 435 units per ml. as compared to 726 in cornsteep medium (Higuchi et al., 1946): in grams per liter—lactose 22.5; glucose 7.5; NH_4 lactate 7.1; KH_2PO_4 2.0; $MgSO_4 \cdot 7H_2O$ 0.25; $FeSO_4 \cdot 7H_2O$ 0.20; $CuSO_4 \cdot 5H_2O$ 0.005; $ZnSO_4 \cdot 7H_2O$ 0.02; $AlCl_3$ 0.00027; $K_2Cr_2O_7$ 0.000053; β-phenylethylamine 0.5. (See also Gordon et al., 1947.)

An enormous amount of work devoted to development of synthetic media was done under Government auspices at Pennsylvania State College by Stone and Farrell. This work has been summarized only in the briefest fashion (1946). Composition of the medium yielding best results with X-1612 follows: lactose, USP 1.5%; glucose, tech. 0.5; NH_4NO_3 0.5; acetic acid, glacial 0.4; KNO_3 0.35; KH_2PO_4 0.20; $MgSO_4 \cdot 7H_2O$ 0.05; $FeSO_4 \cdot 7H_2O$ 0.02; $ZnSO_4 \cdot 7H_2O$ 0.004; $CuSO_4 \cdot 7H_2O$ 0.0005; l-leucine 0.05; phenylacetamide 0.025. In stirred bottle submerged culture 384 units per ml. were obtained in 108 hours, slightly better than yields in corn steep medium, though taking appreciably longer. In the absence of the leucine the yield was 294 and in the absence of both leucine and phenylacetamide only 167. The presence of the leucine did not alter significantly the differential assay ratio, as did phenyacetamide, indicating that leucine increased the total penicillin G synthesis, but did not alter the type of penicillin. Presumably the leucine furnishes some precursor for the azlactone portion of the penicillin structure. The effect of leucine on Q176 in synthetic medium is not known, though being a direct-line progeny of X-1612 it might be expected to respond in similar fashion as the parent.

METABOLIC CHANGES DURING PENICILLIN FERMENTATION

The bulk of published information on this subject has come from a Government-sponsored project at the University of Wisconsin under the leadership of M. J. Johnson and W. H. Peterson. (See also Gordon et al., 1947.) Because different strains behave differently, and because it is likely that all strains prior to Q176 are obsolete, specific details will be given for Q176 whenever possible, though in many cases certain features revealed about the earlier strains have general applicability. A mass of information describing the chemical changes taking place in submerged penicillin fermentations in various media is furnished by Koffler et al. (1945a). Three general trends characterize penicillin fermentations, and these phases, occurring at different stages of the fermentation, are summarized in Table 3. The essence of the Wisconsin work on the metabolism of penicillin producing molds has been summarized by Johnson (1946).

TABLE 3

CHANGES CHARACTERIZING THE THREE PHASES OF PENICILLIN FORMATION[1]

	Phase 1	Phase 2	Phase 3
Penicillin.....	Slight production	Maximum rate of production	Concentration falls
pH..........	Sharp rise	Plateau or slight drop	Rise
Mycelium	Rapid growth, high N content	Slow growth, N content lower	Decrease in weight N content
Lactose.......	Used slowly	Used more rapidly	Small remaining amount exhausted
Lactic acid....	Exhausted rapidly		
Ammonia.....	Released into medium	Utilized	Released into medium
Nitrate.......	Used at maximum rate, although slowly	Slow use	Slow use, not exhausted
Non-ammonia Kjeldahl N	Used extensively	Concentration rather stable	Concentration increases
Inorganic phosphorous	Used at maximum rate, although slowly	Slow use	No use or liberation
$Q_{O_2}(N)$........	Maximum	Decreases	Minimum

[1] From Koffler, Emerson, Perlman and Burris (1945).

The corn steep liquor media employed had $NaNO_3$ or phosphate added. The effects of varying the content of the nitrogen and carbon sources were studied in detail. Because the degree of aeration is of critical importance in obtaining optimum penicillin yields, the study these authors made of the gas metabolism of the penicillin producing fungi is of importance. As expected, the most rapidly utilized sugars gave rise to the highest oxygen uptake as measured in the medium containing that sugar:

Carbohydrate	Maximum rate of sugar utilization, g./l./hr.	Maximum O_2 uptake, ml./l./hr.
Lactose.............	0.32	109
Sucrose.............	0.46	150
Glucose.............	0.71	300

Increased aeration is required with glucose media, for the higher rate of glucose utilization necessitates higher oxygen demand. A given culture producing maximum penicillin yields in shake flasks was capable of absorbing oxygen at a maximum of 368 ml. per liter per hour. Yet in production tanks an aeration rate equivalent to 6 to 12 liters oxygen per liter per hour is required. This indicates the crucial problem of accessability of the oxygen to the cells and the importance of efficiently designed aeration equipment. According to Johnson (1946) the percentage of air passing through tanks which is used varies from 1 to 15 per cent, with figures on the lower side generally the rule.

During shake flask experiments plugged with cotton in the conventional manner, the CO_2 content of the flask atmosphere rose up to 4.7 per cent, though 2.5 per cent was more nearly the rule. Systematic experiments revealed that some CO_2 in the atmosphere was essential for maximum penicillin formation and that excess (> 1.0 per cent) was inhibitory. A CO_2 level of 0.25 per cent was optimal if maintained artificially throughout the entire fermentation. Yet maximum yields were always obtained in the cotton-plugged flasks when the CO_2 content over the incubation period ranged from 0.03 to 4.7 per cent, an unexplained discrepancy.

Johnson (1946) utilized the CO_2 content of the effluent air from tank fermentations as a guide to the amount of growth and metabolic activity of the fungus, especially as a function of the amount of aeration supplied. With adequate aeration (about 1.25–1.5 vols. air per minute per vol. culture) a metabolism rate of 10 volumes of CO_2 per 1000 volumes of culture per minute is attained. The influence of aeration rate on tank fermentations is evident from Table 4.

TABLE 4

EFFECT OF AERATION RATE ON TANK FERMENTATION[1,2]

Aeration, vol./min.	Penicillin yield (70 hrs.), units/ml.	CO_2[3]	Age at max. NH_3 level, hr.
0.15	278	2.7	47
1.0	490	8.9	25
1.5	497	10.0	26

[1] From Johnson (1946).
[2] X-1612 in 3 per cent lactose, 4 per cent cornsteep solids, 1 per cent $CaCO_3$.
[3] Volume CO_2 per min./1000 vols. medium, average 20th to 60th hour.

Figure 1 depicts the metabolic changes characteristic of Q176 during a fermentation run in a 100 gallon tank with a regular commercial type medium consisting of 4 per cent lactose, 4 per cent corn steep solids and 1 per cent $CaCO_3$.

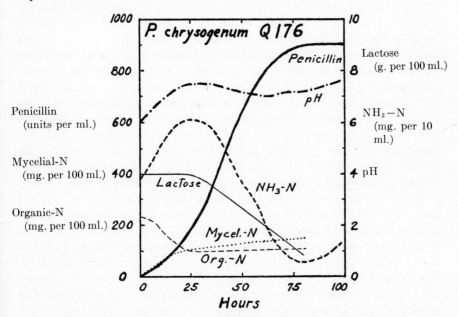

FIG. 1.—Chemical changes during penicillin production by *Penicillium chrysogenum* Q176 (from Gailey *et al.*, 1946).

pH CHANGES

Maximum penicillin yields in normal fermentations invariably are associated with a final pH of the medium between 7 to 8. The pH rise during the first day is typical of corn steep media and when it does not occur, or does so slowly, penicillin production is slow and in low yields. The pH change is due to two things, utilization of lactate ion present in the corn steep liquor and liberation of ammonia from organic nitrogen compounds of the steep liquor. Naturally, a portion of the N is assimilated by the growing mycelium. Lactic acid is consumed very rapidly by the fungus which evidently prefers it as a carbon source to the more slowly attacked lactose, which is utilized at a very slow rate as long as lactate and the organic nitrogen compounds are available as carbon sources (Koffler *et al.*, 1945a). As Fig. 1 shows, the release and accumulation of ammonia coincides with utilization of the organic N.

The most active growth of the mold occurs at the expense of the readily utilizable lactate and organic N compounds as C sources, as Fig. 1 reveals. During the second phase of the fermentation, NH_3-N is rapidly assimilated for growth by the fungus now utilizing lactose as the carbon source. This results in a lowering of the pH during this phase. This reassimilation of ammonia evidently is a prerequisite for a high-penicillin yielding fermentation, for, in general, when the ammonia level in the broth remains high, the penicillin yields are low. As Koffler *et al.*, (1945a) point out, it is not known whether high ammonia is the cause of low yields or the effect of some other factor which is the primary cause of the suppression of penicillin production. The latter explanation is indicated by the fact that ammonia added to a normal fermentation does not suppress penicillin yields. When ammonia utilization is retarded, addition of a rapidly assimilated material like glucose spurs the uptake of NH_3 and results in enhanced penicillin yields. When glucose is substituted for lactose in the original medium, there is no accumulation of ammonia during this phase, due to reutilization by the mold using glucose carbon. Penicillin yields also are much lower. Lactate utilization is also delayed because it is less available than glucose; hence the entire fermentation picture is altered by glucose (Johnson, 1946).

Active penicillin synthesis apparently is associated with the phase of slow mycelial development and ammonia assimilation which occurs at the expense of lactose. Maximum rate of penicillin formation never coincides with maximum rate of cell synthesis, but only when cell synthesis is slowed by the low rate of utilization of lactose. It would appear that penicillin results from a sort of unbalance in the metabolism of the cells, the penicillin synthesis exceeding cell material synthesis, and excreted.

Coinciding with the exhaustion of the lactose, mycelial development ceases, autolysis sets in and a small amount of NH_3 is reliberated, together with non-ammonia Kjeldahl N. Exhaustion of the ammonia often is a cause of cessation of growth. Penicillin synthesis ceases with the depletion of the lactose.

Strain Q176 uses lactose more slowly than its parent, X-1612, and grandparent 1951.B25, and hence reassimilates ammonia N more slowly also (Gailey et al., 1946). Whether this is the reason for the superior penicillin synthesis by Q176 cannot be said.

Similar metabolic studies on X-1612 and Q176 in pilot plant fermenters are given by Gordon et al. (1947).

FERMENTATION ENGINEERING

However promising or successful are laboratory results, the success of any process is assured only upon successful translation into pilot plant and factory scale. The fact that the penicillin process was the first industrial microbiological process requiring aeration in which a contamination-free system is mandatory meant that hitherto unencountered problems had to be solved. In essence, though penicillin production involved little by way of mechanical advancement, it was responsible for the "contamination-proof" philosophy, for contamination is a formidable obstacle in 5,000 to 12,000 gallon tanks through which huge volumes of air are being dispersed continuously. Here the medium conditions are ideal for virtually all possible types of contaminants. In other aerobic processes, such as sorbose production, yeast production, vinegar production, etc., the pH conditions successfully restrict contaminants.

Contamination problems delayed many plants from getting into maximum production during the war for varying lengths of time. As a matter of fact, at one time there was a strong feeling among certain authorities that the surface process should be developed instead of the submerged process, owing to the contamination problems thought to be inherent in the latter. Considerable study was devoted to a search for antiseptic chemicals which could be added to the tank media and which would not suppress growth or penicillin production by the mold but which would prevent or retard contaminants (Knight and Frazier, 1945b). Of thirty-seven chemicals submitted to laboratory tests only boric acid and borax could be used at a level high enough to delay the growth of contaminants and still not interfere with penicillin production. The amount of borax tolerated varied with the penicillin-producing species used, but 0.2–0.3 per cent was successful in controlling contaminations produced artificially by dust, etc. Borax sensitive fungi could be acclimatized to tolerating this level of borax, which did not depress penicillin yields.

Antiseptics as a means of controlling contaminations were never utilized on a large scale because of rapid advances in prevention of entrance of contaminations by proper design and operation practices. Chief among the sources of contaminations were pockets and recesses on the interior of the fermenters and accessories which were not exposed to the full impact of the steam sterilization. These are called "dead spots." Thus, a pipe projecting a few inches from a tank has the culture medium in it but does not reach the sterilization temperature of the main batch because the medium in it is not being agitated. These few milliliters of medium in the pocket are then capable of contaminating the entire batch of 5,000–10,000 gallons of broth after cooling. Another common contamination source is a leaky valve, one side of which contains sterile broth. A microscopic leak suffices to contaminate the batch if the valve itself is not sterile, or if the pipe on the opposite side of the valve is not sterile. Rigorous checking to detect leaky valves, the use of disinfectant greases in the valves, and special three-way cock valves that can be continuously sterilized by passage of steam through the valve cock itself, have minimized valves as a contamination source. Whenever possible, threaded pipe joints should be eliminated in favor of welded or brazed joints.

Sterilization of the huge volumes of compressed air which are forced through the medium at a high rate was another major problem. Again considerable experimentation on pilot or plant scales has solved this problem. A sizable reduction in the bacterial count of the air occurs as a result of the high temperature generated during compression. Through special devices such as electrical precipitation of dust particles, electrically heated tubes, ultraviolet light tubes, and disinfectant scrubbing towers, it is possible to sterilize the air, but used universally today is simple mechanical filtration of the air through glass wool, activated carbon packed in a long pipe, or through plain porcelain filters of pore size 1.5μ (Gordon et al., 1947).

Another source of contamination during the operation of a tank is via the inoculum. Whether the tank be the initial seed tank being inoculated from a laboratory flask, or a 10,000 gallon tank being inoculated from a 1,000 gallon seed tank, it is a prime requisite to ascertain the purity of the inoculum at the time it is used. Microscopic examination is not entirely reliable even in the hands of one experienced in penicillin microbiology for two reasons: (a) the contamination may have entered relatively recently, being too small in numbers to detect in a microscopic field or (b) production medium has millions of dead bacterial cells per ml. from the spontaneous fermentation of corn steeps liquor soon after its manufacture. Only actively motile contaminants would therefore be detectable amid the large numbers of dead cells.

It is customary to inoculate a small sample of the inoculum into test broth that favors the growth of contaminating bacteria if they are present. This may be done 8–16 hours before intended use of the inoculum. The use of rigorous precautions of this sort is the most economical way to operate the plant in the long run, for the loss in output from a production tank is very great financially, and can be eliminated by detecting a contaminated inoculum before it is used and substituting another seed tank inoculum of proved purity.

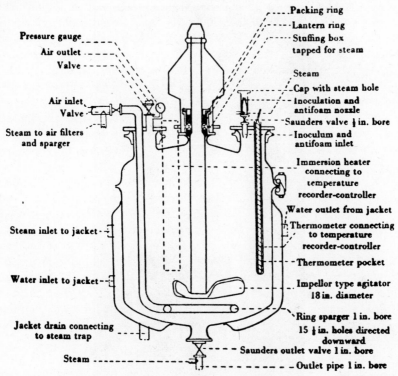

FIG. 2.—Diagrammatic vertical section of pilot-plant apparatus for penicillin production (from Gordon *et al.*, 1947).

Details of design and operation of a "sterile room" in which inoculum preparation is done in order to reduce the incidence of contamination are described by Grenfell *et al.* (1947).

Other aspects of fermentation engineering had to do with the design of efficient agitators and aerating devices, specialized instrumentation, sterile gasket seals, maintenance of pipe lines and other sterile areas in the equipment under constant steam "seal," automatic temperature control, devices for obtaining culture samples periodically under aseptic conditions, and for inoculating seed tanks and adding antifoam materials during the fermentation.

The large evolution of energy in the form of heat from the oxidation of the lactose and other organic nutrients must be dissipated by cold water or brine circulating continuously in coils or in the jackets of the fermenters. Otherwise the heat evolution is so great the temperature would rapidly rise to the point of inhibition of the fungus. Description of fermenter design, construction and operation on a pilot plant scale,

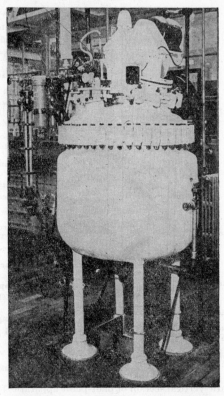

FIG. 3.—Fifty gallon pilot plant penicillin fermenter (from Gordon *et al.*, 1947).

as well as photographs and diagrams of specialized accessories are available from several sources: (Stefaniak *et al.*, 1946a; Jacobs *et al.*, 1948; Gordon *et al.*, 1947; Taylor, 1947). Figures 2 and 3 show a representative penicillin fermenter, in this case of 50-gallon capacity, but comparable in virtually every respect to fermenters of 5,000–15,000 gallon capacity.

It will be noted that the rotary type fermenter advocated for many years by the USDA group for use in aerobic microbiological processes (Gastrock, *et al.*, 1938) is unsatisfactory as compared to the vertical stationary type tank depicted in Figs. 2 and 3, and universally employed for the penicillin (and streptomycin) process.

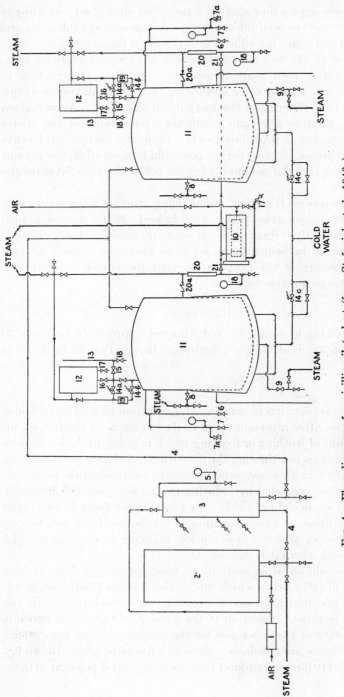

FIG. 4.—Flow diagram of penicillin pilot plant (from Stefaniak *et al.*, 1946a).

1. Steam-jacketed air sterilizer for seed tank. 2. Seed tank. 3. Measuring tank for inoculum. 4. Inoculum line. 5. Inoculum pressure gage. 6. Air vent throttling valve. 7. Exhaust air throttling valve. 7a. Safety valve. 8. Sampling valve. 9. Drain valve. 10. Steam-jacketed air sterilizer for fermenters. 11. Fermenter. 12. Vessel containing antifoam agent. 13. Antifoam agent standpipe. 14a, 14b, 14c. Magnetic valves. 15, 16. Magnetic valves for fermenters. 17. Condensate valve. 18. Drain valve for antifoam agent. 19. Holding chamber for antifoam agent. 20. Rotameter. 20a. Check valve. 21. Air flow regulating valve.

Figure 4 represents a flow sheet of a penicillin pilot plant consisting of two fermenters and one seed tank and a special measuring tank to control the amount of inoculum introduced into the main fermenters.

Stefaniak *et al.* (1946a) report the effect of various factors on penicillin production in pilot plant fermenters. Air flow of about 0.25 to 1 volume per minute per volume culture medium gives maximum yields, depending on the efficiency of the mechanical agitation. At any given aeration rate, there is a certain minimum r.p.m. value of the stirrer required for maximum penicillin yields. Ordinary carbon steel tanks and equipment are satisfactory for the penicillin fermentation, the amount of iron dissolving into the medium being far below the toxic level for the fungus.

Though this process is aerobic, unlike many others it is not accelerated by air pressures above atmosphere, and, indeed, 40 lbs per square inch pressure significantly retards the process (Stefaniak *et al.*, 1946b). Operating practice in penicillin plants is to maintain a small internal positive air pressure in the tanks to prevent the entrance of air contaminants through possible leaks.

TEMPERATURE

Penicillin yields in tanks are not affected appreciably between 20 and 29°C., but 32° is definitely injurious. In practice 23 to 25°C. is employed.

FOAMING

The intense application of aeration and agitation to corn steep liquor media generates, after a certain stage of development of the fungus, an excessive amount of frothing or foaming which may fill up the head space in the tank and spew out through the air outlet. A sizable portion of the batch can be lost in this way, and it creates contamination problems. The foam may be controlled by reducing the air flow, but this generally results in reduced penicillin yields. In practice the foam is controlled by periodic addition of small amounts of sterile antifoam substances, which, by virtue of their surface tension reducing properties, cut the foam to the point where it is manageable.

Foaming is believed due, partially at least, to the synthesis by the mold of fats and fatty acids, which, under the alkaline conditions developed, behave essentially as soaps, creating very stable foams in the proteinaceous medium. Selection of the appropriate antifoam depends on lack of toxicity of the substance for the process. Many commercial synthetic antifoams are available. Several antifoams were studied by Stefaniak *et al.* (1946b), who found lard, lard oil, and 3 per cent octadecanol in lard oil were non-toxic. An antifoam may have excellent foam breaking qualities, but its toxicity renders it valueless for penicillin fermentation. Soybean oil, castor oil, and other natural vegetable oils work, but apparently the mold hydrolyzes them, contributing fatty acids as impurities in the extraction. Mineral oil containing a few per cent octadecanol circumnavigates this difficulty. It is believed that the industry generally utilizes commercially available synthetic antifoams. Antifoams may be added by hand to the fermenters under appropriate aseptic precautions, but in large production tanks it is done mechanically. Design details of an electrical automatic antifoam-adding device which allows antifoam to enter when the foam reaches a certain level, are described by Stefaniak et al. (1946a).

Addition of a few drops of a non-toxic antifoam to submerged flask cultures almost always results in enhanced yields and an accelerated fermentation. This is believed to be ascribable to increased rate of entrance of oxygen into the cells as a result of lowering of the surface tension. In this connection see Stokes and Koffler (1949).

EXTRACTION AND PURIFICATION OF PENICILLIN

When the penicillin batch reaches maturity, the penicillin potency plateaus off for several hours than falls. At maximum potency the batch is pumped to a holding tank equipped with brine coils and cooled to 0 to 5°C. Maintenance of this low temperature is essential during the extraction procedure owing to the instability of penicillin during certain steps. A slurry of diatomaceous earth (filter-aid; filter-cel) is mixed in to facilitate separation of the gelatinous mycelium solids by means of a continuous-type rotary filter.

Two main types of extraction procedures are employed, namely, solvent process and carbon process. The principles and operating details of both these extraction processes on a pilot plant scale are described by Whitmore et al. (1946) and Gordon et al. (1947).

1. SOLVENT PROCESS

This embodies the principles employed in the original Abraham et al. paper (1940). The penicillins are strong acids which are soluble in amyl acetate and other immiscible fat solvents at pH 2.0–2.5. The acidification is done with mineral acids, usually phosphoric acid. The partition coefficient of 30:1 in amyl acetate permits a high concentration and volume reduction when this step is conducted efficiently. The efficiency depends on speed to minimize the time required to hold the penicillin at the low pH where it is very unstable, and on contact between solvent and aqueous phase to secure complete extraction.

The speed is accomplished by continuous-flow mixing of solvent, broth and acid so that only a small portion of the broth is acid at any one time, the solvent containing the penicillin being immediately reextracted with alkali or buffer at approximately neutral pH so that the penicillin is taken into the aqueous phase again as the salt. All solutions are cooled to $\sim 5°C.$, which also minimizes acid inactivation of penicillin.

Intimate contact between solvent and acidified broth is achieved by conducting the extraction in a continuous-flow high speed line homogenizer which emulsifies the solvent and water, creating the ideal conditions for instantaneous passage of the penicillin from the water particles into the solvent dropules.

The emulsion passes immediately to a continuous-flow centrifuge which separates the two liquids based on differences in specific gravity much on the principle of the cream separator. The penicillin-containing amyl acetate now flows into a second line homogenizer and is there extracted with phosphate buffer and separated in a second centrifuge. The process is repeated once more in essentially the same fashion, each successive extracting liquid being a smaller volume so that a very large concentration (volume reduction) of penicillin has been achieved in the final (penicillin) rich aqueous solution. The second aqueous extraction is done with NaOH or $NaHCO_3$, yielding a solution of the sodium salt of penicillin. The volume of aqueous salt solution at this stage represents a 100- to 200-fold volume reduction from the original broths.

The different penicillins have different pK's and this property permits a gross separation depending on the pH to which the final aqueous extraction is adjusted. Thus, if NaOH is added to pH of about 5.8, penicillins G and F are extracted mainly, most of the K remaining. The latter is now extracted at pH 6.8–7.0, this fraction consisting mainly of K with smaller amounts of G. The virtual suppression of K by use of precursors renders this type of separation of the penicillins superfluous.

The concentration procedure accomplishes a high degree of purification also, but other organic acid impurities, including the orange-yellow pigments, chrysogenin and penetrinic acid (Clutterbuck et al., 1932; Stodola et al., 1945) are present in the final rich water. These are eliminated by treatment of the rich water with certain organic bases which readily form crystalline salts with penicillin G, and which are so insoluble in cold solvents that complete recoveries of penicillin G are obtained if the crude material has a penicillin G content exceeding 50 per cent and a potency of > 800 units per mg (Sheehan et al., 1946) though Boon (1948) believes it should be 90 per cent. N-ethylpiperidine is one such base whose salt with penicillin G is insoluble in cold amyl acetate-acetone mixtures. Use of phenylacetic acid precursors with strain

Q176 gives preponderately penicillin G, as we have seen.   The organic salt is decomposed under appropriate conditions, yielding aqueous solution of pure sodium penicillin, the article of commerce.   After distribution in appropriate amounts into vials, the solutions are frozen and dried *in vacuo* (freeze drying; lyophilization).

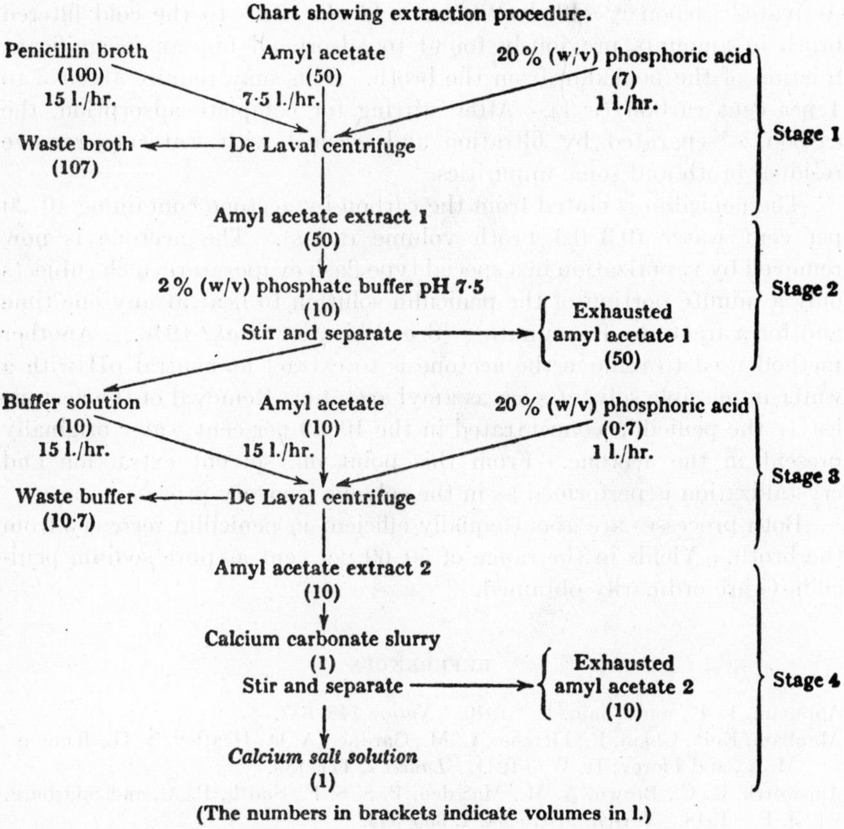

Chart showing extraction procedure.

Penicillin broth (100) 15 l./hr. — Amyl acetate (50) 7·5 l./hr. — 20% (w/v) phosphoric acid (7) 1 l./hr.

Waste broth (107) ← De Laval centrifuge

Stage 1

Amyl acetate extract 1 (50)

2% (w/v) phosphate buffer pH 7·5 (10)
Stir and separate → Exhausted amyl acetate 1 (50)

Stage 2

Buffer solution (10) 15 l./hr. — Amyl acetate (10) 15 l./hr. — 20% (w/v) phosphoric acid (0·7) 1 l./hr.

Waste buffer (10·7) ← De Laval centrifuge

Stage 3

Amyl acetate extract 2 (10)

Calcium carbonate slurry (1)
Stir and separate → Exhausted amyl acetate 2 (10)

Stage 4

Calcium salt solution (1)

(The numbers in brackets indicate volumes in l.)

FIG. 5.—Chart showing solvent extraction procedure for penicillin (from Gordon *et al.*, 1947).

Pure crystalline sodium penicillin G can be obtained from freeze-dried amorphous sodium penicillin G by dissolving in dry acetone whereupon it crystallizes almost at once.   The crystalline material may then be distributed by weighing into vials.

Figure 5 depicts a typical solvent extraction procedure showing the volumes and rates of flow of the various liquids.   In this case, the final rich water solution was prepared as the calcium salt instead of sodium.

2. CARBON ADSORPTION METHODS

These differ from the solvent method only in the first stage where the primary concentration of the penicillin is achieved by adsorption on activated carbon and elution. Solvent extraction is applied from this point on, similar to the corresponding stages in the solvent process. Activated carbon is added (Whitmore *et al.*, 1946) to the cold filtered broth in amounts previously found to adsorb all but an insignificant fraction of the penicillin from the broth. This may require about 3 to 4 per cent carbon (*w/v*). After stirring for complete adsorption, the carbon is separated by filtration and washed with water to remove residual broth and some impurities.

The penicillin is eluted from the carbon by acetone containing 10–20 per cent water (0.3–0.4 broth volume ratios). The acetone is now removed by vaporization in a special type flash evaporator which subjects only a minute portion of the penicillin solution to heat at any one time and for a fraction of a minute. (See Whitmore *et al.*, 1946.) Another method used to remove the acetone is to extract at neutral pH with a water-immiscible solvent such as amyl acetate. Removal of the acetone leaves the penicillin concentrated in the 10–20 per cent water originally present in the acetone. From this point on, solvent extraction and crystallization is performed as in the solvent recovery process.

Both processes are about equally efficient in penicillin recovery from the broth. Yields in the range of 50–60 per cent as pure sodium penicillin G are ordinarily obtained.

REFERENCES

Abraham, E. P., and Chain, E. 1940. *Nature* **146**, 837.

Abraham, E. P., Chain, E., Fletcher, C. M., Gardner, A. D., Heatley, N. G., Jennings, M. A., and Florey, H. W. 1941. *Lancet* **2**, 177–189.

Ainsworth, G. C., Brown, A. M., Marsden, P. S. S. F., Smith, P. A., and Spilsburg, J. F. 1948. *J. Gen. Microbiol.* **1**, 335–343.

Bachus, M. P., Stauffer, J. F., and Johnson, M. J. 1946. *J. Am. Chem. Soc.* **68**, 152–153.

Behrens, O. K. 1948. In Chemistry of Penicillin. Princeton University Press, Princeton, New Jersey.

Benedict, R. G. 1946. Cited in Raper (1946).

Benedict, R. G., Schmidt, W. H., and Coghill, R. D. 1945. *Arch. Biochem.* **8**, 377–384.

Boon, W. R. 1948. *Analyst* **73**, 202–207.

Bowden, J. P., and Peterson, W. H. 1946. *Arch. Biochem.* **9**, 387–399.

Bulletin of the U. S. Army Medical Dept. **6**, 562, 1946.

Bush, M. T., and Goth, A. 1943. *J. Pharmacol. Exp.* **78**, 164–169.

Chain, E., Florey, H. W., Gardner, A. D., Jennings, M. A., Orr-Ewing, J., Sanders, A. F., and Heatley, N. G. 1940. *Lancet* **2**, 226–228.

Clutterbuck, P. W., Lovell, R., and Raistrick, H.   1932.   *Biochem. J.* **26,** 1907–1918.

Coghill, R. G.   1944.   *Chem. Eng. News* **22,** 588–593.

Cook, R. P., and Brown, M. B.   1947.   *Nature* **159,** 376–377.

Cook, A. H., and Lacey, M. S.   1944.   *Nature* **153,** 460.

Cook, R. P., and Tulloch, W. J.   1944.   *J. Path. Bact.* **56,** 555–565.

Cook, R. P., Tulloch, W. J., Brown, M. B., and Brodie, J.   1945.   *Biochem. J.* **39,** xxiii.

Dorrell, W. W., and Page, R. M.   1947.   *J. Bact.* **53,** 360–361.

du Vigneaud, V., Carpenter, F. G., Holley, R. W., Livermore, A. H., and Rachele, J. R.   1946.   *Science* **104,** 431–434.

Duthie, E. S.   1944.   *Brit. J. Exptl. Path.* **25,** 76–100.

Fleming, A.   1929.   *Brit. J. Exptl. Path.* **10,** 226–236.

Fleming, A., and MacLean, I. G.   1930.   *Brit. J. Exptl. Path.* **11,** 127–134.

Florey, H. W., Heatley, N. G., Jennings, M. A., and Williams, T. L.   1944.   *Nature* **154,** 268.

Foster, J. W.   1945.   *Science* **101,** 205.   1949.   U. S. Patent 2,458,495 (C.A. **43,** 2278).

Foster, J. W., and Karow, E. O.   1945.   *J. Bact.* **49,** 19–29.

Foster, J. W., McDaniel, L. E., Woodruff, H. B., and Stokes, J. L.   1945.   *J. Bact.* **50,** 365–368.

Foster, J. W., Woodruff, H. B., and McDaniel, L. E.   1943.   *J. Bact.* **46,** 421–433.

Foster, J. W., Woodruff, H. B., and McDaniel, L. E.   1946a.   *J. Bact.* **51,** 465–478.

Foster, J. W., Woodruff, H. B., Perlman, D., McDaniel, L. E., Wilker, B. L., and Hendlin, D.   1946b.   *J. Bact.* **51,** 695–698.

Frank, M. C., Calam, C. T., and Gregory, P. H.   1948.   *J. Gen. Microbiol.* **2,** 70–79.

Fried, J., Koerber, W. L., and Wintersteiner, O.   1946.   *J. Biol. Chem.* **163,** 341–342.

Gailey, F. B., Stefaniak, J. J., Olson, B. H., and Johnson, M. J.   1946.   *J. Bact.* **52,** 129–140.

Gastrock, E. A., Porges, N., Wells, P. A., and Moyer, A. J.   1938.   *Ind. Eng. Chem.* **30,** 782–789.

Gilbert, W. J., and Hickey, R. J.   1946.   *J. Bact.* **51,** 731–733.

Goodall, R. R., and Levi, A. A.   1946.   *Nature* **158,** 675–676.

Goodall, R. R., and Levi, A. A.   1947.   *Analyst* **72,** 277–288.

Gordon, J. J., Grenfell, E., Knowles, E., Legge, B. J., McAllister, R. C. A., and White, T.   1947.   *J. Gen. Microbiol.* **1,** 187–202.

Grenfell, E., Legge, B. J., and White, T.   1947.   *J. Gen. Microbiol.* **1,** 171–186.

Halpern, P. E., Siminovitch, D., and McFarlane, W. D.   1945.   *Science* **102,** 230.

Henry, R. J., and Housewright, R. D.   1947.   *J. Biol. Chem.* **167,** 559–571.

Higuchi, K., Jarvis, F. G., Peterson, W. H., and Johnson, M. J.   1946.   *J. Am. Chem. Soc.* **68,** 1669–1670.

Higuchi, K., and Peterson, W. H.   1947.   *Anal. Chem.* **19,** 68–71.

Housewright, R. D., and Henry, R. J.   1947.   *J. Biol. Chem.* **167,** 553–557.

Jacobs, W. L., Wright, R. K., and Hildebrandt, F. M.   1948.   *Ind. Eng. Chem.* **40,** 759–764.

Johnson, M. J.   1946.   *Ann. N. Y. Acad. Sci.* **48,** 57–66.

Keefer, C. S., Blake, F. G., Marshall, E. K., Lockwood, J. S., and Wood, W. B.   1943.   *J. Am. Med. Assoc.* **122,** 1217–1224.

Knight, S. G., and Frazier, W. C.   1945a.   *Science* **102,** 617–618.

Knight, S. G., and Frazier, W. C.   1945b.   *J. Bact.* **50,** 505–516.

Koffler, H., Emerson, R. L., Perlman, D., and Burris, R. H.   1945a.   *J. Bact.* **50,** 517–548.

Koffler, H., Knight, S. G., Emerson, R. L., and Burris, R. H. 1945b. *J. Bact.* **50,** 549–559.

Koffler, H., Knight, S. G., Frazier, W. C., and Burris, R. H. 1946. *J. Bact.* **51,** 385–392.

Koffler, H., Knight, S. G., and Frazier, W. C. 1947. *J. Bact.* **53,** 115–123.

Liggett, R. W., and Koffler, H. 1948. *Bact. Revs.* **12,** 297–311.

McKee, C. M., Rake, G., and Houck, C. L. 1944. *J. Bact.* **49,** 19–29.

McQuarrie, E. B., Leibmann, A. J., Kluener, R. G., and Venosa, A. T. 1944. *Arch. Biochem.* **5,** 307–316.

Medical Research Committee, 1945. *Science* **102,** 627–629.

Morgan, J. F., and Campbell, M. E. 1947. *J. Biol. Chem.* **169,** 337–343.

Moyer, A. J., and Coghill, R. D. 1946a. *J. Bact.* **51,** 57–78.

Moyer, A. J., and Coghill, R. D. 1946b. *J. Bact.* **51,** 79–92.

Moyer, A. J., and Coghill, R. D. 1947. *J. Bact.* **53,** 329–341.

Peck, S. M., and Hewitt, W. L. 1945. *Pub. Health Reports* **60,** 148–152.

Pratt, R., and Dufrenoy, J. 1945. *Science* **102,** 428–429.

Pratt, R., and Hok, K. A. 1946. *Am. J. Botany* **33,** 149–156.

Raper, K. B. 1946. *Annals N. Y. Acad. Sci.* **48,** 41–52.

Raper, K. B., and Fennell, D. I. 1946. *J. Bact.* **51,** 761–777.

Raper, K. B., and Alexander, D. F. 1945. *J. Elisha Mitchell Sci. Soc.* **61,** 74–113.

Raper, K. B., Alexander, D. F., and Coghill, R. D. 1944. *J. Bact.* **48,** 639–659.

Reid, R. D. 1935. *J. Bact.* **39,** 215–221.

Richards, A. N. 1943. *J. Am. Med. Assoc.* **122,** 235–236.

Robbins, W. J. 1946. Cited in Raper (1946).

Rode, L. J., Foster, J. W., and Schuhardt, V. T. 1947. *J. Bact.* **53,** 565–566.

Savage, G. M., and Vander Brook, M. J. 1946. *J. Bact.* **52,** 385–391.

Schmidt, W. H., Ward, G. E., and Coghill, R. D. 1945. *J. Bact.* **49,** 411–412.

Sheehan, J., Mader, W. J., and Cram, D. J. 1946. *J. Am. Chem. Soc.* **68,** 2407.

Starks, O. B., and Koffler, H. 1949. *Science* **109,** 495–496.

Stefaniak, J. J., Gailey, F. B., Brown, C. S., and Johnson, M. J. 1946a. *Ind. Eng. Chem.* **38,** 666–671.

Stefaniak, J. J., Gailey, F. B., Jarvis, F. G., and Johnson, M. J. 1946b. *J. Bact.* **52,** 119–127.

Stevenson, H. 1948. *Chem. Eng. News* **26,** 2164.

Stodola, F. H., Wachtel, J. L., Moyer, A. J., and Coghill, R. D. 1945. *J. Biol. Chem.* **159,** 67–70.

Stone, R. W., and Farrell, M. A. 1946. *Science* **104,** 445–446.

Stone, R. W., Patterson, H. T., and Farrell, M. A. 1946. *J. Bact.* **51,** 598.

Taylor, T. H. M. 1947. *Chem. Eng. Progress* **43,** 155–159.

Thom, C. 1944. *J. Bact.* **48,** 120–121.

Thom, C. 1945. *Mycologia* **37,** 460–475.

Umezawa, H., Suzuki, S., and Takeuchi, T. 1948. *Japanese Med. J.* **1,** 73–76.

Ungar, J. 1948. *J. Gen. Microbiol.* **2,** xiii–xv.

Waksman, S. A., and Bugie, E. 1943. *Proc. Nat. Acad. Sci.* **29,** 282–288.

White, A. G. C., Krampitz, L. O., and Werkman, C. H. 1945. *Arch. Biochem.* **8,** 303–310.

Whitmore, F. C., and seventeen other authors 1946. *Ind. Eng. Chem.* **38,** 942–948.

Wickerham, L. J. 1946. Cited in Raper (1946).

Wilson, J. E., and du Vigneaud, V. 1948. *Science* **107,** 653.

Woodruff, H. B., and Foster, J. W. 1945. *J. Bact.* **49,** 7–17.

Yermolieva, Z., Kaplun, T., and Levitov, M. 1945. *Ann. Rev. Soviet Med.* **2,** 247–250.

Author Index

Names in parentheses indicate coauthors of the references and are included to assist in locating references where a particular name is not on a given page.

Example: Alexander, D. F., 571 (see Raper), means that Raper *et al.* will be mentioned on page 571, the *et al.* accounting for Alexander. This article can be located under Raper in the list of references. Numbers in italics refer to the pages on which references are listed in bibliographies at the end of each chapter.

A

Abderhalden, E., 108, *143*, 528, *528*
Abraham, E. P., 565, 569, 599, *602*
Acklin, O., 556, 559, *560*
Afanassjewa, M., 305, 306, *324*
Ainsworth, G. C., 567, *602*
Airoldi, R., 433, *444*
Akasi, S., 112, *143*
Albericci, V. J., 473, *479*
Albert, A., 262, *279*
Alexander, D. F., 188, 189, *208*, 571 (see Raper), 572 (see Raper), 573 (see Raper), 574 (see Raper), *604*
Allen, M. C., 548 (see Waksman), *562*
Allen, R. R., 494, *529*
Allison, F. E., 483, *528*
Allsopp, A., 329, 336, 338, 340, 343, *349*
Amann, P. F., 372 (see Kane), *377*, 422 (see Kane), 427 (see Kane), 428 (see Kane), *429*
Amelung, H., 398, *416*
Anderson, A. K., 312, *324*
Anderson, C. G., 476, *479*
Andrews, H. N., 202, *208*
Angeletti, A., 448, 464, *466*
Anson, M. L., 88, *143*
Armbruster, R., 554 (see Dyckerhoff), *561*
Armit, J. W., 431, 444
Armstrong, G. M., 533, 535, *560*
Arnon, D. I., 262, *281*
Aronovsky, S. I., 458 (see Porges), *467*
Asai, T., 284, *295*, 306, 308, 309, *325*, 358, 360, 366, *377*, 432, *445*
Aso, K., 87, 135, 138, *143*, 260, *279*

Auerbach, C., 216, *248*
Awetissowa, A. N., 524, *529*

B

Baba, S., 142, *144*, 346, *349*, 415, *416*
Bach, D., 486, 517, 518, 522, *528*
Bachus, M. P., 572, *602*
Bail, T., 301, *324*
Baker, G. E., 202, *208*
Balfour, B. G., 262 (see Albert), *279*
Ballou, G. A., 548 (see Lineweaver), *562*
Barber, H. H., 125, *144*
Barham, N. H., 431, 434, 435, 439, 443, *444*
Barinova, S. A., 369, *376*, 400, *416*
Barker, H. A., 71, *74*, 130, 131, *144*
Barnard, D., 442, *444*
Barsony, G., 554 (see Toth), *562*
Baudisch, O., 262, *279*
Beadle, G. W., 17, *25*, 202, 203, 204, 205, *208*, 225, 229, 235, 237, 239, 248, *248*, *249*, *250*
Becker, D., 99 (see Hilpert), *145*
Behr, G., 88, 90, 93, 105, 142, 143, *144*, *146*, 534, *562*
Behrens, O. K., 579, 580, 585, 586, *602*
Belin, P., 115, 122, *144*
Bell, T. T., 242, *250*
Bender, I., 358, *376*
Benedict, R. G., 569, 573, *602*
Bennet-Clark, T. A., 339, 340, 341, *349*
Berger, J., 107 (see Woolley), 527, *528*
Bernhauer, K., 42, 65, 72, *74*, 125, 132, 133, 135, *144*, 275, *279*, 291, *295*, 310, 316, *324*, 339, 340, 341, 342, 345, *349*, *349*, 356, 364, 374, 376, *376*, 382, 383,

605

I

Ichihara, K., 510, 511 (see Kotake), 512
(see Kotake), 513 (see Kotake), *529,
530*
Iglauer, A., 388 (see Bernhauer), *416*
Ingelman, B., 141, *145*
Ingold, C. T., 184, *208*
Inoue, T., 375 (see Sakaguchi), *377*
Ishida, S., 515, *531*
Istin, M., 162, *183*
Itto, G., 465, *466*
Itzerott, D., 486, 487, 488, *529*
Iwanoff, K. S., 266, *279*
Iwanoff, N. N., 5, *25*, 518, 520, 521, 522,
524, 525, *529*

J

Jacobs, W. L., 40 (see Erb), *75*, 596, *603*
Jacobson, K. A., 511, 529
Jacques, A. G., 413, *418*
Jacquot, R., 130, *145*, 331, 332, 338, *349*
Jaffe, H., 319 (see Gould), *324*
Jahiel, R., 222, *249*
Jamieson, G. S., *147*
Jansen, E. F., 548, *561*
Jarvis, F. G., 582 (see Higuchi), 588 (see
Higuchi), 596 (see Stefaniak), 598
(see Stefaniak), *603, 604*
Javallier, M., 268, 276, *279*
Jennings, M. A., 565 (see Chain, Abra-
ham), 573 (see Florey), *602, 603*
Jensen, H. L., 277, *279*
Johnson, J. R., 536 (see Dutcher), *561*
Johnson, M. J., 131 (see Koepsell), 260,
261, *280*, 387 (see Perlman), 388 (see
Perlman), 389, 390, 392, 393, 394, 395,
408, 527 (see Berger), *528*, 568 (see
Gailey), 572 (see Bachus), 582 (see
Higuchi), 588 (see Higuchi), 589, 590,
591 (and see Gailey), 592, 593 (see
Gailey), 596 (see Stefaniak), 597 (see
Stefaniak), 598 (see Stefaniak), 599
(see Stefaniak), *602, 603, 604*
Jones, J. K. N., *144*
Jones, L. R., 458 (see Roberts), *467*
Jones, W. N., 484, *529*
Jordan, J., 258
Joslyn, D. A., 540 (see Smith), *562*
Junitzky, N., 306, *324*

K

Kalb, L., 99, *145*
Kalnitsky, A., 401, *417*
Kamen, M. D., 368 (see Foster, 1941),
370 (see Foster, 1941), *376*, 409 (see
Foster), *417*
Kane, J. H., 372 (see Doscher), *376*, 422,
427, 428, *429*, 453 (see Currie), *466*
Kane, J. N., 372, *377*
Kanel, E., 284, *295*, 374, *377*
Kaplan, N., 397 (see Doudoroff), *417*
Kaplun, T., 573 (see Yermolieva), *604*
Kapur, S. N., 448, *466*
Kardo-Syssojeva, E., 447, *466*
Karow, E. O., *183*, 383, 388, 389, 390,
391, 392, 393, 394, 397, 413, *417, 444*,
573 (see Foster), *603*
Karström, H., 64, *75*, 306, 313, *324*
Kasselbach, E., 483, *529*
Katagiri, H., 434, 435, 441, 442, *444*
Katzman, P. A., 458 (see Roberts), *467*
Katznelson, H., 87, *145*
Kauffman-Cosla, D., 274, 276, *279*
Kavanagh, F., 113, *146*, 316, *325*
Kazdan, R., 222 (see Jahiel), *249*
Keane, J., 541 (see Hardiman), *561*
Keefer, C. S., 566, *603*
Keilin, D., 458, 460, 461, 462, 463, *466*
Keseling, J., 552 (see Rippel), *562*
Kertesz, Z. I., 547, 548, *561*
Kidder, G. W., 242, *249*
Killian, C., 465, *467*
Kingery, L. B., 499 (see Mosher), *530*
Kinoshita, K., 419, 420, 421, *429*, 435,
437, *445*
Kinsey, V. E., 218, *249*
Kintoff, W., 127, 128, 129, 130, *144, 145*
Kirsanowa, V., 400 (see Gudlet), 407
(see Gudlet), *417*
Kita, D. A., 388 (see Perlman), *418*
Kitahara, K., 435, 441, 442, *444*
Klammerth, O. O. L., 312, 319, *324*
Klein, G., 490, *529*
Klein, L., 435 (see Challenger), 441 (see
Challenger), 443 (see Challenger), *444*
Kleinzeller, A., 131, *145*, 373, *377*
Klotz, L. J., 84, *145*, 486, *529*
Kluener, R. G., 569 (see McQuarrie), *604*
Kluyver, A. J., 3, *26*, 51, 66, 68, 69, *75,*

Pauli, R., 461, *466*

Pearce, A. A., 339 (see Chughtai), *349*, 404, *417*, 541, *562*

Pearson, L. K., 125, *145*

Peck, R. L., 126, *145*

Peck, S. M., 573, *604*

Peltier, G. L., 487, *529*

Penan, H., 259 (see Cliquet), *279*

Penner, M. A., 540 (see Smith), *562*

Perlman, D., 65 (see Foster), *75*, 332, *350*, 387, 388, *418*, 577 (see Foster), 589 (see Koffler), 592 (see Koffler), *603*

Perquin, L. H. C., 51, 66, 68, 69, *75*, 165, *183*, 259, 275, *280*, 303, *324*, 379, 387, 389, 390, 393, *417*, *418*, 434, 435, *445*, 447, 450, *467*

Perrier, A., 115, *145*, 402, *418*

Perwozwansky, W. W., 448, *467*

Peterson, W. H., 88, 89 (see Bohonos), 94, 102 (see Pruess), 103 (see Pruess, Gorcica), 104 (see Bohonos), 105 (see Bohonos), 107 (see Woolley, Skinner), 108, 109 (see Bohonos), 113, 115 (see Prill), 119 (see Pruess), 120 (see Pruess), 121 (see Pruess, Prill), 124 (see Prill), 132 (see Pruess, Wenck), 133 (see Pruess, Wenck), 134 (see Prill), 136 (and see Woolley), *144*, *145*, *146*, *147*, 152 (see Pruess), *183*, 388 (see Perlman), 391, *418*, 472 (see Norman), 473, *480*, 527 (see Berger), *528*, 536 (see Woolley), *562*, 576 (see Bowden), 577 (see Bowden), 582 (see Higuchi), 588 (see Higuchi) 589, *602*, *603*

Peukert, M., 101, *145*

Peyros, E., 383, 408, *417*

Pfaff, H., 549, 550, *562*

Pfeffer, W., 252, 265, *280*, 336, *350*

Pfeiffer, S. E., 151 (see Tanner), *183*

Phillips, H., 99, *147*

Pierce, J. G., 239, *249*

Pistschimuka, P., 516, *529*

Pisula, F., 527, *528*

Pjukow, D., 487, *531*

Plattner, P. A., 494, *530*

Plumlee, C. H., 535, *562*

Pollard, A. H., 535, *562*

Pontecorvo, G., 202, 203, *208*, 211, *250*

Pontillon, C., 123, 124, 125, 137, *145*

Pool, J. C., 553 (see Nicholson), 554 (see Nicholson), *562*

Porges, N., 49, *75*, 78, 83, 123, *145*, 266, 267, 274, 275, 276, *280*, 455 (see Gastrock), 457, 458, *466*, *467*, 596 (see Gastrock), *603*

Pottevin, H., 550, 552, 553, 554, *562*

Potzelt, G., 125, 132, 133, 135, *144*

Pratt, R., 578, 588, *604*

Prelog, V., 134, *147*

Prescott, S. C., 66, *75* (see Doelger), 383, 385, 398, *417*, *418*

Price, N. V., 533 (see Nicholson), 554 (see Nicholson), *562*

Prickett, P. S., 133, *145*

Prill, E. A., 115, 121, 123, 124, 134, 136 (see Woolley), *145*, *147*

Pringsheim, H., 100, *146*, 515, *530*

Prodinger, W., 261, *280*

Proskuriakow, N.J., 95, *146*, 548, 549, *562*

Pruess, L. M., 102, 103, 119, 120, 121, 132, 133, *146*, 152, *183*

Puziss, M., 508 (see Emerson), *529*

Q

Quastel, J. H., 492, *530*

Quilico, A., 86, *146*, 268, 269, *280*

R

Rachels, J. R., 579 (see du Vigneaud), *603*

Raciborkski, 541, *562*

Raistrick, H., 6, *26*, 30 (see Birkinshaw), *75* (see Birkinshaw), 108 (see Birkinshaw), 113 (see Oxford), 125 (and see Clutterbuck), 134, *144*, *145*, 153, 154, *183*, 270, 305 (see Birkinshaw), 307, 308, *324*, *325*, 332, 334, 340, 342, *350*, 352 (and see Clutterbuck), 372 (see Birkinshaw), 375 (see Birkinshaw), *376*, *377*, 400, *418*, 421 (see Calam), 423 (see Calam), *429*, 431 (see Birkinshaw), 432 (see Birkinshaw), 433, 434, 439 (see Birkinshaw), 441 (see Birkinshaw), *444*, 448, 450 (see Coulthard), 458 (see Coulthard), 462 (see Coulthard), *466*, 470 (see Birkinshaw), 471, 472 (and see Birkinshaw), 473 (and

Subject Index

A

Acetaldehyde, and oxalate formation, 339; as intermediate in acid formation, 309–310; as intermediate in kojate synthesis, 439–443; bisulfite and fixation, 403–404; from alcohol, 312; in aerated Fusarium cultures, 313–314; in alcohol fermentation, 309–310; in citric synthesis, 403–404; in fat synthesis, 127–130; sulfite trap of, 316; sulfite trapping in fat synthesis, 128; sulfite trapping in sterol synthesis, 135; trapping in kojate synthesis, 441–442

Acetamide, 517

Acetate, condensation in organic acid synthesis, 406; condensation to C_4 dicarboxylic acids, 342–344; evidence against role in citrate synthesis, 405, 407–408; formation, 339; from succinic acid split, 401; intracellular, from sugar; 404; oxidation and NH_3 assimilation, 503; utilization by fungi, 336, 339

Acetic acid and carboxylic acid formation, 310–311; as precursor of oxalate, 339–345; as precursor of sterols, 134; from alcohol, 404; from citric acid breakdown, 415; in citric acid synthesis, 400–411; in fat synthesis, 127; in fumaric acid formation, 360–364, 366; in synthesis of fatty acids, 130–131; pathways of metabolism, 181; toxicity, 406

Acetic acid bacteria, and kojic acid synthesis, 432; gluconic acid formation by, 446

Acetoacetic acid, 131; from butyric acid, 560

Acetobacter, oxidative metabolism of, 9, 432, 446

Acetoin, and 2:3-butylene glycol, 312, 558

Acetone, from isopropanol, 534; by decarboxylation of acetoacetic acid, 557; from butyric acid, 560; from citric acid breakdown, 415

Acetone-dried preparations, 306

Acetonedicarboxylic acid from citric acid breakdown, 415

N-acetylglucosamine, 91

Acetylmethylcarbinol, and 2:3 butylene glycol 312, 558

Acetyl phosphate, 310; as metabolic intermediate, 406; in fatty acid synthesis, 131

Acid formation in relation to growth, 166–167

Acid-producing fungi, detection of, 29; isolation of 31

Aconitic acid, as itaconic acid precursor, 421; conversion to citric acid, 411–412; from citrate, 412; in citrate metabolism, 401–402, 411; in citric synthesis, 399

Acquired characteristics and shunt metabolism, 246–248

Acquired characters, 245–248

"Acquired" mutant characteristics, theory of 245–248

Activated carbon process for penicillin recovery, 602

Activation, heat, of Neurospora ascospores, 229

Adaptation mechanisms, 64–66; in citric acid formation, 396

Adaptive enzyme formation, examples in fungi, 64–65

Adaptive enzymes, 306

Adaptive enzymes, galactase in Fusarium, 313; mass action theory, 551; pectase as, 549; pectinase as, 549; polygalacturonidase as, 550; tannase as, 552

Adenine, from fungus nucleic acid, 113; precursor in pigment synthesis, 246; precursor pigment, 271

Ascospore formation in Neurospora, 228–232

Aspergillin, 268–269

Aspergillus, literature compilation, 5

Aspergillus oryzae, use in "koji," 41

Assays, for penicillins, 581; using deficiency mutants, 248

Assimilation, of phenyl acetyl group into penicillin, 580; of preformed nutrients, 257, 494; of preformed organic nutrients, 257

Autoinhibition by *p*-aminobenzoic acid, 245

Autointoxication by NH₃ and amines, 515

Autolysis, chemical changes accompanying, 88–89; cultural changes accompanying, 87; -resistant protein, 89

B

B vitamins, mold assays for, 21, 42

Back-mutation, 212, 215, 245

Bacterial contaminations in penicillin production, 569

Bacterial metabolism, 3

Barium, apparent toxic effect of, 263

Barker's theory of fatty acid synthesis, 130–131

Basidiomycetes, number of species, 76

Benzene ring, biosynthesis of, 178

Benzoic acid from hippuric acid, 527

Benzophenone derivatives, 539, 541

Benzylpenicillin, 578–580; hydrolytic products of, 579; synthesis of, 579

Betaine, 536; from *A. oryzae* mycelium, 113; from *A. oryzae* spores, 87

Biocatalysis, trace elements and, 253, 263

Biochemical deficiency mutants, 703, 816; frequency distribution, 225–226; isolation of, 228–235

Biochemical, mutants, 226–228; mutability, 185–186

Biochemical syntheses, 235–248; appreciation and implication, 17–20; evolution of, 207–208

Biological removal of trace elements, 261

Bionic acids, 4

Biosynthetic penicillins, 585–586

Biotin, and CO₂ fixation in aspartate,

502; biosynthesis of, 241

Biotypes, 185

Birefringence in cell walls of fungi, 98–99

Bisulfite, fixation of acetaldehyde in citrate synthesis, 403–404; increase in glycerol by, 309; trap in alcohol fermentation, 309–310; trapping of acetaldehyde, 316; trapping of acetaldehyde in oxalate formation, 339

"Blended" vegetative mycelium as inoculum, 62, 575–576

Blasenzelle, 301

Boric acid, as stimulator of penicillin production, 587; in determination of mannitol, 470; inhibition of penicillin contaminants, 493; resistance of fungi, 455–456; solubilization of Ca gluconate, 455–456

Bottle production of penicillin, 567–570

Bound glycogen in fungi, 473

Bound sterols, 134

Bran cultures, for industrial scale processes, 39–40; for preparation of inoculum, 39

Bromine, organic compounds of in fungi, 539; -oxidizable S compounds, 535

Buffer and kojic acid production, 436

sec-Butyl carbinol, 514

2:3-Butylene glycol, dehydrogenation of, 312; from acetoin, 558

Butylnitroso (*p-tert*-butyl-*o*-nitrosophenol), 262

Butyraldehyde, 128

Butyric acid, products of breakdown, 560; synthesis, 131

Butyrylphosphate, 131

C

Cacodylic acid, 545

Cadaverine, 515

Calciferol, 132

Calcium carbonate, and citric acid accumulation, 383; and colchicine action, 215; and fumarate formation, 354; and gluconic acid, 447; and itaconic process, 420; and precipitation of Ca gluconate, 453–456; limitation of in gluconate process, 454; purification method for trace elements, 260

131; unsaturated, 560

Fatty materials in cell walls, 96–98

"Ferment," 297

Fermentation, and giant cells, 302; capacity, 304–305; definition, colloquial and scientific, 296, 386; engineering, 593–598; powers, 307–308; products of molds and bacteria compared, 10, 11

Fermentative assimilation, 313

Fermenters, industrial, 595–597

Ferric chloride, colorimetric test for mold products, 29–30

Fibrous structure of conidiospores and cell walls, 96

Flash evaporator, 602

Flavicin (Δ³-pentenylpenicillin), 584

Flavonols, 443

Flavoprotein, amino acid oxidase as, 460; glucose aerodehydrogenase as, 460

Floor process of fat synthesis, 117

Flow diagram, of penicillin pilot plant, 597; of solvent extraction of penicillin, 601

Fluoride poisoned, cultures, 322; gluconic acid formation, 464

Foaming, control, by antifoam substances, 58; by reduction of air flow, 58–59; in penicillin fermentation, 598–599; in submerged cultures, 57–59

Foamogenic substances, 58

Folic acid peptides, 494

Food, fungi in, 5; as stimulus to mold metabolism, 5

Formaldehyde from methanol, 312

Formic acid, as precursor of oxalate, 170, 345–346; formation from glycolic acid, 345; from oxalate, 346; industrial manufacture of oxalate, 333; metabolism of fungi, 11; transformations by fungi, 345–346

Formic dehydrogenase, 345

Formicodehydrase, 345

Freeze drying of penicillin, 601

Fruiting structures, 3

Fructose, oxidation, 461; reduction to mannitol, 471

Fructuronic acid in oxalate formation, 337

Fumarase, 365

Fumaric acid, age of culture and, 359; and lactic acid formation, 353; C₂ condensation in, 360–364; carbon dioxide inhibition of, anaerobically, 371; commercial use of, 372; formation of free, 357; fungi forming, 352–353; general aspects of growth cultures, 352–356; industrial production of, 372; mechanism of, 359–364; product balance in, 360, 367; replacement cultures, 356–358; strain specificity, 358–359; theoretical aspects of, 369–370; via CO₂ fixation, 366–369; zinc and, 354–356

Fumaric acid-producing fungi, unsaturation test for, 30

Fumaroalanide, 371–372

Fumaromono-dl-alanide, 371–372

Fumaryl-dl-alanide, 371–372

Fumaryl-glycidic acid, 375

Fumigatin, 177

Fungi, accounting for bulk of protoplasm in soil, 16; as analytical tools, 20, 42; importance in economy of soil, 5; in natural processes, 13; number of species known, 76; role in soil, 14

Fungi Imperfecti, number of species, 76

Fungicides, as stimulus of mold metabolism, 5

"Fungin," 92

Fungisterol, 132

"Fungus cellulose," 95

Fungus-starch, 473

Fusarium, submerged process for fat production, 118

Fusel oils, origin of, 514–515

Fusion nucleus, 193–194

G

Galactans synthesized by fungi, 475

Galactocaralose, 475

β-Galactofuranose, 475, 477

Galactose, fermentation by adaptive enzyme, 313; from capreolinose hydrolysis, 477; from varianose hydrolysis, 477; oxidation, 461

D-Galactonic acid, 464; as stimulator of enzymes, 550; from pectin hydrolysis, 465, 549

Gall nuts, 4, 551, 552

allantoic acid, 526; from C$_4$ dicarboxylic acids, 342, 344; from citric acid breakdown, 415

Gosio gas, 542

Griseofulvin, 539

Growth factors, guanine for *Phycomyces blakesleeanus*, 113; hypoxanthine for *Phycomyces blakesleeanus*, 113

Growth, amounts of, 151–152; amounts of, factors influencing, 151–153; metabolic aspects of, 148–153

Guaiacol test for lactic acid, 30

Guanidase, 524–525

Guanidine, urea from, 524–525

Guanine, as growth factor for *Phycomyces blakesleeanus*, 113

Guanosine, 241

Gums synthesized by fungi, 477

H

Halogen metabolism of fungi, 537–541

Haploid mycelium, 194

Harden-Young equation, 321

Heat, activation of Neurospora ascospores, 229, 318; evolution during factory fermentations, 595–596; evolution in bottle penicillin production, 569; liberation by fungi, 157; of combustion of mold mycelium, 158

Helminthosporin, 177

Hematins, 265

Hemicellulose, 80, 81

Hemocyanins, 265

n-Heptylpenicillin (penicillin K), 581–584

Heterocaryons, as survival mechanism, 205; in penicillin production, 202; in spore pigmentation, 204; method for resolving, 201; multiple, 204; nuclear ratios in, 204

Heterocaryosis, 198–207, 210–211; and evolution of sexual reproduction, 205–207

Heterosis, 198

Heterothallism, 194

Heterozygosity, 196

Hexadeca-heptanol acid, 130

Hexadienal, 128, 129, 130

Hexamethyleneamine as a mutating chemical, 214

Hexonic acids, 464

Hexosamine, in autolysis resistant protein, 104; in chitin, 91, 95

Hexosans synthesized by fungi, 472–476

Hexose, diphosphate accumulation, 320–321; from sorbitol, 312; phosphates, 323

Hexylenaldehyde, 130

High energy irradiation, 222

"Higher fungi," 3

Hippuricase, 527

Histaminase, 517

Historical development of mold metabolism, 3, 4

Homocysteine, in biosynthesis of methionine, 238

Homogenization of mold mycelium, 70

Homoserine in synthesis of amino acids, 238

Homozygosity, 196

Hordenine, tyrosol from, 516

Horowitz's theory of biochemical evolution, 207

"Hot-house" cultures, 16

Humic substances and spore pigment, 269, 271

Hybrid vigor, 203

Hybridization as a means of developing desired characteristics, 19, 20, 193–196

Hydrogen acceptors and glucose aerodehydrogenase, 462

Hydrogen peroxide, and iodide oxidation, 541; antibiotic activity of, 461; as mutating agent, 221; catalase destruction of, 460–461; formation by glucose aerodehydrogenase, 460–461; formation by xanthine oxidase, 460; from amino acid oxidation, 508; generated by ultraviolet irradiation, 221

Hydrogen sulfide, from inorganic S compounds, 534; from sulfate, 536; sulfur as H acceptor, 534

Hydrolytic deamination, of amines, 516; of amino acids, 513

α-Hydroxy acids, from amino acids, 509–513; mechanisms of formation, 513

α-Hydroxyalanine in mold products, 495

3-Hydroxyanthranilic acid in synthesis of nicotinic acid, 239

p-Hydroxybenzoic acid in synthesis of

benzene ring, 178

p-Hydroxybenzylpenicillin, 580; precursors of, 580–581

β-Hydroxybutyric acid from butyric acid, 560

ω-Hydroxyemodin, 177

ω-Hydroxyemodinanthranol, 177

β-Hydroxy fatty acids as precursors of ketones, 559–560

3-Hydroxy-2-hydroxymethyl-γ-pyrone, 438

Hydroxylamine, as intermediate in amino acid synthesis, 491–492; from oxidation of ammonia, 491–492; from reduction of nitrite and nitrate, 490–491; in bacterial nitrification, 492; utilization as N source, 491

Hydroxymethyl hydroxy-γ-pyrone, 430

p-Hydroxyphenyl alcohol from tyrosine, 511, 512

p-Hydroxyphenyllactic acid, from p-hydroxyphenylpyruvic acid, 512; from tyrosine, 511–512

p-Hydroxyphenylpyruvic acid, from tyrosine, 510; reduction of, 512

Hydroxyproline inhibition of growth, 501

8-Hydroxyquinoline(oxine), 262

β-Hydroxyvaleric acid from valeric acid, 560

Hypoxanthine, as growth factor for *Phycomyces blakesleeanus*, 113; from fungus nucleic acid, 113; oxidation, 460

I

Idose from varianose hydrolysis, 477

Imbibition changes due to irradiation, 222

Imino acids, 508, 513

Inconstant type mycelium, 200, 201

Indole, in tryptophane synthesis, 237; nucleus in gliotoxin, 526

Induced mutations, 213–235; acquired characteristics in, 245–248; as assay organisms, 248; by chemicals, 213–221; by hydrogen peroxide, 221; by irradiation, 221–235; carbohydrate metabolism of, 226–228; comparison with natural forms, 214

Industrial, alcoholic fermentation of pentoses, 311; applications of molds, 21–25; citric acid production, 380–381, 384–386; fermentations, development of, 22; production of fumaric acid, 372; production of lactic acid, 285; utilization as stimulus to metabolism, 5

Infiltrating materials in cell walls, 96–97

Inheritance of pathogenicity, 195–196

Inhibition of growth, by carbon dioxide, 413; by oxine, 262; of oxalate formation by organic acids, 337

Inhibitors, of catalase, 461; of dehydrogenases, 463

Inoculation techniques, 62–64; "blended" vegetative mycelium, 62; methods in surface penicillin production, 567; pregerminated spores, 62

Inoculum, amount of and itaconate yields, 428; blended, 575–576; scheme for industrial, 191; vegetative, preparation for tank penicillin production, 575

Inosine, biosynthesis of, 241; from adenosine, 526; in synthesis of adenosine, 241

meso-Inositol, 317

Intercellular symbiosis, 205

Intergeneric series, 185

Intracellular, internuclear symbiosis, 206; intranuclear symbiosis, 206

Invertase and Mucoraceae, 284; stimulation by products of, 550

"Iodide oxidase," 541

Iodide, oxidation to iodine, 541; potassium, as a mutating chemical, 214

Iodoacetic acid inhibition of *Neurospora crassa* hyphae, 54

Iodoform from kojic acid oxidation by iodine, 433

Ion, absorption resins, 259; antagonism, 267, 577

Ion exchangers, 388

Iron-containing enzymes (hematins), 265; pigment, 268–269

Iron, influence on citric acid production, 394; influence on light decomposition of oxalate, 327; influence on metabolism, 276; kojate red coloration, 271; metabolic products reacting with, 432–433; storage in spores, 260

diates, 169–171

Meconic acid in opium, 443

Medium constituents, made mutagenic by irradiation, 221; influence on mutations, 221

Meiosis, 206–207; in Neurospora, 233

Melanin, 515; -type substances, 271

Melibiose from raffinose, 397–398

Mellein, 177

Mendelian, inheritance in Neurospora, 233; segregation, 193–197

Mercaptan, methyl, 536

Mercury, combination with sulfhydryl groups, 258

Mesaconic acid from itaconic acid, 420

Mesoxalic acid, 526

Metabolic, changes during penicillin formation, 589–593; products of fungi compared to bacterial products, 9, 10; sequences, 172–180

Metabolism, alteration due to environment, 11; general considerations of mold, 148–183; of precursors, 245–248

Metallic coenzymes, 264–265

Metal-protein complex, 263–264

Metaphosphatase, 141

Metaphosphate in mycelium, 141

Methane and pentose fermentation, 313

Methaneseleninic acid, 546

Methaneselenonic acid, 546

Methanol, dehydrogenation of, 312; from dimethylamine, 516; oxalate from, 346

Methionine, biosynthesis of, 238; deficiency mutants, 216; thiol and alkyl sulfide from, 537

Methods of mold metabolism, 12, 13

Methodology of mold metabolism, 27–75

Methyl alcohol, dehydrogenation of, 312; from dimethyl amine, 516; oxalate from, 346

Methyl alkyl ketones from fatty acids, 556–560

Methyl alkyl selenides, 544

Methyl amyl ketone, 556

Methylarsonic acid, 545

Methyl-bis (β-chloroethyl) amine (nitrogen mustard), 216

Methyl crotonaldehyde in sterol synthesis, 135

Methyl donors, 537, 544–545

Methyl ethyl ketone from valerate, 560

Methyl glyoxal, 315; in Chaetomium fermentation, 323

Methyl heptyl ketone, 556

Methylmercaptan, 536

Methyl nonyl ketone, 556

Methyl pentose, 86, 95

n-Methylproline methylbetaine (stachhydrine), 113

Methyl propyl ketone, 556

γ-Methyl-tetronic acid, 174

Methylated alkyl sulfides, 536–537

Methylation of, alkyl arsonates, 543; alkyl selenic acids, 544; arsenious acid, mechanism, 545; of alkyl selenium compounds, 544; selenious acid, mechanism, 546; sulfate, 536; thiols, 537

Methylene succinic acid, 419

"Microelements," 251

Micronutrients, 251

Microscopic appearance of, fungi under anaerobiosis, 298–302; mutants, 225

Mildew, 2

Minerals, assimilation of and trace elements, 276; content of fungi, 137–143; content of spores, 138, 139; in corn steep liquor, 577; nutrition, historic work in mold metabolism, 4

Mineral oil preservation of cultures, 190

Minioluteic acid, 126, 412

Molasses, for fat production, 117–118; metabolic fate of by A. wentii, 150; purification and use for citric acid process, 388–389; toxicity of, 389

Mold, black, bread, definition, water, white, 2

Mold assays for, amino acids, 21, 42; arsenic, 21, 42; B vitamins, 21, 42; copper, 21; phosphorus in soil, 21, 42; potassium in soils, 21, 42; soil fertility, 21; thiamine, 21; trace elements, 21

Mold bran, 39–41

Mold metabolism, and oxalate formation, 330; general, 148–183; historical development, 2; modern developments, 5; relation to bacterial metabolism, 3; studies, 12

Mold physiology, historical significance, 4

Molds, as agents of chemical synthesis, 6; as agents of dissimilation, 9; as

Penicillin G, 578–580; isolation in pure form, 600; yields in factory production, 602
Penicillin K (n-heptylpenicillin), 581–585
Penicillin precursors, 578–586; influence on type of penicillin, 582
Penicillin production, by heterocaryons, 202–203; enhancement as acquired characteristic, 246; stimulation by radium, 222; total monthly, 567
Penicillin X (p-hydroxybenzylpenicillin), 580–585; fungi producing, 573
Penicillinase, by bacterial contaminants, 569
Penicillium chrysogenum Q176, development of, 572
Penicillium digitatum, FeCl₃ test for, 30
Penicillins, chemical and biological properties of, 584–585; methods for differentiating, 581–583; natural, structures of, 583–585; pK values of, 600; solubility in amyl acetate, 599
Δ²-Pentenylpenicillin (penicillin F), 581, 584
Δ³-Pentenylpenicillin (flavicin), 584
Pentonic acids, 464
Pentosans synthesized by fungi, 472
Pentose fermentation, 311–313
Peptides, 527, 528; in mold metabolism, 494–495
Peptone, oxalate from, 329, 346–348
Permeation of substrates and pH, 362
Permeability, membrane and pH, 362, 487–488, 492
Pfeffer's solution, 252
pH, and asparagine breakdown, 517; and carbon dioxide inhibition of growth, 413; and chitin content of mycelium, 94; and citric acid production, 381–383; and differential N source and utilization of N source, 486–489; and fat synthesis, 123, 124; and fumarate formation, 353; and gluconic acid production, 447, 453–456; and itaconic acid formation, 423–424, 427–428; and kojic acid production, 435–436; and membrane permeability, 487–488; and oxalate accumulation, 328, 331–334; and penicillin extractability, 599–600; and permeability, 362, 487–488,

498; and pigment colors, 271; and pyridoxineless mutants, 244; and starch synthesis, 475; and urease formation, 523; and viability of stock cultures, 190; change as a means of detecting acid-formers, 31; changes in penicillin fermentation, 570, 591–592; influence on organic acid production, 48; internal of mycelium, 489; mutants, 244; of medium and intracellular pH, 488; sterol synthesis, 133; tolerance of microorganisms, 381–382; trends and notatin formation, 570; trends and surface penicillin production, 569–570
Phenolic acids, FeCl₃ test for, 30
Phenylacetamide as penicillin precursor, 582, 588
Phenylacetic acid as penicillin precursor, 257, 579–580
Phenylacetyl compounds, as benzyl penicillin precursors, 579–580; isotopic labeled, 580
Phenylalanine and benzylpenicillin precursor, 580
β-Phenylethylamine, as benzylpenicillin precursor, 580; in corn steep liquor, 580
Phenylpyruvic acid from phenylalanine, 511
Phloroglucinol in tannin, 551
Phoenicin, 177
Phosphatase action, 322–323; in glycerol production, 470
Phosphate, and citric acid production, 392; carriers, 322; donors, 322–323; fractions in fungi, 322; transformations in fungi, 322–324
Phosphatides, 135–136
Phosphoglyceraldehyde, 128
Phosphoglyceric acid in Fusarium fermentation, 322, 323
Phospholipides, 124, 135–136, 323; hydrolysis products, 136
Phosphoprotein, from A. niger, 103; from A. oryzae, 105; from Rhizopus japonicus, 106
Phosphorus, in fungi, 140–141; in soils, mold assay for, 21
Phosphorylation in fermentation, 320–324
Photosensitive nitrogen containing com-

S

Saccharic acid from glucose, 465

Saltation, 193, 210

Salts, influence on dissimilation in replacement cultures, 69

Saprophytic fungi, 2

Scandium, requirements of fungi, 277

Schimmelpilze, 2

Sclerotiorine, 540

Sclerotiose, 473

Screening processes for detection of fungi forming various metabolic products, 32, 35

Sectoring, 210–211, induced by staling products, 220, 221

Seed tanks, contaminations in, 594; in penicillin production, 575

Segregation in mutation work, 216

Selection, as a mechanism of adaptation, 66; for increased acid production, 66

Selective culture principles, 34, 35

Selective permeability, 488–489, 493, 498

Serine in typtophane synthesis, 237

Serylglycylaspartic acid, 495

Serylglycylglutamic acid, 495

Sex, as a mutable character, 212

Sexual, bodies, 2; fusion mechanism, 194–195; mating of Neurospora, 229–232

Sex-linked characters, 196

Sexual reproduction, and generation of variants, 193; evolution of, 205–207; in natural variation, 193–197

Sexuality and fumaric acid formation, 359

Shadow cells, 77

Shake cultures, applications, 12, 13

Shaking machines for submerged growth, 60–61

Shallow pans, mycelium growth in, 152; process for fat production, 117

Shikimic acid in synthesis of benzene ring, 178

Shoyu-Moromi, 515

Shunt metabolism, 164–169; and acquired characteristics, 246–248; and carbohydrate production, 468-469; and carbohydrate synthesis, 479; and citric acid, 383, 393; and kojic acid synthesis, 440; and orotic acid, 240; and reserve

materials, 181–183; and starch synthesis, 474; and the carbohydrate concentration, 357; and the zinc effect, 356; and trace elements, 274; in fat synthesis, 122; of cis-aconitic acid, 402, 411

Silver in mold mycelium, 278

Sodium chloride, and itaconate yields, 425; stimulation of sporulation by, 568

Sodium in mycelium, 139, 143

Sodium penicillin G crystallization, 600-601

Soil cultures, 189–190

Soil, fertility, mold assays in determining, 21; fungi, as stimulus to mold metabolism, 5; microbiology and mold metabolism, 4, 15; population balance, dependence on synthetic activities of organisms, 16; role of fungi in, 162–167

Solids, spore production on loose, 568–569

Solvent process of penicillin extraction, 599–601, 602

Sorbitol, dehydrogenation of, 312

Soy sauce, manufacture as stimulus of mold metabolism, 5, 515

Species groups, 185–186

Spectroscopic detection of trace element impurities, 256

Spherical cells, 301

Sphingosine, 137

Spiculosporic acid, 125–126

Spontaneous mutations, 209–213

Spore, germination inhibition by $CaCO_3$, 45–46; inoculum for surface culture, 45; pregermination as a mutation enrichment, 235; starch, 474

Spores, of penicillin cultures, submerged production of, 575; oat hulls as carrier for, 569; production and use as inoculum in penicillin production, 568; proximate composition of, 86–87; trace elements and, 266–269; trace element storage in, 259–260; viability of Penicillium, 576

Squalene as precursor of sterols, 134

Stachhydrine, from A. oryzae mycelium, 113; in Aspergillus oryzae spores, 87

Staining of cell walls, 92; interference with, 96–98

Z